14-120-1309

ADVANCES IN CARBOHYDRATE CHEMISTRY

VOLUME 14

Zemplén Géza

Advances in Carbohydrate Chemistry

Editor
MELVILLE L. WOLFROM

Associate Editor
R. STUART TIPSON

Board of Advisors

HERMANN O. L. FISCHER
R. C. HOCKETT
W. W. PIGMAN

C. B. PURVES
J. C. SOWDEN
ROY L. WHISTLER

Board of Advisors for the British Isles

E. L. HIRST   STANLEY PEAT   MAURICE STACEY

Volume 14

1959

ACADEMIC PRESS   NEW YORK and LONDON

LIST OF CONTRIBUTORS

LAURENS ANDERSON, *Department of Biochemistry, University of Wisconsin, Madison, Wisconsin*

S. J. ANGYAL, *School of Chemistry, University of New South Wales, Sydney, Australia*

G. O. ASPINALL, *Department of Chemistry, The University of Edinburgh, Scotland*

G. P. ELLIS, *Organic Chemistry Section, Research Department, Benger Laboratories Ltd., Holmes Chapel, Cheshire, England*

A. B. FOSTER, *Department of Chemistry, The University of Birmingham, England*

J. J. FOX, *Sloan-Kettering Institute for Cancer Research, New York, New York*

D. HORTON, *Sebright School, Wolverley, Worcestershire, England*

G. A. LEVVY, *Rowett Research Institute, Bucksburn, Aberdeenshire, Scotland*

C. A. MARSH, *Rowett Research Institute, Bucksburn, Aberdeenshire, Scotland*

L. MESTER, *Centre National de la Recherche Scientifique, Université de Paris, Faculté de Pharmacie, Paris, France*

A. S. PERLIN, *Prairie Regional Laboratory, National Research Council, Saskatoon, Saskatchewan, Canada*

I. WEMPEN, *Sloan-Kettering Institute for Cancer Research, New York, New York*

PREFACE

In Volume 14 of this series, we bring up to date three significant topics previously covered in other volumes. These concern areas of research in which there has been exceptional activity with resultant progress; they are, respectively, the amino sugars (Foster and Horton), the hemicelluloses (Aspinall), and the inositols (Angyal and Anderson). The topic of nucleic acids has twice been summarized in this series, but the unusually fertile studies current in this sector of carbohydrate investigation call for renewed coverage, and the chapter on pyrimidine nucleosides (Fox and Wempen) is part of a projected series of chapters covering subdivisions of this rapidly expanding subject. The action on sugars of the oxidizing agent lead tetraacetate is delineated by Perlin, as a continuation of our series of chapters devoted to the action of oxidizing agents structurally specific toward carbohydrates. From time to time, we have offered summaries relating to enzymes affecting carbohydrates, and Levvy and Marsh herein describe β-glucuronidase. Ellis gives a succinct summary of the present moot status of the Maillard (non-enzymic) browning reaction effected between sugars and amino acids. Finally, an obituary of the late Géza Zemplén is provided by Mester, one of the later coworkers of this distinguished disciple of Emil Fischer.

For the past six years, the Subject Indexes have been compiled by one of us (R. S. T.); the task has this year been assumed by Dr. Joseph D. Moyer. Dr. D. Horton assisted in the final editing.

Columbus, Ohio   M. L. WOLFROM
Washington, D. C.   R. STUART TIPSON

CONTENTS

Action of Lead Tetraacetate on the Sugars

A. S. PERLIN

The Maillard Reaction

G. P. ELLIS

The Cyclitols

S. J. Angyal and Laurens Anderson

Aspects of the Chemistry of the Amino Sugars

A. B. Foster and D. Horton

Pyrimidine Nucleosides

J. J. Fox and I. Wempen

Preparation and Properties of β-Glucuronidase

G. A. LEVVY AND C. A. MARSH

Structural Chemistry of the Hemicelluloses

G. O. ASPINALL

GÉZA ZEMPLÉN

1883–1956

At the turn of the century, Emil Fischer's laboratory in Berlin was the center of the then rapidly advancing organic chemistry, particularly in the fields of carbohydrates and proteins. Scientists from all over the world flocked to his laboratory, eager to learn the secrets of the great master.

In September, 1907, a young Hungarian scientist, on a government fellowship, arrived in Berlin to work in this famous institute. His talent, preparative skill, and diligence soon aroused Fischer's interest in the young man and, within a short time, he was selected to work in Fischer's private laboratory. Before long, he was achieving one interesting result after another: a new method for the preparation of aminohydroxy carboxylic acids, a new way to prepare piperidone derivatives, the resolution of the synthetic dl-proline into its optically active components, and a study of the effects of enzymes upon cellobiose. During his three-year stay in Berlin, he published eight papers with Emil Fischer and two with E. Abderhalden and H. Pringsheim.

Who was this young scientist? He was Géza Zemplén, an Associate Professor of Chemistry at the School of Forestry and Mining of Selmecbánya, Hungary. Even in his student years he had distinguished himself; he graduated from the high school in Fiume at the age of sixteen. Later, he became a member and student of the famous Eötvös Collegium, and completed his studies in natural sciences *summa cum laude* at the Pázmány Péter University, Budapest, where, in 1904, he received his degree of Doctor of Philosophy. In 1905, he was appointed an Assistant Professor, and, in 1907, an Associate Professor at the School of Forestry and Mining, Selmecbánya. Here, he soon published several papers relating to forestry. He had always been greatly interested in botany and the natural products occurring in plants, such as sugars, polysaccharides, glycosides, and dyes. It was only natural that this interest should have been developed further in Emil Fischer's laboratory.

Géza Zemplén was born in Trencsén, Hungary, on October 26, 1883. His father was a post inspector, who reared his children with great love, but also with iron discipline, for he wished to make real men of them. In this he was highly successful, for Géza became Professor of Organic Chemistry at the University of Technical Sciences, Budapest, where his brother, Gyözö, became Professor of Theoretical Physics. A third son, Szilárd, attained a high rank in the Austro-Hungarian Navy.

1

When Géza was a child, his father was transferred to Fiume, the Adriatic seaport of Hungary. The natural beauty of this Dalmatian Coast location was a source of inspiration to the young boy. Here he was able to come in close contact with, and soon developed an ardent love for, Italian music, art, and poetry. Throughout his life he entertained his circle of students and friends by singing Italian songs, and reciting from Dante's "Divine Comedy" and other works which he knew by heart. He was not only fond of folk music, however, but had a great love for the opera, particularly the works of the great Italian composers as well as of Wagner. His musical proficiency was stimulated by his close friendship with Zoltán Kodály, the renowned Hungarian composer, with whom he spent much time during his college years. As an art enthusiast, he painstakingly collected art albums and etchings, and spoke of the masterpieces with the same reverence he accorded his great teacher, Emil Fischer.

The accomplishments and impressions of his years in Berlin, the momentum of research in the world-famous institute, plus the powerful personality of Emil Fischer, were decisive factors in the development of the young scientist. With a thorough knowledge of the modern methods of research at his command, he returned to his home in Hungary in the Fall of 1910. In 1912, he was appointed Privatdozent at the Pázmány Péter University. Meanwhile, he continued the work begun in Berlin, editing the chapters on Carbohydrates and Proteins in Abderhalden's "Biochemisches Handlexikon" and "Handbuch der biochemischen Arbeitsmethoden."

In recognition of his early accomplishments, he was appointed Head of the newly established Organic Chemical Institute of the Royal József Technical University of Budapest. Unfortunately, however, his appointment came on the eve of the First World War and his Institute could not be sufficiently equipped. When the war broke out, he could not even hope to get the necessary equipment for the continuation of his scientific work; only substantial assistance from Lajos Ilosvay, the Professor of Chemistry, enabled him to surmount the initial difficulties. Zemplén never forgot this aid and often remarked "I am eternally grateful to our great scientist, Lajos Ilosvay, who so generously and to the limit of his ability supported the pursuits of the young Institute." These difficulties, however, did not dampen the enthusiasm of the young scientist. He established close connection with various industries, particularly with the Chinoin Pharmaceutical Manufacturing Company of Budapest, and, with the aid of his able assistants, Zoltán Földy, Andor Bartha, and György Schwalm, he solved many industrial problems, which secured for him the financial means to continue his scientific research. Under such conditions, it was quite natural that he selected his assistants on the basis of their talent, ability, and ambition, maintaining the same type of discipline in his laboratory as he had observed at Emil Fischer's institute. As strict as he was during working hours, he was just as congenial and jovial in his social life. He usually gathered his coworkers and friends together in one of the famous Buda restaurants or at one of the resorts along the Danube. At such times, they spent many enjoyable hours, drinking good Hungarian wine, singing, and joking, usually until the early hours. Nevertheless, he always appeared at his laboratory by eight o'clock the next morning, the ever-present cigar in his mouth, ready to begin his work with "full steam ahead." He was determined to obtain the "first crystals" from some hopeless sirups or tars, and only after he obtained them did he give the work over to his assistants.

After the First World War, he obtained considerable financial assistance from the National Science Foundation of Hungary, the Széchenyi Scientific Society, and the Hungarian Academy of Sciences, but he still had to supplement his income by doing private consulting work for industry.

Despite various difficulties, he continued his research work without interruption. The following resumé will give an indication of the wide scope of his achievements.

In the early 1920's, while attempting to obtain the sodium salt of D-glucose, with the cooperation of Alfons Kunz, he discovered a new process for the catalytic saponification of sugar acetates, using sodium methoxide, a method which has now become a standard procedure. The process was modified and somewhat improved later, with the assistance of Eugen Pacsu and Árpád Gerecs.

This novel method of saponification opened up a new way for the degradation of complex sugars containing an aldehydic group. When the acetylated nitriles of acids of such sugars are treated with sodium methoxide in alcoholic solution, the cyanide group is split off *together* with the acetyl groups, and a new aldose results having one less carbon atom. Wohl's method is not applicable to the degradation of complex carbohydrates, because the intermediate products obtained are not the aldoses themselves, but their diacetamide derivatives. Acetamide can be removed from these by acid hydrolysis only, a procedure which, however, also splits the polysaccharide linkages at the same time. The Ruff degradation, while avoiding this difficulty, has the drawback of low yields, owing to the further oxidative decomposition of aldoses. This new degradation process not only makes possible the preparation of a great number of new bioses, but is also very useful in the determination of the position of linkage between the two sugar residues in such important oligosaccharides as cellobiose, maltose, lactose, turanose, and melezitose. This is because the degradation may only be continued to the carbon atom adjacent to the position of linkage. The proof, by this procedure, of the configuration of cellobiose and maltose contributed greatly to the elucidation of the structure of cellulose and starch. This work was done with the assistance of Géza Braun, Dénes Kiss, Zoltán Csürös, Sándor Müller, Alajos Jókay and Zoltán Bruckner.

His proof of the structure of amygdalin was of great importance. This work was done with Alexander Hoffmann, and was later confirmed by synthesis, with the assistance of Alfons Kunz.

While studying the effect of trimethylamine on Karrer's "Cellal," with the co-operation of Zoltán Csürös and Zoltán Bruckner, he succeeded in explaining the reaction and proved the structure of the compound. He obtained, with Géza Braun, some new derivatives of salicin.

The method for the cleavage of glycosidic linkages with hydrogen bromide in glacial acetic acid solution was refined; it served as a potent tool for the identification of the sugar moieties in several glycosides. Complex carbohydrates were isolated in the form of well crystallized "acetobromo" derivatives (poly-O-acetylglycosyl bromides). Applying this procedure, he succeeded in proving the structure of solanin, in co-operation with Árpád Gerecs.

In the meantime, he was gaining steady recognition for his achievements; in 1923, he became a correspondent of the Hungarian Academy of Sciences, and, in 1927, a full member. In 1928, he received the Academy's Major Award, and, in 1931, the Corvin Laurel.

At the end of the 1920's, his attention was directed to the synthesis of glycosides and oligosaccharides. Up to this time, all syntheses of glycosides had started with the α-D-"acetohalogeno" derivatives (poly-O-acetyl-α-D-glycosyl halides), but, due to Walden inversion, the resulting product was invariably the β-D-glycoside. By the application of sublimed ferric chloride, however, he succeeded, with the co-operation of Árpád Gerecs, Zoltán Csürös and Zoltán Bruckner, in obtaining the α-D-glycosides directly. With Zoltán Csürös, he split tri-O-acetyl-"levoglucosan" through the agency of titanium tetrachloride, and converted it into a crystalline 2,3,4-tri-O-acetyl-D-glucopyranosyl chloride. This compound later proved a very important starting material for the synthesis of oligosaccharides. He described the discovery of this method in the following (translated) statement: "It was by accident that I discovered the usefulness of mercuric acetate in the synthesis of glycosides. My intention was to reduce acetobromocellobiose with amalgamated aluminum shavings in benzene solution; during these experiments, I observed that, when a mixture of acetobromoglucose, phenol, mercuric acetate, and granulated aluminum was briefly heated on the water-bath, optically pure phenyl hepta-O-acetyl-α-cellobioside was formed in good yield."

On further investigation with the assistance of Árpád Gerecs, it was found that this procedure was eminently suitable for the preparation of alkyl glycosides and, with the application of the proper amounts of alcohols, either the α- or the β-D-glycosides could be obtained.

The success of the mercuric acetate–glycoside syntheses led to the synthesis of oligosaccharides. He selected, for the alcoholic component, methyl 2,3,4-tri-O-acetyl-β-D-glucoside, a compound obtained from the 2,3,4-tri-O-acetyl-D-glucosyl chloride. When the glucoside was reacted with hepta-O-acetylcellobiosyl bromide, both the α-(1 $\rightarrow$ 6) and β-(1 $\rightarrow$ 6) forms of the methyl 6-O-cellobiosyl-β-D-glucoside were obtained. This work was done with Zoltán Bruckner and Árpád Gerecs. In much the same manner, he succeeded in obtaining some other oligosaccharides, among them a crystalline derivative of cellobiosyl-gentiobiose.

He further observed that α-"acetochloro"-6-O-cellobiosyl-β-D-glucose (and α-"acetochloro"-gentiobiose) may be obtained in one operation from 2,3,4-tri-O-acetyl-D-glucosyl chloride plus "acetobromo"-cellobiose (or "acetobromo"-D-glucose), in benzene solution in the presence of mercuric acetate. The explanation is that coupling on the free hydroxyl group in the sixth position occurs much faster than the splitting of chloride ion from the triacetyl chloride.

Among the natural glycosides, the disaccharides composed of L-rhamnose and D-glucose occur rather frequently. Zemplén's attention was now focused on the synthesis of these disaccharides. One of the best known of these glycosides, rutin, occurs in *Ruta hortensis* and in numerous other plants. With the co-operation of Árpád Gerecs, he obtained from tri-O-acetyl-L-rhamnosyl bromide and 2,3,4-tri-O-acetyl-D-glucosyl chloride, the polyacetate of 6-O-β-L-rhamnosyl-α-D-glucosyl chloride, which, when treated with silver acetate in acetic anhydride solution, gave 6-O-β-L-rhamnosyl-D-glucose heptaacetate. This latter sugar proved to be identical with the heptaacetate of rutinose, a biose obtained by the enzymic or acetic acid hydrolysis of rutin.

The successful synthesis of rutinose made possible the determination of the structure and synthesis of other glycosides which contain rutinose. With the co-operation of Albin Tettamanti, he determined the structure of hesperidin and neohesperidin; and, with Rezsö Bognár and László Mester, the structure of neolinarin. Starting with the acetate of rutinosyl bromide and the appropriate aglycon, he synthesized the lusitanicoside (with Árpád Gerecs); and linarin, pectolinarin, and hesperidin with Rezsö Bognár.

The further application of the mercuric acetate method made possible the synthesis of primeverose [6-O-β-D-xylosyl-D-glucose] and also isoprimeverose [6-O-α-D-xylosyl-D-glucose] from 2,3,4-tri-O-acetyl-α-D-glucosyl chloride and tri-O-acetyl-D-xylosyl bromide. After the preparation of these sugars in larger quantities, the naturally occurring primeverosides could readily be synthesized. The most important of these primeverosides is ruberythric acid. This important glycoside, occurring in madder root, was synthesized with the co-operation of Rezső Bognár, thus proving it to be definitely the 2-alizarin β-primeveroside.

With the co-operation of Árpád Gerecs, he proved the structure of robinobiose, a newly discovered sugar obtained from robinin glycoside. This new disaccharide proved to be a derivative of 6-O-β-L-rhamnosyl-D-galactose; it was obtained from 2,3,4-tri-O-acetyl-D-galactosyl chloride plus the triacetate of L-rhamnosyl bromide, in the presence of mercuric acetate. Later, with Rezső Bognár, he succeeded in proving the structure of the glycoside of robinin itself.

In the early 1940's, Zemplén's attention was centered on the synthesis of flavone glycosides and he soon solved the most difficult problems in the preparation of important, naturally occurring, active principles. With Rezső Bognár, he accomplished the synthesis of phloridzin, a problem which had intrigued him for a number of years. After several unsuccessful experiments, he finally hit on the right solution, by first reacting tetra-O-acetyl-D-glucosyl bromide with 4-benzoyl-phloracetophenone. The resulting glucoside was then coupled with p-hydroxybenzaldehyde in an alkaline medium, to yield the corresponding chalcone. Finally, the "benzylidene" double bond of the chalcone was hydrogenated, to yield the long-sought-after phloridzin. Thus, the road was opened for the preparation of a number of similar flavone glycosides. The synthesis of glucohesperetin, salipurposide, isosalipurposide and other important glycosides, was accomplished in rapid succession. Shortly thereafter, he solved the problem of the transformation of the flavanone series into the flavone series *by dehydrogenation with bromine*, the most important example being the transformation of hesperidin into diosmin.

In the meantime, in co-operation with László Mester, he realized the synthesis of numerous flavone glycosides containing the sugar moiety in unusual positions, such as asebotin, sakuranin, and apigenin-5 D-glucoside. Later, with Rezső Bognár and Lorant Farkas, he published important results on the synthesis of such isoflavone glycosides as genistin and ononin and, finally, on the structure of sophoricoside and sophorabioside.

In recognition of his numerous accomplishments, he received international acclaim. He became a member of the Kaiserlich Deutsche Akademie der Naturforscher zu Halle and a correspondent of the Schlesische Gesellschaft für Vaterländische Kultur. Finally, in 1940, he was awarded the A. W. Hofmann Gold Medal.

Outstanding as he was as a scientist, he was also a brilliant pedagogue. Under his guidance, some forty classes of chemical engineers graduated from the University of Technical Sciences, where, for a number of years, he was Dean of the Department of Chemistry. He placed great emphasis on the importance of teaching and, with extreme care, selected the ablest of his students to become his assistants. These assistants, in whom he had instilled a deep love of science, formed a close, intimate circle, and were bound together throughout their lives by their mutual love and respect for the strong personality of Géza Zemplén. Former assistants, who had become professors or executives of industrial concerns, never missed an opportunity to get together, after scientific meetings or on festive occasions, to reminisce about their unforgettable days in Zemplén's laboratory.

The second World War brought nearly complete destruction of Zemplén's Institute; nothing but the four walls remained after the siege of Budapest. Most of his equipment and his valuable collection of irreplaceable specimens and other materials were destroyed. His lifelong work lay under a heap of rubble, unexploded grenades, and the like. Yet, even this dreadful sight could not break his indomitable spirit. With the assistance of his students, he began restoration work almost immediately and, after months of long, hard work, some of the equipment was salvaged. This enabled them to resume scientific work in the basement, which they used until 1949, when the Institute was completely rebuilt.

In 1947, while the reconstruction was in progress, he received and accepted an invitation from Father Hunter Guthrie, Dean of Georgetown University, Washington, D. C., to conduct scientific research there as a Visiting Professor. The invitation was sponsored jointly by Dr. Robert C. Hockett, Scientific Director of the Sugar Research Foundation, and by Georgetown University. During his absence, the reconstruction of the Institute had been directed by Rezsö Bognár, László Mester, and Nora Schuller, who had kept him constantly informed of its progress.

At the beginning of 1948, he arrived unexpectedly at the airport of Budapest. "I have come home to die," he said to his assistants who were highly excited by his surprising return. Unfortunately, he had hardly established himself in his laboratory at Georgetown, when he was stricken with cancer and had to undergo surgery and other treatment. There was little hope of complete recovery, however, so he decided to return to Hungary.

When he was back there, his condition improved steadily—to such an extent, indeed, that he was able to take over personal direction of the remaining reconstruction work. Zemplén also managed to resume his scientific work on the synthesis of derivatives of allolactose and melibiose, in cooperation with Rezsö Bognár, and the synthesis of acaciin, with the assistance of László Mester and Andreas Messmer.

In 1950, his health again failed. Every effort was made to save him; he even attempted self-treatment which was successful in somewhat delaying the progress of his illness. By this time, he was confined to his home, but scientific research still remained uppermost in his mind. He supervised the investigations on the preparation of formazans from carbohydrates, and reported many interesting results in the field of carbohydrates with the help of his coworkers, László Mester, Lajos Kisfaludy, István Döry, Andreas Messmer, Elemér Móczár, Ede Eckhart, Joseph Schawartz and Ádám Major. Meanwhile, he completed his textbook on organic chemistry, which he dedicated "to my coworkers, past and present, whose devoted assistance contributed so much to the successes I have known."

During his illness, he received many honors. In 1948, he was presented with the Kossuth Award, and became Honorary President of the Hungarian Chemical Society, a position he held for a number of years. His friends and students, as well as scientists from abroad, came to his bedside. All the while, his wife, Sara Rau, selflessly cared for him, doing all in her power to alleviate his suffering. On July 24th, 1956, in Budapest, he passed away, and his death brought mourning throughout the scientific world.

It is very difficult to characterize in just a few words a diverse personality such as Géza Zemplén. He was a man of extremely strong will-power, with a tremendous capacity for work, and one in whom were combined a love of science and of the arts. Those who did not have the opportunity of spending some time with him socially, of listening to his colorful and witty stories, or of being with him in his laboratory to observe the workings of his creative mind, could not really know Géza Zemplén. Those who did know him intimately, admired him as a brilliant scientist and a truly great man.

L. MESTER*

* Grateful acknowledgment is made Dr. G. Braun for his kind assistance and rectifications.

ACTION OF LEAD TETRAACETATE ON THE SUGARS

By A. S. Perlin

*Prairie Regional Laboratory, National Research Council,
Saskatoon, Saskatchewan, Canada*

I. Introduction

Lead tetraacetate appears to have been first used as an organic oxidant by Dimroth, Friedemann, and Kammerer,[1] in place of such established reagents as the dioxides of manganese and lead. It is more readily soluble in a variety of reaction media and hence is particularly convenient for quantitative use, but it also shows distinctive properties of its own. Lead tetraacetate functions smoothly as a dehydrogenating agent under mild conditions,[1-3] converting, for example, hydroquinones to quinones. In hot acetic acid it was found particularly effective in replacing an active hydrogen with an acetoxy residue.[4] Thus, diethyl malonate was acetoxylated readily, and acetone was oxidized to 1,3-dihydroxy-2-propanone diacetate, although

(1) O. Dimroth, O. Friedemann and H. Kammerer, *Ber.*, **53**, 481 (1920).
(2) O. Dimroth and V. Hilcken, *Ber.*, **54**, 3050 (1921).
(3) O. Dimroth and F. Frister, *Ber.*, **55**, 1223 (1922).
(4) O. Dimroth and R. Schweizer, *Ber.*, **56**, 1375 (1923).

in low yield. Criegee[5] found that lead tetraacetate reacts with unsaturated compounds, either by substituting acetoxyl for hydrogen or by adding two acetoxy residues to the double bond. Cyclohexene, for example, treated with one mole of the reagent in acetic acid at 80°, gives cyclohexene-1-ol acetate and *cis*- and *trans*-1,2-cyclohexanediol diacetates.

These and related reactions of lead tetraacetate have been widely used in synthetic organic chemistry, and are the subject of several reviews.[6-10] However, they have found relatively few applications in the carbohydrate field specifically. One important application has been the synthesis of ketones by way of acetoxylation of suitable unsaturated compounds. By treating 1,2-O-isopropylidene-2-propene-1,2-diol (I) in benzene at 50° with

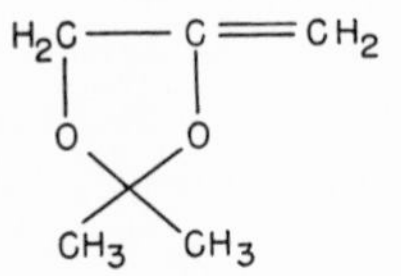

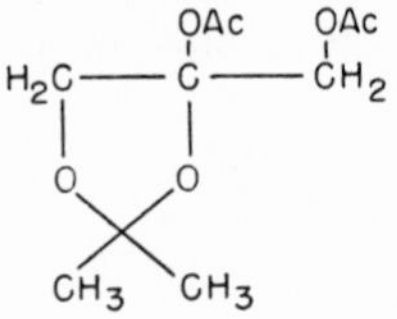

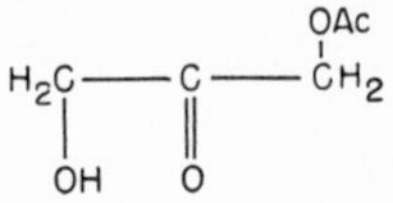

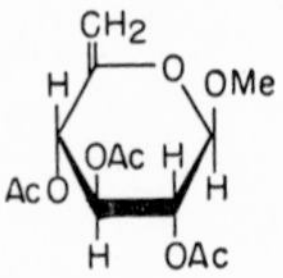

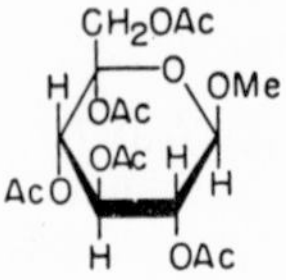

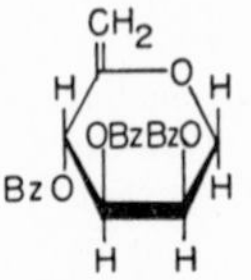

lead tetraacetate, Fischer, Baer, and Feldmann[11, 12] obtained a high yield of the diacetate (II). Saponification and hydrolysis of II afforded 1,3-dihydroxy-2-propanone, and hydrolysis alone gave 1-acetoxy-3-hydroxy-2 propanone (III) which was used recently in the synthesis of 1,3-dihydroxy-2-propanone phosphate.[13] Lead tetraacetate similarly converted the methyl

(5) R. Criegee, *Ann.*, **481**, 263 (1920).

(6) R. Criegee, *Angew. Chem.*, **53**, 321 (1940).

(7) L. F. Fieser, "Experiments in Organic Chemistry," John Wiley and Sons, Inc., New York, N. Y., 1941, p. 436.

(8) R. Criegee, in "Neuere Methoden der Präparativen Organischen Chemie," W. Foerst, ed., Verlag Chemie, GMBH, Weinheim, 1949, p. 21.

(9) W. A. Waters, in "Organic Chemistry," H. Gilman, ed., John Wiley and Sons, Inc., New York, N. Y., 1953, p. 1185.

(10) R. Criegee, *Angew. Chem.*, **70**, 173 (1958).

(11) H. O. L. Fischer, E. Baer and L. Feldmann, *Ber.*, **63**, 1732 (1930).

(12) H. O. L. Fischer and E. Baer, *Ber.*, **65**, 345 (1932).

(13) C. E. Ballou and H. O. L. Fischer, *J. Am. Chem. Soc.*, **78**, 1659 (1956).

β-D-glucoseenide-5,6 triacetate (IV) to a 5-acetoxy-tetraacetate (V),[14] and the unsaturated product VI derived from 1,5-anhydro-2,3,4-tri-O-benzoyl-6-deoxy-6-iodo-D-mannitol gave the corresponding 1,2-diacetate of D-fructose.[15] In some instances, lead tetraacetate was found highly effective for substitution of reactive halogen by acetoxyl, as illustrated in the conversion of 2,3,4-tri-O-acetyl-6-bromo-6-deoxy-α-D-glucopyranosyl bromide to the 6-bromo-6-deoxy β-tetraacetate,[16] and of 2-O-acetyl-3,6-anhydro-5-O-tosyl-α-D-glucosyl bromide to an α,β-mixture of the corresponding 1,2-diacetate.[17]

The property of lead tetraacetate with which carbohydrate chemists have been almost exclusively concerned is its ability to cleave oxidatively 1,2-glycol groups, a reaction which was discovered by Criegee.[18] This reaction, together with the closely related periodate oxidation,[19, 20] has provided a most substantial impetus to carbohydrate research during the past 25 years. Both reagents act smoothly and quantitatively at room temperature, and have been used as alternative means for detecting *vic*-diols and for analytical and preparative purposes.[21] In addition, however, *lead tetraacetate is especially suitable for differentiating between various kinds of glycol groups.* Hence, it has been particularly employed in certain types of structural studies for which periodate has not appeared so well adapted or has not been as fully evaluated. Since an earlier Chapter[22] deals with the periodate oxidation of carbohydrates, the present article emphasizes these specialized aspects of glycol-cleavage with lead tetraacetate rather than those uses of the reagent for which periodate may be equally, or more, effective. In certain instances, brief reference will be made to contrasting behavior on the part of the two oxidants.

II. Mechanism of Glycol-cleavage Oxidation by Lead Tetraacetate

In studying the oxidation of saturated alcohols in cold acetic acid by lead tetraacetate, Criegee[18] discovered that only those alcohols which con-

(14) B. Helferich and N. M. Bigelow, *Z. physiol. Chem., Hoppe-Seyler's*, **200**, 263 (1931).

(15) L. Zervas and I. Papadimitriou, *Ber.*, **73**, 174 (1940).

(16) H. Ohle and V. Marecek, *Ber.*, **63**, 612 (1930).

(17) H. Ohle and E. Euler, *Ber.*, **63**, 1796 (1930).

(18) R. Criegee, *Ber.*, **64**, 260 (1931).

(19) L. Malaprade, *Bull. soc. chim. France*, [4] **39**, 325 (1926).

(20) P. F. Fleury and J. Lange, *Compt. rend.*, **195**, 1395 (1932).

(21) Early comparative studies on the oxidation behavior of the two reagents were made by (a) P. Karrer and R. Hirohata, *Helv. Chim. Acta*, **16**, 959 (1933), and (b) R. Criegee, *Sitzber. Ges. Beförder. ges. Naturw. Marburg*, **69**, 25 (1934); *Chem. Zentr.*, **105**(II), 2515 (1934).

(22) J. M. Bobbitt, *Advances in Carbohydrate Chem.*, **11**, 1 (1956).

tain *at least two free, adjacent hydroxyl groups* (VII) were oxidized, yielding aldehydes or ketones (VIII). A large number of α-glycols which were examined followed second-order kinetics, but rates of reaction differed markedly (see Table I) and these differences were correlated with steric factors.[23, 24] Thus, *cis*-glycols were found to be more easily attacked than *trans*-, and the differences between *cis*- and *trans*- in five-membered rings was greater than in six-membered rings because, in the former, an "even arrangement" was more extremely favorable or unfavorable. Aliphatic glycols possessed properties both of *cis*- and *trans*-compounds because of high rotational freedom, and they generally gave intermediate, oxidation-rate constants. These steric effects strongly resembled those of borate-complexing[25] and acetona-

TABLE I

Rate of Oxidation of vic-*Diols by Lead Tetraacetate*[a]

Diol	Configuration	Ring size	$k_{20°}$
1,2-Acenaphthanediol	*cis*	5	120,000
1,2-Diphenyl-1,2-acenaphthanediol	*cis*	5	33,100
	trans	5	284
1,2-Cyclopentanediol[24]	*cis*	5	40,000
	trans	5	12.8
Methyl α-D-mannofuranoside	*cis*	5	900
D-Mannono-1,4-lactone	*cis*	5	39
D-Arabinono-1,4-lactone	*trans*	5	<0.01
1,2-Cyclohexanediol	*cis*	6	5.0
	trans	6	0.22
1,2-O-Isopropylidene-α-D-glucofuranose	aliphatic	—	0.63
Ethylene glycol	aliphatic	—	0.03

[a] Data from Ref. 23, unless otherwise noted.

tion of glycols, and led to formulation[23] of a hypothetical, five-membered, cyclic intermediate (IX) for the lead tetraacetate reaction, by analogy with Böeseken's cyclic, borate–glycol structure.[25]

Although carbinols were found not to be oxidized by lead tetraacetate in acetic acid, they were attacked in less polar solvents, and glycol-cleavage was also more rapid in these solvents[23]; for example, the rate of oxidation of *trans*-1,2-cyclohexanediol in tetrachloroethane was 5,000 times that in acetic acid. The kinetics was no longer true second-order in the media of low polarity, but approached this state as the concentration of acetic acid

(23) R. Criegee, L. Kraft and B. Rank, *Ann.*, **507**, 159 (1933).

(24) R. Criegee, E. Büchner and W. Walther, *Ber.*, **73**, 571 (1940).

(25) This subject has been reviewed by J. Böeseken, *Advances in Carbohydrate Chem.*, **4**, 189 (1949).

was increased. To explain these properties, it was suggested[23] that the first step in the oxidation of an α-glycol is an esterification, forming X together

$$
\begin{array}{ccc}
\text{R}_2\text{C} \text{---} \text{OH} & \text{R}_2\text{C} = \text{O} & \text{R}_2\text{C} \text{---} \text{O} \\
| & & | \qquad \qquad \text{Pb(OAc)}_2 \\
\text{R}_2\text{C} \text{---} \text{OH} & \text{R}_2\text{C} = \text{O} & \text{R}_2\text{C} \text{---} \text{O} \\
\\
\text{VII} & \text{VIII} & \text{IX}
\end{array}
$$

$$
\begin{array}{c}
\text{R}_2\text{C} \text{---} \text{O} \text{---} \text{Pb(OAc)}_3 \\
| \\
\text{R}_2\text{C} \text{---} \text{OH} \\
\\
\text{X}
\end{array}
$$

with one mole of acetic acid per mole. Cyclization of the ester then was depicted, giving IX in the rate-determining step (which was dependent on the stereochemistry of the glycol group). Since acetic acid was a product, the esterification process also influenced the reaction rate in acetic acid solution by a mass-action effect, and the kinetics was second-order. In other solvents, however, oxidation proceeded more readily to completion. Strong support for the esterification step was provided[26] by the fact that electron-releasing groups accelerate α-glycol oxidation whereas electron-attracting groups retard it, in accordance with the expectation that the Pb—OR bond should be formed more easily with an increased availability of electrons on the oxygen atoms.

Water[27, 28] and methanol[28] accelerated glycol-cleavage, but these appeared to take a positive part in the reaction, giving a hydrolysis product, such as "nascent" lead dioxide,[28] which was more effective than lead tetraacetate itself. Change in dielectric constant may, however, be a more important reason for this enhancing effect.[26] Baer[29, 30] suggested that, in the oxidation of α-keto acids, water or alcohol functioned as part of a "pseudoglycol" for they greatly facilitated decarboxylation; and he showed, by analogy, that acetylcholine could be prepared by the action of lead tetraacetate on a mixture of pyruvic acid and choline chloride in dry acetic acid. Acetate salts were also found to accelerate glycol-cleavage,[28] possibly as basic catalysts, for their effectiveness increased with basicity.

Heidt, Gladding, and Purves[31] pointed out that a specific group of prop-

(26) J. P. Cordner and K. H. Pausacker, *J. Chem. Soc.*, 102 (1953).

(27) E. Baer, J. M. Grosheintz and H. O. L. Fischer, *J. Am. Chem. Soc.*, **61**, 2607 (1939).

(28) R. Criegee and E. Büchner, *Ber.*, **73**, 563 (1940).

(29) E. Baer, *J. Am. Chem. Soc.*, **62**, 1597, 1600 (1940).

(30) E. Baer, *J. Am. Chem. Soc.*, **64**, 1416 (1942).

(31) L. J. Heidt, E. K. Gladding and C. B. Purves, *Tappi*, **121**, 81 (1945).

erties is associated with glycol-cleavage ability. Thus, lead tetraacetate and the related periodic acid possess equally high oxidation potentials and approximately the same effective diameter for the central atom, and undergo a two-valence, electron change. It was predicted that other oxidants having all of these properties—one or another was lacking among the properties of several common oxidants examined—would also cleave α-diols. Sodium perbismuthate and trivalent silver ion were found to fulfil the requirements and were shown, in fact, to produce formaldehyde from ethylene glycol.

The oxidation step has been represented[10, 32] as a transfer of an electron pair from oxygen to Pb^{IV}, with formation of lead diacetate and acetoxy anion, as follows.

$$R—O\overset{\frown}{—}Pb(OAc)_3 \rightarrow RO^{\oplus} + Pb(OAc)_3{}^{\ominus} \rightarrow Pb(OAc)_2 + AcO^{\ominus}$$
$$X$$

In an α-glycol, this transfer is facilitated by simultaneous displacement of an electron pair from the second O—H bond, but it is more difficult with a carbinol because it involves an electron pair of a C—H bond.[10] A mechanism involving free acetoxy radicals instead of a heterolytic process was proposed by Waters,[33] but it was not consistent with subsequent experimental findings on the dissociation of tetravalent lead compounds.[34-36] Homolytic bond fission of the ester X appeared to be an alternative possibility,[26] but, like the free-radical mechanism of Waters, it did not adequately explain rate differences between cis- and trans-diols. Cordner and Pausacker[26] suggested that these differences were due to stronger association by hydrogen bonds in trans- than in cis-glycols, but this hypothesis was not supported by infrared studies on hydrogen bonding in vic-diols.[32, 37-39]

The concept of a cyclic intermediate[23, 40] has been more successful in explaining cis–trans variations. However, the cleavage of some compounds, such as trans-9,10-decalindiol[24] and alicyclic diols containing 9 or more carbon atoms,[32, 41] was not readily accommodated by this mechanism, and

(32) R. Criegee, E. Höger, G. Huber, P. Kruck, F. Marktscheffel and H. Schellenberger, *Ann.*, **599**, 81 (1956).

(33) W. A. Waters, *Nature*, **158**, 380 (1946).

(34) M. S. Kharasch, H. N. Friedlander and W. H. Urry, *J. Org. Chem.*, **14**, 91 (1949).

(35) M. S. Kharasch, H. N. Friedlander and W. H. Urry, *J. Org. Chem.*, **16**, 533 (1951).

(36) W. A. Mosher and C. L. Kehr, *J. Am. Chem. Soc.*, **75**, 3172 (1953).

(37) L. P. Kuhn, *J. Am. Chem. Soc.*, **76**, 4323 (1954).

(38) E. L. Eliel and C. Pillar, *J. Am. Chem. Soc.*, **77**, 3600 (1955).

(39) E. J. Moriconi, F. T. Wallenberger and W. F. O'Connor, *J. Am. Chem. Soc.*, **80**, 656 (1958).

(40) R. Criegee, *Ann.*, **522**, 75 (1936).

(41) V. Prelog, K. Schenker and W. Küng, *Helv. Chim. Acta*, **36**, 471 (1953).

Criegee's original proposals have recently been modified[32] to avoid the necessity of a 5-membered, transition, ring form. The tendency of Pb^{IV} to abstract an electron pair from an oxygen atom was regarded as the driving force of the reaction. This condition could promote a concerted, electron displacement within X, as indicated in XI.[32, 42] Alternatively, proton re-

XI

moval from X could be effected by a "Lewis base" (B:), such as a molecule of acetic acid solvent or, better, of water, alcohol, or acetate anion. These various pathways, including the possibility of cyclization as in IX, thus provided several alternatives. The specific mechanism utilized would then be determined by the chemical and steric properties of the diol.

III. Oxidative Cleavage of *vic*-Diols in Acyclic Systems

With the discovery of the cleavage of glycols by lead tetraacetate, Criegee[18] recognized its applicability to the sugars with their many hydroxyl groups. Glyceritol and mannitol were among the first to be examined.[43] They consumed oxidant smoothly in glacial acetic acid at 50°, yielding two moles of formaldehyde per mole, a measurement which was to serve as an elegant diagnostic test for terminal, 1,2-glycol groups, particularly in sensitive types of compounds.

A series of polyhydric alcohols, ranging from ethylene glycol to hexitols was examined, at 20° and in the presence of a large excess of lead tetraacetate, by Hockett and coworkers.[44] The compounds yielded a family of oxidation-rate curves in which the position of a curve was a function of the number of free carbinol groups in an unbroken series, but there was no simple stoichiometric relation between the number of alcohol groups and the amount of oxidant consumed. At least part of this complexity appeared to be caused by simultaneous oxidation of the formic acid produced in the reaction. The formic acid was converted smoothly to carbon dioxide in about quantitative yield when water was added to the acetic acid solution and the reaction temperature was raised[45, 46] to 35–45°. However, other

(42) A concerted electron-displacement within IX has been considered by W. Rigby, *J. Chem. Soc.*, 1907 (1950).

(43) R. Criegee, *Ann.*, **495**, 211 (1932).

(44) R. C. Hockett, M. T. Dienes, H. G. Fletcher, Jr., and H. E. Ramsden, *J. Am. Chem. Soc.*, **66**, 467 (1944).

(45) J. M. Grosheintz, *J. Am. Chem. Soc.*, **61**, 3379 (1939).

(46) S. Abraham, *J. Am. Chem. Soc.*, **72**, 4050 (1950).

side-reactions now appeared to take place as well, for carbon dioxide evolved under these conditions from glyceritol-*1-C*[14] contained 4.5% of tracer.[47] Most likely, the contamination originated through oxidation of some formaldehyde produced, but it was also possible that enolization of newly-formed aldehydes had occurred.[47] Acetate salts had been shown to enhance rates of glycol-cleavage by lead tetraacetate,[28] and they were also found to promote the oxidation of formic acid to carbon dioxide, affording an alternative method for measuring formic acid in these oxidations.[48, 49] The acetate-catalyzed reaction gave stoichiometric data with polyhydric alcohols at room temperature, both for uptake of lead tetraacetate and for yield of formic acid. Furthermore, incorporation of tracer in carbon dioxide produced from glyceritol-*1-C*[14] was only 0.1%, increasing to 0.4% by prolonged oxidation, showing that undesirable side-reactions were minimized substantially under these conditions.[50]

Comparative oxidations of D-mannitol, D-glucitol, and galactitol in glacial acetic acid[44] and of the first two alditols in 50% acetic acid[51] suggested that the configuration of the alditol exerts little influence on the course of the reactions. This is surprising, because large differences in rate have been found between DL and *meso*-1,2-diols,[32, 52] the former being much more rapidly oxidized, probably because of a less hindered orientation.[53] However, when hexitols were compared with lower alditols, the latter were found to be oxidized with greater difficulty.[51, 54] For example, in 50% acetic acid at 0°, the percentage of the theoretical uptake of lead tetraacetate found[51] in a one-minute reaction time was D-mannitol, 100; glyceritol, 10; and ethylene glycol, 4. These results suggest that a *vic*-diol containing two secondary hydroxyl groups can be oxidized more readily than one containing a primary *and* a secondary hydroxyl group, in agreement with observations on simple aliphatic 1,2-diols.[32] Presumably, then, oxidation should occur more readily toward the center of the hexitol chains than at the ends. The effect is to increase the probability that glycerose or a tetrose (or both) will be formed initially as a product common to each of the hexitols, thus minimizing differences between over-all oxidation rates.[55]

(47) A. P. Doerschuk, *J. Am. Chem. Soc.*, **73**, 5453 (1951). Periodate oxidation yielded formic acid containing only 0.25% of tracer.

(48) A. S. Perlin, *Anal. Chem.*, **26**, 1053 (1954).

(49) A. S. Perlin, *J. Am. Chem. Soc.*, **76**, 5505 (1954).

(50) C. Brice and A. S. Perlin, *Can. J. Biochem. and Physiol.*, **35**, 7 (1957).

(51) P. F. Fleury, J. E. Courtois and A. Bieder, *Bull. soc. chim. France*, 118 (1952).

(52) H. J. Backer and H. Bos, *Rec. trav. chim.*, **57**, 967 (1938).

(53) H. H. Wasserman, in "Steric Effects in Organic Chemistry," M. S. Newman, ed., John Wiley and Sons, Inc., New York, N. Y., 1956, p. 381.

(54) L. Vargha, *Nature*, **162**, 927 (1948).

(55) Recent studies on the periodate oxidation of polyhydric alcohols [(a) J. C. P.

Presence of a tertiary hydroxyl group in a *vic*-diol may increase resistance to lead tetraacetate oxidation,[56] but is not a general effect for all glycols of this type.[32] The 4,5,6-triol in 3-*O*-benzyl-2-*C*-(hydroxymethyl)-D-*arabino*-hexitol (XII) appeared to be attacked more readily than the tertiary glycol, for the compound consumed two moles of lead tetraacetate per mole rapidly, giving 2-*O*-benzyl-3-*C*-(hydroxymethyl)-D-*glycero*-tetrose (2-*O*-benzyl-D-apiose, XIII) in moderate yield. This step facilitated the preparation of synthetic D-apiose.[57]

In addition to stereochemical influences, polar effects might be important in determining the initial site of oxidative attack on certain derivatives of polyhydric alcohols. Müller and Varga[58] found that the polyhydroxy furoic ester derivative (XIV) gave the 2-*C*-formyl derivative (XV) in about 80 %

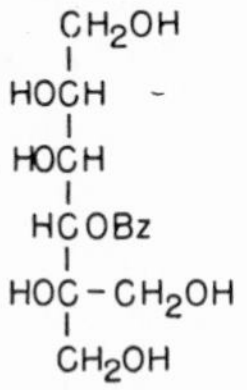

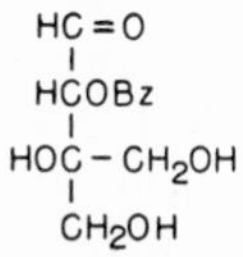

yield with only one mole of lead tetraacetate per mole, and D-glycerose was also obtained. The pyrrole analog of XIV gave similar results. Splitting of the polyhydric alcohol chain in these compounds occurred, therefore, pref-

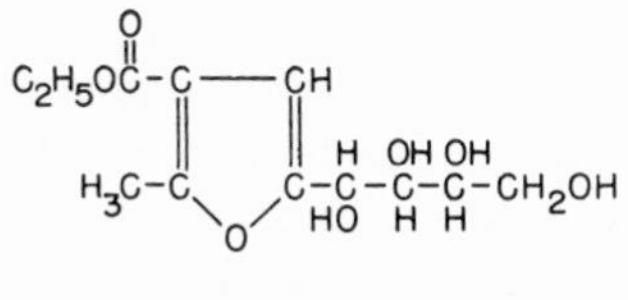

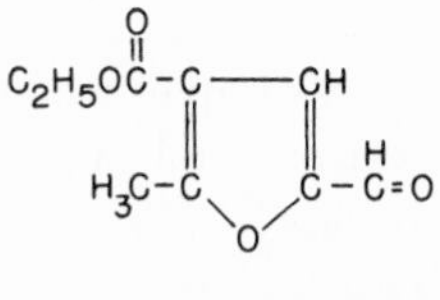

Schwarz, *J. Chem. Soc.*, 276 (1957); (b) J. E. Courtois and M. Guernet, *Bull. soc. chim. France*, 1388 (1957)] have shown that α-glycols containing only secondary hydroxyl groups are generally oxidized most readily and that the *threo* (*trans*)-configuration is favored. The position of initial cleavage in the hexitols was found to vary accordingly.

(56) C. Djerassi, E. Farkas, L. H. Liu and G. H. Thomas, *J. Am. Chem. Soc.*, **77**, 5330 (1955).

(57) P. A. J. Gorin and A. S. Perlin, *Can. J. Chem.*, **36**, 480 (1958).

(58) S. Müller and I. Varga, *Ber.*, **72**, 1993 (1939).

erentially at the *vic*-diol adjacent to the ring, possibly due to inductive effects akin to those observed with benzpinacols[26] or with α-glycols located in the β position relative to a double bond.[32, 59] A quinoxaline analog of XIV also gave the corresponding *C*-formyl derivative in high yield with one mole of lead tetraacetate per mole, but the oxidation of imidazole polyhydric alcohols followed a different, undetermined, pathway.

Since substitution of hydroxyl groups in an alditol decreases the possibilities for glycol cleavage, Criegee[43] recognized the value of lead tetraacetate oxidation as a tool for locating the positions of substituent groups, especially in compounds sensitive to elevated temperatures or strong reagents. Examination of sirupy "2-*O*-acetyl-glyceritol" showed that the preparation contained, in fact, 40% of oxidizable glycol and, hence, was admixed with the 1-*O*-acetyl derivative (or was changed to it). Similarly, Carrara found that glyceritol 1-phosphate could be determined, in the presence of the 2-phosphate, from measurement of the lead tetraacetate uptake.[60] E. Fischer's tetra-*O*-benzoyl-D-mannitol was shown by Brigl and Grüner[61] to be the 1,2,5,6-derivative, for it gave 2,3-di-*O*-benzoyl-D-glycerose in high yield. A di-*O*-tosyl derivative of D-mannitol was found to be the 2,4-diester, for it consumed one mole of lead tetraacetate per mole and yielded 2,4-di-*O*-tosyl-D-arabinose.[62] The preparation of 2,3-*O*-isopropylidene-D-glycerose from di-*O*-isopropylidene-D-mannitol showed that the latter was the 1,2:5,6-di-acetal.[63] This latter application was especially fruitful, for it permitted the preparation of 1,2-*O*-isopropylidene-L-glyceritol, a key compound in subsequent syntheses of glycerides and phospholipids.[64]

These early examples were followed in the succeeding years by numerous other applications and, together with the analogous cleavage by periodate, oxidation by lead tetraacetate has come to constitute probably the most important single means for determining the structure of substituted polyhydric alcohols. Its use for such problems has been particularly well illustrated by Hockett and Fletcher[65] in a study of the di- and tri-benzoates of D-glucitol and D-mannitol. In addition, it has furnished a large variety of useful products, ranging from derivatives of glyoxal and ethylene glycol to those of pentoses, some examples of which have already been given. The great majority of applications to polyhydric alcohols concern their cyclic

(59) C. Djerassi and R. Ehrlich, *J. Org. Chem.*, **19**, 1351 (1954).

(60) G. Carrara, *Giorn. chim. ind. ed-appl.*, **14**, 236 (1932); *Chem. Abstracts*, **26**, 5069 (1932).

(61) P. Brigl and H. Grüner, *Ber.*, **66**, 931 (1933).

(62) A. Müller, *Ber.*, **67**, 830 (1934).

(63) H. O. L. Fischer and E. Baer, *Helv. Chim. Acta*, **17**, 622 (1934).

(64) E. Baer and H. O. L. Fischer, *J. Biol. Chem.*, **128**, 463 (1939).

(65) R. C. Hockett and H. G. Fletcher, Jr., *J. Am. Chem. Soc.*, **66**, 469 (1944).

acetals and these have already been described in detail by Barker and Bourne[66] in an earlier Volume. These authors also tabulated the various combinations of oxidant uptake and production of formic acid and formaldehyde expected for each class of derivative, and indicated preparative uses for the reactions. To avoid unnecessary repetition, therefore, the present Chapter includes only a few references to the oxidations cited by Barker and Bourne.

The reaction of sugar dithioacetals with lead tetraacetate may be complicated by dehydrogenation of the thioacetal groups, in addition to normal glycol-cleavage, depending on the reaction conditions.[67] The latter reaction was found to be favored in non-ionizing solvents, but, in a solvent of medium or high dielectric constant,[68] the thio group was cleaved from the molecule. Thus, the dibenzyl dithioacetals of a group of sugars and sugar acetates in acetic acid yielded dibenzyl disulfide, probably through formation of an intermediate thiol[69] (RSH) and with production of an *aldehydo* diacetate, as follows.

$$\begin{array}{ccc} \text{SR} & & \text{OAc} \\ | & & | \\ \text{X--CH} + \text{Pb(OAc)}_4 \rightarrow \text{RS--S--R} + \text{X--CH} + \text{Pb(OAc)}_2 \\ | & & | \\ \text{SR} & & \text{OAc} \end{array}$$

As the proportion of benzene in the solvent was increased, dehydrogenation of dithioacetals was less pronounced and α-diol scission was more evident.

Using benzene as solvent, Schmidt and Wernicke[70] prepared glyoxal hemi-(dibenzyl dithioacetal) from 4,5-O-isopropylidene-D-fucose dibenzyl dithioacetal. Instead of the corresponding diethyl derivative (XVI), Wolfrom and Usdin[71] obtained ethyl trithio-orthoglyoxylate (XVII) by scission (with lead tetraacetate in dioxane) of the diethyl dithioacetal of D-galactose, L-arabinose, or DL-glycerose. It appeared likely that the trithio derivative resulted from bimolecular disproportionation of the product actually expected, as follows.

$$2 \begin{array}{c} \text{CH(SC}_2\text{H}_5)_2 \\ | \\ \text{CHO} \end{array} \rightarrow \begin{array}{c} \text{C(SC}_2\text{H}_5)_3 \\ | \\ \text{CHO} \end{array} + \begin{array}{c} \text{CH}_2\text{OH} \\ | \\ \text{CHO} \end{array} + \text{C}_2\text{H}_5\text{SH}$$

$$\text{XVI} \qquad\qquad \text{XVII}$$

(66) S. A. Barker and E. J. Bourne, *Advances in Carbohydrate Chem.*, **7**, 137 (1952).

(67) E. J. Bourne, W. M. Corbett, M. Stacey and R. Stephens, *Chem. & Ind.* (London), 106 (1954).

(68) The oxidation of sulfides to sulfoxides by lead tetraacetate has been correlated similarly with the dielectric constant of the solvent [H. E. Barron, G. W. K. Cavill, E. R. Cole, P. T. Gilham and D. H. Soloman, *Chem. & Ind.* (London), 76 (1954)].

(69) Compare L. Field and J. E. Lawson, *J. Am. Chem. Soc.*, **80**, 838 (1958).

(70) O. T. Schmidt and E. Wernicke, *Ann.*, **556**, 179 (1944).

(71) M. L. Wolfrom and E. Usdin, *J. Am. Chem. Soc.*, **75**, 4619 (1953).

In both of these studies, the solvents used promoted glycol-cleavage preferentially.

Lead tetraacetate oxidation, in acetic acid, of a mono-O-benzylidene derivative of L-arabinose diethyl dithioacetal yielded formaldehyde, indicating that the benzylidene group was[72] at positions 2 and 3. However, allowance had to be made for the rapid uptake of about one mole of lead tetraacetate (per mole) by the thio group, as shown from an examination of the reaction with the corresponding di-O-benzylidene and tetra-O-acetyl derivatives. In agreement with this finding, 2,3-di-O-benzoyl-D-arabinose dibenzyl dithioacetal yielded no formaldehyde with one mole of lead tetra- acetate per mole (in *acetic acid*), but two moles of oxidant per mole produced one mole of formaldehyde.[73, 74] By contrast, one mole of the corresponding 4,5-O-isopropylidene-dithioacetal with only one mole of lead tetraacetate in *benzene* gave a good yield of 2,3-O-isopropylidene-D-glycerose. This difference between a 2,3 and a 4,5 derivative appeared to reflect differing reactivity between an α-glycol adjacent to the dithioacetal group and one further removed.[73] A more probable explanation,[67] however, lies in the fact that the 4,5-mono-O-isopropylidene acetal had been oxidized in benzene and the 2,3-dibenzoate in acetic acid.

IV. Oxidative Cleavage of *vic*-Diols in Alicyclic Systems

1. *Stereochemical Considerations*

As noted earlier, certain generalizations can be made about the lead tetraacetate–glycol reaction in terms of the type of glycol concerned. Among these are: (a) a compound possessing a *cis*-glycol group is oxidized more rapidly than is its *trans* isomer; and (b) rate differences between *cis–trans* isomeric pairs are greater for five-membered ring compounds than for acyclic or for six-membered ring compounds. It was clear from the outset[43] that, if the basis for such generalizations was sufficiently broad, the oxidation behavior of an unknown carbohydrate might help to define other structural features than simply the presence or absence of a 1,2-glycol group. Consequently, lead tetraacetate has received particular attention as a reagent for examining ring size, configuration, and ring shape—factors which determine the type of glycol present. An understanding of glycol-cleavage oxidation in terms of the stereochemistry of the sugar molecules attacked has been greatly facilitated by modern views on stereochemical influences

(72) C. F. Huebner, R. A. Pankratz and K. P. Link, *J. Am. Chem. Soc.*, **72**, 4811 (1950).

(73) S. B. Baker, *J. Am. Chem. Soc.*, **74**, 827 (1952).

(74) The dibenzyl dithioacetal group is stable to oxidative attack by periodate; L. Hough and M. I. Taha, *J. Chem. Soc.*, 3994 (1957).

in organic chemistry.[53, 75, 76] It may be useful to refer briefly, here, to this development.

The geometry of the —O—C—C—O— grouping was considered[23, 24] to be the most important steric factor determining reaction rates, and oxidation was fastest, therefore, with the glycol having the "most orderly arrangement." In agreement with this concept, the effective diameter of an oxidant was found to be critical in determining whether or not glycol-fission could occur.[31] However, the actual distance between the hydroxyl groups, as judged by intermolecular hydrogen bonding, was thought to have a relatively minor effect on rates of oxidation by lead tetraacetate.[37, 77] Possibly, this was an under-evaluation for it equated a molecule "at rest" with a "reacting" molecule, thereby neglecting possible conformational changes in the activated species.[32, 39]

Studies on the closely analogous reactions of cuprammonium hydroxide and of lead tetraacetate with 1,2-diols led Reeves[75, 78, 79] to emphasize the significance, for glycol-complexing, of "coplanarity"; that is, the closer the two hydroxyl groups approach each other *in a plane*, the more favorable the arrangement. Hence, the angles which can be subtended by the pair of carbon–oxygen bonds were carefully evaluated, reference being made to the concepts of Hassel and Ottar on the shapes of pyranose rings.[80] The tetrahydrofuran ring appears to be nearly planar,[81] although it can be found in a highly puckered form.[82] This planarity, Reeves noted, tends to fix a *cis*-1,2-glycol group rigidly in the 0° (eclipsed) orientation (as shown in the Newman projection[83] by XVIII) and the *trans*- at an angle of 120°. Consequently, bridging by Pb^{IV} may take place much more readily with the *cis*- than with the *trans*-glycol, a conclusion which is in accordance with the extremely rapid oxidation of five-membered, *cis* compounds and with the markedly lower rates for the *trans* isomers (see Table I, p. 12).

(75) R. E. Reeves, *Advances in Carbohydrate Chem.*, **6**, 107 (1951).

(76) D. H. R. Barton and R. C. Cookson, *Quart. Revs.* (London), **10**, 44 (1956).

(77) Recent studies on complexing of *vic*-diols with borate and with cuprammonium hydroxide have also suggested that there is little correlation between 0—0 distance and complex formation; H. Kwart and G. C. Gatos, *J. Am. Chem. Soc.*, **80**, 881 (1958).

(78) R. E. Reeves, *Anal. Chem.*, **21**, 751 (1949).

(79) R. E. Reeves, *J. Am. Chem. Soc.*, **72**, 1499 (1950).

(80) O. Hassel and B. Ottar, *Acta Chem. Scand.*, **1**, 929 (1947). A relationship between the reactivity of anomeric sugars and their stereochemistry was recognized many years ago by H. S. Isbell [*J. Research Natl. Bur. Standards*, **18**, 505 (1937)], but newer physical and chemical methods had first to be developed before these relationships could be clearly defined.

(81) For a discussion of the stereochemistry of the tetrahydrofuran ring, see J. A. Mills, *Advances in Carbohydrate Chem.*, **10**, 1 (1955).

(82) C. A. Beevers and W. Cochran, *Proc. Roy. Soc.* (London), **190A**, 257 (1947).

(83) M. S. Newman, *J. Chem. Educ.*, **32**, 344 (1955).

In the pyranose ring, the true *cis* orientation is encountered in boat forms (for example, XIX) or in the half-chair forms (for example, XX) and again, as illustrated by the very rapid uptake of lead tetraacetate by methyl 2,6-anhydro-α-D-altropyranoside,[84] which is known to have a boat conformation,

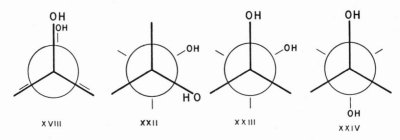

the 0° angle is optimal for glycol-cleavage or copper complexing.[79, 80] The preferred, chair conformations of cyclohexane and pyranose rings are essentially strainless[81, 85] (XXI represents Reeves' *C1* form) and a vicinal glycol on these rings may have (a) an equatorial–equatorial orientation (*e,e*; *trans*) in which the bonds subtend a 60° angle (XXII), (b) an axial–equatorial (*a,e*; *cis*) also having a 60° angle (XXIII), or (c) an axial–axial orientation (*a,a*; *trans*) subtending an angle of 180° (XXIV). Although the angles represented in XXII and XXIII are approximately equal, deformation about the carbon–carbon bond of the *cis*-glycol causes decreased ring-puckering as coplanarity is approached, but increased puckering results when the two equatorial hydroxyl groups of the *trans* isomer (XXII) are brought closer together.[86] Greater energy must be expended by the *trans*

(84) D. A. Rosenfeld, N. K. Richtmyer and C. S. Hudson, *J. Am. Chem. Soc.*, **70**, 2201 (1948).

(85) Recent evidence by J. S. Brimacombe, A. B. Foster and D. H. Whiffen, *Abstracts Papers Am. Chem. Soc.*, **132**, 2D (1957), indicates that the pyran ring has greater flexibility than the cyclohexane ring.

(86) S. J. Angyal and C. G. MacDonald, *J. Chem. Soc.*, 686 (1952).

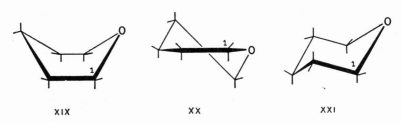

isomer, therefore, and its oxidation rate is noticeably lower than that of the *cis* isomer (see Table I). The a,a-orientation is least favorable to formation of a planar, cyclic intermediate, and, consequently, it is oxidized even more slowly than the e,e-*trans* form.[23, 87]

Stereochemical considerations such as these serve to rationalize most lead tetraacetate–glycol oxidations in terms of a planar, cyclic intermediate (IX). It has been noted already, however, that some *vic*-diols which *cannot* form a planar intermediate of this kind are *nevertheless* cleaved by lead tetraacetate.[24] Other compounds are known (for example, certain derivatives of 9,10-dihydro-9,10-phenanthrenediol and 4,5-dihydro-4,5-pyrenediol) in which the *trans* isomer of a 6-membered-ring pair is oxidized more rapidly than the *cis* isomer.[32, 39] The rate of oxidation of *trans*-1,2-cyclopentanediol (120° orientation), though much lower than that of the *cis* isomer (0° orientation), is substantially higher than the rates for *cis*- or *trans*-1,2-cyclohexanediol (60° orientation) (see Table I). Some *trans*-glycols on the furan ring also show similar behavior (see below). Among the steroids, 22α,5α-spirostan-2β,3α-diol (which possesses a *vic*-diol in an a,a relationship) is oxidized more rapidly than the corresponding a,e-*cis* and e,e-*trans* isomers.[59] Such exceptions may involve oxidation pathways represented by Criegee's modified mechanisms.[32] In others, bulky substituents may force a diol into a conformation favoring a planar, cyclic intermediate.[39] A factor of probable significance in some of these reactions is the fact that lead tetraacetate oxidation is an *irreversible* decomposition, and, hence, may be driven progressively to completion by formation of even a small amount of the proper intermediate.[53] Sometimes, polar effects may be of greater importance than steric factors in determining relative rates.[26]

This lack of an entirely consistent pattern has not prevented the successful application of glycol-cleavage by lead tetraacetate to a wide variety of structural problems. In relating oxidation data to structure, it has been necessary only to recognize that a single approach to a chemical problem is never fully adequate and that other lines of evidence must be sought.

2. *Five-membered Rings*

The oxidation of 1,2-*O*-isopropylidene-D-glucofuranose with lead tetraacetate was found by Criegee to yield formaldehyde,[43] which confirmed the presence of a furanose ring in the sugar derivative. The major oxidation fragment, 1,2-*O*-isopropylidene-5-*aldehydo*-D-*xylo*-pentodialdose, was characterized subsequently by Iwadare,[88] and has recently been shown to crys-

---

(87) The relationship between rates of oxidation by lead tetraacetate and the stereochemistry of *trans*-decalin-2,3-diols as well as of 1,2-cyclohexanediols has been considered recently by M. E. Ali and L. N. Owen, *J. Chem. Soc.*, 2119 (1958).

(88) K. Iwadare, *Bull. Chem. Soc. Japan*, **16**, 40 (1941).

tallize[89] as a so-called "dimer." Criegee extended this criterion of ring size to several other hexose derivatives.[43] When treated with one mole of oxidant in acetic acid at 55°, ethyl α-D-glucofuranoside and D-glucono-1,4-lactone each yielded almost a mole of formaldehyde per mole. However, methyl α-D-mannofuranoside (XXV) and D-mannono-1,4-lactone yielded only about 10 percent of the theoretical value of one mole per mole. The explanation for these contrasting data appeared to lie in the markedly different oxidation rates of *cis, trans,* and aliphatic glycol groups present in the compounds. In the D-glucose derivatives, the 5,6-glycol was attacked about 100 times faster than the 2,3-*trans*-glycol in the ring (see Table I), but, in the D-mannose derivatives, the *cis*-ring glycol group was oxidized preferentially, giving XXVI from the methyl furanoside. Rapid, cyclic hemiacetal formation could then convert XXVI to XXVII, stabilizing the terminal glycol against attack by the oxidant.

Criegee reasoned that if the 2,3-glycol of the D-mannofuranoside complexed with borate under the reaction conditions, attack at the 5,6-glycol would be enhanced. The formaldehyde yield was, in fact, increased from 12 to 67 percent with borate present, but the corresponding lactone showed little change. The latter effect was due, possibly, not to lack of complexing at the 2,3-glycol but to an unexpectedly large borate affinity for the 5,6-glycol group, because the rate of oxidation of the D-glucose derivatives was also lower in boric acid–acetic acid.[90]

Hockett, Nickerson, and Reeder,[91] using a very large excess of lead tetraacetate in acetic acid at 20°, observed an oxidation pattern for methyl α-D-mannofuranoside consistent with that noted by Criegee. One mole of reagent per mole was consumed very rapidly, and further oxidation was slow, as expected for the sequence XXV → XXVII. Presence of a small but finite amount of XXVI was thought to account for the slow, continuing oxidation.

The rapid oxidation step was demonstrated more clearly by the reaction of methyl α,β-D-erythrofuranoside[92] (XXVIII), another 5-membered ring glycoside containing a *cis*-glycol group. This mixed glycoside was obtained by the action of methanol (containing hydrogen chloride) on D-erythrose. By analogy with the behavior of DL-glycerose,[93] other products of the reaction could have been the dimethyl acetal (XXIX) and a dimeric deriva-

(89) R. Schaffer and H. S. Isbell, *J. Am. Chem. Soc.,* **79,** 3864 (1957).

(90) At pH 10, the 5,6-glycol group of D-glucofuranosides appears to have little importance in formation of borate complexes; A. B. Foster and M. Stacey, *J. Chem. Soc.,* 1778 (1955).

(91) R. C. Hockett, M. H. Nickerson and W. H. Reeder III, *J. Am. Chem. Soc.,* **66,** 472 (1944).

(92) R. C. Hockett and C. W. Maynard, Jr., *J. Am. Chem. Soc.,* **61,** 2111 (1939).

(93) H. O. L. Fischer and C. Taube, *Ber.,* **60,** 1706 (1927).

tive (XXX). However, the rate and extent of oxidation were consistent with structure XXVIII, and this conclusion was confirmed by an oxidation with bromine following the lead tetraacetate oxidation. A dicarboxylic acid

XXV   XXVI   XXVII

XXVIII   XXIX   XXX

such as is given by methyl pentopyranosides[94] was obtained, and the specific rotation of the salt showed that the proportion of the α to β anomer in the original glycoside mixture was[95, 95a] 58 to 42.

Ethyl β-D-galactofuranoside (XXXI) consumed two moles of lead tetraacetate per mole relatively slowly and formaldehyde was produced simultaneously, but overoxidation was very extensive.[91] Because the ring-glycol

XXXI   XXXII   XXXIII

was in the less reactive *trans* form, most molecules, statistically, were expected to be attacked outside the ring first, giving XXXII. Evidence in favor of this interpretation is obtained by comparing the relative rates of oxidation of the 5,6-acyclic diol grouping of ethyl 2-deoxy-α,β-2-D-*lyxo*-hexofuranoside[96] with the 3,4-*trans*-glycol grouping of methyl α-D-fructofuranoside,[97] the former being considerably more reactive. Compound XXXII

(94) E. L. Jackson and C. S. Hudson, *J. Am. Chem. Soc.*, **59**, 994 (1937).

(95) Treatment of di-*O*-formyl-D-erythrose with methanolic hydrogen chloride has yielded a much higher proportion of the β isomer; J. N. Baxter and A. S. Perlin, *Chem. Inst. Canada, Abstracts 4th Western Conference*, Sept. 4, 1958, p. 23.

(95a) The β isomer exclusively was obtained by C. E. Ballou, *Abstracts Papers Am. Chem. Soc.*, **134**, 9D (1958).

(96) A. B. Foster, W. G. Overend and M. Stacey, *J. Chem. Soc.*, 974 (1951).

(97) R. C. Hockett and W. S. McClenahan, *J. Am. Chem. Soc.*, **61**, 1667 (1939).

was sterically impeded from intramolecular, hemiacetal formation, and further oxidation gave the hypothetical trialdehyde (XXXIII). The active hydrogen atom of the malonaldehyde residue of XXXIII could then be attacked further, perhaps by acetoxylation,[4] and the consumption of oxidant proceeded well beyond the theoretical value of two moles per mole.[98] Under the same reaction conditions, 2,4-pentanedione (acetylacetone) readily took up about three moles of lead tetraacetate per mole.

These oxidation patterns were sufficiently characteristic and different from each other to assist in structural assignment for other hexose derivatives having furanose rings. For example, the structure of 3,6-anhydro-D-glucitol was confirmed by the fact that the compound consumes lead tetraacetate at a rate identical with that of methyl α-D-mannofuranoside. Another monoanhydro-D-glucitol (Arlitan) was oxidized[99] at the same rate as ethyl β-D-galactofuranoside and 3,6-anhydro-D-galactitol, and it yielded formaldehyde. Hence, it was assigned the 1,4-ring structure (which was confirmed subsequently by other evidence).

A monoanhydro derivative of D-mannitol dibenzoate, thought to be 2,4-anhydro-1,6-di-O-benzoyl-D-mannitol,[100] was shown[101] to have, actually, a 1,4-anhydro-D-mannitol (1,4-D-mannitan) structure. Removal of the benzoate groups thus afforded an anhydro derivative which consumed lead tetraacetate at the rate for methyl D-mannofuranoside. When the original compound was treated with benzaldehyde and zinc chloride, and the benzoyl groups subsequently removed, the resulting monobenzylidene derivative also consumed one mole of lead tetraacetate per mole but yielded no formaldehyde. Hence, the benzylidene group appeared to have been introduced at the 5,6 positions, accompanied by migration of a benzoate group, possibly from position 6 to 3. Reeves[102] later showed that the benzylidene group had itself migrated from the 2,3- to the 5,6-position, a migration probably caused by prolonged solution in acetic acid prior to the addition of lead tetraacetate. Freshly dissolved in acetic acid, the mono-O-benzylidene-D-mannitan consumed one mole of oxidant per mole, and yielded a mole of formaldehyde.

A different monoanhydro-di-O-benzoyl-D-hexitol prepared from D-mannitol, designated 2,5-anhydro-1,6-di-O-benzoyl-D-mannitol (XXXIV, R = benzoyl),[100] was reported to consume no lead tetraacetate, presumably

(98) The analogous oxidation of active methylene groups formed during the oxidation of a variety of carbohydrates by periodate has been considered in detail.[22]

(99) R. C. Hockett, M. Conley, M. Yusem and R. I. Mason, *J. Am. Chem. Soc.*, **68**, 922 (1946).

(100) P. Brigl and H. Grüner, *Ber.*, **67**, 1582 (1934).

(101) R. C. Hockett, H. G. Fletcher, Jr., E. Sheffield, R. M. Goepp, Jr., and S. Solzberg, *J. Am. Chem. Soc.*, **68**, 930 (1946).

(102) R. E. Reeves, *J. Am. Chem. Soc.*, **71**, 2868 (1949).

XXXIV   XXXV   XXXVI

because of the unfavorable *trans*-glycol grouping on the 5-membered ring. Later work[103] contradicted this finding, the compound being shown to take up one mole of oxidant per mole relatively rapidly, and the rate was enhanced by removal of the benzoate groups. No formaldehyde was liberated, in agreement with the assignment of a 2,5-ring, but the dialdehyde produced was optically inactive, suggesting that it was probably the bis(3-*O*-benzoyl-DL-glycerose)-2 ether (XXXV, R = benzoyl). Therefore, the anhydrohexitol must have possessed the D-*glucitol* configuration (XXXVI), for the corresponding D-mannitol derivative should have yielded a dis-symmetric, optically active product, showing that inversion had accompanied anhydridation. This latter oxidation method had been employed earlier by Vargha and Puskás[104] in showing that 2,5-anhydro-1,6-di-*O*-tosyl-L-iditol yields the optically active bis(3-*O*-tosyl-L-glycerose)-2 ether.

The 1,6-anhydro-β-D-aldohexofuranoses[105] represent a somewhat special instance of compounds possessing the furan ring, for the 1,6-oxygen bridge present introduces extra rigidity. Consequently, the *trans*-2,3-glycol grouping of the D-glucitol and galactitol derivatives are so disposed as to be completely resistant to glycol-cleavage. This unusual behavior has been considered fully in an earlier Volume.[106] The corresponding dianhydride possessing a *cis*-2,3-glycol grouping is not known as yet, but, by contrast, it should consume one mole of lead tetraacetate per mole very rapidly.

Earlier, it was noted that *trans*-1,2-cyclopentanediol is oxidized more rapidly than might be expected for a *trans*-glycol subtending an angle of 120°, its rate being about 60 times that of *trans*-1,2-cyclohexanediol (60° orientation). In analogous fashion, a given weight of methyl α-D-fructofuranoside consumes lead tetraacetate more rapidly than the same weight of methyl α-D-glucopyranoside.[97] Hockett and Zief[107] equated the relative oxidation rates of these two glycosides with those of the D-fructofuranosyl and D-glucopyranosyl residues, respectively, in sucrose (XXXVII). Conse-

(103) R. C. Hockett, M. Zief and R. M. Goepp, Jr., *J. Am. Chem. Soc.*, **68**, 935 (1946).

(104) L. Vargha and T. Puskás, *Ber.*, **76**, 859 (1943).

(105) R. J. Dimler, H. A. Davis and G. E. Hilbert, *J. Am. Chem. Soc.*, **68**, 1377 (1946).

(106) R. J. Dimler, *Advances in Carbohydrate Chem.*, **7**, 37 (1952).

(107) R. C. Hockett and M. Zief, *J. Am. Chem. Soc.*, **72**, 2130 (1950).

quently, it has been found[108] that, when treated with one mole of lead tetra-acetate per mole, sucrose is attacked preferentially at the D-fructose unit.

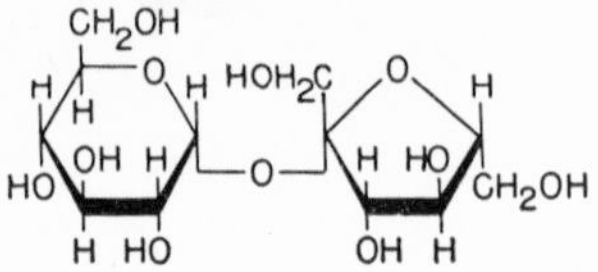

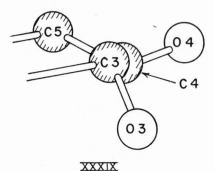

XXXVII 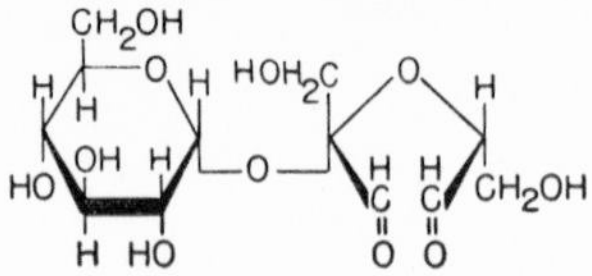   XXXVIII

affording mainly the dialdehyde (XXXVIII). (By contrast, periodate oxidized the D-glucose residue much more readily, in agreement with the observation that methyl L-arabinofuranoside is oxidized by periodate with much greater difficulty than are pyranosides.[94] This difference between the two oxidants was also apparent in the degradation of raffinose and stachyose to sucrose.[109]) X-ray crystallography has shown[82] that, in the D-fructosyl residue of the sucrose–sodium bromide dihydrate complex, the ring-oxygen atom and C2, C3, and C5 lie essentially in one plane, and the ring is puckered at C4, so that the hydroxyl groups at C3 and C4 are forced toward co-planarity (as in XXXIX). In addition, the angles which the 3- and 4-hy-

XXXIX

droxyl bonds make with the adjacent ring bonds are unusually large, tending further to bring the hydroxyl groups into the mean plane of the residue. This conformation is probably imposed by forces within the crystal lattice and cannot be taken to represent the D-fructofuranosyl unit in solution. Nevertheless, it is clear that, under suitable conditions, the furanose ring *can be* distorted so as to favor formation of a planar, cyclic intermediate, a formation which might occur in the lead-complex, transition state. Possibly, then, the anomalous oxidation behavior in general of *trans*-1,2-diol

(108) A. K. Mitra and A. S. Perlin, *Abstracts Papers Am. Chem. Soc.*, **134,** 8D (1958).

(109) A. K. Mitra and A. S. Perlin, *Can. J. Chem.*, **36,** 1079 (1957).

groupings of 5-membered rings may be related to this unusual, conformational feature.

3. Six-membered Rings

The ring structure of methyl pyranosides was found by Criegee to be stable to lead tetraacetate oxidation,[43] for methyl α-D-glucopyranoside and methyl α-D-mannopyranoside consume about two moles of oxidant per mole *without* concomitant production of formaldehyde. It was possible, therefore, to distinguish between aldohexofuranosides and aldohexopyranosides by this method.

In determining the constitution of shikimic and quinic acids, Fischer and Dangschat[110] examined the lead tetraacetate oxidation of $1,2,3$-triol groupings of the cyclohexane ring. Dihydroshikimic acid methyl ester (XL) and the 1-amino compound (derived from it by way of the Curtius degradation) each consumed, as expected, about two moles of lead tetraacetate or periodate, per mole. The dialdehydes obtained in these reactions were further oxidized with bromine to the corresponding dicarboxylic acids, methyl dihydroshikimate giving tricarballylic acid in 34% yield. An 89% yield of citric acid was obtained from methyl quinate, using aqueous acetic acid as the solvent for lead tetraacetate.[27] Similarly, lead tetraacetate cleavage followed by bromine oxidation was utilized[110a] to determine the configuration of conduritol and of *meso*-inositol. The former was converted by way of the $3,6$-di-O-acetyl-$1,2$-O-isopropylidene derivative to galactaric acid,[111] and the other cyclitol, by way of the $1,2,3,4$-tetraacetate, to DL-idaric acid.[112] This sequence of two consecutive oxidations in converting cyclic-sugar derivatives to open-chain dicarboxylic acids was later utilized in studies on the configurations of glycosides.[94, 113, 114]

Fischer and Dangschat[115] also applied lead tetraacetate oxidation to locate the position of a single, free hydroxyl group on a six-membered ring. Thus, the mono-O-isopropylidene acetal of quinic acid lactone (XLI) was

(110) H. O. L. Fischer and G. Dangschat, *Helv. Chim. Acta*, **17**, 1200 (1934).
(110a) See S. J. Angyal and L. Anderson, this Volume, p. 135.
(111) H. O. L. Fischer and G. Dangschat, *Naturwissenschaften*, **27**, 756 (1939).
(112) G. Dangschat, *Naturwissenschaften*, **30**, 146 (1942).
(113) W. D. Maclay and C. S. Hudson, *J. Am. Chem. Soc.*, **60**, 2059 (1938).
(114) W. S. McClenahan and R. C. Hockett, *J. Am. Chem. Soc.*, **60**, 2061 (1938).
(115) H. O. L. Fischer and G. Dangschat, *Ber.*, **65**, 1009 (1932).

first converted (with methylmagnesium iodide) to the glycol (XLII); this
was degraded to the cyclohexanone derivative, showing that the hydroxyl
group had been adjacent to the carboxyl group.

A 1,2,3-triol grouping in a six-membered ring presents *two* points of
attack, and these may not possess equivalent reactivity. In methyl α-D-
mannopyranoside (XLIII), the 2,3-*cis*-glycol group should be attacked
more readily than the 3,4-*trans*-diol. McClenahan and Hockett[114] attempted
to limit (localize) the point of initial cleavage by examining the product
given with one mole of lead tetraacetate per mole. A large proportion of unoxidized D-mannoside remained and triose phenylosazone was isolated, but
the expected D-erythrose was not found. It was suggested that, if the hydroxy aldehyde (XLIV) was formed first, it must in turn be degraded very
rapidly, a possibility which was clarified later[97] (see below). In the presence
of excess lead tetraacetate, methyl D-aldohexopyranosides (for example,
XLIII) yielded the dialdehyde (XLV), and subsequent oxidation with

XLIII   XLIV   XLV, (R = H)
                                                 XLVII, (R = CHO)

hypobromite afforded the corresponding dicarboxylic acid which was the
same as that produced by periodate–hypobromite oxidations of the glycosides.[94, 113] Curiously, the dialdehydes obtained by lead tetraacetate
cleavage were reported[114] to have specific rotations substantially higher than
those of the dialdehydes given by periodate,[94, 116] but closer agreement (on
this point) between the two oxidants has been found more recently.[117] In
converting methyl α- and β-L-arabinopyranosides to the corresponding dialdehydes in aqueous acetic acid, three moles of lead tetraacetate per mole
were required, one mole of oxidant being consumed by the formic acid
liberated.[45] This reaction is useful for determining the activity of C3 in
C^{14}-labeled methyl glycopyranosides.[46]

A thorough study of the oxidation behavior of a wide variety of glycopyranosides under carefully standardized conditions was undertaken by
Hockett and coworkers[97, 118] in order to examine the usefulness of lead tetraacetate for determining hydroxyl configuration. Their results may be summarized as follows. (1) At least two moles of oxidant per mole were always

(116) F. Smith and J. W. van Cleve, *J. Am. Chem. Soc.*, **77**, 3901 (1955).

(117) A. J. Charlson and A. S. Perlin, *Can. J. Chem.*, **34**, 1804 (1956).

(118) R. C. Hockett, M. T. Dienes and H. E. Ramsden, *J. Am. Chem. Soc.*, **65**, 1474 (1943).

consumed ultimately, but side-reactions, such as the oxidation of liberated formic acid, often prevented the uptake from levelling off at this theoretical value. (2) All glycosides having a *cis*-glycol grouping consumed a first mole of lead tetraacetate, per mole, more rapidly than those containing only *trans*-glycol groupings. Since the initial rate of cleavage was probably the rate-determining step, glycosides possessing a *trans-trans*-triol all yielded similar oxidation-rate curves; these rates were low and the curves showed no marked breaks (represented by methyl α-D-glucopyranoside; see curve 1, Fig. 1). (3) Glycopyranosides having one *cis*- and one *trans*-glycol group-

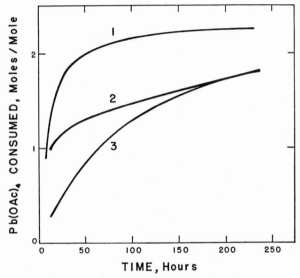

Fig. 1.—Rates of Consumption[97] of Lead Tetraacetate by the Methyl α-D-Pyranosides of Mannose (1), Galactose (2), and Glucose (3), in Glacial Acetic Acid (Temp. 20°).

ing could be classified into two categories: (a) those consuming a second mole at a rapid speed, comparable with that of the first mole, and (b) those in which uptake of the second mole was slower than that of the first.

In group (a) were D-mannosides, D-fructosides, and D-gulosides. Their behavior (represented by curve 2, Fig. 1) was exemplified by that of methyl α-D-mannopyranoside (XLIII). Oxidation was presumed to take place first at the 2,3-*cis*-glycol grouping, yielding a dialdehyde (XLIV) which was in equilibrium with a mixture of *cis*- and *trans*-hemiacetal glycols[119] (for example, XLVI). Being in a 5-membered ring, the new *cis*-glycol group was

(119) B. Helferich [*Ber.*, **64,** 104 (1931)] had noted the tendency of γ-hydroxy aldehydes to cyclize.

rapidly attacked by a second mole of lead tetraacetate and the rate was maintained by a shift in the equilibrium. This rapid, secondary oxidation could have accounted for the earlier failure[114] to find D-erythrose after treating the D-mannoside with one mole of lead tetraacetate per mole. The final product would thus be a formate ester of XLV (namely, XLVII), by analogy with the ozonolysis of D-ribal (D-arabinal) to mono-O-formyl-D-erythrose.[120] An oxidation-rate curve almost identical with that of methyl α-D-mannopyranoside was obtained for styracitol (a 1,5-anhydro-D-hexitol), which, accordingly, was assigned a D-mannitan structure. The same structure for styracitol was assigned by Freudenberg and Rogers[121] from lead tetraacetate oxidation data.

Group (b) was represented by methyl α-D-galactopyranoside. Here, rapid consumption of the first mole of oxidant (per mole) by the 3,4-*cis*-glycol was depicted as giving a hydroxy aldehyde (XLVIII) which was *not* favorably disposed for internal, hemiacetal formation, and was attacked relatively slowly by the second mole of lead tetraacetate (see curve 3, Fig. 1). In agreement with these views, methyl 6-O-trityl-α-D-mannopyranoside and methyl 6-deoxy-α-L-mannopyranoside, being unable to form a hemiacetal as in XLVI, gave oxidation-rate curves analogous to those of group (b).

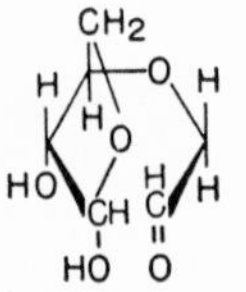

XLVI 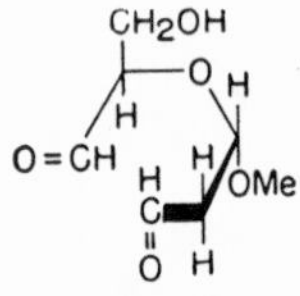   XLVIII

A glycoside containing two *cis*-glycol groups was not available for comparison with the other types examined, but 1-O-benzoyl-D-talopyranose[122, 123] has been oxidized[123] under similar conditions (as a representative of this class of pyranose compounds) and found to consume two moles of lead tetraacetate per mole very rapidly.

Little difference in reaction rates was observed between the anomeric glycosides or between the corresponding methyl and phenyl glycosides.[97, 118] This point might bear re-examination in view of the extensive side-reactions encountered in almost all of the oxidations, for, with the anomeric 2-deoxy-

(120) G. E. Felton and W. Freudenberg, *J. Am. Chem. Soc.*, **57**, 1637 (1935).

(121) W. Freudenberg and E. F. Rogers, *J. Am. Chem. Soc.*, **59**, 1602 (1937).

(122) H. S. Isbell, J. E. Stewart, H. L. Frush, J. D. Moyer and F. A. Smith, *J. Research Natl. Bur. Standards*, **57**, 179 (1956).

(123) H. B. Wood, Jr., and H. G. Fletcher, Jr., *J. Am. Chem. Soc.*, **79**, 3234 (1957).

D-*erythro*-pentopyranosides, the α anomer consumes lead tetraacetate almost twice as rapidly as does the β.[124]

Lead tetraacetate oxidation-rates were used by Hockett and Mowery[125] to compare the relative ease of tritylation of the secondary hydroxyl groups of methyl α-D-arabinopyranoside and methyl 6-deoxy-α-L-galactopyranoside. For the main monotrityl ether obtained from each glycoside, lead tetraacetate uptake was relatively fast, indicative of a free 3,4-*cis*-glycol group.[125a] Acetylation of the main methyl di-O-trityl-α-D-arabinoside, followed by detritylation, afforded a monoacetate. The results of oxidation of the latter suggested that the trityloxy groups had been located at C2 and C3, for the slow consumption of lead tetraacetate observed is characteristic of a *trans*-diol. The over-all results indicated that tritylation of secondary hydroxyl groups in those glycosides proceeded preferentially at the hydroxyl group of C2.

As noted earlier, side-reactions accompanying the lead tetraacetate oxidation of glycopyranosides tend to obscure the stoichiometry of the reaction.[118] By utilizing the "potassium acetate-catalyzed" reaction,[28, 49] it was possible to account for the production of formic acid and to demonstrate clearly that cleavage of the 1,2,3-triol grouping in methyl glycopyranosides by lead tetraacetate *is*, in fact, stoichiometric.[49] In glacial acetic acid, the uptake of oxidant always levelled off at the theoretical value of two moles per mole, but the essential features of the oxidations remained the same as in the *absence* of potassium acetate. Thus, methyl α-D-mannopyranoside consumed two moles of reagent (per mole) rapidly, methyl α-D-galactopyranoside took up the first mole rapidly and the second more slowly, and methyl α-D-glucopyranoside showed a relatively slow consumption of both moles of oxidant.

In these catalyzed oxidations, formic acid production did not parallel the uptake of lead tetraacetate[49] and, particularly with the D-mannopyranoside and D-galactopyranoside, fell far short of the theoretical value of one mole per mole (see Fig. 2). Methyl α-D-mannoside yielded only one third of a mole of free acid per mole, a result which agreed well with the earlier formulation[97] of the ester (XLVII) as the reaction product to be expected. The almost equally low yield of formic acid from methyl α-D-galactopyrano-

(124) R. E. Deriaz, W. G. Overend, M. Stacey and L. F. Wiggins, *J. Chem. Soc.*, 2836 (1949).

(125) R. C. Hockett and D. F. Mowery, Jr., *J. Am. Chem. Soc.*, **65**, 403 (1943).

(125a) Differences in reactivity between a *cis*- and a *trans*-1,2-diol group on the tetrahydropyran ring are clearly illustrated by the comparative rates of oxidation of some 1,5-anhydro-2-deoxy-pentitols and -hexitols [H. F. Bauer and D. E. Stuetz, *J. Am. Chem. Soc.*, **78**, 4097 (1956); E. von Rudloff and A. P. Tulloch, *Can. J. Chem.*, **35**, 1504 (1957)].

side was not in accord with the suggestion[97] that oxidation of the free hydroxy aldehyde (XLVIII) was responsible for the slow consumption of the
second mole of lead tetraacetate. However, compound XLVIII may exist
in equilibrium with several cyclic modifications,[126] such as a hydrate, a
dimeric form, or an intramolecular hemiacetal.[127] Of these possibilities, a
7-membered, internal hemiacetal (XLIX) appeared to account most satisfactorily for the high yield of formate ester (XLVII).[49] Supporting the as-

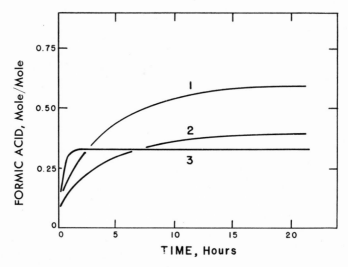

FIG. 2.—Rates of Production[49] of Formic Acid (CO_2 Evolution) during Oxidation
of the Methyl α-D-Pyranosides of Glucose (1), Galactose (2), and Mannose (3), with
Lead Tetraacetate in Glacial Acetic Acid Containing Potassium Acetate (Temp. 27°).

sumption that formate ester formation involved the primary carbinol group
was the fact that methyl β-L-arabinopyranoside yields one mole of formic
acid per mole at a rate close to that of the lead tetraacetate uptake. Theoretically, the hydroxy aldehyde derived from the arabinopyranoside by
primary cleavage of the 3,4-*cis*-diol should be analogous to XLVIII but,
having a hydrogen atom in place of the primary carbinol group, it cannot
form a cyclic hemiacetal such as XLIX. Similarly, methyl α-D-lyxopyrano-
side (which, unlike methyl α-D-mannopyranoside, cannot form a hemiacetal
analogous to XLVI) *also* gave the theoretical yield of free formic acid.

Presence of water in the acetic acid used as solvent in the catalyzed oxi-

(126) J. H. Michell and C. B. Purves, *J. Am. Chem. Soc.*, **64**, 589 (1942).
(127) See (a) G. N. Richards, *J. Chem. Soc.*, 3222 (1957), and (b) I. J. Goldstein,
B. A. Lewis and F. Smith, *J. Am. Chem. Soc.*, **80**, 939 (1958) for discussions of these
structural types and for references to the earlier literature.

$$CH_2$$

XLIX

dations serves to minimize ester formation, rather than simply to promote ester hydrolysis.[49] Thus, when 2 % of water was added after about 1.5 moles of lead tetraacetate per mole had been consumed, a rapid increase in the rate of acid production was found, but there was little change if the water was added after the theoretical two moles of lead tetracetate per mole had been consumed. Methyl α-D-galactopyranoside was particularly sensitive to these changes in the solvent, in agreement with the suggestion that ester formation requires a favorably oriented intermediate. In 90 % acetic acid, the yield of free formic acid was always close to the theoretical value of one mole per mole, but slow overoxidation was evident, indicating a lowered specificity for the reagent in the presence of more than a few percent of water.

4. *Reducing Sugars*

The reducing sugars will be considered separately from other alicyclic compounds, because their oxidation behavior differs in several respects. These differences appear to be mainly related to the presence of the unsubstituted hemiacetal structure and to the resulting great diversity of stereochemical possibilities. In solution, a reducing sugar may exist as a 5-, a 6-, or a 7-membered ring (in any of the conformations possible for these rings) and each of the various conformations may be present as either the α or the β anomer, or both (see Fig. 3). A small proportion of some (or all)

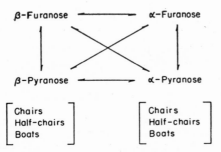

Fig. 3.—Hypothetical Representation of an Equilibrium Solution of a Reducing Sugar.

reducing sugars may even be present in solution in the aldehydo form.[128] Early studies by Böeseken on borate complexing[25] and by Isbell and Hudson on bromine oxidation[129] provided strong evidence that the predominant ring-forms of reducing sugars in solution are pyranose. Further, a striking stereochemical affinity between the methyl glycopyranosides and the reducing sugars was deduced through conformational analysis by Reeves,[79] the $C1$-pyranose, chair conformation being regarded as the most generally stable form.

a. Aldoses.—The oxidation of aldohexoses with lead tetraacetate, examined first by Criegee,[43] appears to involve cyclic forms chiefly. In warm acetic acid, D-glucose, D-mannose, and D-galactose consume three to four moles of lead tetraacetate per mole without concurrently yielding formaldehyde, which suggests that the 5,6-glycol grouping in these sugars is protected against oxidative attack by the 1,5-hemiacetal O-bridge. Similarly, a cyclic, pyranose structure for D-glucosone has been postulated[130] from the fact that the compound consumes about two moles of oxidant per mole fairly rapidly, without liberation of formaldehyde. By analogy with the ozonolysis of D-ribal (D-arabinal),[120] or with the lead tetraacetate oxidation of XLVI, the product from D-glucopyranose (L) should be a formate ester of D-glycerose (LI). However, Hockett and Zief[107] noted that, at 20°, two moles of oxidant per mole were taken up very quickly and a slow oxidation followed at an almost linear rate, a result not in accord with the formulated sequence L → LI.

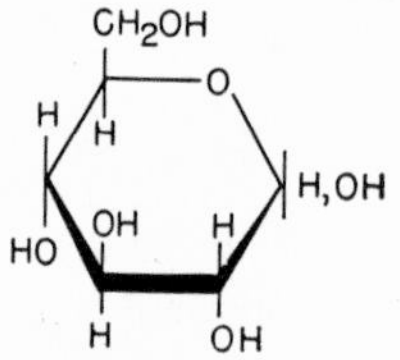

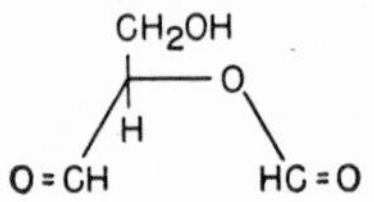

Oxidations of reducing sugars with lead tetraacetate have been re-examined more recently.[131-133] At 0°, or at 25°, in acetic acid and in the presence of excess lead tetraacetate, one mole of D-glucose took up only two moles of oxidant[132, 133] (see Fig. 4), as had been observed by Hockett and Zief. The product of this reaction was *not* a triose derivative (LI) but a diformate ester of D-erythrose.[132] (Oxidation of D-glucose with a limited pro-

(128) S. M. Cantor and Q. P. Peniston, *J. Am. Chem. Soc.*, **62**, 2113 (1940).
(129) H. S. Isbell and C. S. Hudson, *Bur. Standards J. Research* **8**, 327 (1932).
(130) C. S. Becker and C. E. May, *J. Am. Chem. Soc.*, **71**, 1491 (1949).
(131) A. S. Perlin, *J. Am. Chem. Soc.*, **76**, 2595 (1954).
(132) A. S. Perlin and C. Brice, *Can. J. Chem.*, **33**, 1216 (1955).
(133) A. S. Perlin and C. Brice, *Can. J. Chem.*, **34**, 541 (1956).

portion of periodate has afforded D-glycerose formate,[134] suggesting that the reaction primarily involves the degradation of D-glucopyranose (L). Kinetic studies of the oxidation[134(a)] support this suggestion. However, more recent examination[134(b)] of the products formed by partial oxidation has shown that compounds ranging from glycolaldehyde to unoxidized D-glucose may be simultaneously present in the reaction mixture.) D-Galactose

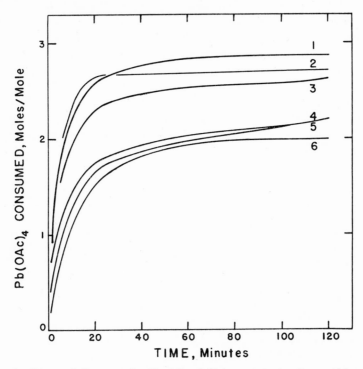

FIG. 4.—Rates of Consumption[133] of Lead Tetraacetate by Some Aldoses: (1) D-Mannose, (2) L-Rhamnose, (3) D-Altrose, (4) D-Allose, (5) D-Galactose, and (6) D-Glucose (Temp. 0°).

showed similar behavior, but the product formed was D-threose esterified with 1.8 formate groups per molecule. Other aldoses also rapidly consumed two moles of lead tetraacetate per mole (see Fig. 4), some proceeding well beyond this level, but in no instance was the consumption of three moles per mole (expected of a pyranose sugar) attained. D-Mannose approached the latter value most closely (2.8 moles per mole) and yielded a mixture of

(134) (a) C. Schöpf and H. Wild, *Ber.*, **87**, 1571 (1954). (b) F. S. H. Head, *Chem. & Ind.* (London), 360 (1958). (c) L. Hough, T. J. Taylor, G. H. S. Thomas and B. M. Woods, *J. Chem. Soc.*, 1212 (1958). (d) S. A. Warsi and W. J. Whelan, *Chem. & Ind.* (London), 71 (1958).

D-glycerose diformate and D-erythrose diformate. When only one mole of oxidant was added to a solution of one mole of the sugar, D-glucose and D-mannose yielded D-arabinose, D-galactose gave D-lyxose, and D-altrose and D-allose yielded D-ribose, all presumably as monoformate esters. In each of these latter oxidations, the corresponding tetrose was also produced, but the relative yield of pentose and tetrose varied widely, depending on the parent sugar. With one mole of lead tetraacetate per mole, D-glucose-1-C^{14} gave a mixture of radioactive esters of D-arabinose and D-erythrose, and saponification converted these to the inactive pentose and tetrose; hence C1 had been retained initially by each product.[131]

A reducing sugar can provide several points for attack by lead tetraacetate. However, to account for the very rapid rates of oxidation, the origin of formate groups in the products, and the generation of pentose formates and tetrose formates in high yield from aldohexoses, it has been suggested[131, 133] that the reactions primarily concern the α-hydroxy hemiacetal glycol group.

By far the most rapid glycol-cleavage oxidations involve vic-diols possessing the true cis (0°) orientation.[78] Reducing sugars exhibit rates of lead tetraacetate uptake in this extreme range[78] and, by analogy, their reactions should concern glycol groups in which the true cis orientation is attained or approached. Stable chair-conformations cannot fulfil this requirement for, in these, the minimum projected angle between vic-diols is 60°. Zero-degree orientation is found, however, in furanose, boat, and half-chair conformations. The proportion of the latter forms in an equilibrium solution of a reducing sugar in acetic acid may be very small, but the steric requirements of the lead-glycol complex might force the sugar to assume such normally unfavored conformations as these.[135, 136] Since subsequent decomposition is irreversible,[23] the equilibrium would be displaced at a rate depending on the speed of interconversion between the various forms (see Fig. 3). Pyranose–furanose[137] and conformational[79] interconversions take place with extreme rapidity, and the attainment of mutarotational equilibrium is immeasurably fast in acetic acid.[133] It is feasible, therefore, that the rapid reaction of reducing sugars with lead tetraacetate involves preferential oxidation of conformers which usually occur as minor components in an equilibrium solution of the sugars, or are initially completely absent.

(135) Reeves[78] has noted that reducing sugars can interfere with the direct titration of true cis-diols with lead tetraacetate in acetic acid, possibly because they can usually form furanose rings.

(136) Borate complexing appears to involve the generation of a substantial proportion of furanose sugars in solution,[25] although virtually none of the furanose forms may be present before the addition of borate.

(137) H. S. Isbell and W. W. Pigman, J. Research Natl. Bur. Standards, **20**, 773 (1938).

For oxidation to cease at a level of two moles per mole, as with D-glucose, D-galactose, and D-allose (group A), it appears necessary that one of the formate groups be introduced at the C2 hydroxyl group of the derived tetrose ester. This can occur most directly by oxidation, initially, of a furanose sugar so as to give a pentose 3-formate. For example, α-D-gluco-furanose (LII) provides a true *cis*-glycol at C1 and C2, facilitating com-plex-formation. Oxidation gives 3-*O*-formyl-D-arabinose (LIII), and a simi-lar attack at the newly formed α-hydroxy hemiacetal of the latter by a second mole of lead tetraacetate (per mole) yields di-*O*-formyl-D-erythrose. A 2,3-isomer (LIV) would be the final product if β-D-arabinofuranose 3-formate were the species attacked, and the β-D-pyranose would yield the 2,4-diformate. Similarly, α-D-galactofuranose may first give 3-*O*-formyl-D-lyxose and, subsequently, D-threose diformate.

LII   LIII   LIV

Rapid consumption of lead tetraacetate by D-mannose, D-altrose, and L-rhamnose does not cease at two moles per mole, but continues to a level of 2.5 to 2.8 moles per mole[133] (see Fig. 4). More extensive oxidation of these sugars (group B) than of those in the D-glucose group probably originates in steric differences. Some obvious differences between the sugars of the two groups (considering stable chair-conformations predominant at the start of the reaction) are (a) the orientation of the C2-hydroxyl group is equa-torial in group A, and is axial in group B; (b) *cis*-1,2-hydroxy-hemiacetal glycols can be given by α anomers in group A, and by β anomers in group B; (c) the *e*–*a* combination in β anomers of group B incorporates the highly unfavorable Δ2 condition[138] and, therefore, is less stable than the *e*,*e*-1,2-glycol in group A.[75, 79] In terms of a sugar solution at equilibrium (see Fig. 3), members of the D-glucose group are assumed to be oxidized preferentially as α-furanose forms, the equilibrium being displaced toward the left. Oxi-dation of sugars in group B may be regarded as proceeding to the right, but the unstable β-pyranose chair-form is less likely to be encountered than are β-conformers in which the Δ2 condition is absent. Some of the latter forms, for example, the *B3* boat[75] or the half-chair, possess a 1,2-hydroxy-hemi-acetal group having 0° orientation and, therefore, can be oxidized in compe-tition with the β-furanose isomer. Such competition may account for the

(138) Reeves[75] rates the Δ2 condition as by far the largest "instability factor"; Mills[81] suggests, however, that this evaluation may be somewhat high.

observed lead tetraacetate uptake of between two and three moles per mole (the theoretical values for a furanose and a pyranose ring, respectively) and production of a mixture of triose formates and tetrose formates.[133]

α,β-L-Idose was found to consume about 2.1 moles of oxidant per mole,[139] although the *configuration* of C2 in this sugar is the same (relative to C5) as in L-mannose. However, α-D- and α-L-idopyranose tend to adopt the orientation[79, 140] in which the C2-hydroxyl group is equatorial instead of axial. This condition gives idose closer identity with the glucose group and may account for the observed similarity in oxidation behavior. Possibly, the somewhat lower consumption of oxidant by D-altrose (2.5 moles per mole) than by D-mannose (2.8 moles per mole) is related to the same situation, for the conformation of D-altrose appears to be represented best by a mixture of the two possibilities.[79]

Detailed structures of the pentose, tetrose, and triose formates produced in these oxidations have not yet been assigned with certainty.[133] In the tetrose diformates, one ester group is probably situated at the C2 oxygen atom, because of its resistance to further oxidation. A 3,4-diformate might be stabilized by dimerization, but DL-glycerose, which is known to exist as a stable dimer,[93] is oxidized much more rapidly by lead tetraacetate than are di-*O*-formyl-D-erythrose or di-*O*-formyl-D-threose.[95] Against the 3,4-assignment also is the fact that D-*glycero*-L-*gulo*-heptose and D-*erythro*-L-*galacto*-octose rapidly consume about two moles of lead tetraacetate per mole, yielding formate esters of D-arabinose and D-glucose, respectively, in almost quantitative yield.[133] If the latter were esterified at positions 3 and 4, by analogy with the hypothetical formation of a tetrose 3,4-diformate, dimerization would not have had precedence over ring formation, and a third mole of oxidant per mole should have been consumed readily.[141] It appears more probable that the initial oxidation step introduces a formate group at position 3 of the primary product and, hence, at position 2 of the final product. Thus, in addition to fulfilling the requirements for rapid glycol-scission by affording a true *cis*-1,2-diol, α-D-glucofuranose can lead directly to formation of D-erythrose esterified at position 2.

An alternative type of mechanism, involving migration of formate groups, has also been considered in terms of these oxidation results.[133] If 4-*O*-formyl-D-arabinose were the initial product from cleavage of a favorably oriented

(139) P. A. J. Gorin and A. S. Perlin, *Can. J. Chem.*, **36**, 661 (1958).

(140) See H. S. Isbell, *J. Research Natl. Bur. Standards*, **57**, 171 (1956).

(141) The reactions of the heptose and the octose illustrate clearly that failure of the 5,6-terminal glycol group in the aldohexoses (or D-glucosone) to consume lead tetraacetate and yield formaldehyde need not imply protection by a 1,5-oxygen bridge, for, even in the pyranose form, the higher sugars possess a free terminal *vic*-diol or a 1,2,3-triol group.

D-glucopyranose conformer, migration of the formate to position 3 could account for the results observed.

   b. *Partially-substituted Aldoses.*—Partially-substituted aldoses have shown oxidation behavior (see Fig. 5) which is generally consistent with the mechanisms just considered. Substitution of the C6-hydroxyl group in D-glucose (as in the 6-methyl ether) did not alter the rate of uptake of lead tetraacetate[142]; 6-deoxy-D-glucose also gave virtually the same kinetic

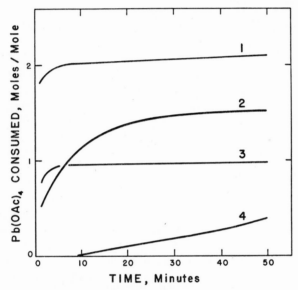

Fig. 5.—Rates of Consumption[142] of Lead Tetraacetate by D-Glucose and Some of its Derivatives: (1) D-Glucose (approximately the same rate curve is given by the 6-O-methyl, 6-deoxy, and 5,6-carbonate derivatives), (2) 4-O-Methyl-, (3) 3-O-Methyl-, and (4) 2-O-Methyl-D-glucose.

data.[95] These results imply that the primary carbinol group need not take part in the oxidation of D-glucose itself. If the compound was forced to assume a furanose ring, as in D-glucose 5,6-carbonate, the rate was again materially unaltered, and a tetrose derivative was again produced.[95] When the furanose ring could not be formed, as in 4-O-methyl-D-glucose, the rate of oxidation was markedly lower.[142] Mahoney and Purves[143] observed that very little reaction takes place when C2 of a sugar is blocked by methoxyl, which is in accord with the formulated initial attack on the α-hydroxy-hemiacetal group, but substitution at C3 permitted one mole of lead tetra-

   (142) A. J. Charlson and A. S. Perlin, *Can. J. Chem.*, **34**, 1200 (1956).
   (143) J. F. Mahoney and C. B. Purves, *J. Am. Chem. Soc.*, **64**, 9 (1942).

acetate per mole to be consumed very rapidly,[142-146] further oxidation being prevented by the substituent group at C2 of the product and by the formate ester group derived[142] from C1. Mono-O-methyl-D-galactose derivatives have afforded data which are similar to those obtained for the D-glucose derivatives,[142] as have disaccharides of corresponding structure (see below).

c. Ketoses.—Hockett and Zief[107] found that D-fructose, like D-glucose, rapidly consumes two moles of lead tetraacetate per mole. This result was confirmed,[133] and similar data were obtained with L-sorbose, L-*gluco*-heptulose, and D-*altro*-heptulose (sedoheptulose), all of these ketoses giving almost identical figures. A formate–glycolate diester of D-glycerose was obtained from D-fructose (D-*arabino*-hexulose), L-sorbose (L-*xylo*-hexulose) gave the corresponding L-glycerose derivative,[133, 147] and D-*altro*-heptulose afforded the corresponding diester of D-erythrose.[50] By analogy with the oxidation of D-glucose, formation of these diesters has been described[133] by assuming, for example, that β-D-fructofuranose (LV) is the species chiefly concerned in the initial cleavage reaction. Preferential attack on the 2,3-hemiacetal[148] group then yields 3-O-glycolyl-D-erythrose (LVI) which, in turn, is degraded to 3-O-formyl-2-O-glycolyl-D-glycerose (LVII).

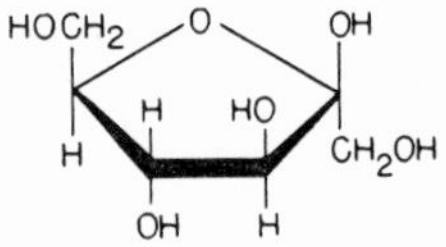

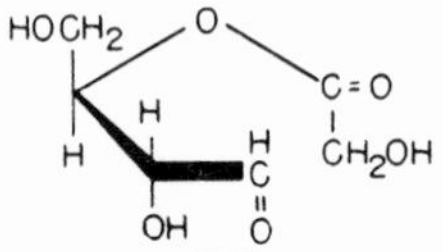

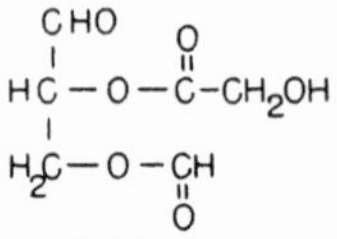

d. Some Applications of the Lead Tetraacetate Reaction to Reducing Sugars. —The characteristics of these reactions have rendered lead tetraacetate oxidation useful for stepwise degradation of reducing sugars, and have thus provided a simple method for directly preparing some relatively rare carbohydrates from readily available, higher members of the series, usually in high yield. In particular, the tetroses D-erythrose and D-threose have been obtained from D-glucose and D-galactose,[132, 133] respectively, and D- and L-glycerose from D-fructose and L-sorbose, respectively.[147] Other rare sugars which have been similarly prepared are D-*arabino*-penturonic acid from

(144) T. E. Timell, *Svensk Papperstidn.*, 52 (1948).

(145) J. Fried and D. E. Walz, *J. Am. Chem. Soc.*, **74**, 5468 (1952).

(146) J. E. Milks and C. B. Purves, *J. Am. Chem. Soc.*, **78**, 3738 (1956).

(147) A. S. Perlin and C. Brice, *Can. J. Chem.*, **34**, 85 (1956).

(148) By contrast, periodate mainly attacks the 1,2-position of D-fructose, giving rise to esterified glyoxylic acid, Y. Khouvine and G. Arragon, *Bull. soc. chim. France*, **8,** 676 (1941); D. B. Sprinson and E. Chargaff, *J. Biol. Chem.*, **164,** 433 (1946); see Ref. 134(c).

D-glucuronolactone, D-*erythro*-tetruronic acid from potassium D-glucuronate, and D-*threo*-tetruronic from D-galacturonic acid.[149]

Degradation of partially substituted sugars has also been utilized to obtain the corresponding, lower sugar. Thus, 3,6-di-O-methyl-D-glucose yielded 2,5-di-O-methyl-D-arabinose.[145] Oxidation of D-glucose 6-phosphate[150] at 0° has given the important intermediary metabolite, D-erythrose 4-phosphate.[151] At room temperature, the oxidation mixture yields D-glycerose 3-phosphate and D-erythrose 4-phosphate in almost equimolar proportions, and addition of D-glycerose 3-phosphate-isomerase plus aldolase to the mixed product has made possible a ready synthesis of D-*altro*-heptulose 1,7-diphosphate.[152] Oxidation of D-ribose 5-phosphate[152] or of D-fructose 6-phosphate[150] has been utilized for preparing D-glycerose 3-phosphate.

In addition to its preparative uses, selective lead tetraacetate oxidation has been employed for determining the distribution of radioactivity in some labeled reducing sugars.[153] Oxidative degradation of one mole of D-fructose-*1,6-C*[14]$_2$, followed by hydrolysis of the D-glycerose diester obtained, afforded a mole each of glycolic-*2-C*[14] acid (comprising C1 and C2 of the ketose), formic acid (from C3), and D-glycerose-*3-C*[14] (from C4, C5, and C6). These products were readily separable and could be degraded further, if necessary, so as to provide an assay of each carbon atom individually.[50]

Other applications of the lead tetraacetate–reducing sugar reaction are considered in the following Section on oligosaccharides.

e. Oligosaccharides.—Maltose and lactose, like reducing monosaccharides, appear to be oxidized as cyclic compounds by lead tetraacetate in acetic acid[43] at 50°. Thus, they readily take up about three moles of oxidant per mole, without liberating formaldehyde. Prolonged oxidation in warm acetic acid, however, led to a much more extensive oxidation of maltose than of melibiose, and it was suggested by Ahlborg[154] that the reaction could be used for distinguishing between disaccharides having these two types of linkage.

At 27°, in 90% acetic acid containing potassium acetate, melibiose

(149) P. A. J. Gorin and A. S. Perlin, *Can. J. Chem.*, **34**, 693 (1956).

(150) J. N. Baxter, A. S. Perlin and F. J. Simpson, *Can. J. Biochem. and Physiol.*, **37**, 199 (1959).

(151) C. E. Ballou, H. O. L. Fischer and D. L. MacDonald, *J. Am. Chem. Soc.*, **77**, 5967 (1955).

(152) V. Klybas, M. Schramm and E. Racker, *Arch. Biochem. Biophys.*, **80**, 229 (1959).

(153) The combined activity of C1 to C5 of D-glucose-C[14] and of C1 to C4 of L-arabinose-C[14] was determined[46] by use of warm, aqueous acetic acid as solvent, the formic acid liberated being converted directly to carbon dioxide by excess lead tetraacetate.

(154) K. Ahlborg, *Svensk Kem. Tidskr.*, **54**, 205 (1942).

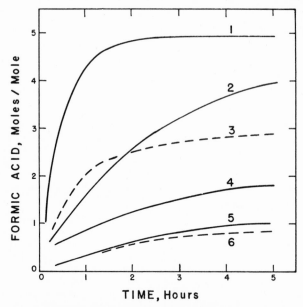

(LVIII) yields much more formic acid than does maltose (LIX), and its lead tetraacetate consumption is proportionately higher.[155] Other disaccharides were examined[142, 155] under the latter conditions, and also in 98 % acetic acid without potassium acetate.[156] Each position of the glycosidic

Fig. 6.—Rates of Production[142, 155] of Formic Acid (CO_2 Evolution) during "Potassium Acetate-catalyzed" Lead Tetraacetate Oxidation of Reducing Disaccharides: (1) 6-*O*-α-D-Galactopyranosyl-D-glucose, (2) 2-*O*-α-D-Mannopyranosyl-D-mannose, (3) 5-*O*-Methyl-D-glucose plus Methyl α-D-Glucopyranoside, (4) 3-*O*-β-D-Glucopyranosyl-D-glucose, (5) 4-*O*-α-D-Glucopyranosyl-D-glucose, and (6) Methyl α-D-Glucopyranoside.

(155) A. S. Perlin, *Anal. Chem.*, **27**, 396 (1955).

(156) It should, perhaps, be emphasized that the two reactions used, distinguished as "normal" (uncatalyzed) and "potassium acetate-catalyzed," yield different kinds of data. The catalyzed reactions are greatly accelerated and may involve less stabili-

linkage was found to be associated with a characteristic oxidation-pattern, determined chiefly by the reaction properties of the reducing end-unit of the disaccharide. For convenience, these data are considered separately, but it will be evident that the two reactions are complementary. Together, they have afforded a group of criteria sufficiently distinctive to be of help in determining the structure of unknown disaccharides.[157-163]

(i) *"Potassium Acetate-catalyzed" Oxidations.*—In general, these oxidations involve (a) the reducing end-unit, starting from the hemiacetal group and proceeding stepwise along the carbon chain to the glycosidic linkage, and (b) the nonreducing end, as in the catalyzed oxidations of the corresponding methyl glycoside.[49, 164]

Hexopyranose disaccharides having a $(1 \rightarrow 6)$-linkage rapidly yield about five moles of formic acid per mole (see Fig. 6), that is, one from the nonreducing end and four from the reducing end-unit, and consume about six moles of oxidant per mole, the data corresponding to conversion of LVIII to LX. In the 1,4-hexopyranoses (for example, LIX), formic acid appeared

LX   LXI

to be derived almost exclusively from the nonreducing end-unit, and the reducing end-unit was oxidized to a tetrose diformate (as in LXI). A $(1 \rightarrow 3)$-linkage prevented oxidation from proceeding beyond an initial consumption of one mole (per mole) by the reducing end-unit, and the pen-

___

zation by formate esters, so that extensive degradation may occur, both with the reducing and nonreducing end-units. In the uncatalyzed oxidations, early periods of the reaction are examined and selective stages, particularly during degradation of the reducing end-unit, become more apparent.

(157) E. L. Hirst and A. S. Perlin, *J. Chem. Soc.*, 2622 (1954).

(158) B. O. Lindgren, *Acta Chem. Scand.*, **11**, 1365 (1957).

(159) A. Wickström, *Acta Chem. Scand.*, **11**, 1473 (1957).

(160) P. A. J. Gorin and A. S. Perlin, *Can. J. Chem.*, **34**, 1804 (1957).

(161) J. K. N. Jones and W. H. Nicholson, *J. Chem. Soc.*, 27 (1958).

(162) J. H. Pazur, C. L. Tipton, T. Budovich and J. M. Marsh, *J. Am. Chem. Soc.*, **80**, 119 (1958).

(163) C. P. J. Glaudemans and T. E. Timell, *J. Am. Chem. Soc.*, **80**, 941 (1958).

(163a) J. K. Gillham, A. S. Perlin and T. E. Timell, *Can. J. Chem.*, **36**, 1741 (1958).

(164) The data obtained are similar to those given by periodate oxidation of reducing disaccharides[22] [see, particularly, G. Neumüller and E. Vasseur, *Arkiv Kemi*, **5**, 235 (1953) for a discussion of these periodate oxidations].

tose derivative formed (LXII) was stabilized against further rapid degradation by the presence of a formate ester. Production of formic acid from a $(1 \rightarrow 2)$-linked hexose disaccharide (LXIII) and the concomitant lead tetraacetate uptake were substantially greater than with $(1 \rightarrow 3)$- and $(1 \rightarrow 4)$-linked compounds, but extensive overoxidation was apparent (Fig. 6), presumably because of the hydroxymalonaldehyde structure of the product (LXIV). Oxidation of the 5,6-glycol group of the reducing end-unit occurred

readily, and a mole of formaldehyde was liberated per mole, in contrast to the little or no formaldehyde from other linkage types. Wickström[159] has reported that 2-O-D-galactopyranosyl-D-galactose was not oxidized as readily as is indicated in Fig. 6 and that somewhat less than one mole of formaldehyde per mole was produced, but the over-all data were consistent only with a $(1 \rightarrow 2)$-structure. Acid production and lead tetraacetate uptake by 5-O-methyl-D-glucose suggested that a 1,5-hexopyranose disaccharide (LXV) should yield three moles of formic acid and consume five moles of oxidant per mole, affording LXVI.[165]

Oxidation patterns exhibited by 2-, 3-, 4-, and 6-O-methyl-D-hexoses were in close agreement with those of the corresponding disaccharides, allowance being made for the contribution of the nonreducing end-unit of the latter.[155] In assessing this contribution, it was found that disaccharides having different nonreducing end-units differed from each other, as did the corresponding methyl glycopyranosides. A more rapid liberation of formic acid from lactose than from maltose thus reflected the more vigorous oxidation of a D-galactopyranosyl than of a D-glucopyranosyl residue. The oxidation behavior of pentose disaccharides and of some disaccharides containing

(165) A. S. Perlin, unpublished results.

both ketose and uronic acid residues was examined,[142, 155] and the results obtained could be rationalized readily by considerations similar to those already applied to aldohexose disaccharides.

Analogies were drawn[117] between the trialdehydes produced in these catalyzed oxidations and the dialdehydes formed by glycol-cleavage of methyl glycosides.[94, 114, 116] For example, the trialdehyde (LX) given by a $(1 \rightarrow 6)$-aldohexopyranose disaccharide differs from the dialdehyde (XLV) only in that the former is a derivative of glycolaldehyde rather than of methanol. In their classical studies on configuration, Jackson and Hudson[94] had related the rotatory power of such dialdehydes as XLV to configuration. Accordingly, this method was extended to the trialdehydes.[117] The configuration of the glycosidic linkages in disaccharides which could be degraded to LX (or to its β anomer) could thereby be defined from the specific rotation of the oxidation product. Consistent results were obtained with a number of compounds examined, α-D isomers giving on oxidation a value of about $+80°$, and β-D isomers about $-110°$. Similarly, the linkage in disaccharides yielding the trialdehyde (LXI) or its anomer could be designated α or β from the specific rotation of the oxidation product obtained. Such compounds as 2-O-α- and 2-O-β-D-glucopyranosyl-D-erythritol[142] *also* yielded anomeric trialdehydes, but these were compensated internally by the presence of D- and L-glycerose residues (LXVII, compare with XXXV), and therefore could not be used for assigning configuration

LXVII

Reactions of higher oligosaccharides were closely analogous to those of related disaccharides.[166] However, in three homologous series of $(1 \rightarrow 4)$-linked compounds—those of xylobiose, maltose, and cellobiose—the central units were resistant to oxidation, and the reactions appeared to involve the two end-units almost exclusively. The resistant, internal residues contained a 2,3-*trans*-glycol group situated between the glycosidic center and the 4-O-linkage.[167] Complexing of the glycol with lead tetraacetate may have been hindered by this type of linkage, but then, differences would have been expected between α- and β-linked compounds, for example, maltotriose and

(166) A. S. Perlin and A. R. Lansdown, *Can. J. Chem.*, **34**, 451 (1956).

(167) The $(1 \rightarrow 6)$-linked, internal D-glucose unit of raffinose was readily oxidized under the same conditions (see Ref. 166).

cellotriose. Alternatively, the glycol group may have been held in too rigid a *trans* orientation for an adequate approach to coplanarity. When the reducing end-unit was replaced by a phenyl or benzyl aglycon (as in phenyl and benzyl maltosides), the "internal" unit was still unoxidized.[166] A less bulky aglycon, as in methyl lactoside, failed to alleviate the resistance to attack by lead tetraacetate, but methyl 4-*O*-methyl-D-glucoside *was* oxidized, suggesting that a large substituent at C4 is of prime importance.[168] Oxidation of oligosaccharides in which central residues were unaffected by lead tetraacetate has constituted a unique means for stepwise degradation of these compounds.

(ii) *"Normal" (Uncatalyzed) Oxidations.*—Under normal oxidation conditions, reducing oligosaccharides exhibit reactions analogous to those of the partially substituted monosaccharides described earlier.[142] This close similarity has been related to the extremely rapid attack of lead tetraacetate on α-hydroxy-hemiacetal glycol groups and the relatively slow reaction with glycosides, the reducing end-units being degraded selectively. Therefore, oxidation rates of reducing, hexose disaccharides were closely represented by the data in Fig. 5 for the corresponding mono-*O*-methyl-hexoses, and the same considerations applied to both classes of compound.[142]

Because of its selectivity, lead tetraacetate oxidation has been used for preparing disaccharides by stepwise degradation of other disaccharides,[142] in a manner analogous to the shortening of the carbon chain of monosaccharides and partially-substituted derivatives. On oxidation with two moles of lead tetraacetate per mole, melibiose, maltose, and cellobiose gave (in high yield), respectively, 4-*O*-α-D-galactopyranosyl-D-erythrose and 2-*O*-α- and 2-*O*-β-D-glucopyranosyl-D-erythrose.[142] These reactions were equivalent to *two* successive single degradations by other procedures[169] for descending the sugar series.

The fact that polyhydric alcohols are generally attacked more readily than glycopyranosides[24, 44, 114] was utilized to carry the selective degradation of cellobiose a step further.[142] Reduction of the *O*-D-glucosyl-D-erythrose obtained gave the corresponding erythritol derivative (LXVIII) which, with one mole of lead tetraacetate (per mole) yielded primarily 2-*O*-β-D-glucopyranosyl-L-glycerose (LXIX). The latter was then reduced to 2-*O*-β-D-glucopyranosyl-glyceritol (LXX). Maltose was converted by the same sequence of reactions to 2-*O*-α-D-glucopyranosyl-glyceritol.[170] Asymmetry

(168) P. A. J. Gorin and A. S. Perlin, unpublished results.

(169) Reviewed by W. L. Evans, D. D. Reynolds and E. A. Talley, *Advances in Carbohydrate Chem.*, **6**, 27 (1951).

(170) A. J. Charlson, P. A. J. Gorin and A. S. Perlin, *Can. J. Chem.*, **34**, 1811 (1956).

$$CH_2OH$$
$$HCO-R$$
$$HCOH$$
$$CH_2OH$$

$$CH_2OH$$
$$HCO-R$$
$$HC=O$$

$$CH_2OH$$
$$HCO-R$$
$$CH_2OH$$

(R = D−Glucopyranosyl)

LXVIII   LXIX   LXX

survived only in the D-glucosyl residues of these two compounds, and they constituted, therefore, an α,β anomeric pair of D-glucopyranosides. D-Glucoside LXX, having $[\alpha]_D$ −30°, was defined by Hudson's rules[171] as the β anomer, and the second D-glucoside, $[\alpha]_D$ +121°, as the α anomer, thereby providing confirmation of the assigned linkage configurations in cellobiose and maltose. Similarly, degradation of lactose[170] gave 2-O-β-D-galactopyranosyl-glyceritol, $[\alpha]_D$ −2°, which was different from a naturally occurring 2-O-D-galactopyranosyl-glyceritol, $[\alpha]_D$ +185°. By definition, the latter member of this pair was the α anomer, and that derived from lactose, the β anomer. By this method, configuration has been determined for the glycosidic linkages of a variety of disaccharides obtained by partial degradation of polysaccharides. These applications have afforded the α,β anomeric pairs of 2-O-glycopyranosyl-glyceritols of D-glucose, D-galactose, D-mannose,[170] D-xylose, and L-arabinose,[172] and the fully methylated 2-O-D-glucopyranosyl-glyceritols,[173] which serve as reference standards for determining configuration in other disaccharides.

Selective, lead tetraacetate oxidations of this type have been extended to higher oligosaccharides as well. A trisaccharide obtained from *Saccharomyces rouxii* mannan[160] was shown to be O-α-D-mannopyranosyl-(1 → 2)-O-α-D-mannopyranosyl-(1 → 2)-D-mannose (LXXI) by a series of reactions (see Fig. 7) involving preferential removal either of the nonreducing or of the reducing end-unit.[174] Reduction of LXXI gave a mannotriitol (LXXII) which was degraded with three moles of lead tetraacetate (per mole), followed by reduction to a 2-O-mannobiosyl-glyceritol (LXXIII). The central residue of the latter was relatively resistant to attack by lead tetraacetate, and hence the nonreducing end-unit was oxidized preferentially to the dialdehyde (LXXIV). Treatment of LXXIV with phenylhydrazine acetate, according to the method of Barry,[175] yielded 2-O-α-D-mannopyranosyl-glyceritol (LXXV), showing that the (1 → 2)-linkage between the central

(171) C. S. Hudson, *J. Am. Chem. Soc.*, **60**, 1537 (1938).
(172) A. J. Charlson, P. A. J. Gorin and A. S. Perlin, *Can. J. Chem.*, **35**, 365 (1957).
(173) P. A. J. Gorin and A. S. Perlin, *Can. J. Chem.*, **36**, 999 (1958).
(174) P. A. J. Gorin and A. S. Perlin, *Can. J. Chem.*, **35**, 262 (1957).
(175) V. C. Barry, *Nature*, **152**, 537 (1943).

residue and the reducing end-unit of the trisaccharide possesses the α-D configuration. Bromine oxidation converted the trisaccharide to LXXVI, and oxidation with three moles of lead tetraacetate per mole then gave the L-*glycero*-triouronic acid derivative (LXXVII). The latter proved readily

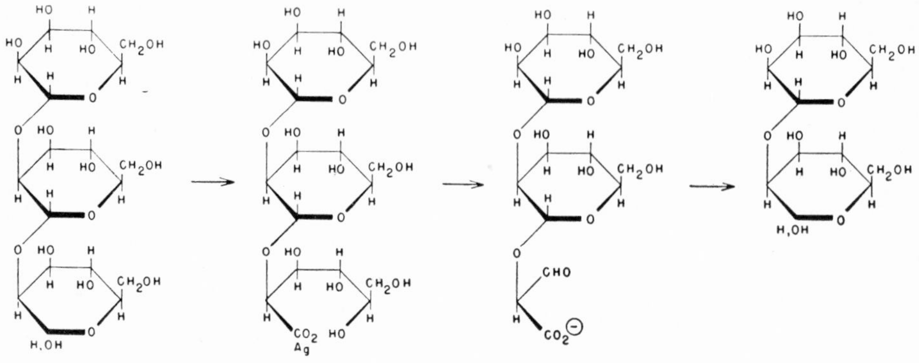

LXXI LXXVI LXXVII LXXVIII

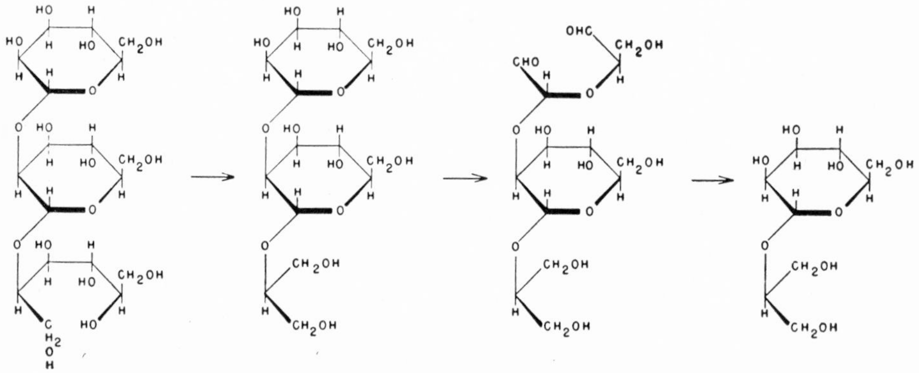

LXXII LXXIII LXXIV LXXV

FIG. 7.—Stepwise Degradation of *O*-α-D-Mannopyranosyl-(1 → 2)-*O*-α-D-mannopyranosyl-(1 → 2)-D-mannose.[174]

hydrolyzable, affording 2-*O*-α-D-mannopyranosyl-D-mannose (LXXVIII).[160] Therefore, the glycosidic linkage between the nonreducing end-unit and the central residue of the trisaccharide also possesses the (1 → 2)-α-D-glycosidic linkage.

Conversion of the reducing end-unit in 2-*O*-(4-*O*-methyl-D-glucosyluronic acid)-D-xylose to a tartronic semialdehyde residue (as in LXXVII) facilitated the ready isolation of 4-*O*-methyl-D-glucuronic acid by acid hydrolysis.[176] By contrast, the parent aldobiouronic acid was highly resistant to acid hydrolysis.

Manninotriose (LXXIX), a trisaccharide obtained by hydrolysis of the labile sucrose-linkage in stachyose, was degraded to establish the configuration of the D-galactopyranose nonreducing end-unit.[177] Two moles of lead tetraacetate per mole were rapidly consumed by the trisaccharide, giving the D-erythrose derivative (LXXX). In the latter, the glycosidic linkage attached to the reducing end-unit was now at position 4 (instead of at C6

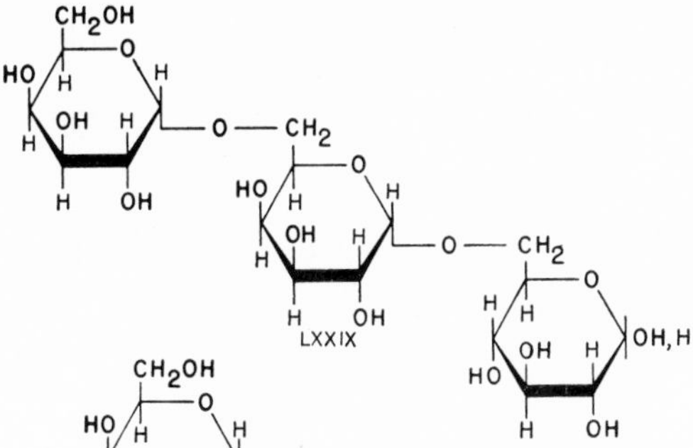

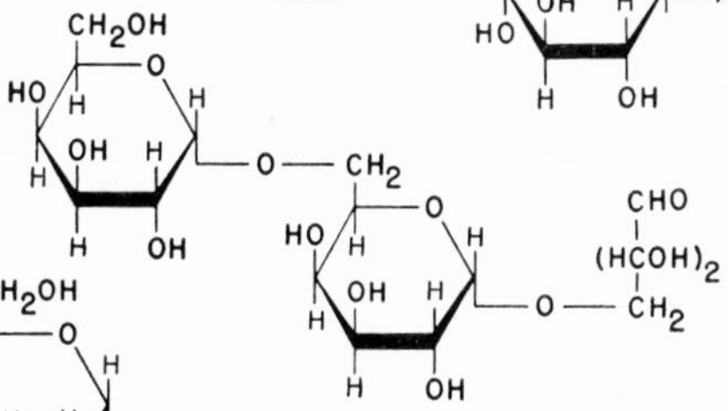

as in the parent compound), and hence was more liable to scission by alkali.[127, 178] In agreement with this, mild alkali treatment afforded as the product 6-O-α-D-galactopyranosyl-D-galactose (LXXXI). Partial oxidation by lead tetraacetate was also used in furnishing a chemical proof for the presence of the sucrose linkage in stachyose.[109] In this degradation, the D-galactose residues (represented in LXXIX) were oxidized and the resulting dialdehydes were cleaved with alkali, affording sucrose. However, the D-fructofuranosyl residue consumed a high proportion of the lead tetra-

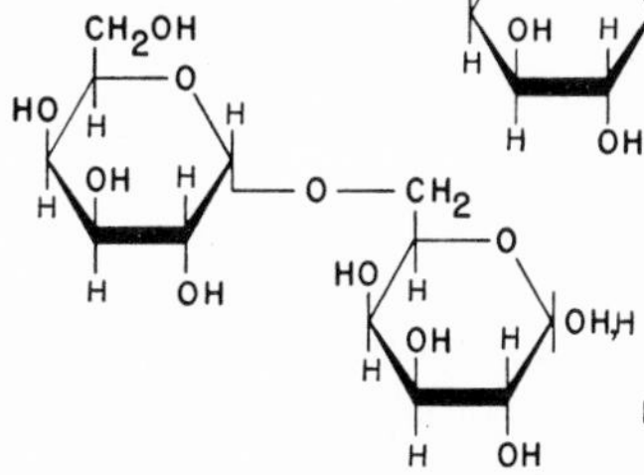

(176) P. A. J. Gorin, *Can. J. Chem.*, **35**, 595 (1957).

(177) A. K. Mitra and A. S. Perlin, unpublished results.

(178) J. Kenner and G. N. Richards, *J. Chem. Soc.*, 2916 (1956), and earlier papers in this series.

acetate added, in agreement with the behavior noted earlier,[108] which made
for a low yield of sucrose. Periodate oxidation was more specific for the
D-galactose residues and gave a higher yield of the disaccharide.[109]

f. Polysaccharides.—Very few oxidations of polysaccharides have been
carried out with lead tetraacetate, a situation in marked contrast to the
voluminous literature on polysaccharide oxidations with periodate.[22] The
main reason for this discrepancy has undoubtedly been the fact that polysaccharides are insoluble in the solvents generally used for lead tetraacetate
oxidation.

A partially acetylated cellulose, being readily soluble in acetic acid, was
examined by Cramer, Hockett, and Purves.[179] Using conditions which had
been standardized for the oxidation of glycopyranosides,[114] they found a
small uptake of oxidant; this was regarded as due to a true glycol split,
followed by a slower non-specific reaction. The data corresponded to one
free 2,3-glycol group per 100–150 units, but, on the basis that substitution
of cellulose is purely random, this figure should have been 30–35 units. It
was therefore concluded that substitution of secondary hydroxyl groups is
not a random process. Using the same oxidation conditions with a technical
O-ethylcellulose, Mahoney and Purves[143] found very few 2,3-glycol groups
unsubstituted, the data being consistent with other information on the distribution of ethoxy groups in the polymer.

Benzylation of cellulose monoalkoxide was expected to give mainly the
2-O-benzyl derivative[180] and, in agreement with this expectation, Wolfrom
and El-Taraboulsi[180] found no detectable 2,3-glycol groups in the product
(by the method of Cramer, Hockett, and Purves[179]).

A procedure for estimating mannan in wood cellulose based on differential
rates of oxidation by lead tetraacetate has been proposed by Steinmann and
White.[181] The *cis*-2,3-glycol grouping of the mannan present was expected to
oxidize more readily than the *trans*-2,3-glycol group of the cellulose. A plot
of the lead tetraacetate uptake with time (for several acetylation-grade
pulps) showed, in fact, that there was an initial rapid oxidation which then
approached a low, linear rate. Extrapolation of the rate curves to zero
time gave values for mannan which agreed satisfactorily with the D-mannose contents of these materials, as determined by hydrazone precipitation
after hydrolysis. However, it has been pointed out[182] that the mannan contents were low (2 % or less) and that a correlation between the two analytical
methods was determined over a narrow range.

Each of these polysaccharide oxidations has involved a very small or a

(179) F. B. Cramer, R. C. Hockett and C. B. Purves, *J. Am. Chem. Soc.*, **61**, 3463
(1939).
(180) M. L. Wolfrom and M. A. El-Taraboulsi, *J. Am. Chem. Soc.*, **76**, 2216 (1954).
(181) H. W. Steinmann and B. B. White, *Tappi*, **37**, 225 (1954).
(182) W. J. Polglase, *Advances in Carbohydrate Chem.*, **10**, 283 (1955).

negligible lead tetraacetate consumption, which was to be expected with the particular polymers examined. Control oxidations on polysaccharides possessing a known proportion of free *vic*-diols were not carried out, presumably due to the unavailability of suitable reference materials. Rather, the oxidation behavior of simple glycosides was taken as a reference point. No instance has been found in the literature of a polysaccharide–lead tetraacetate reaction in which a large proportion of oxidant was reduced. Several polysaccharides examined by the "potassium-catalyzed" oxidation showed no significant uptake of lead tetraacetate,[166] although the same materials were readily oxidized by periodate. Resistance was attributed mainly to insolubility of the substrates in acetic acid, but it was pointed out that many oligosaccharides which contain free α-glycol groups and are *soluble* in the reaction medium are resistant, nevertheless, to lead tetraacetate oxidation.[166]

Contradictory evidence has been given on the use of lead tetraacetate as a histochemical reagent for detecting polysaccharides. It has been described as equal to periodate or chromic acid for producing aldehydes[183]; these are subsequently located in the tissue sections by means of carbonyl reagents. Catalysis of the lead tetraacetate reaction by potassium acetate or sodium acetate was found to be highly beneficial for speeding the staining procedure,[183, 184] which was to be expected for true glycol-cleavage.[28] Little or no reaction was observed when glacial acetic acid was used as solvent in the absence of sodium acetate.[184] However, Crippa has reported[185] that lead tetraacetate in glacial acetic acid without acetate salts readily permits staining of glycogen and polysaccharides in general.

Because of the small amount of information available and the inconsistencies found in that reported, it is at present difficult to evaluate lead tetraacetate as a reagent for examining polysaccharides or partially-substituted polysaccharides.

V. Oxidative Cleavage of Nitrogen-containing Carbohydrates

An amino group is generally equivalent to a hydroxyl group in cleavage-reactions with lead tetraacetate—α-amino alcohols, α-amino acids, and α-diamines all being attacked oxidatively.[6, 23, 30] By analogy with *vic*-diol scission, the oxidation of an α-amino alcohol may take place by way of a cyclic *N*-analog of IX, giving rise to an imine-aldehyde.[186] However the presence of an extra hydrogen atom on the amino group, as compared with the hydroxyl group, makes for increased oxidation possibilities. Unless

(183) J. F. Lhotka, *Stain Technol.*, **27**, 213 (1952).

(184) N. Shimizu and T. Kumamoto, *Stain Technol.*, **27**, 97 (1952).

(185) A. Crippa, *Boll. soc. ital. biol. sper.*, **27**, 599 (1951); *Chem. Abstracts*, **47**, 10597 (1953).

(186) G. E. McCasland and D. A. Smith, *J. Am. Chem. Soc.*, **73**, 5164 (1951).

suitably protected, the imine may, in turn, be dehydrogenated by the reagent, to give the nitrile; for example, phenylaminoacetic acid yields benzonitrile.[23] This secondary type of reaction probably accounted for a continuing, slow overoxidation of 2-aminocyclanols when excess lead tetraacetate was present,[186] in contrast to the stoichiometric uptake by simple 1,2-diols, and for the lack of agreement found with second- or first-order rate-equations.[186]

Because of the extra hydrogen atom, also, some partially-substituted α-amines are readily oxidized and yield products which find no counterpart in the cleavage of glycol groups; for example, a N-tosyl derivative afforded the stable imine, RCH=N—tosyl.[6] A N-carbethoxy group also permitted scission to occur,[187] the mono-O-benzylidene-D-"glucosaminic" acid derivative (LXXXII) being degraded to the glyoxylate derivative (LXXXIII). This reaction was taken as evidence in favor of a 4,6-acetal structure for the compound. Introduction of a N-benzoyl group prevented attack on L-serine by lead tetraacetate, but the isomeric N-benzoyl-isoserine was oxidized, presumably at the carbinol–carboxyl bond, permitting these two amino acids to be readily distinguished.[188] By contrast, methyl N-benzoyl-D-"glucosaminate" was vigorously overoxidized by lead tetraacetate, possibly because the α-benzamido-aldehyde (LXXXIV), expected as the product, was unstable.[189]

LXXXII LXXXIII LXXXIV

The N-acetyl group may impart stability toward attack by lead tetraacetate, a fact utilized by Wolfrom, Lemieux, and Olin[190] to establish a stereochemical relationship between the carbohydrate standard, D-glycerose, and the amino acid standard, L-serine. D-Glucosamine, possessing the D-glycerose configuration at C2, was converted by way of the N-acetyl diethyl dithioacetal to 2-acetamido-1,2-dideoxy-D-galactitol. Oxidation with lead tetraacetate, followed by bromine oxidation, afforded N-acetyl-

(187) P. Karrer and J. Meyer, *Helv. Chim. Acta*, **20**, 407 (1937).

(188) F. Knoop, F. Ditt, W. Hecksteden, J. Maier, W. Merz and R. Härle, *Z. physiol. Chem., Hoppe-Seyler's*, **239**, 30 (1936).

(189) A. Neuberger, *J. Chem. Soc.*, 47 (1941).

(190) M. L. Wolfrom, R. U. Lemieux and S. M. Olin, *J. Am. Chem. Soc.*, **71**, 2870 (1949).

$L(+)$-alanine, which is related to $L(-)$-serine. An interchange of groups on the reference carbon atom is involved in this series of reactions.

The action of aqueous ammonia on penta-O-acetyl-*aldehydo*-D-glucose or on hexa-O-acetyl-α-D-glucoheptonic nitrile yielded a N-acetyl-D-glucosamine which was shown to be a D-glucofuranose derivative,[191] for it consumed lead tetraacetate at a rate characteristic of alkyl D-glucofuranosides[91] and yielded formaldehyde. The compound was also prepared from penta-O-acetyl-β-D-glucose plus methanolic ammonia, and its structure was again checked by lead tetraacetate oxidation.[192] Both oxidations involved the uptake of considerably more than two moles of lead tetraacetate per mole, which was regarded by Ellis and Honeyman[193] as being due to the failure of the N-acetyl group to stabilize the ring. On this basis, overoxidation might also have been expected with N-acetyl-D-glucopyranosylamine, but the latter consumed only slightly more than two moles of lead tetraacetate per mole.[192] More probably, the hydroxy-malonaldehyde structure of the trialdehyde formed (analogous to **XXXIII**) induced overoxidation, just as with the alkyl D-glucofuranosides.[91]

Glycol cleavage of diacetamides proceeds smoothly and without apparent attack on the N-substituted carbon atom,[44] 1,1-bis(acetamido)-1-deoxy-D-erythritol and -D-threitol giving rate curves similar to that of glyceritol. Rate curves for pentitol diacetamides resembled those of erythritol.

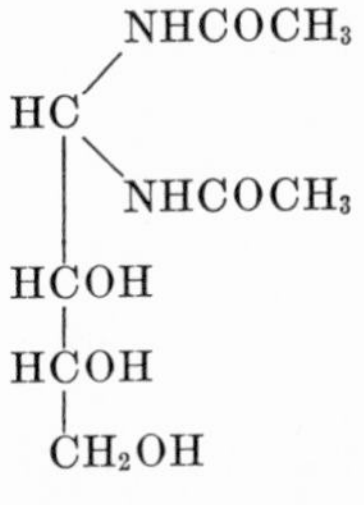

$$
\begin{array}{l}
\qquad\quad NHCOCH_3 \\
\qquad\quad / \\
HC \\
\qquad\quad \backslash \\
\qquad\qquad NHCOCH_3 \\
| \\
HCOH \\
| \\
HCOH \\
| \\
CH_2OH
\end{array}
$$

Some related N-aryl compounds were examined in model experiments in connection with lead tetraacetate cleavage of samandarin derivatives.[194] Oxidation in aqueous acetic acid at 60–70° of 1-deoxy-1-(p-toluidino)-L-arabinitol (**LXXXV**) and -D-mannitol yielded two moles of formaldehyde per mole, one mole being derived from the terminal carbinol group and the second from subsequent hydrolysis of the Schiff base (**LXXXVI**) pro-

(191) R. C. Hockett and L. B. Chandler, *J. Am. Chem. Soc.*, **66**, 957 (1944).

(192) C. Niemann and J. T. Hays, *J. Am. Chem. Soc.*, **67**, 1302 (1945).

(193) G. P. Ellis and J. Honeyman, *Advances in Carbohydrate Chem.*, **10**, 118 (1955).

(194) D. Klein, *Chem. Ber.*, **85**, 253 (1952).

duced. Reference to the lead tetraacetate oxidation of the samandarin derivatives thus suggested that the second mole of formaldehyde was not a

$$
\begin{array}{ll}
\overset{\displaystyle H}{CH_2-N-C_6H_5CH_3\text{-}p} & CH_2=N-C_6H_5CH_3\text{-}p \\
| & \qquad\qquad LXXXVI \\
CHOH & \rightarrow \\
| & \\
(CHOH)_2 & +\ 3\ HCO_2H \\
| & \\
CH_2OH & +\ HCHO \\
LXXXV &
\end{array}
$$

primary product but originated from hydrolysis of an intermediate RN=CH₂ structure.

An α-hydroxy tertiary amine is oxidized with difficulty. At 60°, however, 2-(N,N-diethylamino)ethanol took up lead tetraacetate, but scission occurred between the carbon–nitrogen bond (instead of between the carbon–carbon bond), possibly by a free-radical mechanism.[195]

$$
\begin{array}{ccc}
\overset{\displaystyle C_2H_5}{\diagdown} & & \overset{\displaystyle C_2H_5}{\diagdown} \\
N-CH_2CH_2OH \rightarrow & & NH + \begin{array}{l} CHO \\ | \\ CH_2OH \end{array} \\
\overset{\diagup}{C_2H_5} & & \overset{\diagup}{C_2H_5}
\end{array}
$$

The usefulness of lead tetraacetate oxidation for determining the structure of nucleosides and nucleotides has been largely dependent on the reactivity of the particular aglycon group present. Adenosinetriphosphoric acid, muscle adenylic acid, and adenosine (in 50% acetic acid) all consumed one mole of lead tetraacetate per mole within 5 minutes' reaction time,[196] in accord with the presence of a *cis*-glycol group in the furanose rings. Other D-ribofuranosyl derivatives also consumed one mole per mole within this oxidation period, although slow oxidation occurred with guanine and guanylic acid *beyond* that required by glycol cleavage.[197] Accordingly, the nucleoside 3-phosphates gave a negligible reaction in the short period selected for oxidation, and these conditions were then used for examining products obtained by degrading yeast ribonucleic acid with ribonuclease. A group of N-aryl-glycosylamines (for example, LXXXVII) related to the nucleosides showed variable oxidation behavior.[198] The rate of consumption of lead tetraacetate by several of the compounds fell off at a level of 3 moles per mole, the product of this first stage being represented by LXXXVIII. Mild over-oxidation which followed was attributed to sub-

(195) N. J. Leonard and M. A. Rebenstorf, *J. Am. Chem. Soc.*, **67**, 49 (1945).

(196) G. Fawaz and K. Seraidarian, *J. Am. Chem. Soc.*, **69**, 966 (1947).

(197) R. A. Becker and F. W. Allen, *J. Biol. Chem.*, **195**, 429 (1952).

(198) G. A. Howard, G. W. Kenner, B. Lythgoe and A. R. Todd, *J. Chem. Soc.*, 861 (1946).

LXXXVII   LXXXVIII

sequent breakdown of LXXXVIII, and vigorous over-oxidation, observed
with some compounds, was thought due to simultaneous attack on the
aglycon group. It was concluded, therefore, that glycol-cleavage oxidation[199]
is only moderately satisfactory for determining the structure of a sugar
ring in glycosylamines having a free NH-group attached to the glycosidic
carbon atom. Since oxidation of formic acid was not allowed for in determining the consumption of lead tetraacetate, it might be of interest to
re-examine these glycosides and to take this factor into account.

Posternak[200] studied lead tetraacetate oxidation of two stereoisomeric
inosamines. One of these isomers consumed oxidant many times as rapidly
as the other and, by analogy with the oxidation behavior of *cis*- and *trans*-
cyclohexanediols,[110a] was assigned the *cis* configuration. To enlarge the experimental basis for oxidatively determining the configuration of amino-
cyclanols, McCasland and Smith[186] studied the cleavage rates of simple
2-aminocyclopentanols and 2-aminocyclohexanols. The behavior of these
reference compounds closely paralleled that of the corresponding 1,2-diols:
lead tetraacetate uptake by *cis*-2-aminocyclopentanol was too rapid to be
measured accurately, but it was at least 20 times the rate for the *trans*
isomer; the rate for *cis*-2-aminocyclohexanol was about 20 times that for
the *trans* isomer, but, as with 1,2-diols,[23] its rate was lower than that for
the *trans*-2-aminocyclopentanol. Provided that both epimers were available, the oxidation rates thus appeared to be a useful means for distinguishing between *cis*- and *trans*-2-aminocyclanols.[201]

The action of lead tetraacetate on osazones of C^{14}-labeled sugars in warm
aqueous acetic acid has been employed[46] for determining specific activity
of the oxidizable carbon atoms present, that is, C4, C5, and C6 of D-glucose
phenylosotriazole. In the potassium acetate-catalyzed oxidation, D-glucos-
azone (D-*arabino*-hexose phenylosazone) yielded two moles of formic acid

(199) The overconsumption of periodate by these compounds was generally much
greater than that of lead tetraacetate.

(200) T. Posternak, *Helv. Chim. Acta*, **33**, 1597 (1950).

(201) Under certain conditions, *cis*-2-amino-cyclohexanol was oxidized by periodate *less* rapidly than the *trans* isomer.[186] The reaction was markedly dependent on
initial pH, possibly because of the presence of a salt-forming amino-group and, therefore, was considered unreliable for configurational determinations.[186]

(carbon dioxide) per mole, although slow overoxidation occurred.[165] The reaction was utilized in determining the structure of 6-*O*-isopropyl-D-*arabino*-hexose phenylosazone,[202] which yielded one mole of formic acid per mole.

VI. EXPERIMENTAL CONDITIONS

Lead tetraacetate is generally prepared by the reaction of red lead (lead tetroxide) with acetic acid. Hutchinson and Pollard[203] appear to have first prepared the reagent, using red lead in warm acetic acid containing sufficient acetic anhydride to react with the water formed. A number of modifications of the original method have been recorded, most of which are concerned with variations in the ratios of red lead to acetic acid and acetic anhydride or with reaction temperature. Colson[204] found that lead tetraacetate is also produced when chlorine is bubbled into an acetic acid solution of lead diacetate, and Oesper and Deasy[205] utilized this reaction, in combination with acetolysis of red lead, to improve the yield and purity of the tetraacetate. Electrolytic formation of lead tetraacetate from the diacetate in acetic acid containing sodium acetate was reported to take place with high current efficiency.[206] Several good, laboratory, preparative methods for the reagent have been described.[4, 7, 114, 205, 207, 208] Lead tetraacetate is now also readily available through commercial sources and, because of its increasing industrial significance, may be obtained at moderate price in large quantities.[209]

Instead of lead tetraacetate, red lead itself, suspended in organic solvents containing acetic acid or in aqueous acetic acid, has been used as a glycol-cleaving agent.[54] This procedure permits the generation of lead tetraacetate in the reaction mixture while the concentration of excess oxidant is simultaneously kept at a minimum, and it retards hydrolysis of lead tetraacetate in an aqueous system.

Acetic acid is the reaction medium most commonly used, since it is a good solvent for most sugars and their derivatives. With free sugars and oligosaccharides, it is often advantageous to dissolve the compound first in a small proportion of water[27] and then to dilute this solution with the

(202) P. A. J. Gorin, *J. Org. Chem.*, **24**, 49 (1959).

(203) A. Hutchinson and W. Pollard, *J. Chem. Soc.*, 212 (1896).

(204) A. Colson, *Compt. rend.*, **136**, 1664 (1903).

(205) R. E. Oesper and C. L. Deasy, *J. Am. Chem. Soc.*, **61**, 972 (1939).

(206) C. Shall and W. Melzer, *Z. Elektrochem.*, **28**, 474 (1922); *Chem. Abstracts*, **17**, 698 (1923).

(207) J. C. Bailar, Jr., *Inorg. Syntheses*, **1**, 47 (1939).

(208) A. I. Vogel, "Practical Organic Chemistry," Longmans, Green and Co., Inc., New York, N. Y., 1948, p. 195.

(209) *Chem. Eng. News*, **36**, No. 26, 59 (1958).

appropriate quantity of acetic acid. Mixtures of acetic and propionic acids are suitable for low-temperature reactions.[133] A high percentage of water may sometimes be used—for example, 1,2:5,6-di-O-isopropylidene-D-mannitol was oxidized in water, glycol-cleavage being more rapid than hydrolysis of lead tetraacetate[27]—but, in some instances, water induces undesirable side-reactions, such as hydrolysis[27, 49] or non-specific oxidation.[47, 49] Even in the absence of water, acetic acid may not always be a suitable solvent, because, as indicated with dithioacetals, other types of reactions can be promoted.[67] Such solvents as benzene, ethyl acetate, chloroform, and dioxane are particularly suitable for many derivatives of the sugars. In these media, reactions are rapid, the isolation of products is facilitated by the fact that lead diacetate is usually precipitated from solution, and the solvents themselves are easily removed. Pyridine has frequently been used and, although glycol-cleavage is very rapid in this solvent, steric differences between 1,2-diols are less pronounced than in other media[125] and the side-oxidation of formic acid is enhanced.[165]

In preparative experiments, excess lead tetraacetate may be smoothly reduced by addition of a stoichiometric quantity of hydrazine in acetic acid.[43] Oxalic acid is also useful,[28] additional acid being added to precipitate the divalent lead formed. When no excess of tetravalent lead is present, sulfuric acid, oxalic acid, or a cation-exchange resin may be used for removing divalent lead.

Lead tetraacetate consumption is measured conveniently by iodometry.[4] The reaction mixture is added to excess potassium iodide solution, usually in the presence of sodium acetate,[5] and the iodine liberated is then titrated with standard thiosulfate. Oxidation may also be measured potentiometrically,[78, 210, 211] a procedure especially useful for "fast" glycol groups,[78] or with redox indicators.[211]

Methods which have been used for estimating the formic acid produced during lead tetraacetate oxidation are based on conversion of the acid to carbon dioxide. Grosheintz[45] used excess lead tetraacetate in warm aqueous acetic acid for oxidation of the formic acid. The "potassium acetate-catalyzed" oxidation of formic acid has been carried out at about room temperature in dry or moist acetic acid, and the carbon dioxide evolved was measured on the microscale with the Warburg respirometer.[48, 49] As noted earlier, however, the course of the glycol-cleavage oxidation may itself be altered in these reactions and, consequently, they may not provide a measure of the formic acid produced during the "normal" oxidation of α-glycols. In the latter (non-catalyzed) reaction, the formic acid produced *also* con-

(210) S. Granick and L. Michaelis, *J. Am. Chem. Soc.*, **62**, 2241 (1940).

(211) O. Tomicek and J. Valcha, *Collection Czechoslov. Chem. Communs.*, **16–17**, 113 (1951–2).

sumes lead tetraacetate, but at a relatively low rate.[36, 44, 49] A corrected value for lead tetraacetate uptake can therefore be obtained by measuring the evolved carbon dioxide,[49] but this measurement may not represent the *total* formic acid liberated. Ness and Fletcher[212] applied bromometric estimation of formic acid[213] to the reaction (with lead tetraacetate) of methyl α-D-mannopyranoside and 3,5-di-O-benzoyl-D-ribose, but they noted that it was difficult to distinguish in this way between free and esterified formate.

Formaldehyde produced during lead tetraacetate oxidations may be estimated readily by colorimetric procedures[43, 155] or as the Dimedon (5,5-dimethyl-1,3-cyclohexanedione) derivative.[72] Excess oxidant is first destroyed and the formaldehyde is then distilled,[43] or the reaction mixture is used directly. Failure to reduce excess lead tetraacetate led to an incorrect assignment of structure for di-O-isopropylidene-galactitol, formaldehyde being produced spuriously from the terminal 1,2-glycol groups liberated by accidental hydrolysis of isopropylidene groups.[214]

With a few exceptions, substituent groups have been found stable to conditions used in lead tetraacetate oxidation. Reference has been made to dithioacetals and to some aryl aglycons which may be prone to attack, and to the ineffectiveness of certain N-acyl substituents for protecting α-hydroxy amines from oxidation. Acetals[66] and O-acyl substituents—benzoate,[61, 65, 215] acetate,[43, 125, 179, 216] tosylate,[62] phosphate,[150, 152] and carbonate[95]—appear to be generally stable. However, migration of an O-benzylidene group in acetic acid has been reported,[102] and cognizance must always be taken of the possibility of ester migrations in these, as in other, reactions. Methyl[142, 145] and benzyl[57, 217] ethers have been oxidized without obvious side-reactions, but slow hydrolysis of trityl groups in acetic acid [125, 218] permits cleavage to occur at a correspondingly low rate. In a fast oxidation, as with 6-O-trityl-D-glucose, no appreciable hydrolysis occurs.[95] Stability of an epoxy ring to lead tetraacetate has been demonstrated in the oxidation of conduritol oxide to give 2,3-epoxysuccinaldehyde.[219]

Structural examination of a sugar by lead tetraacetate oxidation should include a preliminary measurement of the oxidation rate and of products

(212) R. K. Ness and H. G. Fletcher, Jr., *J. Am. Chem. Soc.*, **76**, 1663 (1954).

(213) W. Poethke, *Pharm. Zentralhalle*, **86**, 357 (1947); *Chem. Abstracts*, **44**, 9303 (1950).

(214) R. A. Pizzarello and W. Freudenberg, *J. Am. Chem. Soc.*, **61**, 611 (1939).

(215) F. Smith and J. W. Van Cleve, *J. Am. Chem. Soc.*, **77**, 3659 (1955).

(216) P. A. J. Gorin, L. Hough and J. K. N. Jones, *J. Chem. Soc.*, 2699 (1955).

(217) W. T. Haskins, R. M. Hann and C. S. Hudson, *J. Am. Chem. Soc.*, **64**, 132 (1942).

(218) P. E. Verkade, *Rec. trav. chim.*, **57**, 824 (1938).

(219) C. Schöpf and A. Schmetterling, *Angew. Chem.*, **64**, 591 (1952).

formed (such as formic acid and formaldehyde), all of which estimations may be carried out with micro to semimicro quantities of material. Reactions should be effected at the ambient temperature, or lower, to minimize non-specific effects and decomposition of lead tetraacetate, and it may be desirable to try more than one solvent, if possible. On a larger scale, the isolation and characterization of products will be of the utmost importance in clarifying the course of the oxidation. It has become abundantly clear that the action of lead tetraacetate on a sugar can be distinctly different from the action of periodate thereon, that one reagent is sometimes more effective than the other, or that the reactions take different pathways. Hence, it may be advantageous to compare the oxidation behavior with each reagent.

THE MAILLARD REACTION

By G. P. Ellis

*Organic Chemistry Section, Research Department, Benger Laboratories Ltd.,
Holmes Chapel, Cheshire, England*

I. Introduction

A more accurate but longer description of the reaction to be discussed
in this article would be *the interaction which occurs initially between amino*

acids and the glycosidic center of sugars. Later stages of the reaction concern other parts of both molecules. Maillard[1] was the first to study such reactions systematically and to realize some of their relations to the chemistry of natural products. He found that simple amino acids react on warming with certain sugars, to form dark-brown products. This explains why the reaction has also been called *the browning reaction, non-enzymic browning, melanoidin formation,* or *caramelization*; and the brown products have been referred to as *melanoidins, humin-like substances, aterins,* or *orpheins.* Since these names are vague and chemically uninformative, the Maillard reaction will, for the purposes of this review, be defined as *the reaction of the amino group of amino acids, peptides, or proteins with the "glycosidic" hydroxyl group of sugars.* (This reaction is followed by other, more complex, changes which result eventually in the formation of brown pigments and polymers.)

As a result of the very wide chemical interest which the Maillard reaction has attracted since the early years of this century, and of its diverse commercial and biological implications, a vast amount of work thereon has been published. In this article, the chemical aspects of the reaction between simple amino acids and mono- and di-saccharides will be surveyed; the reaction with peptides and proteins will be discussed only when it contributes to our understanding of the mode of interaction between simple amino acids and sugars. The significance of the reaction in the preservation of various foodstuffs has now been reviewed many times[2-9] and continues to be the subject of much investigation.[10-15e] The reaction is also

(1) Louis Maillard was born in 1878, and gained a diploma in Higher Pharmacy and a doctorate in medicine. He was made a qualified teacher in the Faculty of Medicine in Paris in 1904, and in 1919 became Professor of Biological and Medical Chemistry in the Faculty of Algiers. Besides his work on the reaction which bears his name, he made important discoveries in protein chemistry, on the nature of urinary coloring, on the metabolic formation of urea, and in titanium chemistry. His study of the formation of peptides from amino acids in the presence of alcohols led him to use glycerol, and then sugars, in this reaction. He died suddenly in Paris in 1936.

(2) H. D. Lightbody and H. R. Fevold, *Advances in Food Research,* **1,** 149 (1948).

(3) A. F. Ross, *Advances in Food Research,* **1,** 257 (1948).

(4) E. R. Stadtman, *Advances in Food Research,* **1,** 325 (1948).

(5) J. P. Danehy and W. W. Pigman, *Advances in Food Research,* **3,** 241 (1951).

(6) A. Patron, *Inds. agr. et aliment.* (Paris), **68,** 251 (1951).

(7) J. E. Hodge, *J. Agr. Food Chem.,* **1,** 928 (1953).

(8) L. Görnhardt, *Fette, Seifen Anstrichmittel,* **57,** 270, 429 (1955).

(9) S. Adachi, *Kagaku no Ryôiki,* **9,** 363 (1955).

(10) A. R. Deschreider, *Bull. école meunerie belge,* **17,** 96 (1955).

(11) A. T. Markh, *Biokhimiya,* **21,** 636 (1956).

(12) S. Adachi, *Nippon Nôgei-kagaku Kaishi* **30,** 459 (1956).

(13) M. Catalán and M. P. Rodríquez, *Anales bromatol.* (Madrid), **9,** 161 (1957).

(14) A. R. Deschreider, *Bull. école meunerie belge,* **19,** 15 (1957).

(15) R. Andreotti, *Ind. conserve* (Parma), **32,** 83 (1957).

(15a) S. Adachi, *Nippon Nôgei-kagaku Kaishi,* **31,** 93, 97 (1957).

important in the analytical determination of amino acids and carbohydrates[16-25] and has become significant in connection with the nutritional availability of amino acids from proteins.[26-39a] The stimulation of the growth of *Lactobacillus gayoni* in a heated culture-medium has been ascribed to the formation of *N*-D-glucosylglycine,[32] but the growth of *Lactobacillus bulgaricus 09* is inhibited by a product of the reaction of lactose with proteins or certain amino acids.[40] Similarly, the reaction product of glycine and D-glucose is toxic to *Phytophthora fragariae*.[41]

(15b) R. C. Dutra, N. P. Tarassuk and M. Kleiber, *J. Dairy Sci.*, **41**, 1017 (1958).

(15c) S. Omata, T. Ueno and Y. Nakagawa, *Nippon Nôgei-kagaku Kaishi*, **31**, 822 (1957).

(15d) J. E. Hodge, *Abstracts Papers Am. Chem. Soc.*, **134**, 20D (1958).

(15e) W. W. Binkley, *Abstracts Papers Am. Chem. Soc.*, **134**, 20D (1958); *Intern. Sugar J.*, **59**, 64, 178 (1957), **60**, 62, 322 (1958).

(16) D. T. Englis and F. A. Dykins, *Ind. Eng. Chem. Anal. Ed.*, **3**, 17 (1931).

(17) J. A. Ambler and J. B. Sneider, *Ind. Eng. Chem. Anal. Ed.*, **4**, 37 (1932).

(18) A. M. Kuzin and Z. Makaeva, *Biokhimiya*, **4**, 367 (1939); *Chem. Abstracts*, **34**, 1693 (1940).

(19) A. M. Kuzin and O. Polyakova, *Biokhimiya*, **6**, 113 (1941); *Chem. Abstracts*, **35**, 7937 (1941).

(20) C. Enders, *Biochem. Z.*, **314**, 389 (1943).

(21) H. N. Horowitz, M. Ikawa and M. Fling, *Arch. Biochem.*, **25**, 226 (1950).

(22) H. Täufel and H. Iwainsky, *Z. anal. Chem.*, **136**, 31 (1952).

(23) J. Immers and E. Vasseur, *Acta Chem. Scand.*, **6**, 363 (1952).

(24) Y. Nagai, *Tôhoku J. Exptl. Med.*, **61**, 331 (1955).

(25) H. Iwainsky, *Z. Lebensm.-Untersuch. u.-Forsch.*, **100**, 173 (1955).

(26) J. M. Stevens and J. McGinnis, *J. Biol. Chem.*, **171**, 431 (1947).

(27) L. Friedman and O. L. Kline, *J. Nutrition*, **40**, 295 (1950).

(28) J. R. Lowry and R. Theiessen, Jr., *Arch. Biochem.*, **25**, 148 (1950).

(29) L. Friedman and O. L. Kline, *J. Biol. Chem.*, **184**, 599 (1950).

(30) D. R. Clandinin, J. M. Stevens, A. B. Morrison and A. R. Robblee, *J. Biol. Chem.*, **190**, 219 (1951).

(31) K. V. Giri, P. B. R. Rao and R. Rajagopalan, *Food Research*, **18**, 217 (1953).

(32) D. Rogers, T. E. King and V. H. Cheldelin, *Proc. Soc. Exptl. Biol. Med.*, **82**, 140 (1953).

(33) P. de Lange and L. P. v. d. Mijll Dekker, *Nature*, **173**, 1040 (1954).

(34) J. Mauron, F. Mottu, E. Bujard and R. H. Engli, *Arch. Biochem. Biophys.*, **59**, 433 (1955).

(35) L. J. Schroeder, M. Iacobellis and A. H. Smith *J. Nutrition*, **55**, 97 (1955).

(36) H. D. Cremer and E. Menden, *Z. Lebensm.-Untersuch. u.-Forsch.*, **104**, 33 (1956).

(37) J. E. Folk, *Arch. Biochem. Biophys.*, **64**, 6 (1956).

(38) D. S. Miller, *J. Sci. Food Agr.*, **7**, 337 (1956).

(39) S. Sentheshanmuganathan and A. A. Hoover, *Biochem. J.*, **68**, 621 (1958). J. Mauron and F. Mottu, *Arch. Biochem. Biophys.*, **77**, 312 (1958).

(39a) K. M. Clegg and N. Davies, *Proc. Nutrition Soc.* (Engl. and Scot.), **17**, No. 1, 1 (1958).

(40) L. Viswanathan and P. S. Sarma, *Nature*, **180**, 1370 (1957).

(41) W. E. McKeen, *Science*, **123**, 509 (1956).

II. Nomenclature

When the structure of a compound is known, the current British–American practice[42] will be followed. No specific recommendation was made for naming Amadori rearrangement products, but, under Rule 8, the systematic name for the Amadori product of N-D-glucosyl-DL-leucine could be 1-(DL-1-carboxy-3-methylbutyl)amino-1-deoxy-D-fructose (I or II), and this name conflicts with the requirement that the carboxyl function takes precedence and that the name should end in "acid." Consequently, this compound should be named as N-(D-*arabino*-tetrahydroxy-2-oxohexyl)-DL-leucine. A shorter and equally unambiguous name would be 1-(DL-leucino)-1-deoxy-D-fructose. (This is sometimes shortened to DL-leucino-deoxyfructose. Such compounds have also been called fructose-leucine, but this is not recommended since it may be confused with such expressions as "the fructose–leucine system.[11])

$$
\begin{array}{ccc}
CO_2H & & CO_2H \\
| & & | \\
H_2CNHCHCH_2CH(CH_3)_2 & & H_2CNHCHCH_2CH(CH_3)_2 \\
| & & | \\
CO & & C-OH \\
| & \rightleftharpoons & | \\
HOCH & & HOCH \\
| & & | \\
HCOH & & HCOH \\
| & & | \\
HCOH & & HCOH \\
| & & | \\
CH_2OH & & H_2CO \\
\mathbf{I} & & \mathbf{II}
\end{array}
$$

$$
\begin{array}{c}
CO_2H \\
| \\
HCNHCHCH_2CH(CH_3)_2 \\
\| \\
COH \\
| \\
HOCH \\
| \\
HCOH \\
| \\
HCOH \\
| \\
CH_2OH \\
\mathbf{III}
\end{array}
$$

Such compounds as III are not systematically named herein, but are referred to as the enolic form—in this case, of DL-leucino-deoxyfructose.

III. Scope of the Reaction

The interaction of amino acids and sugars falls into two general types. The first is the simple, controlled condensation of the reactants; this leads

(42) Editorial Report on Nomenclature, *J. Chem. Soc.*, 5108 (1952); *Chem. Eng. News*, **31**, 1776 (1953).

to compounds which are identifiable as *N*-substituted glycosylamines or, occasionally, their Amadori rearrangement products. The second is the typical Maillard reaction, which leads to a mixture of products of increasing complexity if conditions are conducive.

1. N-*Substituted Glycosylamines*[43] *and Amadori Products*[44]

When aldoses are heated in methanol,[45] ethanol,[45] or water[46] with compounds containing a primary amino group, solid glycosylamines (IV) separate on cooling or on adding ether. Occasionally, an acidic catalyst such as ammonium chloride[47] or hydrogen chloride[48] may be necessary, especially if the amine is a weak base. Too much acid must not be present, however, as the glycosylamine may then rearrange to the 1-amino-1-deoxy-2-ketose derivative (V) (the Amadori "rearrangement"[44]). The presence or absence of water in the reaction solvent may have an effect in determining which isomer crystallizes.[49-51] The reactions may be summarized as follows.

$$\begin{array}{ccccc}
\text{HCOH} & & \text{HCNHR} & & \text{H}_2\text{CNHR} \\
| & + \text{RNH}_2 \rightarrow & | & \xrightarrow{\text{H}^\oplus} & \text{HOC} \\
\text{HCOH} & & \text{HCOH} & & \\
| & & | & & \\
& & \text{IV} & & \text{V}
\end{array}$$

Ketoses react readily with aliphatic amino compounds,[52, 53] but much less readily with aromatic amines.[54] The ketosylamines (VI) formed can *also* rearrange by undergoing an Amadori "rearrangement" in reverse, so that a 2-amino-2-deoxy-D-glucose (D-glucosamine) derivative (VII) is formed from D-fructose and an amine.[53, 55] Sometimes the D-fructosylamine derivative (VI) has not been isolated. The α-anomer of the D-fructosylamine is shown for convenience in VI and in other formulas in this article, although the β configuration is equally possible.

Aldoses have been condensed with a number of amino acids and their esters to yield *N*-substituted glycosylamines. For example, D-glucose has

(43) G. P. Ellis and J. Honeyman, *Advances in Carbohydrate Chem.*, **10**, 95 (1955).

(44) J. E. Hodge, *Advances in Carbohydrate Chem.*, **10**, 169 (1955).

(45) B. Sorokin, *Ber.*, **19**, 513 (1886); *J. prakt. Chem.*, [2] **37**, 291 (1888).

(46) F. Weygand, *Ber.*, **72**, 1663 (1939).

(47) R. Kuhn and R. Ströbele, *Ber.*, **70**, 773 (1937).

(48) R. Kuhn and L. Birkofer, *Ber.*, **71**, 621 (1938).

(49) G. P. Ellis and J. Honeyman, *J. Chem. Soc.*, 1490 (1952).

(50) S. Tsuiki, *Tôhoku J. Exptl. Med.*, **61**, 267, 365 (1955).

(51) L. Rosen, J. W. Woods and W. Pigman, *J. Org. Chem.*, **22**, 1727 (1957).

(52) J. G. Erickson, *J. Am. Chem. Soc.*, **75**, 2784 (1953).

(53) J. F. Carson, *J. Am. Chem. Soc.*, **77**, 1881 (1955).

(54) C. P. Barry and J. Honeyman, *J. Chem. Soc.*, 4147 (1952).

(55) K. Heyns, H. Paulsen and H. Breuer, *Angew. Chem.*, **68**, 334 (1956).

$$\underset{\text{VI}}{\begin{array}{c} \text{HOH}_2\text{C—COH} \\ | \\ \text{HOCH} \\ | \\ \text{HCOH} \\ | \\ \text{HCOH} \\ | \\ \text{H}_2\text{CO} \end{array}} \quad\xrightarrow{\text{RNH}_2}\quad \underset{\text{}}{\begin{array}{c} \text{HOH}_2\text{C—CNHR} \\ | \\ \text{HOCH} \\ | \\ \text{HCOH} \\ | \\ \text{HCOH} \\ | \\ \text{H}_2\text{CO} \end{array}} \quad\rightarrow\quad \underset{\text{VII}}{\begin{array}{c} \text{HCOH} \\ | \\ \text{HCNHR} \\ | \\ \text{HOCH} \\ | \\ \text{HCOH} \\ | \\ \text{HCO} \\ | \\ \text{CH}_2\text{OH} \end{array}}$$

afforded the N-D-glucosyl derivatives of m-, o-, and p-aminobenzoic acid,[56, 57] and of p-aminosalicylic acid,[56, 58] glycine,[56] lysine,[56] and serine.[56] However, Ågren and Taylor[59] have shown that the presence of a carboxyl group tended to inhibit the reaction of an amino compound with D-glucose. The reaction between a DL-amino acid and an aldose has been used for resolving the former into its stereoisomers by taking advantage of their different solubilities.[60]

After β-D-glucosyl fluoride and an amino acid have been kept at room temperature in an aqueous solution at pH 7–8, the sodium salt of the N-D-glucosylamino acid may be isolated as an amorphous powder.[61] No catalyst is required in these reactions. When D-glucose and DL-phenylalanine are refluxed together in dry methanol, the main product is the Amadori re-arrangement compound, 1-deoxy-1-phenylalanino-D-fructose.[62] This kind of product is also given by several other amino acids.[63-65] The yields obtained in most of these reactions are very low; and, since the products have seldom been obtained crystalline, it is difficult to purify them by conventional procedures. Ion-exchange chromatography is frequently used.[64] A crystal-line product was, however, obtained from glycine isopropyl ester and 4,6-O-benzylidene-D-glucose.[66] An improved yield of 1-deoxy-1-N-sarcosyl-D-fructose was given when refluxing N,N-dimethylformamide was used as the solvent.[67] The benzyloxycarbonyl method of peptide synthesis, when

(56) See Reference 43, Table XII, pp. 136–150.

(57) F. Micheel and B. Schleppinghoff, *Chem. Ber.*, **89**, 1702 (1956).

(58) Laboratoires francois de chimiotherapie and A. Girard, French Pat. 1,015,573 (1952); *Chem. Abstracts*, **52**, 1217 (1958).

(59) G. Ågren and A. Taylor, *Arkiv Kemi, Mineral. Geol.*, **14B**, No. 14, 6 pp. (1940).

(60) K. Maurer and B. Schiedt, *Z. physiol. Chem., Hoppe-Seyler's*, **213**, 110 (1932).

(61) F. Micheel and A. Klemer, *Chem. Ber.*, **84**, 212 (1951); **85**, 1083 (1952).

(62) A. Gottschalk, *Biochem. J.*, **52**, 455 (1952).

(63) A. Abrams, P. H. Lowy and H. Borsook, *J. Am. Chem. Soc.*, **77**, 4794 (1955).

(64) P. H. Lowy and H. Borsook, *J. Am. Chem. Soc.*, **78**, 3175 (1956).

(65) K. Täufel, H. Iwainsky and H. Bergner, *Ernährungsforschung*, **1**, 719 (1956).

(66) F. Micheel and A. Frowein, *Angew. Chem.*, **69**, 562 (1957); *Chem. Ber.*, **90**, 1599 (1957).

(67) A. Klemer and F. Micheel, *Chem. Ber.*, **89**, 1242 (1956).

applied to 4,6-O-benzylidene-D-glucose with N-benzyloxycarbonylglycyl chloride, gives N-D-glucosylglycine.[68]

Although much work has been done in an attempt to elucidate the structure of N-substituted glycosylamines, rigid proof of their structures has not yet been achieved.[43] Spectroscopic evidence is inconclusive,[69] whilst chemical methods are of limited value because equilibrium between open-chain, pyranose, and furanose forms is possible. However, all such derivatives as ethers and esters so far prepared directly from N-glycosylamines have been shown to be pyranoid, and periodate oxidation of some N-glycosylamines has confirmed this conclusion.[70, 71]

2. The Maillard Reaction

Whereas the conditions under which N-substituted glycosylamines are formed from sugars plus amines (or amino acids) are fairly well defined, the conditions under which the Maillard reaction occurs may be varied widely. These variables, which include temperature, moisture content, and pH, will be discussed in the following Sections; the comparative reactivity of individual amino acids and sugars will also receive consideration. Several stages of the Maillard reaction have been identified, chiefly by the various compounds which have been isolated. These compounds exhibit increasing complexity, or are degradation products either of the sugar or of the initial, carbohydrate–amine reaction product. Dark-brown, insoluble, polymeric compounds are formed in the later stages.

The Maillard reaction has been studied from several viewpoints and these differing approaches have sometimes been reflected in the particular molecular proportions of sugar and amino acid which were used in the experiments. Thus, the reaction has been regarded as the decomposition or polymerization of the carbohydrate by a small molecular-proportion of amino acid.[20, 72-77]

When an amino acid is heated with D-glucose in a stream of oxygen at 130°, decarboxylation and deamination occur according to the following equation. Very little free ammonia can be detected, since it quickly com-

(68) M. Bergmann, L. Zervas and J. Overhoff, Z. physiol. Chem., Hoppe-Seyler's, **224**, 52 (1934).

(69) F. Legay, Compt. rend., **234**, 1612 (1952).

(70) I. Kawashiro, Yakugaku Zasshi, **73**, 943 (1953); Chem. Abstracts, **48**, 10630 (1954).

(71) I. Kawashiro, Yakugaku Zasshi, **74**, 33 (1954); Chem. Abstracts, **49**, 1586 (1955).

(72) L. C. Maillard, Compt. rend., **154**, 66 (1912).

(73) J. A. Ambler, Ind. Eng. Chem., **21**, 47 (1929).

(74) F. Lieben and B. Baumiger, Biochem. Z., **292**, 371 (1937).

(75) J. Benek and F. Lieben, Biochem. Z., **292**, 376 (1937).

(76) C. Enders, Wochschr. Brau., **60**, 98 (1943); Chem. Abstracts, **39**, 1962 (1945).

(77) A. P. Patton and P. Chism, Nature, **167**, 406 (1951).

$$RCHCO_2H + [O] \rightarrow RCHO + CO_2 + NH_3$$
$$\underset{NH_2}{|}$$

bines with the sugar. The reaction is more intense at pH 9.2 than at pH 11.9, and it is irreversible.[75, 78-80] Browning is usually most intense when the proportion of amino acid to sugar is about[72, 74] 1:2, but, at high temperature, more sugar reacts per mole of amino acid.[81] There may be a connection between this phenomenon and the formation of diglycosylamines from aldoses plus ammonia.[82-85] Recently, an Amadori type of product was described[85a] which contains two sugar moieties to each molecule of glycine. When glycine sodium salt was heated for 12 minutes at 100° with an excess of either D-glucose or D-mannose, a 20 % yield of this product was obtained. Alternatively, the sodium salt of 1-deoxy-1-glycino-D-fructose may be similarly treated for 6–7 minutes with D-glucose or D-mannose to give a 40 % yield of the N,N-di-(1-deoxy-D-fructose) compound. An excess of amino acid has been used in the preparation of sample melanoidins,[86] but kinetic studies (see Section VIII) suggest that at least the *first* stage of the reaction involves a 1:1 reaction between the components.

The Elson–Morgan[87] test for hexosamines is also given by the products of the Maillard reaction[88] and, since free sugars, amino acids, and hexosamines are frequently present together in protein hydrolyzates from natural sources, it is important to be able to identify hexosamines in the presence of D-glucose and such amino acids as lysine or glycine. Horowitz, Ikawa, and Fling[21] have shown that D-glucose, D-fructose, D-galactose, L-sorbose, L-fucose, and D-xylose give rise to compounds which react positively to the Elson–Morgan test. Means of distinguishing between the two kinds of reaction have been described.[23, 88, 89] If the unknown compound gives a red color with the Erhlich reagent (p-dimethylaminobenzaldehyde in hydrochloric acid) after treatment with sodium carbonate solution not containing 2,4-pentanedione (acetylacetone), a sugar–amino acid mixture is pres-

(78) S. Akabori, *Ber.*, **66**, 143 (1933).

(79) J. Watanabe, *J. Biochem.* (Tokyo), **16**, 163 (1932).

(80) J. Watanabe, *J. Biochem.* (Tokyo), **17**, 147 (1933).

(81) A. G. Zabrodskii and V. A. Vitorskaya, *Biokhimiya*, **19**, 738 (1954).

(82) H. S. Isbell and H. L. Frush, *J. Research Natl. Bur. Standards*, **46**, 132 (1951).

(83) I. D. Raacke-Fels, *Arch. Biochem. Biophys.*, **43**, 289 (1953).

(84) R. J. Bayly, E. J. Bourne and M. Stacey, *Nature*, **169**, 876 (1952).

(85) S. Lewin and Z. Kosinski, *Trans. Faraday Soc.*, **54**, 222 (1958).

(85a) E. F. L. J. Anet, *Chem. & Ind.* (London), 1438 (1958).

(86) M. L. Wolfrom, R. C. Schlicht, A. W. Langer, Jr., and C. S. Rooney, *J. Am. Chem. Soc.*, **75**, 1013 (1953).

(87) L. A. Elson and W. T. J. Morgan, *Biochem. J.*, **27**, 1824 (1933).

(88) E. Vasseur and J. Immers, *Arkiv Kemi*, **1**, 253 (1949).

(89) J. Immers and E. Vasseur, *Nature*, **165**, 898 (1950).

ent (since D-glucosamine does not give a color under these conditions). The
optimum pH for producing the red color from D-glucosamine is 9.5, but
with sugar–amino acid mixtures it is 10.8–11.2. The absorption maximum
for the color produced by D-glucosamine plus the Erhlich reagent is at 530
mμ, and this drifts to 510 mμ on letting the solution stand, whereas the
corresponding red color obtained from the Maillard reaction product has
two maxima, at 570 and 510 mμ, respectively.

IV. EXPERIMENTAL METHODS

1. *Preparation of* N-*Glycosylamino Acids and Esters*

a. *4-*(D-*Glucosylamino)-2-hydroxybenzoic Acid.*[90]—

Sodium *p*-aminosalicylate dihydrate (21.1 g.) and D-glucose (19.8 g.) were dissolved in water (100 ml.) and the solution was brought to pH 5.5 with formic acid.
After 3 days at room temperature, the solution was cooled to 0°, treated with 10%
formic acid, and allowed to stand for one hour at 0° to crystallize. Colorless needles
(29 g., 92% yield) were isolated; m. p., 152° with browning but no liberation of gas;
$[\alpha]_D$ −143° (in pyridine).

b. *4-*(D-*Glucosylamino)benzoic Acid, 2-Diethylaminoethyl Ester, Hydro-*
chloride.[91]—

Procaine hydrochloride (5.1 g.) and D-glucose (3.4 g.) were refluxed in absolute
ethanol (67 ml.) for about 1.5 hours. A little undissolved D-glucose was removed by
filtration, and the yellowish-brown, viscous oil was triturated to give a solid, m. p.
138–142° and then 176–178°. Recrystallization from a 1:1 mixture of 96% ethanol
and methanol gave crystals of the hydrate, m. p. 142–144°. The anhydrous compound,
m. p. 176–178°, was obtained by recrystallization from absolute ethanol.

c. N-D-*Glucosyl- and* N-*Lactosyl-glycine, Copper Salts.*[92]—

The poly-*O*-acetylaldosyl bromide was reacted with diethyl formamidomalonate
to give diethyl poly-*O*-acetylglycosylformamidomalonate which, on treatment with
barium hydroxide, afforded the glycosylglycine. The copper salt was then prepared.
For example:

(90) G. Haberland, *Arzneimittel-Forsch.*, **1**, 298 (1951).

d. N-D-*Glucosylglycine, Sodium Salt.*[61]—

D-Glucosyl fluoride (500 mg.) and an equivalent amount of glycine in water (25 ml.) containing sodium bicarbonate was kept at room temperature for 1 day, and then for 3 days at 36–39°, at pH 7–8. The solution was now evaporated to dryness under diminished pressure, and a methanol extract was made. Addition of absolute ether precipitated the product (180 mg., 25% yield) as a colorless, amorphous material, $[\alpha]_D$ +15.4° (in water).

e. N-D-*Glucosylsarcosine.*[93]—

Tetra-*O*-acetyl-D-glucosyl bromide (4.1 g.) and sarcosine ethyl ester (2.4 g.) were warmed together on a waterbath at 50° and the mixture became dark-brown. The sirup was kept at room temperature for 20 hours, whereupon crystals formed. Dry ether was added, sarcosine ester hydrochloride was removed by filtration, and the solution was quickly washed with water and dried. Removal of the ether gave a yellow sirup which, on treatment with methanol, gave needles of tetra-*O*-acetyl-*N*-D-gluco-sylsarcosine (3.5 g., 79% yield); after recrystallization from methanol, m.p. 87–88° (no dec.). This compound was treated at 0° with methanol (100 ml.) saturated with ammonia. After removal of the solvent, crystals of *N*-D-glucosylsarcosine (1.7 g., 88% yield), m.p. 169–170°, were obtained.

2. Amadori Rearrangement Products

a. Reaction of D-*Glucose with* DL-*Phenylalanine.*[62]—

D-Glucose (5 g.) and DL-phenylalanine (700 mg.) in dried methanol (140 ml.) were refluxed for 4–5 hours. The solvent was removed under diminished pressure at 35° and the excess of D-glucose was fermented with bakers' yeast (5 g.) at 26° for 7 hours. After removal of the yeast and concentration of the filtrate to dryness, the brittle residue was freed of unchanged amino acid by treatment with methanol. An amorphous powder (1.34 g.) remained; this could not be obtained in a crystalline state. Chromatography indicated that the material was mainly 1-deoxy-1-(DL-phenylal-anino)-D-fructose.

b. 1-Deoxy-1-sarcosyl-D-fructose.[67]—

Sarcosine (1 g.) and dry, powdered D-glucose (10 g.) in *N,N*-dimethylformamide (30 ml.) were heated at 100°. Dissolution was complete in ten minutes, and the mixture was heated for a further 30 minutes. The yellow sirup remaining after removal of the solvent under diminished pressure was freed of D-glucose with bakers' yeast. After 5 days, paper-chromatographic examination showed that no D-glucose or D-mannose remained. The solution was decolorized and the water was removed by evaporation under diminished pressure. Purification from methanol and ether gave an amorphous powder (2 g., 70% yield), $[\alpha]_D$ − 49 ± 1° (in water).

(91) H. Grasshof and U. Lippold, *Arnzeimittel-Forsch.*, **3**, 42 (1953).

(92) J. V. Koštíř and M. Queisnerová, *Chem. listy*, **43**, 277 (1949); *Chem. Abstracts*, **45**, 553 (1951).

(93) K. Maurer, *Ber.*, **59**, 827 (1926).

3. Glyconyl Peptides[94]

Glycine (0.75 g.) was dissolved in water (50 ml.); sodium bicarbonate (1.7 g.) was added and the solution was cooled in an ice-bath. Penta-O-acetyl-D-gluconyl chloride (4.3 g.) in chloroform (50 ml.) was added in portions during 1 hour. After shaking the solution for a further hour at room temperature, the bicarbonate layer was separated, acidified to pH 2, and cooled in ice. The crystals (2.4 g., 52% yield) were removed by filtration| and dried. Esterification gave (penta-O-acetyl-D-gluconyl)glycine ethyl ester, m.p. 114–116°, $[\alpha]_D$ +18.3° (in 1% ethanol). Treatment of this compound (4.9 g.) with hot barium methoxide[95] gave D-gluconylglycine ethyl ester (2.4 g.), m.p. 110–111°, $[\alpha]_D$ +35.3° (in 1% ethanol). This ester was dissolved in water, and N sodium hydroxide (9 ml.) was added. After 0.5 hour at room temperature, N hydrochloric acid (20 ml.) was added, and the solution was evaporated to dryness under diminished pressure. The residue was taken up in hot ethanol (20 ml.), the sodium chloride was removed by filtration, and ether was added to incipient turbidity. After one day at −5°, the amorphous powder was removed by filtration and dried over calcium chloride.

4. Later Stages of the Maillard Reaction

The brown product or melanoidin which results from the Maillard reaction has been isolated from the products from various mixtures of reactants by numerous workers. A selection of these is given below. Maillard[72, 96-99] studied the interaction of D-glucose and other reducing sugars with glycine and several other amino acids at 34°, 40°, 100°, and 150°.

For example, a mixture of powdered D-glucose (4 g., 0.02 mole), glycine (1 g., 0.0013 mole), and water (3–4 ml.) was heated *on a steambath*. The solution had a light-yellow color at first, but darkening became more pronounced with increasing speed, until the mixture was brown and of thicker consistency. Bubbles of gas caused a foam on the surface, and a spongy, voluminous mass of dry, shiny, brown plates was obtained. On adding a little water, evolution of gas continued for a long time, and the final product was amorphous. In a similar experiment performed *at 40°*, the solution remained clear until 27 hours had elapsed, when it assumed a light-yellow tint. At 44 hours, it was orange colored; at 68 hours, the clear, brown solution liberated many small gas bubbles; after 110 hours, the deep-brown solution was covered with foam and a brown, insoluble mass appeared. When the temperature was maintained *at 34°*, 204 hours elapsed before the reaction mixture became dark brown; but, *at 150°*, the evolution of gas and the coloration were very rapid. As the water vaporized, the residual mass rapidly swelled out of the vessel.

When an *excess of glycine* was heated *at 170°* with D-glucose and water,

(94) D. G. Doherty, *J. Biol. Chem.*, **201**, 857 (1953).
(95) G. Zemplén and E. Pacsu, *Ber.*, **62**, 1613 (1929).
(96) L. C. Maillard, *Compt. rend.*, **155**, 1554 (1912).
(97) L. C. Maillard, *Compt. rend. soc. biol.*, **72**, 599 (1913).
(98) L. C. Maillard, *Ann. chim.* (Paris), [11] **5**, 258 (1916).
(99) L. C. Maillard, *Ann. chim.* (Paris), [11] **7**, 113 (1917).

a dark-brown crust formed. This was boiled with water and the suspension was filtered. The filtrate was found to contain glycine. Enders and Theis[100] prepared a sample of melanoidin in a similar way, using *less* than the equimolar proportion of glycine. Tan, Wolfrom, and Langer[101] prepared a brown material from D-xylose plus glycine by heating equimolar proportions, or by treating 0.1 mole of the sugar with one mole of the amino acid at 95° for between 20 and 90 hours. The brown pigment was isolated by filtration dialysis, coagulation, and centrifugation. Wolfrom, Cavalieri, and Cavalieri[102] also prepared sample pigments under defined conditions of pH at 90–95°, for use as color standards (with which to compare the colors of pigments formed from other amino acids and sugars). The intensity of the color was measured at 490 mμ. A similar melanoidin pigment was prepared by Lewis, Esselen, and Fellers[103] from D-glucose–glycine, for use as a color comparator in a study of the liberation of carbon dioxide in the Maillard reaction.

V. Reaction Conditions and Their Effects

1. *Introduction*

The formation of N-glycosylamino acids, as mentioned in the previous Section, takes place under rather clearly defined conditions and will not be discussed further. The present Section will be concerned with the effect, on the Maillard reaction, of (a) external conditions and (b) the presence or absence of substances other than the amino acid and the sugar.

It is first of all necessary to mention some of the characteristics of the Maillard reaction and to summarize the various means by which its progress has been followed. Only a few typical references will be mentioned in this Section, but others will be cited later.

The most obvious characteristic is, of course, the formation of a yellow or brown coloration. This becomes progressively darker with time, until it is dark-brown or even black,[97, 103, 104] but, if the first step in the Maillard reaction is the formation of the glycosylamine[7, 105] (which is usually colorless[43]), it is obvious that the rate of color formation alone is not a safe

(100) C. Enders and K. Theis, *Brennstoff-Chem.*, **19**, 360, 402, 439 (1938); *Chem. Abstracts*, **34**, 440 (1940).

(101) T.-L. Tan, M. L. Wolfrom and A. W. Langer, Jr., *J. Am. Chem. Soc.*, **72**, 5090 (1950).

(102) M. L. Wolfrom, L. F. Cavalieri and D. K. Cavalieri, *J. Am. Chem. Soc.*, **69**, 2411 (1947).

(103) V. M. Lewis, W. B. Esselen, Jr., and C. R. Fellers, *Ind. Eng. Chem.*, **41**, 2587 (1949).

(104) D. Nomura and M. Kawano, *Hakkô Kôgaku Zasshi*, **32**, 442 (1954).

(105) L. Petit, *Compt. rend.*, **242**, 829 (1956).

guide to the progress of the interaction of sugars with amino acids.[106] The optical density of the solution at a particular wavelength (usually, 420 or 490 mμ) has, nevertheless, frequently been used as a supposed measure of the progress of the reaction.[101, 107-109] The liberation of carbon dioxide was noted by Maillard[72] as a characteristic of the sugar–amino acid reaction and, more recently, this evolution has been correlated with the development of color.[103, 104, 109] But, in dilute solution of sugars and amino acids, carbon dioxide is *not* released.[110]

Chromatography[65, 83, 106, 111-114a] and spectroscopy[24, 101, 115, 116] (in both the ultraviolet and infrared regions) have been widely used in identifying some of the reaction products and in estimating the speed of their formation. Frankel and Katchalsky[117-121] used potentiometric titration and a colorimetric method in their study of the speed and extent of the interaction of sugars and amino acids. Both methods gave results which were in agreement with those given by measurement of the decrease in free amino group in the system.[120] The latter method has been used by other workers.[122, 123]

Polarimetry,[124-126] cryoscopy,[127, 128] polarography,[104, 129] determination of

(106) C. O. Chichester, F. H. Stadtman and G. Mackinney, *J. Am. Chem. Soc.*, **74**, 3418 (1952).

(107) V. A. Haas, E. R. Stadtman, F. H. Stadtman and G. Mackinney, *J. Am. Chem. Soc.*, **70**, 3376 (1948).

(108) G. Haugaard, L. Tumerman and H. Silvestri, *J. Am. Chem. Soc.*, **73**, 4594 (1951).

(109) F. H. Stadtman, C. O. Chichester and G. Mackinney, *J. Am. Chem. Soc.*, **74**, 3194 (1952).

(110) L. Grünhut and J. Weber, *Biochem. Z.*, **121**, 109 (1921).

(111) K. Täufel and H. Iwainsky, *Biochem. Z.*, **323**, 299 (1952).

(112) K. Täufel, H. Iwainsky and H. Bergner, *Ernährungsforschung*, **1**, 704 (1956).

(113) K. Täufel, H. Iwainsky and H. Bergner, *Ernährungsforschung*, **1**, 714 (1956).

(114) J. Dubourg and P. Devillers, *Bull. soc. chim. France*, 333 (1957).

(114a) D. L. Ingles and T. M. Reynolds, *Australian J. Chem.*, **11**, 575 (1958).

(115) M. L. Wolfrom, D. K. Kolb and A. W. Langer, Jr., *J. Am. Chem. Soc.*, **75**, 3471 (1953).

(116) E. L. Richards, *Biochem. J.*, **64**, 639 (1956).

(117) M. Frankel and A. Katchalsky, *Biochem. J.*, **31**, 1595 (1937).

(118) M. Frankel and A. Katchalsky, *Biochem. J.*, **32**, 1904 (1938).

(119) A. Katchalsky, *Biochem. J.*, **35**, 1024 (1941).

(120) M. Frankel and A. Katchalsky, *Biochem. J.*, **35**, 1028 (1941).

(121) M. Frankel and A. Katchalsky, *Biochem. J.*, **35**, 1034 (1941).

(122) H. Borsook and H. Wasteneys, *Biochem. J.*, **19**, 1128 (1925).

(123) G. Boretti, *Chim. e ind.* (Milan), **26**, 31 (1944).

(124) C. Neuberg and M. Kobel, *Biochem. Z.*, **162**, 496 (1925).

(125) H. von Euler and K. Josephson, *Z. physiol. Chem., Hoppe-Seyler's*, **153**, 1 (1926).

(126) F. A. Dykins and D. T. Englis, *Ind. Eng. Chem. Anal. Ed.*, **3**, 21 (1931).

the content of carbonyl group,[130] the use of radioactive tracers,[86, 106, 109, 131] and determination of the amount of water formed[132] are some of the other methods which have been used. From an appraisal of several ways of following the changes which occur in the Maillard reaction, Menden and Cremer[133] concluded that enzymic hydrolysis with pancreatin followed by determination of the free amino acids with ninhydrin provided a satisfactory procedure.

2. Temperature

The effect of temperature on the interaction of D-glucose and glycine was investigated by Maillard[98] (as mentioned in Section IV, 4), but, as he only examined (in detail) the melanoidin formed in the reaction carried out *at 100°*, his conclusions regarding effect of temperature on the reaction are based on his visual observations of the rate of (a) browning, (b) gas release in the form of bubbles, and (c) increase in viscosity. For the temperatures studied (34°, 40°, 100°, and 150°), the rate of reaction appeared to increase with the temperature. This general statement has since been confirmed by several investigators, some of whom have provided quantitative data. Because of the biological implications of the reaction, much of the work has been carried out at temperatures between about 20° and 60°. However, the potential importance of the reaction in relation to the loss of nutritive value observed when casein and other proteins are heated has stimulated research into the Maillard reaction at higher temperatures.[28, 30, 35, 134] Lea and Hannan[135] showed that the rate of the D-glucose–casein reaction, as measured by the decrease in amino-nitrogen content, increases uniformly with temperature (between 0° and 90°).

In a kinetic study of the reaction of various amino acids with aldoses, Haugaard, Tumerman, and Silvestri[108] applied a new method (see Section VIII) for following the course of the reaction. With D-glucose and DL-leucine as reactants (and an initial pH of 9.2), the reaction constants for the formation of the Schiff base at the three temperatures studied were as follows:

(127) H. von Euler, E. Brunius and K. Josephson, *Z. physiol. Chem., Hoppe-Seyler's*, **155**, 259 (1926).

(128) H. von Euler and E. Brunius, *Ber.*, **59**, 1581 (1926).

(129) D. Nomura, *Hakkô Kôgaku Zasshi*, **33**, 247 (1955).

(130) C. Enders and S. Sigurdsson, *Ber.*, **76**, 560 (1943).

(131) A. Abrams and H. Borsook, *J. Am. Chem. Soc.*, **75**, 6299 (1953).

(132) M. F. Mashkovtsev, *Biokhimiya*, **15**, 528 (1950); *Chem. Abstracts*, **45**, 3564 (1951).

(133) E. Menden and H. D. Cremer, *Z. Lebensm.-Untersuch. u.-Forsch.*, **104**, 105 (1956).

(134) L. J. Schroeder, M. Iacobellis, H. Lees and A. H. Smith, *J. Nutrition*, **50**, 351 (1953).

(135) C. H. Lea and R. S. Hannan, *Biochim. et Biophys. Acta*, **3**, 313 (1949).

at 0°, 0.11 × 10⁻⁶; at 23.9°, 2.61 × 10⁻⁶; and at 40°, 11.4 × 10⁻⁶ (see also Fig. 1). Katchalsky and Sharon,[136] using a potentiometric method, deduced that the observed rate-constant for the interaction of the positive oxonium ion of D-glucose and the glycine anion bears a linear relation to the temperature. These workers also gave a graphical representation of the temperature dependence of the analogous reactions of α-alanine and of asparagine, but the temperature range studied was comparatively narrow, namely, 25° to

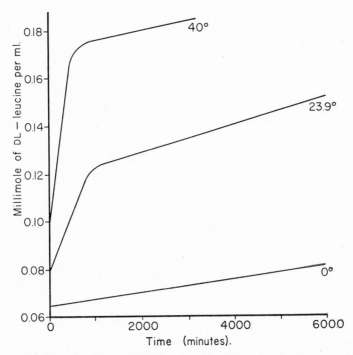

FIG. 1.—The Reaction Rate of D-Glucose with DL-Leucine in Aqueous Solution at pH 9.2 and at Different Temperatures, as Indicated by the Amino Acid Saturation Technique.[108]

45°. Another study of the D-glucose–glycine reaction, under different conditions and over a wider temperature range, is of interest.[116] A mixture of D-glucose (0.25 mole) and glycine (0.06 mole) was dissolved in water and the solution was brought to pH 6.7 with hydrochloric acid and sodium hydroxide. The solution was evaporated to dryness under diminished pressure and the product was stored in air-tight jars at a relative humidity of 70% at 0°, 22°, 37°, and 55°, respectively. Some of the jars kept at each temperature were opened at intervals and the spectral absorption at 350

(136) A. Katchalsky and N. Sharon, *Biochim. et Biophys. Acta*, **10,** 290 (1953).

mμ of the contents of each was measured. The results showed practically no reaction after 32 days at 0°, but, at 55°, the spectral absorption increased from the first day.

Potentiometric measurements have shown[137] that the equilibrium constant for the D-glucose–L-histidine reaction falls as the temperature is raised from 20° to 50°; the reaction is, therefore, exothermic. The heat of reaction for the 40–50° range was about twice that for the 20–40° range,

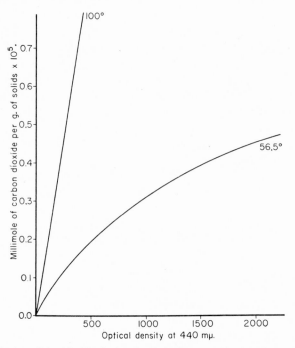

Fig. 2.—Carbon Dioxide Evolution in Relation to Pigment Production at 100° and at 56.5° in the Reaction of D-Glucose (2.4 Moles) and Glycine (1 Mole) in Water.[109]

both figures being deduced on the assumption that equimolar quantities of the reactants had taken part. Evidence for this assumption was obtained from the straight-line relationship which exists between the antilog of pH depression and the D-glucose concentration at various temperatures for the first steady state. Such a change in the heat of reaction may indicate a difference in the type of combination which is taking place, but, since the plot of antilog ΔpH against D-glucose concentration is a straight line at all temperatures from 20° to 50°, the reaction is still one of combination between one mole each of D-glucose and L-histidine. Lewin suggests that the

(137) S. Lewin, *Biochem. J.*, **63**, 14 (1956).

different heat of reaction may indicate a change in the equilibrium between various forms of the sugar or the various ionic forms of the amino acid. The reactions of glycine and DL-α-alanine with D-glucose have been similarly studied.[85]

The effect of temperature on the Maillard reaction is also reflected in other ways. The brown pigment isolated from the reaction of D-glucose with glycine at 100° contains a higher proportion of carbon than that obtained when the same reaction is conducted[106] at 56.5°. Complementary to this observation is that made by the same authors[109]—that more pigment is produced per millimole of carbon dioxide at 56.5° than at 100°. Thus, the amount of carbon dioxide released per unit optical density is greater at 100° than at 56.5° (see Fig. 2). The density of color reached in 2 hours at 100° requires 250 hours at 56.5°. An interesting comparison with these figures is the observation that the reaction between D-glucose and casein proceeds twenty times faster at 60° than[138] at 37°. Moreover, different products may be formed at different temperatures, as was shown by a chromatographic study[106] of the D-glucose–glycine reaction at 56.5° and 100°. However, all the spots on the chromatogram were not identified. The reaction temperature also has an effect on the reversibility; for example, the reaction of D-glucose with glycine in dilute aqueous solution at 25° is reversible,[16] but, at 100°, this reaction is not reversible.[79] When N-D-glucosylglycine ethyl ester is heated at 90–92° in water, an initial sudden increase in pH is followed by a slow decrease.[139] This observation is explained by supposing that the compound is quickly hydrolyzed to a large extent to D-glucose and glycine ester, and that the latter is then slowly hydrolyzed to glycine. The D-glucosylamine is slowly hydrolyzed in aqueous solution, even at room temperature. However, the reversibility or non-reversibility of the aldose–amino acid reaction may depend on the pH, as well as on the temperature (see the following Sub-section).

3. *Effect of* pH

Since the basic amino group disappears in the Maillard reaction, the pH of an aqueous solution of the reactants will decrease. It is to be expected, therefore, that the initial pH of the solution, or the presence of a buffer, will have an important effect on the progress of the reaction. In an early investigation[122] of the effect of pH on the reaction, individual solutions containing D-glucose and glycine were made in phosphate buffer solutions at pH 7.8, 7.9, 8.3, 8.7, and 9.2, respectively, and kept at 37°. The amino

(138) C. H. Lea, R. S. Hannan and D. N. Rhodes, *Biochim. et Biophys. Acta*, **7**, 366 (1951).

(139) M. L. Wolfrom, R. D. Schuetz and L. F. Cavalieri, *J. Am. Chem. Soc.*, **71**, 3518 (1949).

nitrogen content was determined from time to time during 48 hours by the Van Slyke procedure. Controls for each pH value consisted of the amino acid in the respective buffer solution. The results showed that the amino nitrogen content decreased more, the higher the pH value. Euler and Josephson[125] followed the same reaction polarimetrically for solutions buffered at pH 5.9, 8.1, 8.4, and 9.6, respectively. Higher pH values caused more change in rotation, and this observation was ascribed to interaction between sugar and amino acid, since a control solution of D-glucose at pH 8.3 showed no rotational change over a similar period of time. Englis and Dykins,[16] however, threw some doubt on these results; they showed that the D-glucose–glycine complex formed at 25° is decomposed into its components on acidification. When the reaction occurred at 35°, complete reversal to the sugar and amino acid was not possible, as some stable reaction-product remained. This discovery meant that the acid conditions of the Van Slyke amino-nitrogen determination might give unreliable results. These workers found, in fact, that, in some experiments, the Van Slyke results showed no decrease in amino-nitrogen concentration in spite of a change in optical rotation. However, it is significant that the mutarotation of D-glucose is more strongly catalyzed at pH 6 by certain amino acids than by strong acids. Histidine is by far the most efficient catalyst of those studied.[140] Measurement of rotational changes is, therefore, *not* a reliable method of following the progress of the reaction between sugars and amino compounds.

The pH depression (ΔpH) which occurs in a mixture of an aldose and an amino acid over a period of time is a widely used criterion of interaction, and its magnitude has been shown to be dependent on the reactants and on the initial alkalinity of the solution.[117] For example, the maximum pH depression for glycine plus an aldose occurs when the initial pH value is between 7 and 8.5. When pH values of 11 or higher are used, the extent of reaction increases continuously with pH, and this observation suggests that a *different* reaction is in progress. (This conclusion is based on the much lower *speed* of reaction and the absence of a marked decrease in pH. Boretti[123] observed a similar change in the reaction, at pH 12, of several D-glucose–amino acid mixtures.) Chromatographic evidence which may support this conclusion was provided by Lewin,[141] who found that D-glucose solutions, initially adjusted to pH 8.4 with alkali, gave D-glucose spots only, on chromatographing a month later. Similarly, D-glucose–amino acid solutions, either initially adjusted to pH 9 or buffered at pH 7.8, kept at 40° for up to 3 days gave spots for D-glucose only. However, when similar experiments were performed at pH values of 10.2, spots for both D-glucose and D-fructose appeared on the chromatograms. By titrating mixtures of

(140) F. H. Westheimer, *J. Org. Chem.*, **2**, 431 (1937).
(141) S. Lewin, *Biochem. J.*, **65**, 30P (1957).

glycine and D-glucose (or D-galactose) with sodium hydroxide, the pH depressions were shown[118] not to be attributable to the acidity of the sugars.[142, 143] Subsequently, Frankel and Katchalsky[120] demonstrated that it is possible to correlate the results obtained by pH depression with those given by the Van Slyke amino-nitrogen method.[144] Shiga[145] maintained that the amount of alkali required to restore the pH is more important than the measured pH drop, but further study[121] of the reaction of D-glucose with glycine and with glycylglycine supported Frankel and Katchalsky's earlier work.[117-120]

The behavior of D-glucose with various amino acids at an initial pH of 5–6, and in a phosphate buffer at pH 7.3–7.8, was studied by Wolfrom,

TABLE I

Browning of Mixtures of D-Glucose and Various Amino Acids[102]

Amino Acid	pH			Absorption, %		pH of buffer			Absorption, %	
	Time (hr.)									
	0	4	6	4	6	0	0.5	1	0.5	1
Glycine	5.3	4.8	4.6	7.3	24.8	7.4	6.6	6.0	87.4	99.8
Sarcosine	5.7	4.5	4.4	0	5.3	7.6	7.3	7.0	7.9	19.1
N,N-Dimethyl- glycine	5.1	4.6	4.5	0	0	7.8	7.8	7.7	0	6.0
DL-Alanine	5.7	5.1	4.8	12.0	36.0	7.3	6.8	6.4	52.2	96.2
2-Aminoisobutyric acid	5.9	5.1	4.8	0	2.3	7.5	7.2	6.7	22.0	85.5

Cavalieri, and Cavalieri.[102] The amount of color, measured at 490 mμ, which was produced after various intervals of time was compared with that of carefully prepared samples from D-glucose and the amino acid at 90–95°, for specified periods and defined pH values. Table I shows that, for three amino acids containing a primary amino group, the degree of browning is considerably greater at pH 7 than at pH 5. This conclusion was confirmed in a study of the interaction of D-xylose with (a) glycine and with (b) DL-alanine over a wider range of pH values.[115] Both reactions were followed by measurement of the light absorption of the soluble, colored product at 490 mμ. Apart from a short induction period, a straight-line relation was ob-

(142) F. Urban and P. A. Shaffer, *J. Biol. Chem.*, **94**, 697 (1932).
(143) E. W. Balson and A. Lawson, *Biochem. J.*, **32**, 230 (1938).
(144) N. Shiga, *J. Biochem.* (Tokyo), **25**, 607 (1937).
(145) N. Shiga, *J. Biochem.* (Tokyo), **27**, 307 (1938).

tained with time, and the slope of this line gave a measure of the first-order, specific reaction constant, k. When log k is plotted against the initial pH value, a significant change in slope appears at pH 6 (which is the iso-electric point for the amino acids studied). The steeper slope of the curve between pH 6.5 and 8.5 is the result of base catalysis, but, between pH 5 and 3, the effect is that either of weak-base or of solvent catalysis. Acid in-hibition accounts for the fall in k values at pH 3 and below. Considerable quantities of 2-furaldehyde were detectable [as its (2,4-dinitrophenyl)hy-drazone] in this pH range. At fractional pH values, the D-xylose–glycine curve showed a minimum. The reaction between L-histidine and D-glucose, at pH values from 5 to 9, shows similar trends. At pH 5–6.5, no combina-tion could be detected potentiometrically, but, at pH 8–9, the pH dropped to the first steady-state within[137, 146] 7 days at 20°, or 2 hours at 50°. Brown-ing occurs both in acidic and in alkaline media, but, since the amine–carbonyl reaction is very feeble in acid, the browning in acid media has been attributed to polymerization of the furan compounds produced.[115] However, other theories concerning this reaction will be mentioned later.

A kinetic study of the reaction of D-glucose with DL-leucine, at 23.9° at three different initial pH values, using a novel method of following the reac-tion (see Section VIII), showed[108] that the extent and rate of reaction in-creases with pH (see Fig. 3). Similar results were obtained when the method was extended to a study of the interaction of sugars with peptides, but it was found that reaction occurs at a lower pH (7.7) than is required for causing amino acids to react with sugars at the same rate.[147] This trend continues into the weakly basic aromatic amino acids, as is shown by the vigorous reaction of p-aminobenzoic acid with aldoses, even at pH 5.3. Peptides, proteins, and aromatic amino acids are thus more reactive toward D-glucose than are aliphatic amino acids, at the pH values found in Nature. By developing an earlier experimental method[117-121] and introducing new theoretical considerations, Katchalsky and Sharon[136] showed that the ex-tent of reaction decreases with rise in hydrogen-ion concentration, but the rate of reaction increases almost linearly with the hydrogen-ion concentra-tion. By plotting the reciprocal of the observed rate-constants for various temperatures against the pH, and by using an equation evolved theoreti-cally, these authors were able to derive rate constants which are independent of pH. Their investigations covered a number of aldoses, amino acids, and peptides, and will be discussed further in Section VIII(p. 110).

The effect of pH and moisture on the reaction between D-glucose and several amino acids and synthetic peptides was thoroughly investigated by

(146) S. Lewin, *Biochem. J.*, **61,** xxv (1955).
(147) G. Haugaard and L. Tumerman, *Arch. Biochem. Biophys.*, **65,** 86 (1956).

Schroeder, Iacobellis, and Smith,[148] who set out to determine whether or not further evidence might be gleaned for the observation[134] that water prevents the deleterious effect of autoclaving on the nutritive value of dried skim-milk. The amino acids used in this study were glycine, L-leucine, and DL-valine; glycyl-L-leucine and glycyl-DL-valine were the peptides chosen.

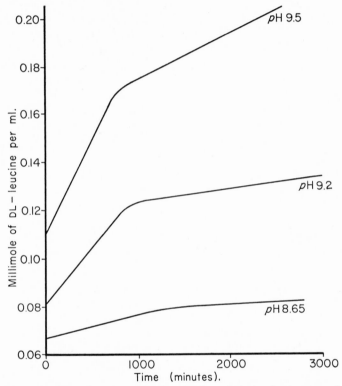

FIG. 3.—The Reaction Rate of D-Glucose with DL-Leucine in Aqueous Solution at 23.9° and at Various pH Values, as Indicated by the Amino Acid Saturation Technique.[108]

Samples of these compounds were separately mixed with D-glucose at various concentrations, and their pH values were checked. Some mixtures were made up in buffer solutions. Total-nitrogen (Kjeldahl) and amino-nitrogen (Pope and Stevens[149, 150]) determinations were carried out on aliquots of

(148) L. J. Schroeder, M. Iacobellis and A. H. Smith, *J. Biol. Chem.*, **212,** 973 (1955).
(149) C. G. Pope and M. F. Stevens, *Biochem. J.*, **33,** 1070 (1939).
(150) W. A. Schroeder, L. M. Kay and R. S. Mills, *Anal. Chem.*, **22,** 760 (1950).

each sample, and the rest of the sample was autoclaved at 15 lb. per sq. in. for 30 minutes. Samples of the amino compound alone, and of D-glucose alone, under the same conditions of pH and concentration were used as controls. The autoclaved samples were subjected to total-nitrogen and amino-nitrogen analysis, to a visual estimate of color, and to paper chroma-

TABLE II

Effect of Autoclaving (at 15 Pounds per Square Inch Pressure, for 30 Minutes) on D-Glucose, L-Lysine, and D-Glucose-L-Lysine Mixtures, in Phosphate Buffer at Various pH Levels[148]

D-*Glucose:* L-*lysine. HCl (millimoles)*	pH		Total N		α-Amino N[a]		Color
	Before auto-claving	*After auto-claving*	*Calcula-ted, mg.*	*After auto-claving, mg.*	*After auto-claving, mg.*	*Loss, %*	
50:0	3.2	3.0	0	0	0		−
	6.0	5.2					++
	8.0	5.9					++++
	9.7	6.2					++++
	11.0	6.5					++++
	6.0[b]	5.3					+
0:50	3.2	3.2	1396.9	1321.5	698.7		−
	6.0	6.0		1313.0	698.0		−
	8.0	8.0		1313.5	698.5		−
	9.7	9.1		1312.8	698.1		−
	11.0	11.0		1314.2	698.5		−
	5.7[b]	5.6		1313.8	698.5		−
10:50[c]	3.2	3.2	1396.9	1319.1	698.3		−
	6.0	5.5		1313.1	698.8		+++
	8.0	7.5		1312.5	502.9	28.0	++++
	9.7	8.0		1314.5	497.3	28.8	++++
	11.0	7.8		1315.1	494.5	29.2	++++
	5.6[b]	5.3		1314.7	697.9		++

[a] α-Amino nitrogen is one half of the total nitrogen.
[b] Unbuffered.
[c] Comparable results were obtained on 10:10, 30:10, 10:30, and 10:50 mixtures.

tography. For comparison, samples made up as above, but *not* autoclaved, were included in the analytical tests. The results showed that *only in the dry, autoclaved* D-glucose–amino acid and D-glucose–peptide mixtures was there a decrease in amino nitrogen, and this decrease was accompanied by browning (see Table II). Moreover, browning and loss of amino nitrogen for any sugar–amino compound mixture both increased with initial pH and were absent in acid medium. However, there was at least the same amount of browning in samples of D-glucose autoclaved alone at pH 6 or higher. These observations suggest that the browning of D-glucose is due to the effect of heat and alkalinity, whereas the Maillard reaction, as evidenced by the loss of amino groups, proceeds only *in the absence of water*. Analytical results were confirmed by chromatography; ninhydrin-reacting spots and spots positive to aniline–phthalic acid decreased on autoclaving the dry-mixed components, whereas, in aqueous medium, only the free aldehyde group (that is, spots reacting to aniline–phthalic acid) decreased. Variation of the molar ratio of the reactants had no appreciable effect on the results. Chromatography of the autoclaved D-glucose samples showed a decrease in the size of the spots reacting to aniline–phthalic acid as the pH increased. This result is thought to indicate a disappearance of the aldehyde group and the formation of acidic intermediates. The effect of phosphates on the intensity of browning[151] will be mentioned later.

These findings were confirmed by the results of further experiments on the chromatography of mixtures of D-glucose with glycine, L-leucine, or L-glutamic acid (autoclaved and unautoclaved; with and without water).[152] The chromatograms were treated with ninhydrin, and only a spot representing the amino acid was detected in mixtures autoclaved with water, or without water, at pH 3.2 or 6.0. However, when the D-glucose–glycine mixture was autoclaved at pH 9.7 and then chromatographed, two spots appeared: one corresponded to glycine (R_f 0.4), the other had the same R_f value (0.2) as an unautoclaved sample of synthetic D-gluconylglycine (see p. 125). On autoclaving, at pH 9.7, a mixture of D-gluconylglycine with D-glucose plus glycine, the same two spots were obtained. Under the conditions used, therefore, the reaction product of D-glucose and glycine is D-gluconylglycine. Similar results were obtained when glycine was replaced by L-leucine or L-glutamic acid. Moreover, browning of autoclaved D-glucose occurred to the same extent in the absence of amino acid as in its presence, provided that the alkalinity of the samples was the same. The destructive effect of increasing pH (on the autoclaved D-glucose samples) was shown by the decrease in the size of the spot positive to aniline–phthalic acid (in the chromatographed samples). In the two investigations[148, 152] just discussed, the progress of the reaction was measured by the loss of amino groups, whereas development of color received only qualitative assessment. In contrast, a recent study laid the main emphasis on the color-producing ability of several amino acids individually treated with D-glucose.[153] Amino acids of three types were chosen: DL-alanine (neutral),

(151) S. Schwimmer and H. S. Olcott, *J. Am. Chem. Soc.*, **75**, 4835 (1953).

(152) M. Iacobellis, *Arch. Biochem. Biophys.*, **59**, 199 (1955).

(153) C. O. Willits, J. C. Underwood, H. G. Lento, Jr., and C. Ricciuti, *Food Research*, **23**, 61 (1958).

L-glutamic acid (acidic), and L-lysine (basic). The final solution was 0.025 M with respect to D-glucose and 0.125 M in the respective amino acid. Each solution was buffered with phosphate at one of six pH values: pH 3, 5, 6, 7, 8, or 9, and was then autoclaved at 10 lb. per sq. in. at 114° for 20 minutes. The results (see Table III) showed that, under this treatment, D-glucose browns in varying degrees by itself, and also with amino acids,

TABLE III

Effect of Individual Amino Acids and pH on the Color Developed in a 0.025 M D-Glucose Solution Heated for 20 Minutes at 114° in an Autoclave[153]

Components	pH	Absorbance at 500 mμ
D-Glucose	3	0.00
	5	0.00
	6	0.00
	7	0.00
	8	0.18
	9	0.48
D-Glucose + DL-alanine	3	0.00
	5	0.00
	6	0.00
	7	0.14
	8	0.20
	9	0.33
D-Glucose + L-glutamic acid	3	0.00
	5	0.00
	6	0.00
	7	0.02
	8	0.12
	9	0.50
D-Glucose + L-lysine	3	0.00
	5	0.00
	6	0.16
	7	0.35
	8	0.65
	9	0.84

but only at pH 6 or above. Furthermore, there is no significant difference in the intensity of the colors produced by D-glucose alone, D-glucose plus L-glutamic acid, and D-glucose plus DL-alanine under these conditions. D-Glucose plus L-lysine, however, gives a more highly colored product in the alkaline range and shows an appreciable color at pH 6. Additional (statistically designed) experiments were performed in order to investigate the effects of concentration, of mixtures of amino acids, and of pH on the reaction. These experiments showed that the effect of pH and the presence of L-lysine act synergistically in producing the brown color with D-glucose. Some of the color produced at pH 8 and 9 must be caused by the alkalinity of the solution, but the fact that color is produced at pH 6 with L-lysine demonstrates the browning action of this amino acid.

A more detailed study of the effect of pH and of different types of amino acid on the browning produced with D-glucose has been reported.[153a] The same amino acids were used as are listed in Table VI, except that DL-lysine hydrochloride replaced L-lysine, and glycine was omitted. The reaction conditions were also similar and, from the experimental results, it is clear that, between pH 5.0 and 9.0, the α-amino acids studied caused very little browning with D-glucose. Under the same reaction conditions, ω-amino acids exhibited some browning, but this was only appreciable at pH 6.5, 7.0, 8.0, and 9.0, and was most pronounced for 4-aminobutyric acid. Of the ω-amino acids, that with the longest chain (6-aminocaproic acid) produced the least color at any particular pH value. αω-Diamino acids showed, however, a different pattern in that, at pH 6.5 and higher values (up to 9.0), browning was considerable and increased from 2,4-diaminobutyric acid through DL-ornithine to DL-lysine.

When the period of heating is extended, some browning occurs even at acid pH. For example, heating of aqueous solutions of D-glucose and glycine, buffered at various acid pH values, for 15 hours at about 100°, produces browning at values down to pH 2. By subtracting, from this degree of coloration, the intensity of the color produced by similar treatment of a D-glucose solution, Smirnov and Geispits[154] obtained a curve representing the color occasioned solely by the D-glucose–glycine reaction. From this graph (see Fig. 4), the browning attributable to the Maillard reaction is seen to begin at pH 4 and to increase with pH, but, in another experiment in which the pH was 0.65 and heating at 100° was continued for 24 hours, estimation of the sugar (by the Bertrand method) and of the amino acid (by the copper-salt method) showed that some combination had occurred at this very low pH (compare with the D-xylose–glycine reaction at a pH of less than unity[115]).

4. Water

The role of water in the Maillard reaction was not systematically studied until rather recently. Most of the early work was conducted with water as the reaction medium, but Ambler[73] mentioned that the concentration of the reactants has an effect on the course of the reaction. The change which occurs in dried eggs on storage stimulated research into the effect of small

(153a) J. C. Underwood, H. G. Lento, Jr., and C. O. Willits, *Food Research*, **24**, 181 (1959).

(154) V. A. Smirnov and K. A. Geispits, *Biokhimiya*, **21**, 633 (1956).

amounts of moisture in this and other foods.[155-157] When dry D-glucose and dry glycine were ground together and stored at 50° there was no apparent change, but, when small proportions (2, 5, and 10%, respectively) of water were added, the mixtures turned brown in 24 hours at 50°. The sample containing 10% of moisture browned the most.[158] A systematic study, by Wolfrom and Rooney,[159] of the influence of water on the browning of a

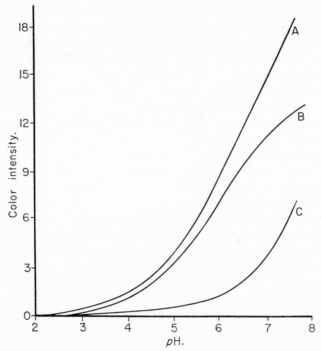

FIG. 4.—Dependence of Color Intensity of a D-Glucose–Glycine Solution on pH. (Curve A: intensity of total color; curve B: intensity of color due to non-melanoidin products; curve C: color from melanoidin formation, by difference between A and B.[154])

D-xylose–glycine (1:5) mixture at 65° showed that maximum browning is reached when the water content is about 30%. If the water content is zero, or above 90%, no browning is observed at 65°. Kato[160] has similarly shown

(155) M. M. Boggs and H. L. Fevold, *Ind. Eng. Chem.*, **38**, 1075 (1946).
(156) H. M. Barnes and C. W. Kaufman, *Ind. Eng. Chem.*, **39**, 1167 (1947).
(157) R. R. Legault, W. F. Talburt, A. M. Mylne and L. H. Bryan, *Ind. Eng. Chem.*, **39**, 1294 (1947).
(158) H. S. Olcott and H. J. Dutton, *Ind. Eng. Chem.*, **37**, 1119 (1945).
(159) M. L. Wolfrom and C. S. Rooney, *J. Am. Chem. Soc.*, **75**, 5435 (1953).
(160) H. Kato, *Bull. Agr. Chem. Soc. Japan.* **20**, 273 (1956).

that, in dilute (0.25 M sugar and 0.5 M glycine) solution, the color produced is about one sixth of that of a solution of double the concentration. In D-glucose–glycine or D-glucose–alanine systems, at temperatures between 20° and 50°, the extent of reaction, as measured by pH depression, increases with D-glucose concentration over the range 0.1 M to 1.3 M, at a constant concentration[85] of amino acid.

The Maillard reaction is sensitive to the relative humidity of the air in contact with the reactants, if the latter do not contain water. Thus, the humidity of the air in contact with dry mixtures of D-glucose and glycine, at 37° and pH 6.7, had a pronounced influence on the optical density (at 350 mμ). Maximum browning occurred when the relative humidity was[116] about 70 %. Hannan and Lea[161] studied the reaction between D-glucose and the terminal amino group of N^2-acetyl-L-lysine at relative humidities varied from 20 to 60 %. Chromatography of freeze-dried mixtures of the components showed that browning was greatest when the relative humidity was 60 %, but the maximum rate of loss of amino groups occurred at 40 %. If a mixture of an aldose and an amino acid is kept in contact with air dried with calcium chloride, no reaction is observed.[162] On the other hand, a high content of water has been reported to retard the formation of melanoidin from D-glucose plus glycine.[163] Similarly, the reaction of methionine with D-glucose at 125° (in an autoclave) proceeds more vigorously in the absence of an excessive amount of water than when an 8 % solution is heated.[164] This difference was apparent from measurements of the brown color, the fluorescence, and the amino-nitrogen content.

Results which contradicted much of the previous work were recorded by Schroeder, Iacobellis, and Smith,[148] whose work has already been mentioned in Section V,3. The analysis of amino nitrogen and the chromatographic examination of the product after autoclaving, for many samples of D-glucose with and without an amino acid, showed that interaction occurs only in the *absence* of water, but that some color is formed in the presence and in the absence of amino compounds and at pH 6 or higher. These conclusions have some features in common with those of Rosen, Johnson, and Pigman[165] on the browning of N-phenyl-D-glucosylamine at 30°. Various proportions of water and hydrogen chloride were added to methanolic solutions of the D-glucosylamine, and the degree of browning was measured

(161) R. S. Hannan and C. H. Lea, *Nature*, **168**, 744 (1951).

(162) G. P. Volgunov and M. T. Pokhno, *Biokhimiya*, **15**, 67 (1950); *Chem. Abstracts*, **44**, 5542 (1950).

(163) M. F. Mashkovtsev, *Biokhimiya*, **16**, 615 (1951); *Chem. Abstracts*, **46**, 11114 (1952).

(164) W. D. Graham, P. Y. Hsu and J. McGinnis, *Science*, **10**, 217 (1949).

(165) L. Rosen, K. C. Johnson and W. W. Pigman, *J. Am. Chem. Soc.*, **75**, 3460 (1953).

at intervals of the 400–450 mμ range. In all the experiments, the rate of browning was greatest under anhydrous conditions; and, for any specific acid-concentration, increase in the water content resulted in a decrease in the rate at which color developed.

5. *Oxygen*

Maillard[98] observed that one of the products of the interaction of D-glucose with glycine is carbon dioxide. He investigated the source of this compound, and, to find out if the oxygen was absorbed from the air, he carried out an experiment in the absence of oxygen. Since carbon dioxide was produced as before, he concluded (from this and other experiments) that decarboxylation of the amino acid produces carbon dioxide, and that oxygen is *not* essential for the reaction to proceed. As part of a study of the changes occurring in dried eggs on storage, Olcott and Dutton[158] found that D-glucose and glycine, in the presence of a small proportion of water, react in air, or oxygen, at the same rate as in high vacuum. Similarly, atmospheric oxygen does *not* contribute significantly[165] to the darkening of N-phenyl-D-glucosylamine in dilute aqueous methanol at 30°, or to the browning of dehydrated vegetables during storage.[157] When solutions of D-xylose–glycine (or alanine) were heated at 100° in an open tube, in a sealed tube, and in a tube sealed under nitrogen, and the light-absorption (at 450 mμ) of the products was determined, no difference in the speed of the reaction could be detected.[160] Lewin,[137] however, found measurable differences between the reaction of D-glucose with L-histidine under aerobic and anaerobic conditions. Although no figures were given, browning was stated to be less pronounced under aerobic than under anaerobic conditions. The extent of depression of pH increased more rapidly in the aerobic experiments, but such a difference only became apparent after the first steady-state (see Fig. 5). The larger pH drop observed for aerobic conditions suggests the formation of acidic products, possibly by oxidation. Changes in pH were more reproducible in the anaerobic than in the aerobic experiments, especially in the later stages of the reaction. Similar results were observed in the interactions of lysine,[166] valine,[166] glutamic acid,[166] glycine,[85] and alanine[85] with D-glucose. At low temperature and low concentration of D-glucose, there was no difference between the aerobic and the anaerobic depression of pH values, but, with increase in these variables, values of pH depression were noticeably greater for the aerobic experiments, whereas browning was more intense under anaerobic conditions. The inhibiting effect of oxygen on browning is apparent also from experiments with D-glucose and glycine in the absence of iron and manganese. Solutions of the mixture, sealed under nitrogen and kept at 50°, developed about two to three times as much color as those

(166) S. Lewin, *Biochem. J.*, **63**, 5P (1956).

sealed under air. Under the same conditions, small proportions of manganese inhibited browning in the presence of oxygen, but had no effect on solutions kept under nitrogen.[167]

This alleged tendency of oxygen to inhibit browning is not confirmed by the results of other workers. Johansen and Nickerson[168] state that, in acidic solution, atmospheric oxygen favors both the interaction of amino groups and color formation. Webb[169] had previously reported that oxygen increases the color developed in lactose solutions. On the other hand, Volgunov and Pokhno,[162] in a systematic investigation of the effects of various factors on the reaction of D-glucose (and D-fructose) with glycine (and

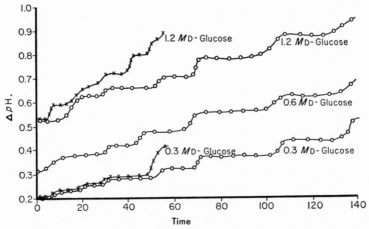

FIG. 5.—Variations of the pH Depressions (ΔpH) with Time in D-Glucose–L-Histidine Solution at 50°. (Histidine concentration, 0.016 M; initial pH, 7.81. O——O Anaerobic conditions; ×——× aerobic conditions.[137] Time in hours.)

tyrosine), found that the presence of oxygen results in a more intense coloration and also affects the nature of the product.

6. *Metals*

The significance of small amounts of metals to the Maillard reaction appears to have been first studied by Webb[169] in 1935, in his work on the color of evaporated milk. The browning of lactose solutions at 49° was found to be positively catalyzed by copper and iron, but retarded by tin. Traces of cupric salts similarly accelerate the browning of amino acids or proteins with D-glucose in weakly alkaline solutions, but they have no ef-

(167) G. S. Bohart and J. F. Carson, *Nature*, **175**, 470 (1955).

(168) G. Johansen and W. J. Nickerson, *Intern. Congr. Biochem. 1st Congr., Cambridge, Engl.*, **1949**, *Abstr. Communs.*, 223.

(169) B. H. Webb, *J. Dairy Sci.*, **18**, 81 (1935).

fect on the rate of loss of amino groups of proteins.[170] Rosen, Johnson, and Pigman[165] did not, however, find any significant difference in the browning of dilute methanolic solutions of N-phenyl-D-glucosylamine with a 0.08 N hydrogen chloride concentration in the absence or presence of 0.1 % of cupric ions. Deschreider,[171, 172] from a study of the browning of heated D-glucose sirups in the presence of amino acids, concluded that browning and the disappearance of amino nitrogen are inhibited, at pH 3.25 or 5.20, by traces of copper, iron, or zinc. The conditions for these experiments were unusual in that the amino acid (glycine, DL-alanine, or aspartic acid) was present to the extent of only 75 to 225 parts per million. Copper was introduced as cupric sulfate, and its concentration ranged from 10 to 40 parts per million. Spectroscopic examination showed the presence of 5-(hydroxymethyl)-2-furaldehyde, whose concentration ran parallel to the intensity of browning. A study of the effect of varying the copper content on the reaction of D-glucose sirup with an amino acid, which was present to the extent of 225 parts per million, showed that the optimum copper concentration was 10–20 parts per million. The reaction conditions were 10 hours' heating at 105°, the initial pH being 5.25. In determining the progress of the reaction, the criteria used were optical density at 420 mμ, the ultraviolet absorption at 282 mμ and the spectrum of 5-(hydroxymethyl)-2-furaldehyde.

In a phosphate-buffered, D-glucose–glycine system at 50°, ferric ions accelerate the reaction four- or five-fold, but manganese ions (Mn$^{\oplus\oplus}$, 0.4 parts per million) reduce the intensity of color by 17 to 24 %. A slight excess of glycine was present in these experiments, and the sensitivity of the reaction to minute proportions of manganese was further shown by the fact that 0.003 parts per million caused a significant inhibition of browning. When 2 parts of manganese per million were present, coloration was reduced by 30 to 40 %, as compared with controls. Reactions which were conducted in tubes sealed under nitrogen showed no sensitivity to manganese.[167] The presence of a ferric phosphate buffer resulted in a greater degree of interaction between D-glucose and glycine than did the presence of sodium phosphate.[173]

Cobalt tends to weaken the color, but it favors the binding of amino groups in acid solution. In neutral solution containing phosphate ions, the metal has no effect.[168]

The lack of uniformity in these results is not surprising in view of the very small proportions which can have a significant effect. A recent obser-

(170) A. Mohammad, H. Fraenkel-Conrat and H. S. Olcott, *Arch. Biochem.*, **24,** 157 (1949).

(171) A. R. Deschreider, *Rev. fermentations et inds. aliment.*, **9,** 25 (1954).

(172) A. R. Deschreider, *Rev. fermentations et inds. aliment.*, **9,** 111 (1954).

(173) B. Baumiger and F. Lieben, *Biochem. Z.*, **292,** 92 (1937).

vation,[174] that N-glycosylamino acids form metal complexes which are more stable to hydrolysis than are the free acids, may have a bearing on the Maillard reaction, and confirms other work[105] which showed that, during melanoidin formation, the amount of copper incorporated with glycine was more than would be expected of the amino acid alone.

7. Phosphates

The ability of phosphates to accelerate the interaction (between D-glucose and the amino groups of glycine or proteins) was noted[122] in 1925 and has since been confirmed by other workers.[160, 169, 175-178] When glycine was used as a buffer in experiments on the effect of heat on lactose, a deeper

TABLE IV

Browning of Glycine with Two Hexoses and Their Phosphates[151]

Mixture	pH		Brown color
	Initial	Final	
D-Glucose + buffer	6.5	6.1	100
D-Fructose + buffer	6.5	6.3	28
D-Glucosyl phosphate + buffer	7.7	7.7	0
D-Glucose 6-phosphate + buffer	6.6	5.9	146
D-Fructose 6-phosphate + buffer	6.6	6.6	82
D-Fructose 1,6-diphosphate + buffer	6.5	6.5	21
D-Glucose, unbuffered	5.4	5.1	8
D-Fructose, unbuffered	5.4	4.8	16

color was produced than when a lactose solution was heated (at 120° for 15 minutes) with conventional buffers at various pH values.[179]

A valuable series of comparative experiments was performed by Schwimmer and Olcott[151] on the reaction of glycine with D-glucose, D-fructose, D-glucose 6-phosphate, D-fructose 6-phosphate, and D-fructose 1,6-diphosphate in the presence and absence of a phosphate buffer at pH 6.5. The rate of browning at 70° (over 18 hours) was determined colorimetrically at 420 mμ. An increase in the rate of browning was observed for the hexose 6-phosphates, as compared with the unsubstituted sugars. Similarly, the

(174) G. Weitzel, H. U. Geyer and A. M. Fretzdorff, *Chem. Ber.*, **90**, 1153 (1957).

(175) G. Ågren, *Acta Physiol. Scand.*, **1**, 105 (1940).

(176) G. Ågren, *Enzymologia*, **9**, 321 (1941).

(177) Y. Tamaki, *Kôgyô Kagaku Zasshi*, **56**, 460 (1953); *Chem. Abstracts*, **48**, 11512 (1954).

(178) K. Kudo and Y. Tamaki, *Kôgyô Kagaku Zasshi*, **57**, 249 (1954); *Chem. Abstracts*, **49**, 2764 (1955).

(179) J. P. Kass and L. S. Palmer, *Ind. Eng. Chem.*, **32**, 1360 (1940).

extent of browning of D-fructose and D-glucose was much greater in the presence of a buffer than in its absence.

Masking of the aldehyde group of D-glucose, for example, in D-glucosyl phosphate, completely inhibited browning. Table IV gives comparative figures for the browning of these carbohydrates with glycine, the intensity of the color of the buffered D-glucose–glycine system at pH 6.5 being taken as 100. The 6-phosphate group of the hexoses was found to be split off and converted into inorganic phosphate at a rate dependent on the progress of browning.

When promoted by sodium hydroxide, the Maillard reaction, as evidenced by a decrease in amino nitrogen, is reversible on addition of acid. However, if the reaction proceeds near neutrality in the presence of phosphate, this is not so.[168]

8. *Miscellaneous*

As might be expected, the manifestations of the Maillard reaction increase with *time*. The depth of color increases with the square of the time.[104, 108] Observations on other characteristics of the reaction are largely qualitative, but, in general, development of insolubility and reducing power, loss of amino nitrogen, and fall in pH increase with time. Fluorescence, however, reaches a maximum and then decreases.[180] Similarly, the production of 5-(hydroxymethyl)-2-furaldehyde from N-phenyl-D-glucosylamine reaches a maximum, but browning increases continuously.[181] Aqueous solutions of D-glucose with individual amino acids were shown by Lewin and his coworkers[85, 137, 146, 166, 182, 183] to exhibit a common pattern of change in pH with time. The pH of the mixture first decreases and then assumes a constant value—*the first steady-state*. After an interval of time, the pH begins to fall again, but it eventually remains constant for some time—*the second steady-state*. This process is repeated a few more times. The duration of each of the steady states depends on the temperature, the concentrations of D-glucose and amino acid, and the particular amino acid present. Browning was apparent from the end of the second steady-state, onward. Initial pH has little effect at 30°, except in the third and subsequent steady-states, where lower initial pH resulted in greater pH depression (ΔpH). The results obtained with D-glucose–histidine are shown graphically in Fig. 5(see p. 91).

The *effect of light* on the Maillard reaction has not been widely studied, but Bohart and Carson[167] have shown clearly that it has a pronounced ef-

(180) L. R. Overby and D. V. Frost, *J. Nutrition*, **46**, 539 (1952).
(181) D. Nomura, *Hakkô Kôgaku Zasshi*, **33**, 279 (1955).
(182) S. Lewin and Z. Kosinski, *Biochem. J.*, **62**, 24P (1956).
(183) S. Lewin and C. Fox, *Biochem. J.*, **63**, 5P (1956).

fect under certain conditions. When samples of a solution of D-glucose–glycine were sealed under nitrogen, those stored at 50° in laboratory illumination became darker than those stored in the dark at the same temperature. However, if partly browned solutions under air or oxygen were exposed to light at 25°, their color was gradually bleached.

Ionizing radiations have been shown to increase the tendency for non-enzymic browning to occur in milk and also in a lactose–casein model system. Fluorescent compounds were formed, but no furans could be detected. Exclusion of carbonyl compounds prevented browning, but some coloration appeared in the absence of free amino groups.[184]

Since the non-enzymic browning of fruits and other foods is usually undesirable, much effort has been directed toward preventing the reactions which cause it. Such methods of inhibition can be classified under two headings: firstly, imposition of unfavorable conditions; and, secondly, addition of inhibitors.

a. *Unfavorable Conditions.*—The roles of moisture, *p*H, and temperature in the Maillard reaction have been discussed. Absence of moisture on the one hand,[155, 185] or use of a very dilute solution on the other,[33, 159] should both tend to minimize browning. Low *p*H[155] and low temperature[135] would also discourage the reaction. L-Lysine is probably the most chromogenic amino acid toward aldoses[153]; and, of the sugars, the pentoses cause most browning. However, the removal of *any* free sugar capable of causing browning would minimize the phenomenon. An enzymic method of removing D-glucose from dried eggs or other foods has been patented,[186] and live cells of *Lactobacillus pentoaceticum* (which have D-ribose oxidase activity) have been reported to minimize the browning of fish.[187] Glucose oxidase has been recommended for counteracting the browning of eggs during drying.[188] Another method for preventing the deterioration, through the Maillard reaction, of dried eggs during storage is to add a simple amino acid which will preferentially react with free sugars, so that none of them are available to react with the protein.[189] Such a melanoidin, formed from a sugar and a simple amino acid, is more soluble than that formed from protein present in dried-egg powder, and it therefore does not interfere

(184) J. H. Wertheim, B. E. Proctor and S. A. Goldblith, *J. Dairy Sci.*, **39**, 1236 (1956).

(185) C. E. Hendel, H. K. Burr and M. M. Boggs, *Food Technol.*, **9**, 627 (1955).

(186) R. R. Baldwin (to Ben L. Sarrett), U. S. Pat. 2,744,017 (1956); *Chem. Abstracts*, **50**, 12348 (1956).

(187) H. L. A. Tarr and H. M. Bissett, *Fisheries Research Board Can., Progr. Repts. Pacific Coast Stas.*, **No. 98**, 3 (1954); *Chem. Abstracts*, **48**, 11670 (1954).

(188) R. W. Kline, T. T. Sonoda and H. L. Hanson, *Food Technol.*, **8**, 343 (1954).

(189) E. C. Bate-Smith and J. R. Hawthorne, *J. Soc. Chem. Ind.* (London), **64**, 297 (1945).

with the latter's normal usability. Addition of any of the common amino acids, except cysteine, maintains the solubility of the dried-egg powder, but accelerates development of fluorescence and color. Cysteine, however, while *retarding* development of both fluorescence and browning, also *maintains* the solubility of the powder.[190]

An unusual method of inhibiting the browning of dried apricot stored at 37° is to extract the samples continuously with ethyl acetate at this temperature. Browning is inhibited only while extraction continues.[107]

b. Addition of Inhibitors.—The most widely used inhibitor of browning is sulfur dioxide, which is an antioxidant and therefore a preservative of vitamin C and of color.[156, 191, 192] The best results were obtained[185] if it was applied as a dilute spray and if, at the same time, the moisture content was lowered to 4%. An improvement on the use of sulfite alone is disclosed in a patent[193] which recommends employing a solution of salt, L-ascorbic acid, and a sulfiting agent because this treatment results in better flavor than when sulfite alone is used. Another patent[194] covers the use of formic acid, urea, thiourea, or benzaldehyde. Formaldehyde,[107, 191, 195] hydroxylamine,[156] hydrazine,[156] and semicarbazide[156] have also been observed to inhibit browning of sugars plus amino acids or proteins. Another reducing agent, sodium borohydride, effectively inhibited the browning of sugars with amines.[196] Traces of formaldehyde increase color formation in lactose–amino acid solutions, but larger proportions retard it. Sodium bisulfite also inhibits browning in this mixture, but this compound could not be used for preventing the discoloration of lactose solutions during sterilization.[169]

Recent work[197] has shown that a combination of sulfite and calcium chloride is more effective than either compound alone in retarding the browning of dehydrated potatoes. No explanation could be given for the effect of calcium chloride, but it causes a small depression in the pH value of the substrate and may block free amino groups. The dehydrating action of calcium chloride may also have an effect in taking up the traces of moisture which may persist after "drying." The mechanism by which sulfurous acid inhibits browning is also not completely understood, but the facile combination of sulfur dioxide with furaldehyde may be significant in this

(190) R. W. Kline and G. F. Stewart, *Ind. Eng. Chem.*, **40**, 919 (1948).

(191) M. A. Joslyn, *Ind. Eng. Chem.*, **33**, 308 (1941).

(192) C. A. Weast and G. Mackinney, *Ind. Eng. Chem.*, **33**, 1409 (1941).

(193) G. Johnson and D. G. Guadagni, U. S. Pat. 2,475,878 (1949); *Chem. Abstracts*, **43**, 7605 (1949).

(194) C. J. Krister, U. S. Pat. 2,315,626 (1943); *Chem. Abstracts*, **37**, 5614 (1943).

(195) D. Nomura, *Hakkô Kôgaku Zasshi*, **33**, 212 (1955).

(196) J. E. Hodge and C. E. Rist, *J. Am. Chem. Soc.*, **75**, 316 (1953).

(197) M. Simon, J. R. Wagner, V. G. Silveira and C. E. Hendel, *Food Technol.*, **9**, 271 (1955).

connection. The sequence of reactions which lead to color formation may be interrupted at the stage where formaldehyde reacts with sulfur dioxide.[198] Intercomparison of the ease with which various sugars combine with sulfur dioxide shows that this interaction is increased when amino acids are present.[199] Moreover, the sulfite content decreases markedly with time, and this has been shown to be the result of irreversible binding.[156]

The addition-compounds of sodium bisulfite (or potassium bisulfite) with numerous sugars have[199a] been prepared in a pure state and have been shown to react with aromatic amines under conditions similar to those under which the free sugars react. N-Substituted glycosylamines are formed, but the reaction with amino acids was not reported.

VI. COMPARATIVE REACTIVITY OF INDIVIDUAL SUGARS AND AMINO ACIDS

The ability to cause browning and to react with amino compounds varies considerably with the sugar used. Similarly, amino acids vary greatly in the ease with which they react with any particular sugar. Maillard[72, 98] came to these conclusions from experiments (a) with D-glucose mixed with various amino acids, and (b) with glycine and each of a number of sugars. His results were not strictly quantitative, since he based his judgments largely on visual observations, except for some polarimetric measurements. Owing to the depth of color produced and the temperature (100°) at which his experiments were performed, the use of a polarimeter was, at that time, almost impossible after the initial stages. In a study of the comparative reactivities of amino acids, he observed the time taken to reach various shades of color; he also noted the time elapsed before the liberation of carbon dioxide started. From these experiments, the amino acids were placed in the following order of decreasing reactivity toward D-glucose: alanine, valine, glycine, glutamic acid, leucine, sarcosine, and tyrosine. However, in a paper[200] contemporaneous with those of Maillard, alanine, leucine, phenylalanine, and glutamic acid were considered not to be important factors in humin formation under acidic conditions. Maillard[72] conducted a set of experiments (with glycine mixed with various sugars, at 100°) which led to this sequence of decreasing reactivity: D-xylose, L-arabinose, hexoses (D-fructose, D-galactose, D-mannose, and D-glucose), and disaccharides (maltose, lactose, and sucrose). The amount of browning with sucrose was very small, and Maillard rightly concluded that a free aldehyde or ketone group was essential to occurrence of the reaction. He also compared the reactions of D-glucose and D-xylose with glycine at 30° and 40°,

(198) M. Ingram and K. Vas, J. Sci. Food Agr., 1, 63 (1950).
(199) M. Ingram and K. Vas, J. Sci. Food Agr., 1, 21 (1950).
(199a) D. L. Ingles, Australian J. Chem., 12, 97 (1959).
(200) M. L. Roxas, J. Biol. Chem., 27, 71 (1916).

and again found that, in a certain time-interval, D-xylose gives a darker brown color and liberates more carbon dioxide than does D-glucose.

Since the publication of Maillard's experiments, the relative reactivities of various sugars and amino acids have been more precisely determined, but the method used for measuring the progress of the reaction may have an important effect on the result. This is clearly shown by a comparison[201] of two methods of following the reaction, namely, determination of amino-nitrogen content using Van Slyke's method, and comparison of color formed (by means of the Lovibond Tintometer). Both methods gave D-xylose, L-arabinose, and D-glucose as the three most reactive sugars toward casein. Van Slyke's method placed lactose, maltose, and D-fructose next, whereas the Tintometer indicated that these three sugars do not produce a brown color with casein. Similar differences in reactivities of amino acids were reported by Deschreider,[172] who measured the optical density of the solution and determined the loss of amino nitrogen and of amino acid on refluxing an aqueous solution of D-glucose and the amino acid at pH 5.25 or 3.20 for 10 hours. The results for the experiments conducted at pH 5.25 are shown graphically in Figs. 6, 7, and 8. These curves also show that the proportion of amino acid present can affect its reactivity toward D-glucose.

Kretovich and Tokareva[202] compared the color produced by pentoses, hexoses, and disaccharides, respectively, with amino acids at 95°, using a more dilute solution than had Maillard.[72] Iodine solutions were used as color standards. Pentoses were the most reactive and disaccharides the least reactive; and glycine, leucine, and alanine showed decreasing reactivity as amino acids.

In comparing the reactivities of various sugars with L-histidine, Lewin[166] found that, up to the end of the first steady-pH state, a decreasing order of reactivity from pentoses through hexoses to disaccharides was again evident. At 20°, the D-ribose–L-histidine system required about one hour to reach the steady state (which lasted three days), whereas a D-glucose–L-histidine solution needed about a week to attain the first steady-state (which lasted about four weeks). The behavior of D-ribose with amino acids has had very little study considering its wide distribution in Nature and its reactivity toward amines.[49] The discovery of free D-ribose[187, 203, 204] in certain varieties of fish, *post mortem*, has stimulated further research into the cause of the browning of fish muscle. This work has shown that the Maillard reaction is indeed a factor and that D-ribose is several times as

(201) V. M. Lewis and C. H. Lea, *Biochim. et Biophys. Acta*, **4**, 532 (1950).

(202) V. L. Kretovich and R. Tokareva, *Biokhimiya*, **13**, 508 (1948); *Chem. Abstracts*, **43**, 4501 (1949).

(203) H. L. A. Tarr, *Nature*, **171**, 344 (1953); *Federation Proc.*, **12**, 279 (1953).

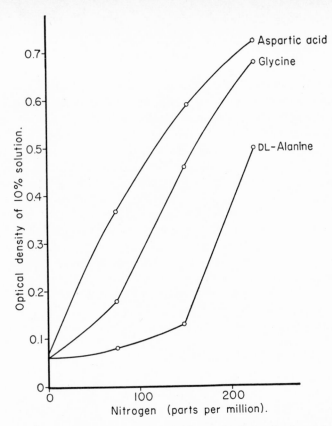

FIG. 6.—The Effect of Different Amino Acids on the Color Produced in 50% D-Glucose Solution at pH 5.25 and at Reflux Temperature for 10 Hours.[172] (This graph also shows the effect of different amino acid concentrations on the degree of browning under these conditions.)

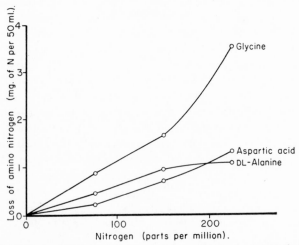

FIG. 7.—The Effect of Different Amino Acids on the Loss of Amino Nitrogen of a 50% D-Glucose Solution Containing the Amino Acid, at pH 5.25 and Reflux Temperature for 10 Hours. (The effect of different amino acid concentrations on the loss of amino nitrogen is also shown.[172])

effective as D-glucose in producing color[204, 205] (compare Ref. 131). Addition of D-ribose to extracts of muscle from codling increased the amount of browning, and only 7 to 16% of the D-ribose could be recovered, as compared with 93% or more of added D-glucose.[206]

By repeated evaporation to dryness of solutions of equimolar amounts of several sugars and amino acids, Grünhut and Weber[110] found that L-arabinose[33] and glutamic acid were the most reactive of those studied. Glutamic acid also produced more color with D-glucose sirup at pH 5.2 than did several other amino acids.[172]

A correlation between the reactivity of the sugar and the proportion of

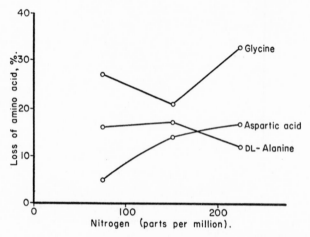

Fig. 8.—The Effect of Various Amino Acids at Different Concentrations on the Percentage of Amino Acid Lost on Heating a 50% Solution of D-Glucose at Reflux Temperature for 10 Hours at pH 5.25 with Amino Acids.[172]

aldehydo form present has been suggested.[207] Van Slyke's amino-nitrogen determination was applied to a glycine–sugar mixture adjusted to pH 9.0. L-Arabinose and D-xylose were the most reactive, followed by D-mannose, D-galactose, and D-glucose (in that order). This order is comparable to that found polarographically for the proportion of aldehydo form of the sugar.[208] A similar order has been found by Katchalsky and Sharon[136] in their determination of the observed rate constants for the reaction of various sugars with glycine. The order of reactivity, L-arabinose > D-xylose >

(204) N. R. Jones, *J. Sci. Food Agr.*, **9**, 672 (1958).

(205) H. L. A. Tarr, *Food Technol.*, **8**, 15 (1954).

(206) N. R. Jones, *Biochem. J.*, **68**, 704 (1958).

(207) S. Araya, *Nippon Seikagakkai Shi*, **19**, 143 (1947); *Chem. Abstracts*, **46**, 2595 (1952).

(208) S. M. Cantor and Q. P. Peniston, *J. Am. Chem. Soc.*, **62**, 2113 (1940).

D-galactose > lactose > D-glucose > maltose, is the same as that of the content of open-chain form, as determined[209] by the color produced with the Schiff reagent.[210] The parallelism between reactivity of the sugar and the proportion of it which exists in the acyclic form has been taken further by Traitteur,[211] who has provided data for (a) the tendency to melanoidin formation with glycine, (b) the proportion of open-chain form, and (c) the velocity of mutarotation, for a number of sugars and certain carbonyl compounds (see Table V). From these figures, it appears that a high proportion of a stable, hemiacetal form of a sugar discourages interaction with amino groups.

TABLE V

Proportion of Acyclic Form of a Sugar, Its Speed of Mutarotation, and Its Ability to Form Melanoidin[211]

	Melanoidin formation[a]	Open-chain form[b]	Speed of mutarotation
D-Glucose	1	1	1
D-Fructose	1.2	—	—
D-Mannose	1.4	2.7	1.7
D-Galactose	2	3.4	1.6
D-Xylose	5.5	7.1	3.2
L-Arabinose	6.7	7.1	4.8
D-Lyxose	—	16.7	10
D-Ribose	Very high	354	Very fast
2-Furaldehyde	>15	—	—
Methylglyoxal	>30	—	—

[a] Compared to D-glucose = 1.

[b] At 20°, in 0.25 M solution at pH 7, the proportion of acyclic form of D-glucose is 0.022% (which is taken as unity).

Although Maillard[72] placed the reactivity of D-fructose (toward amino acids) higher than that of D-galactose, D-mannose, and D-glucose, Shiga,[144] on the basis of Van Slyke amino-nitrogen determinations, concluded that D-fructose combines to a much smaller extent, even at alkaline pH. Similarly, 0.3 M solutions of D-fructose plus either alanine or cysteine, in 0.1 M phosphate buffer at pH 7.4 and 40°, showed no loss of amino groups during 24 hours.[175] Under the same conditions, cysteine reacts with aldohexoses to form a thiazolidine-4-carboxylic acid (VIII), the original C1 of

(209) B. N. Stepanenko and O. G. Serdyuk, *Biokhimiya*, **15**, 155 (1950); *Chem. Abstracts*, **44**, 6769 (1950).

(210) W. C. Tobie, *Ind. Eng. Chem. Anal. Ed.*, **14**, 405 (1942).

(211) H. Traitteur, *Brauwissenschaft*, **9**, 153 (1951).

the sugar being situated in the heterocyclic ring.[212] Euler and Brunius[213]

$$\begin{array}{c}
^{\oplus}\text{HN}\text{---}\text{CHCO}_2\text{H} \\
\text{C}\diagdown\diagup\text{CH}_2 \\
\text{S} \\
\text{HCOH} \\
\text{HOCH} \\
\text{HCOH} \\
\text{HCOH} \\
\text{CH}_2\text{OH} \\
\text{VIII}
\end{array}$$

found that their cryoscopic method indicated that a solution of D-fructose and DL-alanine (0.6 M) reacts to form another compound to the extent of 6.9%. Measurements of pH-depression and browning[166] show that D-fructose reacts with L-histidine in dilute solution at 20°, but apparently not with glycine or alanine,[117, 118] although the increased levorotation of a solution of the latter and D-fructose has been cited as evidence for occurrence of interaction between them.[124, 214] When the amino acid was added to a D-glucose solution, no such rotational change occurred. The interaction of D-fructose (and L-sorbose) with ammonia[215, 216] and aliphatic amines,[52, 53, 217-219] is, however, well established. This reaction was recently extended to amino acids, which react with D-fructose in the presence of ammonium chloride.[55, 220] Anhydrous isopropylamine,[53] propylamine,[218] butylamine,[218] or cyclohexylamine[53] react with D-fructose at room temperature (or below), to give the products of the "reversed Amadori rearrangement" or the *Heyns rearrangement*,[221] but anhydrous *ethylamine* yields crystalline *N*-ethyl-D-fructosylamine (which then undergoes the Heyns rearrangement in methanolic acetic acid[218]). D-Fructose (in aqueous solution) reacts more readily than D-glucose with butylamine, asparagine, and aspartic acid, but the products formed from asparagine do not appear, from their nitrogen content, to be isomeric. Thus, the D-glucose–asparagine

(212) M. P. Schubert, *J. Biol. Chem.*, **130**, 601 (1939).

(213) H. von Euler and E. Brunius, *Z. physiol. Chem.*, *Hoppe-Seyler's*, **161**, 265 (1926).

(214) C. Neuberg and M. Kobel, *Biochem. Z.*, **174**, 464 (1926).

(215) K. Heyns and W. Koch, *Z. Naturforsch.*, **7b**, 486 (1952).

(216) K. Heyns and K. H. Meinecke, *Chem. Ber.*, **86**, 1453 (1953).

(217) K. Heyns, R. Eichstedt and K. H. Meinecke, *Chem. Ber.*, **88**, 1551 (1955).

(218) J. F. Carson, *J. Am. Chem. Soc.*, **77**, 5957 (1955).

(219) J. F. Carson, *J. Am. Chem. Soc.*, **78**, 3728 (1956).

(220) K. Heyns, H. Breuer and H. Paulsen, *Chem. Ber.*, **90**, 1374 (1957).

(221) H. H. Baer, *Fortschr. chem. Forsch.*, **3**, 822 (1958).

product contained 5.7 % nitrogen, whereas its D-fructose analog contained[192] 7.6 %. The reactivity of D-fructose with aliphatic amino compounds, especially those containing the (deactivating) carboxyl group,[59] is in contrast to its low reactivity toward aromatic amines.[54, 222]

In view of the possible role of furans in browning reactions, Rice, Kertesz, and Stotz[223] studied the ability of amino acids to react with 2-furaldehyde. They found that glycine, aspartic acid, and arginine are excellent accelerators of browning reactions at 80° (pH 3.3 to 6.8). Arginine is the most potent throughout the pH range studied.

The alleged high reactivity of glutamic acid[110, 172] in the Maillard reaction is *not* confirmed by recent work on the browning of various amino acids with D-glucose. Willits, Underwood, Lento, and Ricciuti[153] studied the degree of browning produced by autoclaving L-lysine, DL-alanine, and L-glutamic acid at six different pH values for 20 minutes at 114°, and concluded that neither DL-alanine nor L-glutamic acid increases the browning (measured at 500 mμ) over that produced when D-glucose is autoclaved alone at the same pH. The solution containing L-lysine, on the other hand, browned considerably more than an autoclaved solution of D-glucose alone. No color was produced either with or without an amino acid at pH values lower than 6, but, above this figure, the amount of color increased up to a pH of 9, the highest value investigated (see Table II). Of the three acids studied, only L-lysine is a basic amino acid and, as this factor might have a bearing on the browning, the reaction between D-glucose and two other basic amino acids, arginine and histidine, was investigated. No browning comparable with that caused by L-lysine was produced by these two basic amino acids.

Much of the work conducted on the Maillard reaction has been concerned with α-amino acids because they are the main constituents of proteins. Some research has, however, been done on the reaction of sugars with amino acids in which the amino group is separated from the carboxyl group by *more than one* carbon atom. Kubota[224] found that the carboxyl group has an inhibiting effect on the reactivity of the amino group; the magnitude of the inhibition depends on the distance between the two groups. Thus, β-amino acids react at a rate greater than that of α-amino acids, and esterification of the carboxyl group results in an increase in the reaction velocity. L-Lysine contains *two* amino groups, one of which is well separated from the carboxyl function, and its reaction with sugars at 37° has been studied

(222) F. Knotz, *Monatsh.*, **88**, 703 (1957).

(223) R. G. Rice, Z. I. Kertesz and E. H. Stotz, *J. Am. Chem. Soc.*, **69**, 1798 (1947).

(224) T. Kubota, *J. Biochem.* (Tokyo), **34**, 119 (1941); *Chem. Abstracts*, **45**, 1177 (1951).

by several workers. Chromatographic examination of the products showed that one of them is an enol (IX)[225] and that the 6-amino group is more

IX

reactive than the 2-amino group toward D-glucose.[65] The evidence for the enolic structure will be discussed later (see Section VII). A re-investigation of this reaction under the same conditions suggests, however, that the two amino groups *react at about the same rate*, since Folk[226] has shown the presence of both isomers by treating the reaction mixture with 1-fluoro-2,4-dinitrobenzene (which reacts with any remaining amino groups), hydrolyzing off the sugar, and identifying the L-lysine derivative. Paper chromatography and ionophoresis were used for separating and identifying the products. A slow-moving spot (which increased with time) was ascribed to the di-N-substituted glycosyllysine. 2,4-Dinitrophenylation of reaction mixtures which had been standing for 7 days gave bis-(2,4-dinitrophenyl)-L-lysine, 2,4-dinitrophenol, N^6-(2,4-dinitrophenyl)-L-lysine, and N^2-(2,4-dinitrophenyl)-L-lysine. The success of this method depends on (a) the absence of reaction between 1-fluoro-2,4-dinitrobenzene and the group (amino) which has reacted with the sugar, and (b) the ability to split off the sugar completely with acid. Completely reversible hydrolysis of the sugar–amine product is not always obtained, however, since an irreversible reaction may occur, depending on the conditions and duration of the original condensation (see pp. 79 and 80). It is, therefore, not surprising that Folk recovered only about 20 % of the L-lysine lost during storage. Firm conclusions cannot, then, be drawn from this work. Hannan and Lea[161] studied the reaction of D-glucose with N^2-acetyl-L-lysine (at 37° and pH 6.5) at relative humidities varying from 20 to 60 %. Acid hydrolysis of the samples stored at 20 % or 30 % relative humidity did *not* yield D-glucose; neither were the samples reduced catalytically at atmospheric pressure. Both products appear to be formed from equimolar amounts of reactants, but these observations do not provide evidence for a D-glucosylamine structure or for an Amadori type of structure.

The effect of the distance (between the amino and carboxyl functions) on the degree of browning of a series of amino acids with D-glucose was studied by Lento, Underwood, and Willits.[227] Their standardized reaction

(225) A. Gottschalk and S. M. Partridge, *Nature*, **165**, 684 (1950).

(226) J. E. Folk, *Arch. Biochem. Biophys.*, **61**, 150 (1956).

(227) H. G. Lento, Jr., J. C. Underwood and C. O. Willits, *Food Research*, **23**, 68 (1958).

conditions were a 0.1 M solution of both reactants, a buffered pH of 8, and autoclaving of the mixture at 114° at 10 lb. per sq. in. for 20 minutes. Their

TABLE VI

Effect of Various Amino Acids on the Color Developed in a Dilute D-Glucose Solution at[227] pH 8

Amino Acid	Formula	Absorbance at 500 mμ
Glycine	$H_2NCH_2CO_2H$	1.56
DL-α-Alanine	CH_3CHCO_2H $\quad$ | $\quad$ NH_2	0.77
β-Alanine	$H_2N(CH_2)_2CO_2H$	2.00
DL-2-Aminobutyric acid	$CH_3CH_2CHCO_2H$ $\quad$ | $\quad$ NH_2	1.00
4-Aminobutyric acid	$H_2N(CH_2)_3CO_2H$	2.30
2,4-Diaminobutyric acid·2HCl	$H_2N(CH_2)_2CHCO_2H$ $\quad$ | $\quad$ NH_2	0.85
DL-Norvaline	$CH_3(CH_2)_2CHCO_2H$ $\quad$ | $\quad$ NH_2	1.07
5-Aminovaleric acid	$H_2N(CH_2)_4CO_2H$	1.88
DL-Ornithine·HCl	$H_2N(CH_2)_3CHCO_2H$ $\quad$ | $\quad$ NH_2	3.07
DL-Norleucine	$CH_3(CH_2)_3CHCO_2H$ $\quad$ | $\quad$ NH_2	1.21
6-Aminocaproic acid	$H_2N(CH_2)_5CO_2H$	0.70
L-Lysine	$H_2N(CH_2)_4CHCO_2H$ $\quad$ | $\quad$ NH_2	0.70
D-Glucose (alone)		0.64

results are shown in Table VI. Representatives of three types of amino acid were chosen, namely, terminal monoamino acids, α-amino acids, and α,ω-diamino acids. For the terminal amino acids, browning increases from glycine through β-alanine to 4-aminobutyric acid and then decreases through 5-aminovaleric acid and 6-aminocaproic acid. The explanation suggested is that only in the five- and six-carbon monoamino acids can the carbon chain bend so that the amino group comes closer to the carboxyl group and thus has its reactivity decreased. The most intense browning was caused by lysine and by the closely related basic amino acid, ornithine. α-Amino acids having three, four, five, or six carbon atoms produced comparatively little browning (see also p. 87).

The reactivities of a large number of amino acids (in 0.05 M solution) with 0.25 M D-glucose solution at 90° were given by Traitteur[211] in terms of the tendency (taken as unity) for D-glucose alone to form melanoidin. Here, again, lysine (87) led and was followed by 6-aminocaproic acid (41), phenylalanine (39), and β-alanine (27). Tryptophan, which has been reported[228] to be very reactive in respect to humus formation in strongly acid solution, was given a value of 25. Glycine (as 0.05 M solution) had a relative activity of 20, but, when its concentration was 0.1 M, its reactivity (38) was nearly doubled. Ornithine was not mentioned, and so, comparison with the results of Lento, Underwood, and Willits[227] is not possible. It is interesting to note that the low placing (8.5) given to glutamic acid is in keeping with its low browning ability with D-glucose at all pH values[153] from 3 to 9. But Grünhut and Weber's[110] and Deschreider's[172] conclusions regarding its high reactivity were based on more drastic and prolonged interaction, and the results were not compared with those obtainable with lysine. Deschreider[14] divided amino acids into three classes, according to their behavior with sugars. Alanine and glutamic acid represent those mainly responsible for the intense browning and the ability to form "amino acid–sugar complexes." Others, such as tyrosine and phenylalanine, do not reinforce browning but give rise to a compound with an absorption maximum at 279 mμ. Finally, the leucine type of amino acid neither causes browning nor gives rise to a compound with an absorption maximum at 279 mμ.

From a study of the browning of a number of amino compounds with D-glucose at 60°, Beacham and Dull[229] concluded that browning is proportional to the basic strength of the amino compound. Thus butylamine causes more intense browning than glycine. The results discussed above suggest, however, that the basicity of the aglycon is only one of several factors which affect browning. That the concentration of the solution is important is shown by the very small differences between the color produced by fourteen amino acids when heated at 98° for 3 hours with 2%

(228) S. Hori, J. Kato, T. Hino and N. Mizokuchi, *Nippon Nôgei-kagaku Kaishi*, **31**, 19 (1957); *Chem. Abstracts*, **51**, 17015 (1957).

(229) H. H. Beacham and M. F. Dull, *Food Research*, **16**, 439 (1951).

(0.011 M) solutions of D-glucose and D-fructose,[230] and also from Traitteur's work[211] mentioned above.

VII. Properties of Maillard Reaction Products

The physical properties of the brown pigment have been described by numerous workers, but, as the properties depend to a considerable extent on the conditions under which the pigments were formed, uniformity is not readily obtained. The pigment isolated during the initial stages of the reaction, especially at low temperature, is water soluble and acidic to litmus. It is not precipitated in aqueous solution by mineral acids, alkalis, or salts.

The pigment which is formed later, or at higher temperature, is insoluble in water and in cold acids, although hot acids dissolve it slowly. Ammonia dissolves some of the precipitate, but addition of acid causes its reprecipitation. Strong alkali dissolves the pigment to give a brown liquid, from which a brown mass is precipitated by acid. A typical sample had a pH of 3.2, and it absorbed chlorine and bromine.[72, 98, 101, 229, 231] Enders and Theis[100] deduced that the empirical formula of their melanoidin from D-glucose plus glycine was $C_{67}H_{76}N_5O_{32}$, and the repeating unit was found by Wolfrom, Schlicht, Langer, and Rooney[86] to be $C_{6.0}H_{6.4}N_{1.0}O_{2.0}CH_2 \cdot (CO_2H)_{0.5}$. For the polymer made by heating an aqueous solution of D-xylose plus glycine at 95° for 90 hours under nitrogen, the repeating unit was $C_{5.0}H_{4.7}N_{0.8}O_{1.5}CH_2(CO_2H)_{0.3}$. These figures were deduced from experiments in which either the sugar or the amino acid, or both, had a C^{14} atom.

Ambler[73] has determined the elemental composition both of soluble and insoluble fractions of melanoidin from the reaction of D-glucose (0.11 mole) with alanine (0.03 mole) in aqueous solution at reflux temperature. The insoluble melanoidin contained 60.5% of C, 5.3% of H, 3.2% of N, and 31.1% of O, and the soluble fraction contained 58.4% of C, 6.4% of H, 3.27% of N, and 32.1% of O. The difference between the two analyses is small, and, by comparing these figures with those of Maillard's[98] for the melanoidin obtained in the D-glucose–glycine reaction at 100°, it can be seen that the dehydration of the sugar had proceeded further in Maillard's experiment. He analyzed three successive fractions (A, B, and C) of the melanoidin, and obtained the figures shown in Table VII.

Brown products from D-xylose–glycine showed an absorption peak at 320 mμ and, in the infrared, a band at 6.2 μ and also (sometimes), a second one at 5.9 μ, which might be due to doubly-bonded atoms. However, no positive evidence of double bonds was obtained by treatment with

(230) D. Nomura, *Hakkô Kôgaku Zasshi*, **31,** 429 (1953).

(231) C. Enders, *Kolloid-Z.*, **85,** 74 (1938); C. Enders, M. Tschapek and R. Glawe, *ibid.*, **110,** 240 (1948).

bromine, although much hydrogen bromide was present at the end of the treatment.[101] The soluble fraction of the pigment from the D-glucose–glycine reaction at 100° had maximum absorption at 400 mμ and the dry compound was black.[103] Enders and Theis[100] detected the presence of five carboxyl, eight alcoholic, three phenolic, and two carbonyl groups per molecule of the melanoidin prepared by them from D-glucose plus glycine. When distilled with zinc dust, it yielded pyrroles and pyridines, and oxidation with nitric acid gave oxalic and other acids.[231]

N-Glycosylamino acids are stronger acids than the free amino acids.[61] This fact would explain an observation[137] that acidic products are formed during the Maillard reaction; but the enolic form of the Amadori product might *also* be expected to show stronger acidic properties than the simple amino acids. N-D-Glucosylglycine is rapidly hydrolyzed in dilute acetic

TABLE VII

Elemental Analysis of Melanoidin Fractions[98]

Element, %	Fraction		
	A	B	C
Carbon	58.6	59.1	58.9
Hydrogen	4.6	5.0	5.1
Nitrogen	4.4	5.5	6.0
Oxygen	32.4	30.4	30.0

acid and, more slowly, in water.[232] The enol form of the Amadori rearrangement product, on the other hand, is *not* easily hydrolyzed by acid; but, in a sealed tube at 100° for one hour with N sulfuric acid, glycine and 5-(hydroxymethyl)-2-furaldehyde are formed.[116] Further, the 1-amino-1-deoxy-2-ketose derivative shows very strong reducing properties.[7, 62, 116, 232]

With the development of such modern techniques as chromatography and absorption spectroscopy, the identification of reaction products has been increasingly made in terms of R_f values and the wavelengths of absorption peaks. These, together with the spraying of chromatograms with various special reagents, can provide information on the size of the molecule and the functional groups present. So much work of this kind has been done that only a few papers will be discussed in detail, and but brief mention of many others will be made in this and other Sections.

Richards[116] has made a thorough chromatographic and spectrophoto-

(232) W. W. Pigman, E. A. Cleveland, D. H. Couch and J. H. Cleveland, *J. Am. Chem. Soc.*, **73**, 1976 (1951).

metric study of the D-glucose–glycine reaction at low moisture-content. The procedure used for preparing reaction products has been described in Section IV, and the only product, apart from an immobile, brown material, was one with an R_f value of 0.11. Increasing amounts of this latter compound were formed as the reaction time was extended. On acid hydrolysis in a sealed tube, it gave products which corresponded in R_f values, color reactions, and ultraviolet absorption spectra with glycine, 5-(hydroxymethyl)-2-furaldehyde, and unchanged starting-materials. The compound of R_f 0.11 gives D-*arabino*-hexosazone (XIII) with phenylhydrazine, and it releases three moles of formic acid per mole with periodate. It is, therefore, an open-chain compound containing a tetrahydroxybutyl group. All tests for a ketose were negative, but the compound showed reducing power toward Fehling solution, *o*-dinitrobenzene, and ferricyanide at room temperature.[233] Its conversion into D-*arabino*-hexosazone shows that the reducing center and the amino grouping are C1 and C2, although which is at C1 is not known. The absence of a keto group rules out the 1-amino-1-deoxy-ketose type of structure, but this may have been its precursor.[7] No 5-(hydroxymethyl)-2-furaldehyde could be identified chromatographically in the reaction mixture, but the ultraviolet absorption spectrum showed a peak at 290 mμ (compared with 285 mμ for the furan). The peak at 290 mμ may, however, be attributed to the Schiff base (azomethine) of 5-(hydroxymethyl)-2-furaldehyde, which had earlier been suggested[62, 225] as being formed in the D-glucose–lysine and D-glucose–phenylalanine reactions and which can polymerize to brown products. Whereas a compound of R_f 0.05 (presumably corresponding to the compound of R_f 0.11 from D-glucose and glycine) was observed in a D-glucose–lysine mixture after five days, the supposed furaldehyde azomethine did not appear until the reaction had proceeded for 14 days or longer, and it was apparently formed from the compound of R_f 0.05. 5-(Hydroxymethyl)-2-furaldehyde with lysine gave a compound having the same R_f value as the Schiff base obtained from D-glucose plus lysine. The results from infrared spectroscopy support the chemical evidence that the compound of R_f 0.11 is an enol of the type XII. Compounds of very similar properties have been shown to be present in various fruits and vegetables which suffer browning on storage.[234, 235] Such compounds have also been identified in liver.[236] The scheme shown in formulas X–XVI summarizes these postulates.

(233) E. F. L. J. Anet, *Australian J. Chem.*, **10**, 193 (1957).
(234) H. G. Wager, *J. Sci. Food Agr.*, **6**, 57 (1955).
(235) E. F. L. J. Anet and T. M. Reynolds, *Australian J. Chem.*, **10**, 182 (1957).
(236) H. Borsook, A. Abrams and P. H. Lowy, *J. Biol. Chem.*, **215**, 111 (1955).

$$
\begin{array}{cccc}
\begin{array}{c}
\text{CHOH} \\
\text{HCOH} \\
\text{HOCH} \\
\text{HCOH} \\
\text{HCO} \\
\text{CH}_2\text{OH}
\end{array}
&
\begin{array}{c}
\text{HCNHR} \\
\text{HCOH} \\
\text{HOCH} \\
\text{HCOH} \\
\text{HCO} \\
\text{CH}_2\text{OH}
\end{array}
&
\begin{array}{c}
\text{HCNHR} \\
\text{COH} \\
\text{HOCH} \\
\text{HCOH} \\
\text{HCOH} \\
\text{CH}_2\text{OH}
\end{array}
&
\begin{array}{c}
\text{HC=NNHPh} \\
\text{C=NNHPh} \\
\text{HOCH} \\
\text{HCOH} \\
\text{HCOH} \\
\text{CH}_2\text{OH}
\end{array}
\\
\text{X} & \text{XI} & \text{XII} & \text{XIII}
\end{array}
$$

X $\xrightarrow{\text{RNH}_2}$ XI $\rightarrow$ XII $\xrightarrow{\text{PhNHNH}_2}$ XIII

XVI ← XV ← XIV

$$ \text{HOH}_2\text{C} \underset{\text{O}}{\diagdown}\text{CHO} \rightarrow \text{HOH}_2\text{C}\underset{\text{O}}{\diagdown}\text{CH=NR} \leftarrow \text{HOH}_2\text{C}\underset{\text{O}}{\diagdown}\begin{array}{c}\text{HO}\quad\text{OH}\\ \text{CHNHR}\end{array} $$

XVI XV XIV

Compound XII is the enol form of the Amadori rearrangement product, 1-(carboxyalkylamino)-1-deoxy-2-hexulose. Hodge and Rist[237] observed that (2-O-methyl-D-glucosyl)piperidine is stable, whereas the unsubstituted D-glycosylamine decomposes into a tar on standing in the solid state. The 2-methyl ether would not, of course, be able to undergo an Amadori rearrangement.

VIII. Mechanism and Kinetic Studies of the Reaction

These two aspects of such a complex change as the Maillard reaction are considered together, because most of the *kinetic studies* are based on certain assumptions regarding the *mechanism of reaction*. It is convenient to consider first the reaction in acid medium, and then the reaction at pH values of about 6.5 and above.

1. *Maillard Reaction in Acid Medium*

In an attempt to determine which amino acids could cause humin formation when proteins are hydrolyzed by acid, Roxas,[200] in an early paper, described an investigation of the interaction of a number of amino acids in boiling 20 % hydrochloric acid containing D-glucose, D-xylose, or D-fructose. On the basis of this drastic treatment, alanine, leucine, phenylalanine, and glutamic acid were eliminated as important factors in humin formation. Some of the other amino acids reacted and lost the following proportion of their nitrogen: tyrosine, 15 %; cysteine, 3.1 %; arginine, 2.33 %; lysine,

(237) J. E. Hodge and C. E. Rist, *J. Am. Chem. Soc.*, **74**, 1494 (1952).

2.62%; histidine, 1.84%; and tryptophan, 71%. D-Xylose and D-fructose were usually more reactive than D-glucose under these acidic conditions.

When D-glucose (0.5 mole) and glycine (0.2 mole) were heated at 96° in 3% citric acid solution, an insoluble melanoidin was produced and the total nitrogen and amino nitrogen decreased. Color increased and the amount of N-glucosylamine derivative formed was found (by paper chromatography) to increase with time of heating (see Table VIII). The presence of glycine increased the amount of 5-(hydroxymethyl)-2-furaldehyde produced and this increase ran parallel with the degree of browning. Other compounds identified by chromatography, polarography, and spectroscopy

TABLE VIII

Changes in the Various Forms of Nitrogen in a 3% Citric Acid Solution of 0.5 Mole of D-Glucose and 0.2 Mole of Glycine, on Heating at 96° for Various Time Intervals[104]

Time, hours	Total N, %	Amino N, mg./100 ml.	Ammonia N, mg./100 ml.	Color at 500 mμ, %[a]	N-D-Gluco-sylamine
0	0.279	279.0	0	100	—
5	0.279	277.0	0	71	—
8	0.279	276.9	0	53	—
11	0.278	253.9	+	25	+
14	0.274	245.2	20.0	6	+
17	0.270	240.2	22.0	2	+
20	0.256	201.1	30.9	0	++
30	0.216	140.3	33.6	0	+++
40	0.183	72.4	34.5	0	+++

[a] Percentage transmission.

were levulinic acid, formaldehyde, and formic acid.[104] Using the same reactants in solutions buffered at acid pH values, Smirnov and Geispits[145] showed that the contribution of the sugar–amine reaction to the total color formed is significant, especially above pH 4. Further experiments, at pH 0.65, indicated that some combination occurs, since there was a small disappearance of both sugar and amino acid.

Potentiometric determination of the pH of L-histidine solutions with and without D-glucose at 40° showed that, at initial pH values between 5 and 6.5, the pH remained constant for both samples. When the initial pH was above 6.5, alkali had to be added to the D-glucose–histidine mixture in order to maintain the pH.[137] Chromatographic evidence shows that other basic amino acids (such as lysine and arginine) *also* react[238] with D-glucose

(238) B. Jurecka, D. Barszez, Z. Bergman, B. Bulhak and I. Chmielewska, *Przemysl Chem.*, **13**, 343 (1957).

in aqueous solution at pH 5.0–7.6, but the extent of reaction decreases[137] with pH. A similar conclusion was drawn by Deschreider[172] from his investigation of the browning of D-glucose sirups in the presence of small proportions of amino acids. A 50 % aqueous solution of D-glucose containing 75, 150, and 225 parts per million of amino nitrogen (in the form of various amino acids) was heated under reflux for 10 hours at pH 3.2 or 5.25, and the browning and loss of amino nitrogen were measured at the end of the reaction. Although there was some variation amongst the amino acids, the optical density and the disappearance of amino nitrogen during this fairly drastic treatment were much smaller at pH 3.2 than at pH 5.25. For example, the highest optical density at pH 3.2, measured as index of coloration, was about 0.23, whereas, at the higher pH, it was 0.72; the amounts of nitrogen which disappeared were 0.10 mg. and 0.37 mg., respectively. Over the range in concentration of amino acid studied, browning and disappearance of amino nitrogen generally increased with the proportion of amino acid present. At pH 5.25, aspartic acid produced the most intense browning; this was true also at pH 3.2 at the lowest two concentrations, but, at 225 parts per million, glycine gave the most color. In view of other work, to be discussed later in this Section (see p. 124), it is significant that, at pH 3.2, aspartic acid caused browning but suffered no loss of nitrogen. In acid solution, there is a connection between the presence of 5-(hydroxymethyl)-2-furaldehyde and of amino compound and the intensity of color.[239] Thus, the more nitrogenous material there is present, the more colored is the D-glucose sirup and the more intense is the spectrum caused by 5-(hydroxymethyl)-2-furaldehyde. The quantity of the latter increases with time of heating at 105°, such that there is nearly five times as much present after 6 hours as after 2 hours. These workers conclude that yellowing of heated D-glucose sirup is caused by partial pyrolytic decomposition of the sugar into furans. Browning originates from the Maillard reaction between sugar and amino acid, but it could also arise from reaction of furans with amino acids. These results were obtained in a system in which there was a large excess of sugar in relation to amino acid, but substantially similar conclusions were drawn by Nomura and Kawano[104] using a smaller excess of sugar. Kato[239a] has investigated the nature of the colored products formed from the N-D-xylosylamine derived from an aromatic amino acid or aromatic amine at a higher acid concentration than would normally be found in biological systems. Nevertheless, his results are of some interest and show that the color formed from 4-(D-xylosylamino)benzoic acid and N-phenyl-D-xylosylamine in 0.2 M anhydrous methanolic hydrogen chloride (com-

(239) A. R. Deschreider and E. Maes, *Rev. fermentations et inds. aliment.*, **8**, 223 (1953).

(239a) H. Kato, *Bull. Agr. Chem. Soc. Japan*, **22**, 85 (1958).

pare Ref. 165) at 25° consists of melanoidin and a red pigment. The latter compound was isolated and shown to be identical with that formed from 2-furaldehyde and the appropriate amino compound, both by melting point and infrared absorption spectroscopy. Earlier work[239b] had shown that the most likely structure for the compound formed from 2-furaldehyde and aniline is 2-hydroxy-5-phenylamino-1-phenylimino-2,4-pentadiene dihydrochloride and, by analogy, the red compound isolated from 4-(D-xylosylamino)benzoic acid would be:

$$\left[HO_2C\!\!\bigcirc\!\!NHCH\!=\!CHCH\!=\!\underset{\underset{OH}{|}}{C}CH\!=\!NH\!\!\bigcirc\!\!CO_2H \right]^{\oplus} Cl^{\ominus}$$

Moreover, the presence of 2-furaldehyde was demonstrated by the isolation of its (2,4-dinitrophenyl)hydrazone in 20 % yield from 4-(D-xylosylamino)benzoic acid after standing for 20 hours in methanolic hydrogen chloride (0.4 N). This high yield, compared with observations by other workers,[139] can be attributed to the very high concentration of acid.

Maillard[72, 96, 98] concluded that the carbon dioxide released in his experiments came from the carboxyl group of the amino acid. By quantitative measurements on the reactants and reaction products, he found that a considerable amount of water was also formed. This corresponded to twelve moles for every mole of carbon dioxide released, but this amount was thought to be supplied by *several* moles of sugar. Maillard had, however, neglected the possibility of loss of *volatile compounds other than water* (which are now known to be formed). Modern studies with C^{14}-labeled D-glucose have shown that all of the carbon dioxide formed does *not* come from the amino acid. In experiments carried out under conditions very similar to those used by Maillard, the percentage of carbon dioxide emanating from the carboxyl group has been given[109] as over 80 % and also[86] as 90–100 %. The same experiments showed that some of the carboxyl carbon from the amino acid is incorporated in the brown pigment. However, these results were obtained from the reaction of D-glucose with glycine at acid pH values, and they do not of necessity apply to the Maillard reaction in neutral or alkaline media at lower temperatures. The relation of production of carbon dioxide and of browning to temperature has already been discussed (see Section V,2). In hydrochloric acid solution, the carbon dioxide formed is believed to be derived from the sugar, since it is liberated in the absence of amino acid.[228] A comparison of the amount of color produced by D-glucose with various amino acids at 90–95° in acidic and alkaline media was made by Wolfrom, Cavalieri, and Cavalieri.[102] With glycine at an ini-

(239b) W. M. Foley, Jr., G. E. Sanford and H. McKennis, Jr., *J. Am. Chem. Soc.*, **74**, 5489 (1952).

tial pH of 5.3, the percentage absorption at 490 mμ after 6 hours was 24.8, compared with 99.8 after 1 hour when the initial pH was 7.4. The corresponding figures for DL-alanine were 36.0 at an initial pH of 5.7, and 96.2 at an initial pH of 7.3. Leucine, labeled with C^{14} in the carboxyl group, does not cause visible browning on heating at 80° for one hour in a buffer at pH 5, but the results of chromatography suggested the formation of N-D-glucosylleucine (which was the only radioactive product detected). D-Ribose with the labeled leucine, on the other hand, gave a number of radioactive products and considerable browning.[131]

2. *Maillard Reaction in Neutral and Alkaline Media*

It is clear from the preceding Sections that much of the interest in the Maillard reaction centers around its course at pH values between about 6 and 9. The reaction is very much weaker below[115, 172] pH 6.5, and a different type of reaction probably occurs, since larger quantities of free furan compounds are released and their polymerization may be one cause of browning.[7] However, the formation of combined[62, 114, 225, 234, 235] and free[78, 106, 139, 195, 202, 240, 241] furan derivatives has been postulated as the mechanism of browning in alkaline solution. When 2-furaldehyde, itself, in aqueous solution is heated to 80° with individual amino acids, a very pronounced increase in the color is obtained as compared with that given by the aldehyde alone.[223] The increase is much more marked at pH 6.6 than at lower pH values. Arginine, glycine, and aspartic acid were shown to have this effect, but, in dilute hydrochloric acid, glycine does not react with 2-furaldehyde.[242] It is known that, under acid conditions, D-glucose is converted into 5-(hydroxymethyl)-2-furaldehyde,[243, 244] which shows a maximum absorption at about 285 mμ and a weaker peak at 228 mμ. This compound has been identified chromatographically, spectroscopically, and polarographically as a product of the reaction of D-glucose with glycine[104, 106, 139, 195, 241] and lysine,[225] and in browning samples of various fruits.[107, 240]

One of the products of heating an aqueous solution of D-glucose plus glycine was found by Dubourg and Devillers[114] to be decomposed, by heating with hot water or dilute acid, to glycine and 5-(hydroxymethyl)-2-furaldehyde together with a little colored material. The product was separated (from other compounds present) by ion-exchange chromatography, and it had an analysis corresponding to $C_8H_{15}NO_7$. This formula corre-

(240) A. Wahhab, *J. Am. Chem. Soc.*, **70**, 3580 (1948).

(241) L. Petit, *Compt. rend.*, **244**, 2326 (1957).

(242) C. T. Dowell and P. Menaul, *J. Biol. Chem.*, **40**, 131 (1919).

(243) M. L. Wolfrom, R. D. Schuetz and L. F. Cavalieri, *J. Am. Chem. Soc.*, **70**, 514 (1948).

(244) B. Singh, G. R. Dean and S. M. Cantor, *J. Am. Chem. Soc.*, **70**, 517 (1948).

sponds to the product which would be formed by the condensation of one mole each of D-glucose and glycine, with the loss of one mole of water. It could, thus, be either the glucosylamine or its Amadori rearrangement product, but Dubourg and Devillers[114] favored the former possibility. Tests for a ketose would have shown if the latter was present. The compound in solution gives a brown color, slowly on warming, and rapidly on heating with glycine. Wager[234] observed a similar behavior by one of the chromatographic spots from dehydrated carrot. Furan formation is more pronounced if a sugar is heated with an acidic amino acid (such as glutamic acid, whose isoelectric point is at pH 3.1). From glutamic acid and D-glucose at 130°, Akabori[78] identified 5-(hydroxymethyl)-2-furaldehyde, whereas L-arabinose

TABLE IX

Conversion of D-Glucose and D-Xylose to Furans[139]

Sugar	Glycine, molarity	pH		Conversion to furans, %
		Initial	Final	
D-Glucose	0	6.5	4.8	0.124
	0.03	6.4	5.1	0.154
	0.05	6.4	5.2	0.185
	0.075	6.3	5.0	0.222
	0.1	6.2	5.0	0.333
D-Xylose	0	6.7	4.4	0.556
	0.03	6.6	5.1	0.633
	0.05	6.5	5.1	0.850

gave 2-furaldehyde. The amount of furans produced does not rise, on increasing the proportion of sugar in the reacting mixture.

Continuous extraction, with ethyl acetate, of dried apricot samples stored at 57° inhibited browning, but, when the extraction was stopped, browning started. 2-Furaldehyde and 5-(hydroxymethyl)-2-furaldehyde were amongst the compounds found in the extract. When small amounts (up to 0.5 %) of 2-furaldehyde were added to the apricot concentrate, browning increased.[107] A study of the conversion of D-glucose and D-xylose into furans, in the presence and absence of glycine, shows that the percentage conversion measured spectroscopically, although comparatively small, is greater in the presence of glycine.[139] Table IX shows the conversion obtained on refluxing 0.05 M sugar solutions for 1000 minutes, with and without glycine. By plotting the percentage transmission (at 490 mμ) against time, Wolfrom, Schuetz, and Cavalieri[139] showed that only in the presence of glycine did the transmission decrease significantly for solutions of D-galacturonic acid, D-xylose, and 2-furaldehyde heated at 102° (see Fig. 9).

In a series of experiments in which the sugar was increasingly replaced by D-xylose–glycine in the D-xylose–glycine system, color formation increased with the initial amount of the furan added. It was concluded that both the sugar and the furan contribute to browning.[101] Other experiments also

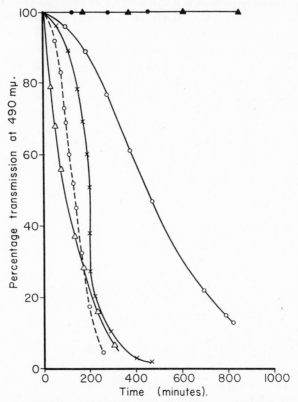

FIG. 9.—Rate of Change in Percentage Transmission (at 490 mμ) of D-Xylose, D-Glucose, D-Galacturonic acid, and 5-(Hydroxymethyl)-2-furaldehyde with Glycine, Compared with the Sugars Alone.[139] [Each constituent (0.25 mole) in aqueous solution at reflux temperature (102°); ●——● D-xylose; ▲——▲ D-glucose; ○——○ D-glucose and glycine; ×——× D-xylose and glycine; △——△ 5-(hydroxymethyl)-2-furaldehyde and glycine; ○- - -○ D-galacturonic acid and glycine.]

showed that the immediate availability of 2-furaldehyde results in earlier browning, thus shortening the so-called "induction period" which has been attributed to the absence of some essential color-producer.[107, 108] The presence of the N-glycosylamine has also been claimed to be a factor shortening the induction period, since 4-(D-xylosylamino)benzoic acid browns more rapidly than a mixture of D-xylose and p-aminobenzoic acid.[245] That such

(245) H. Kato, Bull. Agr. Chem. Soc. Japan, **20**, 279 (1956).

compounds do exist in Nature is shown by the identification of N-D-glucosyl-arginine as a constituent of mulberry leaves.[246]

Many other compounds have been identified as products of the sugar–amino acid reaction. Amongst these are 2,3-butanedione,[195] formaldehyde,[195] pyruvaldehyde,[20, 195, 247, 248] 3-hydroxy-2-butanone,[248] hydroxy-2-propanone,[248] and acetaldehyde.[73] Imidazoles,[195, 249-251] especially 4(5)-methylimidazole, have also been isolated from the reaction under mild conditions, and could have been formed from α-hydroxy ketones or aldehydes plus amino compounds. Following the early identification[247] of pyruvaldehyde as a product of the Maillard reaction, much work was done in an attempt to show that this reactive compound plays a major role in the reaction,[249, 252-254] but, that this is so is by no means certain.[7]

Another possible mechanism[7] for the transformation of sugars with amino acids into colored products is through the Amadori rearrangement,[44] which is the isomerization of an aldosylamine to a ketose derivative, for example, of a D-glucosylamine derivative to a derivative of 1-amino-1-deoxy-D-fructose. Such a conversion has been shown to occur when an amino acid reacts

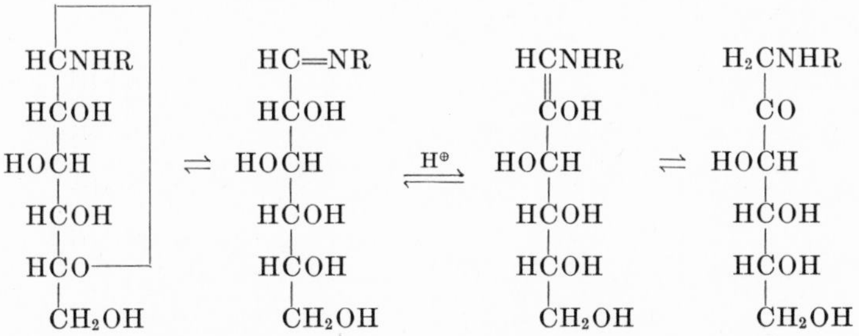

| | XVII | XVIII | XIX |

with an aldose; products which are analytically[65] and chromatographically[116] pure have been isolated. The identification of a N-(D-*arabino*-tetrahydroxy-2-oxohexyl)amino acid in freeze-dried apricots[255] gives weight to this theory. The Amadori rearrangement mechanism is applicable only to N-aldosylamines, but a "reversed Amadori rearrangement" (also called the Heyns

(246) Y. Hamamura and K. Naito, *Nippon Nôgei-kagaku Kaishi*, **30**, 358 (1956).

(247) C. Neuberg and M. Kobel, *Biochem. Z.*, **185**, 477 (1927).

(248) L. Sattler and F. W. Zerban, *Ind. Eng. Chem*, **41**, 1401 (1949).

(249) C. Enders and R. Marquardt, *Naturwissenschaften*, **29**, 46 (1941).

(250) C. Enders, F. Fischler and R. Zellweger, *Brauwissenschaft*, 85 (1948).

(251) L. Hough, J. K. N. Jones and E. L. Richards, *Chem. & Ind.* (London), 545 (1954).

(252) C. Neuberg and M. Kobel, *Biochem. Z.*, **188**, 197 (1927).

(253) C. Neuberg and M. Kobel, *Biochem. Z.*, **200**, 459 (1928).

(254) C. Enders, *Biochem. Z.*, **313**, 352 (1943).

(255) E. F. L. J. Anet and T. M. Reynolds, *Nature*, **177**, 1082 (1956).

rearrangement[221]) has been shown to occur for D-fructosylamine,[112, 215-217, 256] N - alkyl - D - fructosylamines,[53, 217-219] and several N - (D - fructosyl)amino acids[55, 220]; this reversed rearrangement gives a product which is more stable to acid than is the D-fructosylamine. Thus, from D-fructose plus glycine in methanol, N-D-fructosylglycine (XXI) is first formed, and this rearranges, under the catalytic influence of the carboxyl group, to the 2-amino-2-deoxy-D-glucose derivative (XXII). Occasionally, an organic acid (such as oxalic acid) is required as a catalyst. A small amount of the epimeric aldose derivative is formed, in addition[256] to XXII. More recently, Heyns and

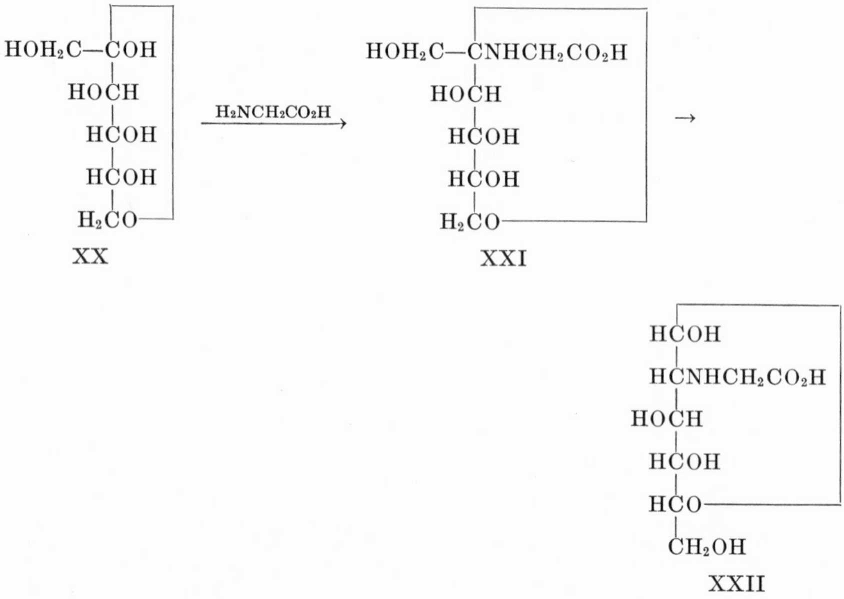

$$
\begin{array}{ccc}
\mathrm{HOH_2C-COH} & \xrightarrow{\mathrm{H_2NCH_2CO_2H}} & \mathrm{HOH_2C-CNHCH_2CO_2H} & \rightarrow \\
\mathrm{HOCH} & & \mathrm{HOCH} \\
\mathrm{HCOH} & & \mathrm{HCOH} \\
\mathrm{HCOH} & & \mathrm{HCOH} \\
\mathrm{H_2CO} & & \mathrm{H_2CO} \\
\mathrm{XX} & & \mathrm{XXI}
\end{array}
$$

$$
\begin{array}{c}
\mathrm{HCOH} \\
\mathrm{HCNHCH_2CO_2H} \\
\mathrm{HOCH} \\
\mathrm{HCOH} \\
\mathrm{HCO} \\
\mathrm{CH_2OH} \\
\mathrm{XXII}
\end{array}
$$

Breuer[256a] isolated not only the two epimeric aldose derivatives but also a small amount of the 1-deoxyketose–amino acid compound. Thus, by heating D-fructose and L-phenylalanine in refluxing methanol for 3 hours, the 2-deoxy-2-L-phenylalanino-D-mannose (XXIIa), 2-deoxy-2-L-phenylalanino-D-glucose (XXIIb), and 1-deoxy-1-L-phenylalanino-D-fructose (XXIIc) derivatives were formed. The properties of the last-named compound were identical with those of the compound obtained from D-glucose –L-phenylalanine by an Amadori rearrangement. It is thus obvious that changes of a character more complex than was expected can take place. Compounds corresponding to XXIIa, XXIIb, and XXIIc were also isolated from the reaction of D-fructose with L-valine, or L-asparagine, the

(256) K. Heyns, H. Paulsen, R. Eichstedt and M. Rolle, *Chem. Ber.*, **90**, 2039 (1957).
(256a) K. Heyns and H. Breuer, *Chem. Ber.*, **91**, 2750 (1958).

three isomers in each reaction being separated from one another by column and paper chromatography. Several compounds of the type XXIIc were obtained in crystalline form for the first time.

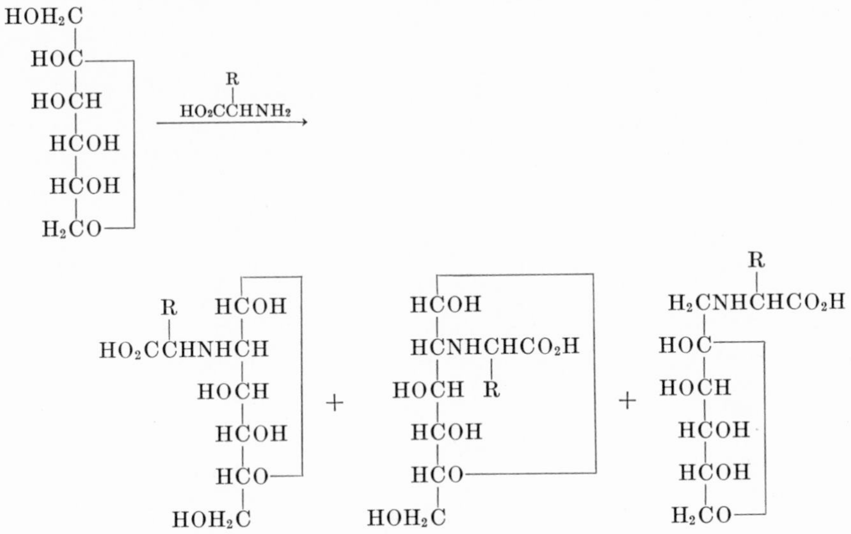

$$HOH_2C$$
$$HOC{-}$$
$$HOCH \qquad HO_2C\overset{R}{C}HNH_2 \longrightarrow$$
$$HCOH$$
$$HCOH$$
$$H_2CO{-}$$

XXIIa
$$\overset{R}{HO_2CCHNHCH}\quad HCOH$$
$$HOCH$$
$$HCOH$$
$$HCO{-}$$
$$HOH_2C$$

$+$

XXIIb
$$HCOH$$
$$HCNHCHCO_2H$$
$$HOCH\ R$$
$$HCOH$$
$$HCO{-}$$
$$HOH_2C$$

$+$

XXIIc
$$\overset{R}{H_2CNHCHCO_2H}$$
$$HOC{-}$$
$$HOCH$$
$$HCOH$$
$$HCOH$$
$$H_2CO{-}$$

The evidence for the formation of such enolic compounds as XVIII from sugars and amino acids has already been discussed in Section VII. Other experiments on the reaction of simpler compounds, such as mono- and di-hydroxy ketones, with amines or amino acids have confirmed the ability of such products to rearrange and then to form brown pigments.[257, 258] This work showed that presence of an α-hydroxy ketone is essential if the re-arrangement (and, hence, the browning) is to proceed. For example, 2,3,4-trideoxyaldopentopyranose (tetrahydropyran-2-ol, XXIII) showed very slight browning with glycine, but 3,4-dideoxy-*glycero*-aldopentopyranose (tetrahydropyran-2,3-diol, XXIV) browned to a greater extent than D-glu-cose. The browning given by 2-deoxy-D-*lyxo*-pentose (a β-hydroxy alde-

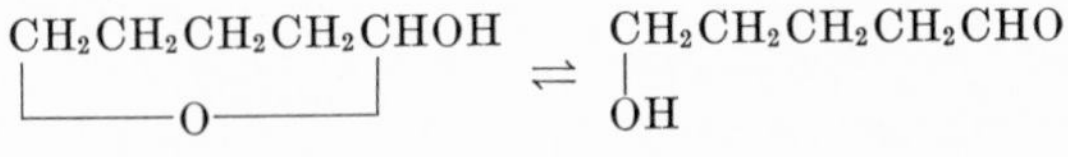

XXIII
$$CH_2CH_2CH_2CH_2CHOH$$
$$\rule{3cm}{0.4pt}O\rule{3cm}{0.4pt}$$
$$\rightleftharpoons$$
$$CH_2CH_2CH_2CH_2CHO$$
$$OH$$

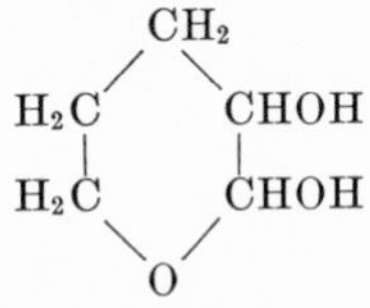

XXIV
$$\begin{array}{c} CH_2 \\ H_2C\diagup\quad\diagdown CHOH \\ H_2C\quad\quad CHOH \\ \diagdown\quad\diagup \\ O \end{array}$$

(257) C. D. Hurd and C. D. Kelso, *J. Am. Chem. Soc.*, **70**, 1484 (1948).
(258) C. D. Hurd and C. M. Buess, *J. Am. Chem. Soc.*, **78**, 5667 (1956).

hyde) with casein[259] is an exception to this rule, but, as an aldol, it can undergo dehydration, which is followed by isomerization to a 4-ketose.[258]

$$
\begin{array}{cccc}
\text{CHO} & \text{CH=NR} & \text{CH=NR} & \text{CH}_2\text{NHR} \\
| & | & | & | \\
\text{CH}_2 & \text{CH}_2 & \text{CH} & \text{CH} \\
| \quad \xrightarrow{\text{RNH}_2} & | & \| & \| \\
\text{CHOH} & \text{CHOH} \;\rightarrow\; & \text{CH} \;\rightarrow\; & \text{CH} \\
| & | & | & | \\
\text{CHOH} & \text{CHOH} & \text{CHOH} & \text{CO} \\
| & | & | & |
\end{array}
$$

Heyns and Stumme[260, 261] have made a systematic investigation of the reaction of α-hydroxy carbonyl compounds with aromatic[260] and aliphatic[261] amines. When such keto alcohols as benzoin and 3-hydroxy-2-butanone were used, it was difficult to draw conclusions as to the mechanism of the reaction. With benzoin, routes A and B both give the same product (XXV), whose assigned structure was confirmed by its infrared spectrum[262] and by its chemical properties. Starting with a substituted benzoin, Cowper and

$$
\begin{array}{ccc}
\text{PhCO} & & \text{PhCO} \\
| & + \text{RNH}_2 \xrightarrow{\text{A}} & | \\
\text{PhCHOH} & & \text{PhCHNHR} \\
& \text{B}\downarrow \quad {}^{B}\nearrow & \text{XXV} \\
& \text{PhC=NR} & \\
& | & \\
& \text{PhCHOH} &
\end{array}
$$

Stevens[263] showed that the course of the reaction involves a rearrangement, as follows.

$$
\text{PhCOCHOHR} + \text{PhNH}_2 \rightarrow \begin{array}{c} \text{PhCHCOR} \\ | \\ \text{NHPh} \end{array}
$$

$$
\text{PhCHOHCOR} + \text{PhNH}_2 \rightarrow \begin{array}{c} \text{PhCOCHR} \\ | \\ \text{NHPh} \end{array}
$$

(where R = p-methoxyphenyl)

Heyns and Stumme[260] have provided further evidence as to the widespread occurrence of this type of rearrangement for compounds in which the α-hydroxy carbonyl group is either terminal or non-terminal, and a detailed electronic mechanism for this rearrangement has been put forward.[264]

Confirmatory evidence for the formation of products of the Amadori type

(259) C. H. Lea and D. N. Rhodes, *Biochim. et Biophys. Acta*, **9**, 56 (1952).

(260) K. Heyns and W. Stumme, *Chem. Ber.*, **89**, 2833 (1956).

(261) K. Heyns and W. Stumme, *Chem. Ber.*, **89**, 2844 (1956).

(262) W. Stuhmer, G. Messwarb and K. D. Ledwoch, *Arch. Pharm.*, **286**, 418 (1953).

(263) R. M. Cowper and T. S. Stevens, *J. Chem. Soc.*, 348 (1940).

(264) (a) L. I. Smith and R. H. Anderson, *J. Org. Chem.*, **16**, 963 (1951). (b) R. H. Anderson, *ibid.*, **19**, 1238 (1954).

was obtained by Täufel, Iwainsky, and Bergner.[65] Their chromatographic study of the interaction of sugars and amino acids showed that one spot, which was recognized as that of the Amadori product, appears in the chromatograms of the reaction of glycine with D-glucose, D-mannose, or D-fructose. This is to be expected for the two aldoses, since the asymmetry of the epimeric center is destroyed in the Amadori rearrangement, but, although D-fructosylamine can yield D-glucosamine derivatives,[220] the latter would not be expected to possess the same R_f values as the isomeric 1-amino-1-

HCNHR	CH₂NHR	HCNHR
HCOH	CO	HOCH
HOCH	HOCH	HOCH
HCOH	HCOH	HCOH
HCO——|	HCOH	HCO——
CH₂OH	CH₂OH	CH₂OH

N-Substituted D-glucosylamine	N-Substituted 1-amino-1-deoxy-D-fructose	N-Substituted D-mannosylamine

deoxyketose compounds. Unfortunately, Täufel and coworkers did not give R_f values for their additional spot.

A direct comparison has been made of the amount of brown color produced by Amadori products alone and that caused by a mixture of sugar and amino acid.[264a] Three Amadori products were prepared—from D-glucose with glycine, L-alanine, or DL-phenylalanine. The amount of browning (measured at 500 mμ) caused when these three compounds were heated at 93° in phosphate buffer (at pH 6.8) was much greater than that arising from the corresponding mixture of D-glucose and amino acid. But paper chromatography, chemical tests, and ultraviolet spectroscopy showed the presence of Amadori products in the mixture of D-glucose and amino acid after heating for up to 165 minutes. However, the shapes of the graphs of absorbance with time, for the browning of the Amadori products, suggest that noncolored products may also be formed.

Hodge[7] has advanced several possible routes for the conversion of the enol form of the 1-amino-1-deoxy-2-ketose into melanoidin, and the evidence to support these mechanisms is considerable. Thus, the enol may be converted into the Schiff base of a furaldehyde, or to a reductone by loss of water. It may also be broken down into smaller fragments (for example, hydroxy-2-propanone or pyruvaldehyde), which react further with amino compounds. The enol may also react with an α-amino acid and be converted to an aldehyde by a Strecker degradation. The compounds thus formed from

(264a) P. Nordin and Y. S. Kim, *J. Agr. Food Chem.*, **6**, 765 (1958).

the enol would be reactive and could react with amines[114] to form polymers containing nitrogen.

Fluorescence has frequently been observed in sugar–amine reaction mixtures, but the compound responsible for this property has not been definitely identified. D-Glucose is essential for the formation of the fluorogen in dried-egg powder,[158] but fluorescence can also arise from the reaction of certain amino acids with paraformaldehyde in concentrated sulfuric acid.[265] Of a large number of amino acids studied, only tyrosine, phenylalanine, and tryptophan gave the blue fluorescence in this way. Investigations on the rate of development of color and of fluorescence in moist D-glucose–glycine mixtures at 50° showed that they proceed at the *same* rate. A further correlation of fluorescence with both browning and decrease in amino-nitrogen

TABLE X

Development of Color and Fluorescence as a Function of Time[180]

	Absorbance at 385 mμ				Fluorescence			
	Time (mins.)							
	0	30	60	120	0	30	60	120
Glycine	0.022	0.022	0.027	0.036	16	20	24	28
D-Glucose	0.029	0.013	0.018	0.036	12	12	12	20
D-Glucose + glycine	0.017	0.446	1.28	opaque	16	120	40	16
D-Glucose + glycine + NaHSO₃	0.004	0.112	0.180	0.319	16	72	144	172

content was found during the autoclaving of methionine in the presence of D-glucose and a small proportion of water.[164] Many other amino acids gave the same result.

Fluorescent compounds are formed in more dilute solutions of sugars with amino acids. Thus, refluxing of solutions (0.1 M or M) of D-glucose–glycine, followed by paper chromatography of the solution after various time-intervals, showed the presence of several fluorescent bands whose R_f values ranged[77, 190] from 0.07 to 0.91. Another significant observation was that, after an initial induction-period, maximum fluorescence was attained after 48 to 72 hours of refluxing, and fluorescence then decreased. The fluorogens were colorless and were believed to be precursors of brown pigments.[77, 180, 190] Furthermore, fluorescence has been observed when browning is inhibited by sodium bisulfite, and, therefore, the absence of browning does not ensure inhibition of the Maillard reaction.[29] When 0.02 %

(265) J. L. Chen, J. D. Medler and R. A. Harte, *J. Am. Chem. Soc.*, **70**, 3145 (1948).

of sodium hydrosulfite was added to a fibrin hydrolyzate–D-glucose solution, fluorescence was more intense, reached a maximum, and then began to decrease before browning became appreciable.[180] Similar effects were observed with an aqueous D-glucose–glycine system. Table X shows the relative rates of production of color and of fluorescence for 0.25 M solutions of D-glucose plus glycine heated at 121°, with and without 0.05 % of sodium sulfite.

The presence of bisulfite (1.5 %) not only retards browning but promotes the accumulation of fluorescent compounds in a mixture of an amino acid and D-xylose. Shore and Pardee[266] made use of this fact in their semiquantitative, chromatographic method of estimating amino acids. The chromatogram was sprayed with D-xylose solution and heated. A spectrophotometer fitted with a filter which absorbed the exciting light and transmitted rays above 400 mμ was then used for measuring the amount of fluorescence. D-Xylose produced more than twice as much fluorescence as D-glucose, but 2-furaldehyde gave no fluorescent compounds with amino acids. The pH also had an effect on the fluorescence, a pH value of 6 to 8 giving the best compromise between the weak fluorescence shown below pH 6 and the increased browning which occurred above pH 8. A lower concentration (either of D-glucose or of glycine) resulted in a decrease in the rate of production of fluorogens. The sensitivity of this rate (to pH) was similar to that of other manifestations of the Maillard reaction. For example, between pH 4 and 6, little change in the rate occurred, whereas, above pH 6, fluorescence increased with the alkalinity. The effect was more pronounced at 49° and 60° than at lower temperatures.[267] Moisture content also seems to have an effect on the production of fluorogens. The time taken to reach a certain fluorescence value for the D-glucose–glycine reaction at 49° changed throughout the range of relative humidity, but was a minimum at 100 % relative humidity (which corresponds to a moisture content of about 30 %).[268] The reaction of D-glucose with N^2-acetyl-L-lysine, at 37° and pH 6.5, did not result in the formation of fluorescent compounds when the relative humidity was 20 %, but, at 30 %, a spot which gave a bright purple fluorescence under ultraviolet light was found on the chromatogram. Elution of this spot gave a material which had an absorption peak at 288 mμ and which reduced ammoniacal silver nitrate and ferricyanide[161] at pH 5.

The presence in Nature of D-glucosamine (a substituted aldohexose) prompted Lea, Rhodes, and Borrell[269] to investigate its behavior toward proteins. A mixture of these reactants (at pH 6.3, a temperature of 37°,

(266) V. G. Shore and A. B. Pardee, *Anal. Chem.*, **28**, 1479 (1956).

(267) J. A. Pearce, *Food Technol.*, **4**, 416 (1950).

(268) J. A. Pearce, *Ind. Eng. Chem.*, **41**, 1514 (1949).

(269) C. H. Lea, D. N. Rhodes and S. Borrell, *Nature*, **169**, 1097 (1952).

and a relative humidity of 70%) underwent rapid and intense browning with accompanying disappearance both of the aldehyde and the amino groups, but the reaction was not of the usual aldehyde–amine type, and presumably the Amadori rearrangement could not occur. An acid was released and the pH decreased. The same kind of reaction occurs at higher temperatures and is accompanied by release of small proportions of ammonia and formic acid.[270] A dark-brown, insoluble melanoidin is formed on prolonged heating, but among the compounds identified chromatographically and by ultraviolet spectroscopy (at the intermediate stage of the reaction) were 2-furaldehyde, 5-(hydroxymethyl)-2-furaldehyde, some fluorescent compounds, and compounds which reacted with ninhydrin, aniline hydrogen phthalate, and 2,6-dichlorophenolindophenol.

A different view of the browning of sugars was taken by Schroeder, Iacobellis, and Smith[148] as a result of their work on the autoclaving of amino acids, with and without D-glucose. As mentioned earlier (see Section V,3), they were able to distinguish between the Maillard reaction and the browning of the sugar. Such browning can occur at various pH values (compare Reference 172) and in the absence of amino acids, whereas the Maillard reaction occurs only in an alkaline medium and in the presence of amino acids. Analytical and chromatographic methods show that, when D-glucose and an excess of amino acid are heated together in the dry state, there is a decrease in the content of amino nitrogen, a reduction in the amount of amino acid present, and a complete disappearance of the sugar. When the same reactions were conducted in the presence of moisture, there was no decrease in amino nitrogen, and ninhydrin-sprayed chromatograms showed spots having R_f values identical with those of the amino acids. Chromatograms sprayed with aniline hydrogen phthalate gave a spot (of R_f 0.39) similar to that of unautoclaved D-glucose solution, but, when the mixture was heated in the presence of water, this spot was very weak, indicating the very small amount of unchanged D-glucose remaining. Autoclaving a D-glucose–amino acid mixture in a non-alkaline medium produced browning at the same rate and to the same extent as that of D-glucose alone at the same pH. The amino-nitrogen content did not change on heating such mixtures, and ninhydrin showed one spot (on the chromatogram) having the same R_f value as the amino acid. There was a decrease in pH, however, and a decrease in the amount of D-glucose present. In an alkaline medium, both browning and the Maillard reaction occurred, the latter being indicated by a decrease in amino nitrogen and the appearance of an extra spot on the chromatograms developed with ninhydrin. From these observations, the conclusion was drawn that the mechanism of browning is the same at all pH values and is independent of the Maillard reaction.

(270) T. V. Drozdova, *Biokhimiya*, **22**, 487 (1957); *Chem. Abstracts*, **52**, 2119 (1958).

Kato's criticism[160] of the work just discussed, on the grounds that the aqueous solutions used were too dilute, does not seem justified. The concentration of a typical sugar–amino acid mixture containing water appears to have been 10 millimoles and 50 millimoles, respectively, in 25 ml. of water —that is, 0.4 M and 2 M, respectively. There is evidence, however, that the concentration of the amino acid has an effect on the intensity of the reaction.[81, 211]

In an attempt to identify the reaction products formed when mixtures of D-glucose and individual amino acids are autoclaved, Iacobellis[152] chromatographically studied such products obtained under various conditions. The chromatograms were treated with ninhydrin, and the spots were identified by chromatographing the reaction mixture with known synthetic compounds and by isolating derivatives of the products. The samples of glycine or of glycine plus D-glucose at acid pH values, whether autoclaved or not, gave only one ninhydrin-positive spot, which corresponded to glycine (R_f 0.39). When the mixture was autoclaved at pH 9.7, two spots were obtained, one corresponding to glycine and the other having R_f about 0.19. Synthetic D-gluconylglycine gave a spot of this R_f value, both by itself and when chromatographed with the autoclaved product. Similar correlations were established for D-gluconyl-L-leucine and D-gluconyl-D-glutamic acid. Color development at any one pH value was identical, no matter whether D-glucose was autoclaved by itself or with an amino acid, and chromatography showed D-glucose spots of a size which decreased as the pH was increased. Browning is, therefore, a consequence of the effect of pH on the sugar, which is converted into acidic intermediates which lack an aldehyde group.

Several physicochemical studies of the Maillard reaction have recently been published and, within the limitations imposed and the assumptions made by the various workers, these studies have elucidated the initial stages of the reaction. Because of the complexity of the subsequent stages, no such studies have yet been made for them. Earlier papers on the kinetics of the reaction have already been mentioned (see Section V,2 and 3). Some of them are contradictory, and others involve factors which could not exist in Nature or which would tend to alter the conditions of the reactions. A new method (of so studying the reaction as to eliminate at least *some* of these objections) was described by Haugaard, Tumerman, and Silvestri,[108] who later extended it to the reaction of D-glucose with peptides.[147] A saturated solution of the amino acid (in equilibrium with an excess of amino acid crystals) is made. The nitrogen content of the filtered solution, determined by the Kjeldahl method, remains constant until the aldose is added to the amino acid solution, at which time some of the latter reacts with sugar and the equilibrium changes, with the result that more amino acid crystals are dissolved. If the soluble nitrogen is now determined, the increase will be a measure of the reaction between the sugar and the amino acid. For this method to succeed, it is necessary for the amino acid solution to regain its saturated state within a reasonable time, throughout the experiment. Vigorous stirring was maintained for this purpose. Moreover, the method would be best suited to a slightly soluble amino acid, since readily measurable differences in soluble nitrogen would then be obtained. The method has been successfully used with DL-leucine and L-valine. The assumption was made that the sugar and the amino acid reacted in equimolar ratio, as shown in the following equation. Although the primary prod-

$$RCHO + H_2NR' \rightleftharpoons RCHNR' + H_2O$$

uct was called a Schiff base, the kinetic method used is independent of the

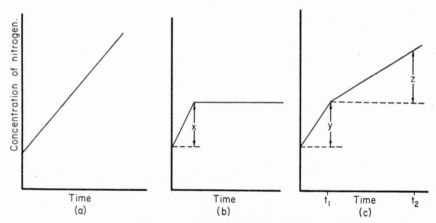

Fig. 10.—Graphs of Nitrogen Concentration–Time for the Reaction of a Sugar with an Amino Acid.[108] (Where x is the amount of Schiff base present at equilibrium; y is the amount of Schiff base present at the stationary state; z is the amount of nitrogen-containing degradation products formed between time t_1 and t_2.)

structure of the product. As it is known that the initial stages of the reaction of a sugar with various amino compounds are reversible,[16, 141] three possible courses for the reaction must be considered: (a) the Schiff base is a very stable compound, or it decomposes to compounds other than the original amino acid; (b) the Schiff base decomposes reversibly, or into the amino acid plus carbohydrate degradation-products; (c) the Schiff base decomposes into various compounds, some of which contain nitrogen. These three possibilities will be apparent in the plots of nitrogen concentration–time, as shown in Fig. 10(a), (b), and (c), respectively.

The following three equations are theoretically derived and express three reaction-constants in terms of the slopes of the above graphs and of the concentration of amino acid (C_A), of aldose (C_C), and of Schiff base at the stationary state (C_S).

$$K_1 = \frac{\text{Slope 1}}{C_A \cdot C_C}$$

where K_1 is the reaction constant for the formation of Schiff base.

$$K_2 = \frac{\text{Slope 1} - \text{Slope 2}}{C_S}$$

where K_2 is the constant for the decomposition of the Schiff base, reversible with respect to the amino acid.

$$K_3 = \frac{\text{Slope 2}}{C_S}$$

where K_3 is the constant for the irreversible decomposition of the Schiff base.

The systems studied by this method were DL-leucine–D-glucose at pH 8.65, 9.2, or 9.5, and a temperature of 0°, 23.9°, or 40°; D-glucose with (a) DL-valine and (b) L-leucine, DL-leucine with (a) L-arabinose and (b) 2,3-di-O-methyl-D-glucose, and L-valine with lactose, all at pH 9.2 and 23.9°. The values of K_1 at 23.9° and pH 9.2 ranged between 0.78×10^{-6} and 4.25×10^{-6}, whereas at 40° it was 11.40×10^{-6} for D-glucose and DL-leucine. D-Glucose and valine gave the highest value and 2,3-di-O-methyl-D-glucose and leucine the lowest. The values of K_2 and K_3 were considerably greater than K_1, except for the 2,3-di-O-methyl-D-glucose–leucine system, for which K_3 was zero. The next lowest values of K_3 were given by the lactose and L-arabinose mixtures mentioned. These figures show that the irreversible decomposition of the Schiff base is blocked by the presence of the 2,3-di-O-methyl groups, and, as these are known to resist enolization of the sugar chain, the significance of the results is obvious.[102, 271-273] The low value of K_3 for the lactose–valine system may possibly be explained by the inability of a disaccharide derivative to undergo an Amadori rearrangement, but this is not likely to be the correct answer, since a lactosylamine has recently been shown to rearrange readily in this way.[274]

Haugaard, Tumerman, and Silvestri[108] also investigated the reaction of D-glucose with glycine in aqueous solution at reflux temperature and measured, at intervals, the absorption (at 490 mμ) of the reaction mixture. The

(271) M. L. Wolfrom and W. L. Lewis, *J. Am. Chem. Soc.*, **50**, 837 (1928).
(272) R. D. Greene and W. L. Lewis, *J. Am. Chem. Soc.*, **50**, 2813 (1928).
(273) D. J. Loder and W. L. Lewis, *J. Am. Chem. Soc.*, **54**, 1040 (1932).
(274) S. Adachi, *Chem. & Ind.* (London), 956 (1957).

rate of coloration is at first very low, but it later increases considerably. This initial lack of browning has been explained by presuming the absence of one of the intermediates necessary for the coloration[107] and, from mathematical considerations (using arguments discussed in their paper), the

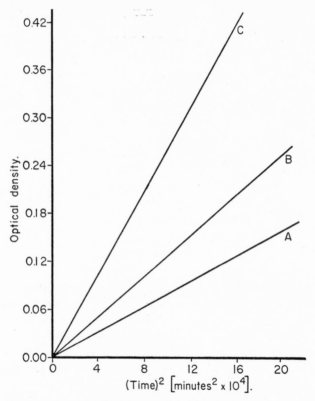

FIG. 11.—The Development of Brown Color in Relation to Time, in the Reaction Between D-Glucose and Glycine in Aqueous Solution[104] at 100°. [Curve A: mixture of D-glucose (9 g.) and glycine (1.5 g.) in water (100 ml.). Curve B: mixture of D-glucose (18 g.) and glycine (1.5 g.) in water (100 ml.). Curve C: mixture of D-glucose (9.g.) and glycine (3 g.) in water (100 ml.).]

authors deduced that the concentration of the brown compound B (C_B) is proportional to the product of the square of the time, the square of the concentration of amino acid, and the concentration of the sugar. The last two terms may be considered as constant in this experiment as they were both large. Thus, we have the following.

$$C_B = k \times C^2_A \times C_C \times t^2$$

$$= k' \times t^2$$

Confirmation of the theory is given by the straight-line plots of the logarithm of the extinction coefficient against the square of the time. This result was subsequently arrived at by Nomura and Kawano[104] from their work on the interaction of D-glucose and glycine at 100°, and was found to be true when the molecular proportions of the reactants and their concentrations were varied (see Fig. 11). The conclusions drawn (from this work[108]) regarding the effect of temperature and pH on the reaction have already been mentioned (Section V,2 and 3).

The interaction of a sugar and an amino acid results in a fall in pH as the amino groups disappear. By following this pH depression potentiometrically, it is possible to measure the rate of reaction. An extension of this method (which also incorporates a new theoretical treatment) has made possible the calculation of (a) rate constants which are independent of pH and concentration, and (b) the energy of activation of several sugar–amino acid systems.[136] Earlier work[82, 275] on the kinetics of glycosylamine formation[119-121] had shown that the reaction occurs between the negative amino acid ion ($R^{\ominus}$) and D-glucose. The amount of $R^{\ominus}$ present depends on the equilibrium $HR \rightleftharpoons H^{\oplus} + R^{\ominus}$, for which

$$K_A = \frac{H^{\oplus} \cdot R^{\ominus}}{HR},$$

and the extent to which it reacts with aldoses will depend on the pH. The various equilibria will then be as follows.

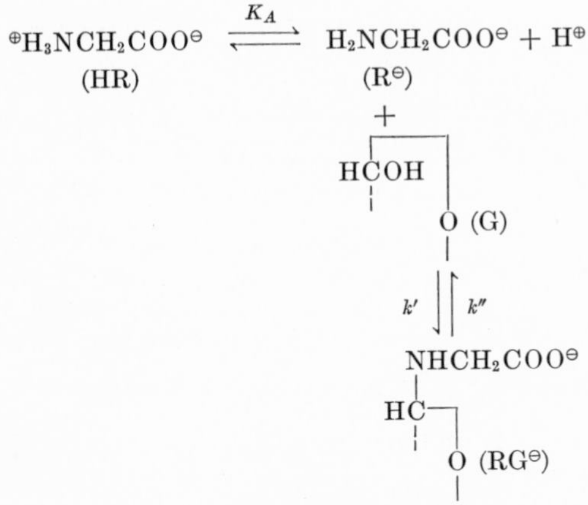

$$\overset{\oplus}{H_3}NCH_2COO^{\ominus} \xrightleftharpoons{K_A} H_2NCH_2COO^{\ominus} + H^{\oplus}$$

(HR) (R$^{\ominus}$)

$$+$$

$$HCOH$$

$$O \text{ (G)}$$

$$k' \Big\Vert k''$$

$$NHCH_2COO^{\ominus}$$

$$HC$$

$$O \text{ (RG}^{\ominus}\text{)}$$

The equilibrium constant, L, is therefore given by

$$L = \frac{RG^{\ominus}}{R^{\ominus} \cdot G} = \frac{k'}{k''}.$$

The rate-determining steps were (a) the nucleophilic attack of the free

(275) H. L. Frush and H. S. Isbell, *J. Research Natl. Bur. Standards*, **47**, 239 (1951).

amino group of the amino acid anion ($R^{\ominus}$) on the oxonium ion ($GH^{\oplus}$), and (b) the formation of the Schiff-base ion by the ionization of the amino group of the reaction product $RG^{\ominus}$, with the opening of the ring in reaction -4 (the reverse of reaction 4). The rate constants are calculated from

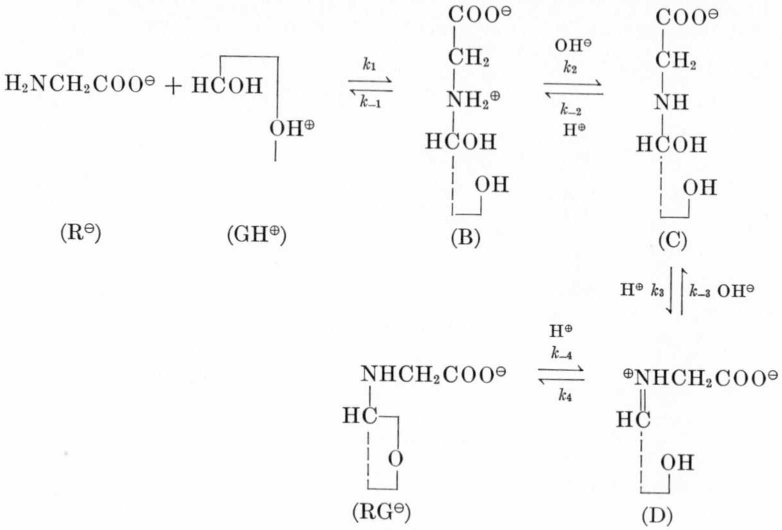

$$
H_2NCH_2COO^{\ominus} + H\overset{|}{C}OH \underset{OH^{\oplus}}{\Big|} \underset{k_{-1}}{\overset{k_1}{\rightleftharpoons}}
\begin{matrix} COO^{\ominus} \\ | \\ CH_2 \\ | \\ NH_2^{\oplus} \\ | \\ H\overset{|}{C}OH \\ |\_\_\_| \quad OH \end{matrix}
\underset{\substack{k_{-2} \\ H^{\oplus}}}{\overset{\substack{OH^{\ominus} \\ k_2}}{\rightleftharpoons}}
\begin{matrix} COO^{\ominus} \\ | \\ CH_2 \\ | \\ NH \\ | \\ H\overset{|}{C}OH \\ |\_\_\_| \quad OH \end{matrix}
$$

$(R^{\ominus})$ $(GH^{\oplus})$ (B)   (C)

$$H^{\oplus} \, k_3 \Big\updownarrow k_{-3} \, OH^{\ominus}$$

$$
\begin{matrix} NHCH_2COO^{\ominus} \\ | \\ H\overset{|}{C}\text{---} \\ \,\_\_\_|\; O \end{matrix}
\underset{k_4}{\overset{\substack{H^{\oplus} \\ k_{-4}}}{\rightleftharpoons}}
\begin{matrix} {}^{\oplus}NHCH_2COO^{\ominus} \\ \| \\ H\overset{|}{C} \\ |\_\_\_|\; OH \end{matrix}
$$

$(RG^{\ominus})$ (D)

the amount of alkali required in order to maintain the pH constant at its initial value. At zero time ($t = 0$), a quantity b_0 of alkali is required, and, after time t, a further addition of alkali Δb, will have been necessary to maintain the pH. At equilibrium, after time t_∞, the final concentration of alkali is b_∞. Katchalsky and Sharon, after making certain limitations that simplify the experiment, deduced theoretically that

$$k' = \frac{L \cdot b_\infty}{A \cdot t \cdot b_0} \cdot \ln \frac{b_\infty - b_0}{b_\infty - b},$$

where A is a constant.

$$k'' = \frac{b_\infty}{A \cdot t \cdot b_0} \cdot \ln \frac{b_\infty - b_0}{b_\infty - b}$$

Now, since $b = b_0 - \Delta b$ and $b_\infty = b_0 + \Delta b_\infty$,

$$k' = \frac{L \cdot b_\infty}{A \cdot t \cdot b_0} \cdot \ln \frac{\Delta b_\infty}{\Delta b_\infty - \Delta b}.$$

Experimental results with D-glucose and glycine, at 25° and pH 7.55, gave a straight-line plot of

$$\ln \frac{\Delta b_\infty}{\Delta b_\infty - \Delta b}$$

against time. From the slope of the line (and from other data), it was possible to calculate the other unknowns, including k'. The observed rate constants k' and k'' were shown to be *independent* of concentration but *dependent* on initial pH. By plotting the reciprocal of k' against the concentration of hydroxyl ion, however, they obtained a straight line whose intercept and slope give rate constants k_α and k_β which are independent of pH. The validity of the reasoning is shown by the straight-line plots obtained for various sugar–amino acid systems, one system being studied at various temperatures from 25° to 45° and at initial pH values from 7.11 to 8.79 (see Section V,2 and 3).

Katchalsky and Sharon's assumption that one molecule of D-glucose reacts with one molecule of the valine anion has been questioned by Lewin and Fox,[183] who claim that data obtained in a study of the glutamic acid–D-glucose reaction cannot be explained by the above scheme. A thorough study is, however, necessary before comparisons can be made between the mechanism of action of an amino dicarboxylic acid and an amino monocarboxylic acid. Lewin[137] has also used the potentiometric method for studying the reaction of D-glucose with L-histidine at temperatures between 20° and 50° and over a pH range 5 to 9. On the whole, pH depression did not vary with changing concentration of histidine at constant D-glucose concentration, except for a slight increase in ΔpH at 30° and 40° as the amino acid concentration was decreased. The equilibrium constant for the first steady-pH state decreased as the temperature was raised, and this indicated that the reaction is exothermic. Up to the end of the first steady-state, there was no difference between the results of aerobic and anaerobic experiments, but, subsequently, ΔpH was greater under aerobic conditions. This suggests that one (or more) of the products of the initial stage of the reaction is sensitive to aerial oxidation and that the oxidation products are acidic. That this oxidation is variable in speed (and, possibly, in character) is shown by the poorer reproducibility of the aerobic as compared with the anaerobic experiments. Browning of the solutions first appeared at the end of the second steady-pH state. Results which are generally of the same type were obtained when histidine was replaced by either glycine or DL-α-alanine.[85] There was some evidence of the formation of a 1:2 amino acid–glucose product, and, at higher temperatures (40° and 50°), the equilibrium constant for such a reaction, being almost independent of temperature, became significant in relation to that of the uni-(D-glucose) reaction.

IX. Summary and Conclusions

Results of the many investigations into the mechanism of the Maillard reaction support one of two main theories. The first assumes the formation of glycosylamines which undergo the Amadori (or, for ketoses, the Heyns) rearrangement. The 1-amino-1-deoxyketose derivative (or 2-amino-2-deoxyaldose derivative) formed may be dehydrated and cyclized to form furan derivatives, or it may enolize. In either case, intermediates which are readily transformed into brown compounds are formed. A third possibility is for the deoxy sugar derivative to react with more amino acid to form colored products. The many workers who have supported this mechanism found also that optimum conditions for occurrence of the Maillard reaction are (a) a fairly low water content, (b) a pH of 7 to 10, and (c) a high temperature. Nevertheless, some reaction occurs under conditions far removed from these, but *in the absence of moisture* there is no reaction. The formation of an acyclic Schiff base as an initial step is not very likely, since replacement of the aldose by salicylaldehyde caused only a very small loss of amino groups.[123]

The second theory of the mechanism of the browning reaction is of recent origin[148] and maintains that the browning reaction and the Maillard reaction are separate and distinct. Browning, according to this school of thought, is due to the effect of pH on the sugar and can occur over a wide range of pH, whereas the Maillard reaction proceeds only in alkaline media. When sugars plus amino acids were heated in the absence of added buffers, there was *no decrease in amino nitrogen unless the reaction was carried out in the dry state*. In alkaline buffers, on the other hand, pH depression, decrease in content of amino nitrogen, and the appearance of color (and of an extra spot on the chromatogram) showed that browning *and* the Maillard reaction proceeded simultaneously. The reaction products in these experiments were shown to be glyconyl-amino acids[152] (which had never before been identified as products of this type of reaction). These investigations need to be extended to include other amino acids—such as L-lysine, which causes intense browning.[153] It would be interesting to know whether this browning is accompanied by comparably high intensity of reaction. Evidence does exist to suggest that browning and disappearance of amino group do not always run parallel.[172] All experiments whose results supported glyconyl-amino acid formation were performed at 120° under pressure, whereas much of the evidence for the Amadori-rearrangement mechanism comes from experiments conducted at lower temperatures and atmospheric pressure. Both mechanisms result in the formation of water, a fact which may be significant when "dry-state" reactions are considered.

Generalizations regarding the Maillard reaction cannot be made, because of the variation in the behavior of different amino acids[77, 156] and because of the profound effects of comparatively small changes in experimental conditions. That less than one part per million of metallic iron can have a measurable inhibiting effect shows the high sensitivity of the reaction.[167] The study of browning in natural systems is further complicated by the high degree of coloring which is produced by *other* compounds which may be present, for example, uronic acids (see Fig. 9),[129, 139, 201, 276, 277] L-ascorbic acid,[11, 230, 276, 278-282a] and other non-nitrogenous carboxylic acids,[283-285] polyphenols,[286] proteins[170, 280, 287, 288] and their hydrolysis products,[289-291] and other compounds.[7, 292-298] Comparatively small changes in the reactants or in the reaction conditions suffice to alter the course of the Maillard reaction, with the result that the melanoidin formed varies with the conditions.[248] Another problem which should not be underestimated is that of accurately determining the extent of the reaction. The formation of copper complexes

(276) J. L. Seaver and Z. I. Kertesz, *J. Am. Chem. Soc.*, **68**, 2178 (1946).

(277) V. A. Haas and E. R. Stadtman, *Ind. Eng. Chem.*, **41**, 983 (1949).

(278) A. Bloch, *Science*, **102**, 209 (1945).

(279) T. Koppanyi, A. E. Vivino and F. P. Veitch, Jr., *Science*, **101**, 541 (1945).

(280) J. B. Thompson, R. B. Kocher and H. W. Fritsche, *Arch. Biochem.*, **18**, 41 (1948).

(281) D. Nomura, *Hakkô Kôgaku Zasshi*, **34**, 317 (1955).

(282) M. A. Joslyn, *Food Research*, **22**, 1 (1957).

(282a) T. Lalikainen, M. A. Joslyn and C. O. Chichester, *J. Agr. Food Chem.*, **6**, 135 (1958).

(283) V. M. Lewis, W. B. Esselen, Jr., and C. R. Fellers, *Ind. Eng. Chem.*, **41**, 2591 (1949).

(284) D. Nomura, *Nippon Nôgei-kagaku Kaishi*, **28**, 923 (1954); *Chem. Abstracts*, **50**, 7343 (1956).

(285) A. Carreras Ledon and J. C. Pita Larrañeta, *Bol. ofic. asoc. téc. azucar.* (Cuba), **8**, 457 (1949–50); *Chem. Abstracts*, **47**, 11775 (1953); *Bol. ofic. asoc. téc. azucar.* (Cuba), **10**, 11 (1951–52); *Chem. Abstracts*, **47**, 12849 (1953).

(286) H. Rinderknecht and L. Jurd, *Nature*, **181**, 1269 (1958).

(287) A. R. Patton, E. G. Hill and E. M. Foreman, *Science*, **107**, 623 (1948).

(288) C. H. Lea, R. S. Hannan and R. I. N. Greaves, *Biochem. J.*, **47**, 626 (1950).

(289) F. Samuely, *Beitr. chem. Physiol. Path.*, **2**, 355 (1902).

(290) L. C. Maillard, *Compt. rend.*, **156**, 1159 (1913).

(291) L. Y. Auerman, V. L. Kretovich, E. A. Alyakrinskaya, V. M. Bazarnova and R. R. Tokareva, *Doklady Akad. Nauk S. S. S. R.*, **92**, 131 (1953); *Chem. Abstracts*, **48**, 898 (1954).

(292) S. M. Manskaya, T. V. Drozdova and K. I. Tobelko, *Doklady Akad. Nauk S. S. S. R.*, **96**, 569 (1954); *Chem. Abstracts*, **48**, 13755 (1954).

(293) F. Micheel and W. Langsfeld, *Chem. Ber.*, **89**, 1246 (1956).

(294) S. Adachi, *Tôhoku J. Agr. Research*, **4**, 167 (1954).

(295) S. Adachi, *Nippon Nôgei-kagaku Kaishi*, **30**, 92, 372 (1956).

(296) S. Adachi, *Nippon Nôgei-kagaku Kaishi*, **30**, 378, 709, 713 (1956).

(297) S. Adachi, *Nature*, **177**, 936 (1956).

(298) S. Adachi, *Nature*, **178**, 1055 (1956).

does not seem to be satisfactory for estimating amino acids,[105, 174] although a recent modification is claimed to give good results.[299] Moreover, the use of ninhydrin for the chromatographic identification of amino acids has been shown to be susceptible to the presence of reducing sugars and to traces of ammonia in the atmosphere.[300]

In spite of the enormous amount of work already done and the many difficulties which beset the researcher, the widespread occurrence of the Maillard reaction and the possibility of applying it to advantage[301-304] justify further study of the fundamental chemical transformations which take place.

(299) A. Cherkin, H. Wolkowitz and M. S. Dunn, *Anal. Chem.*, **28,** 895 (1956).
(300) W. Klinger, *Naturwissenschaften*, **42,** 645 (1955).
(301) C. Franzke and H. Iwainsky, *Deut. Lebensm.-Rundschau*, **50,** 251 (1954).
(302) H. Iwainsky, *Deut. Lebensm.-Rundschau*, **50,** 300 (1954).
(303) H. Iwainsky and C. Franzke, *Deut. Lebensm.-Rundschau*, **52,** 129 (1956).
(304) F. Knorr, *Brauwissenschaft*, **11,** 28 (1958).

THE CYCLITOLS

By S. J. Angyal and Laurens Anderson

School of Chemistry, University of New South Wales, Sydney, Australia

Department of Biochemistry, University of Wisconsin, Madison, Wisconsin

I. INTRODUCTION

The chemistry of the cyclitols (a group of compounds which includes the inositols, quercitols, inosamines, and their derivatives) has undergone considerable expansion since 1948, when Fletcher's excellent review[1] appeared in this Series. The most important developments have been: the synthesis of all hitherto unknown inositol diastereomers; the total synthesis, and the synthesis from D-glucose, of myo-inositol, both of which procedures have been used for the preparation of C^{14}-labeled inositol; the discovery of four new inositol methyl ethers in plants, and the determination of the constitutions of all the naturally occurring methyl ethers; the development of methods for the preparation of partially substituted inositols; and the discovery of inosamines in Nature. Most of the immediate problems in the chemistry of the cyclitols appear to have been solved; a sound foundation has thereby been built for biochemical investigations which have gained impetus and have yielded important results in recent years. The time therefore appears appropriate for another comprehensive review.[2]

The present review is to be regarded as a continuation of Fletcher's article[1]; the facts described therein will not be repeated here unless required for the understanding of recent developments. Because of the considerable expansion of cyclitol chemistry, it is not practicable to cover, as Fletcher did, all compounds of the cyclitol group. Only the inositols, the quercitols, and the inosamines, their derivatives, and some closely related compounds will be discussed; the tetrahydroxycyclo-hexanes and -hexenes, and quinic and shikimic acids—on which subjects many important papers have appeared—are not reviewed here.[3]

1. Nomenclature

The nomenclature of the cyclitols is in a confused state. The peculiar problems associated with the naming and numbering of polysubstituted

(1) H. G. Fletcher, Jr., Advances in Carbohydrate Chem., 3, 45 (1948).

(2) Other recent reviews: (a) G. Dangschat, in "Modern Methods of Plant Analysis," K. Paech and M. V. Tracey, eds., Springer, Berlin, 1955, Vol. 2, p. 64; (b) S. J. Angyal, Quart. Revs. (London), 11, 212 (1957); (c) R. L. Lohmar, Jr., in "The Carbohydrates," W. Pigman, ed., Academic Press Inc., New York, N. Y., 1957, p. 241; (d) G. Dangschat, in "Encyclopedia of Plant Physiology," W. Ruhland, ed., Springer, Berlin, 1957, Vol. 6, p. 363 (occurrence in plants); (e) C. E. Ballou, ibid., Vol. 10, p. 442 (metabolism in plants); (f) "The Vitamins," W. H. Sebrell, Jr., and R. S. Harris, eds., Academic Press Inc., New York, N. Y., 1954, Vol. 2, p. 321 (biochemistry).

(3) It is desirable to point out that the constitution assigned to "tetrahydroxymannocyclitol" (LIV in Ref. 1, p. 68) is no longer accepted, since a compound of that structure and configuration has been synthesized (see Ref. 4) and found to have different physical properties; the structure of "tetrahydroxymannocyclitol" is, therefore, regarded as still unknown.

(4) S. J. Angyal and P. T. Gilham, J. Chem. Soc., 375 (1958).

cyclic systems are not adequately catered for by the internationally recognized rules of nomenclature. Many authors therefore improvised names and numbering rules in their papers to cover their immediate needs until, in the early fifties, two comprehensive systems were proposed to cover all aspects of cyclitol nomenclature: one by Fletcher, Anderson, and Lardy[5] and the other by Angyal and coworkers.[6, 7] The two systems are based on similar principles but differ in details; hence, a compound may have a different name and different numbering in each system. At present, the system of Fletcher, Anderson, and Lardy is used mostly in America, and the one of Angyal and coworkers in Great Britain; however, some important workers in the field, for example, Posternak and McCasland, continue to use their *own* nomenclatures. Neither system has the sanction of any official body.

Under these circumstances, the reviewers make a strong plea to end the confusion by universal adoption of one system of nomenclature. In the meantime, an attempt will be made in this article to avoid the difficulties as far as possible; this is, of course, easier in a review than in original papers. The Fletcher–Anderson–Lardy and the Angyal systems will *both* be used, as set out in the following paragraphs.

a. Naming.—All the cyclohexane*hexols* are called *inositols* and are differentiated from each other by trivial prefixes, as shown in formulas I to IX.[8] To conform with this practice, scyllitol is referred to as *scyllo*-inositol,[6] and the trivial name *meso*-inositol—which is singularly inappropriate, inasmuch as six of its diastereomers are also *meso* forms—has been changed to *myo*-inositol.[5] The same prefixes (Fletcher–Anderson–Lardy) are used in naming derivatives, such as deoxyhalogenoinositols and inosamines, in which one or more hydroxyl groups of an inositol have been replaced by other groups. No trivial prefixes are given to the asymmetric inositols, since there exists only one pair of them; the terms *dextro*, *levo*, and *rac* suffice to describe them.

According to the Angyal proposals, the cyclohexane*pentols* are all called *quercitols*, and these compounds, like the pentahydroxycyclohexanones (*inososes*), are differentiated by trivial prefixes, the same prefix being used for the quercitol and the inosose of the same configuration. These prefixes are shown under the formulas CXXXIX–CXLIV (see p. 190). In the Fletcher–Anderson–Lardy system, these compounds are named as deoxy and keto derivatives, respectively, of inositols. The Angyal names will be

(5) H. G. Fletcher, Jr., L. Anderson and H. A. Lardy, *J. Org. Chem.*, **16,** 1238 (1951).

(6) S. J. Angyal and C. G. Macdonald, *J. Chem. Soc.*, 686 (1952).

(7) S. J. Angyal and P. T. Gilham, *J. Chem. Soc.*, 3691 (1957).

(8) The carbon-bound hydrogen atoms have been omitted for clarity throughout this review.

used in this review, with the Fletcher–Anderson–Lardy names given in parentheses at the first mention and also in the Tables.

I
cis

II
epi

III
allo

IV
neo

V
myo

VI
muco

VII
scyllo

VIII
dextro

IX
levo

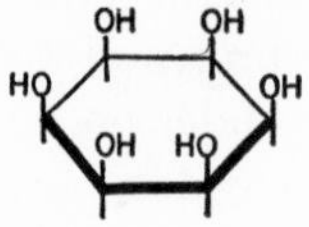

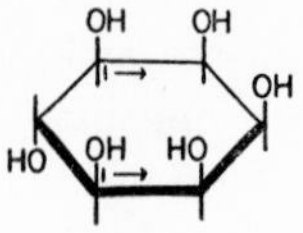

b. Numbering.—In the Angyal system, all cyclitols are numbered according to the following rule. *The larger number of functional groups on one side of the cyclohexane ring shall be described by the lowest possible numbers.* Although it is not stated explicitly, this same rule is used in the Fletcher–Anderson–Lardy system, except as applied to the active inositols. If a hydroxyl group is substituted, or replaced by another group, and if the rule has not determined the numbering unequivocally (as in asymmetrically substituted derivatives of *meso* compounds), this substituted position is given the lowest number in *both* systems. In both systems, equivalent positions in enantiomorphs carry the same number.

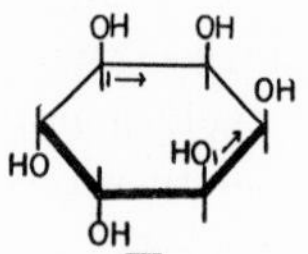

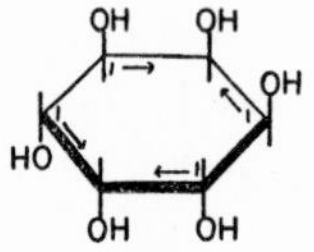

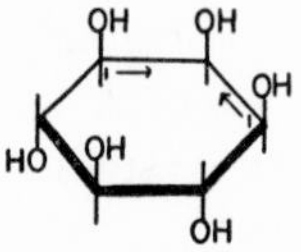

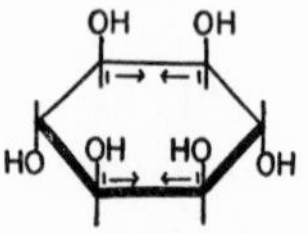

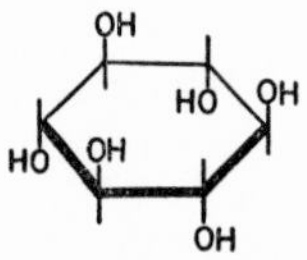

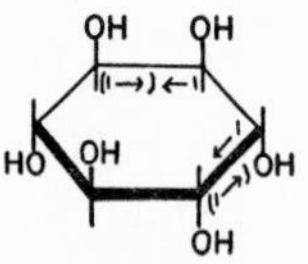

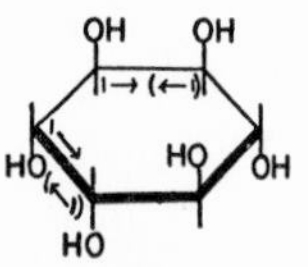

c. Specification of Configuration.—The absolute configuration of nearly every asymmetric cyclitol is now known. The configurations have been established by degradation of the cyclitols to known carbohydrate derivatives. It would be desirable, therefore, to indicate the absolute configuration in the name of the compounds. Both nomenclature systems made provision for doing this: the Angyal system uses the lowest-numbered,[7] and the Fletcher–Anderson–Lardy system the highest-numbered asymmetric carbon atom as the point of reference.[5] But, in view of the fact that this feature of the two systems has not been generally accepted, it has been considered preferable in this review simply to designate asymmetric compounds as (+) or (−), and print their full formulas. (This method is not particularly suitable for indexing and abstracting.) When the text refers to a racemic compound, only one (arbitrarily chosen) enantiomorph will be shown; but, in discussion of optically active compounds, the formulas will always show the correct configuration.

2. *Conformations of the Cyclitols*

The application of conformational analysis[9] has been of considerable value in understanding some reactions of cyclitols; it will, therefore, be

I′
cis

II′
epi

III′
allo

IV′
neo

V′
myo

VI′
muco

VII′
scyllo

VIII′
dextro

IX′
levo

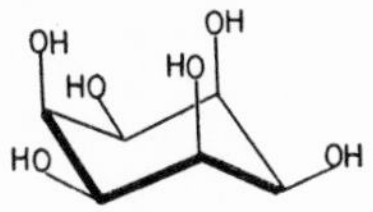

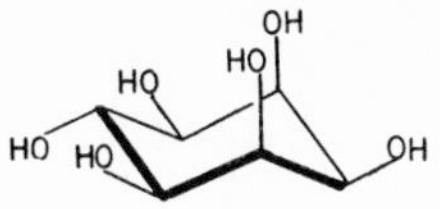

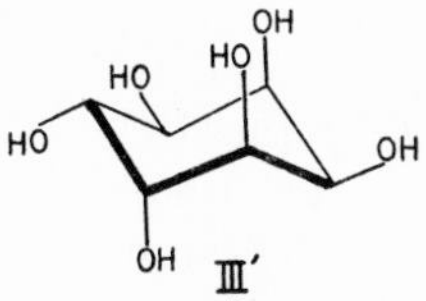

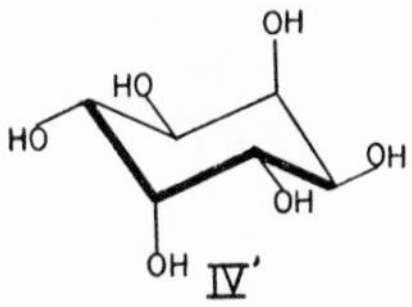

useful to consider the conformations of the cyclitols. It is generally assumed that, for each inositol, the most stable, and therefore the preponderant, conformation is that chair form which has the smaller number of axial hydroxyl groups; these are shown by formulas I′ to IX′. These conformations are deduced from the general tenets of conformational analysis, according to which, *substituent groups on a cyclohexane ring are more stable in the equatorial than in the axial positions*; the conformations are also in ac-

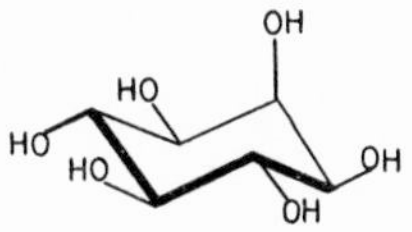

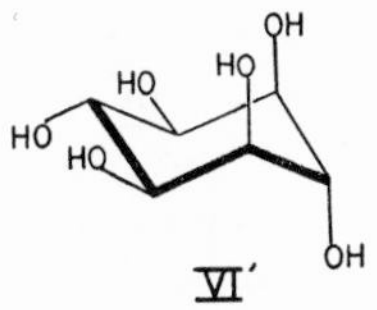

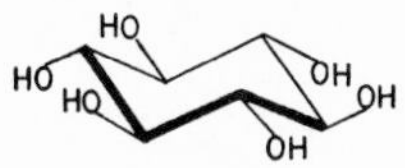

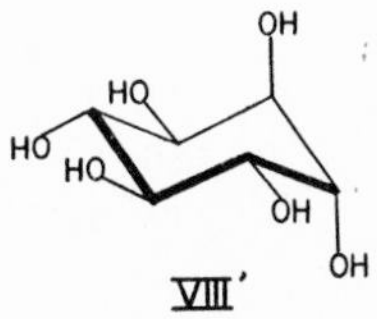

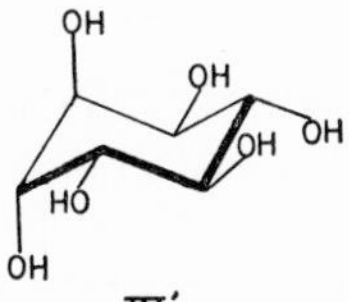

(9) D. H. R. Barton and R. C. Cookson, *Quart. Revs.* (London), **10**, 44 (1956); H. D. Orloff, *Chem. Revs.*, **54**, 347 (1954); W. G. Dauben and K. S. Pitzer, in "Steric Effects in Organic Chemistry," M. S. Newman, ed., John Wiley & Sons, Inc., New York, N. Y., 1956, p. 1; W. Klyne, *Progr. in Stereochem.*, **1**, 36 (1954); J. A. Mills, *Advances in Carbohydrate Chem.*, **10**, 1 (1955).

cordance with certain reactions of the cyclitols, such as dehydrogenation and complex-formation with borate.

Physical evidence also substantiates these assigned conformations. Thus, the absorption band at 873 ± 11 cm^{-1} in the infrared spectra, attributed to deformation of equatorial C—H bonds, is shown by all the cyclitols investigated except *scyllo*-inositol and *scyllo*-quercitol.[10] Nuclear magnetic resonance spectra allow distinction to be made between hydrogen atoms in different positions. The nuclear magnetic resonance spectra of the inositols can be interpreted on the basis of conformations I′ to IX′, and they agree closely with those of the corresponding hexachlorocyclohexanes (whose conformations have been ascertained by other methods); the spectra were made simpler by replacing the hydrogen atoms of the hydroxyl groups, either by acetylation[11] or by deuteration.[12] The dipole moments of cyclitol acetates can also be interpreted on the basis of these conformations.[13] The conformations I′ to IX′ can therefore be regarded as well established.

It is to be noted that, in those inositols which have *three* axial hydroxyl groups, the two possible chair forms are equally stable. In the case of (unsubstituted) *cis*- and *muco*-inositol, the two chair conformations are superimposable and are therefore indistinguishable. In *allo*-inositol, they are mirror images of each other: *allo*-inositol is, therefore, an inseparable, racemic mixture of rotational isomers. Every hydroxyl group in *cis*-, *muco*-, and *allo*-inositol has an equal chance of being axial.

The all-equatorial *scyllo*-inositol (VII′) is the most stable isomer; axial hydroxyl groups, particularly when accumulated on one side of the cyclohexane ring, introduce extra energy. The equilibrium constants of complex-formation with boric acid allow the approximate calculation[14] of the free-energy differences between the isomers; thus, *myo*-inositol (V′, one axial hydroxyl group) is estimated to be less stable by 0.9 kcal./mole, *epi*-inositol (II′, two axial hydroxyl groups on the same side) by 2.8 kcal./mole, and *cis*-inositol (I′, three axial hydroxyl groups on the same side) by 5.7 kcal./mole than *scyllo*-inositol (VII′). In one case, it was possible to confirm these energy relationships experimentally: direct equilibration of *myo*-, *rac*-, and *muco*-inositol gave similar amounts of the first two, but very little *muco*-inositol.[15] The rearrangement and the ring-opening of anhydroinositols

(10) S. A. Barker, E. J. Bourne, R. Stephens and D. H. Whiffen, *J. Chem. Soc.*, 4211 (1954).

(11) R. U. Lemieux, R. K. Kullnig, H. J. Bernstein and W. G. Schneider, *J. Am. Chem. Soc.*, **79**, 1005 (1957).

(12) S. Brownstein, *J. Am. Chem. Soc.*, **81**, 1606 (1959).

(13) C. L. Angyal and S. J. Angyal, *J. Chem. Soc.*, 695 (1952).

(14) S. J. Angyal and D. J. McHugh, *Chem. & Ind.* (London), 1147 (1956).

(15) S. J. Angyal, S. R. Johns and M. Pitman, unpublished work.

(see p. 182) also proceeds in the direction predicted by conformational analysis.

An interesting correlation has been noted[16] between the natural occurrence of the cyclitols and their conformational stability. Inositols which have a high interaction energy owing to the presence of two axial hydroxyl groups on the same side of the ring (*epi*, *allo*, *muco*, and *cis*) have not been found in Nature, whereas all the other configurations do occur in Nature, either as inositols (*myo*, *scyllo*, *dextro*, and *levo*) or as the inosamine (*neo*). The two naturally occurring quercitols also do not contain two axial hydroxyl groups on the same side of the ring. Moreover, in all the inositol methyl ethers which occur in Nature, the methoxyl groups are in equatorial positions; in fact, all the possible *equatorial* monomethyl ethers of *myo*-inositol and the active inositols have been found in Nature, at least in one enantiomorphous form, but none of their *axial* isomers have been so found.

II. The Inositols

1. *Synthesis*

The *myo*, the *dextro*, and the *levo* isomers of inositol are readily obtainable from natural sources, whilst the other diastereomers are usually synthesized from these compounds by a series of reactions which amount to epimerizations at one or more centers. These syntheses will be discussed under the individual inositols; the present Section deals only with syntheses of inositols from non-cyclitol materials.

The first synthesis of *myo*-inositol was described in 1914, long before the configuration of this cyclitol was established. Wieland and Wishart[17] claimed to have obtained *myo*-inositol in more than 50 % yield by the hydrogenation of hexahydroxybenzene. The surprising stereospecificity of this reaction, and the fact that others[18,19] reported their inability to repeat it, called for re-investigation. In 1949, Kuhn, Quadbeck, and Röhm[20] gave details of the reaction and of the palladium catalyst required for its success; they used the more readily available tetrahydroxybenzoquinone as starting material (since it is converted to hexahydroxybenzene during the hydrogenation) and found that the product was a mixture of inositols from which they isolated only the *myo* isomer in 13 % yield.

The products of the hydrogenation were fully investigated by Angyal

(16) S. J. Angyal and J. A. Mills, *Revs. Pure and Appl. Chem.* (Australia), **2**, 185 (1952).

(17) H. Wieland and R. S. Wishart, *Ber.*, **47**, 2082 (1914).

(18) R. C. Anderson and E. S. Wallis, *J. Am. Chem. Soc.*, **70**, 2931 (1948).

(19) M. R. Stetten and D. Stetten, *J. Biol. Chem.*, **164**, 85 (1946).

(20) R. Kuhn, G. Quadbeck and E. Röhm, *Ann.*, **565**, 1 (1949).

and McHugh,[21] who used chromatography on cellulose powder for their separation. Five inositols (*myo*, *rac*, *cis*, *scyllo*, and *epi*), three quercitols (*cis*, *epi*, and *scyllo*) and one inosose (*cis*, X) were isolated; *myo*-inositol, obtained in a yield of 17 %, was the predominant product. Substantial amounts of cyclohexane-tetrols and -triols were also formed.[22]

Tetrahydroxybenzoquinone can also be hydrogenated at high pressure and temperature with a Raney nickel catalyst,[18] to give products ranging from cyclohexanediols to inositols. The yield of *myo*-inositol is small (2–6 %); somewhat larger proportions of *cis*-inositol and *cis*-quercitol are produced.

The preparation of inositols by the hydrogenation of tetrahydroxyquinone amounts to a total synthesis, since the latter can be prepared from the reaction of carbon monoxide with potassium.[23] This synthesis has been utilized for the preparation of *myo*-inositol uniformly labeled[24, 25] with carbon-14.

myo-Inositol has also been synthesized from D-glucose by a series of re-

X
cis—Inosose   XI   XII

actions of which all but the last have already been reported in the earlier review.[1] In slightly alkaline solution, 6-deoxy-6-nitro-D-glucose (and also 6-deoxy-6-nitro-L-idose) cyclized to a mixture of deoxynitroinositols from which three compounds were isolated.[26, 27] The one which predominates under equilibrating conditions ("nitrodesoxyinositol III") has the *scyllo* configuration, as shown[28] by its reduction to aminodeoxy-*scyllo*-inositol (*scyllo*-inosamine, XI). "Nitrodesoxyinositol II" gives a di-*O*-isopropylidene acetal which does not react with lead tetraacetate,[27] and which therefore probably has the *muco* configuration (XII).[29] The configuration of the third nitro compound is not yet known.

(21) S. J. Angyal and D. J. McHugh, *J. Chem. Soc.*, 3682 (1957).

(22) In view of the complexity of the reaction, it seems ironical that Wieland and Wishart[17] recommended this synthesis of *myo*-inositol as a student preparation.

(23) J. Liebig, *Ann.*, **11**, 182 (1834); R. Nietzki and T. Benckiser, *Ber.*, **18**, 1833 (1885).

(24) F. Weygand and E. Schulze, *Z. Naturforsch.*, **11b**, 370 (1956).

(25) S. J. Angyal and M. E. Tate, unpublished work.

(26) J. M. Grosheintz and H. O. L. Fischer, *J. Am. Chem. Soc.*, **70**, 1476, 1479 (1948).

(27) B. Iselin and H. O. L. Fischer, *J. Am. Chem. Soc.*, **70**, 3946 (1948).

(28) T. Posternak, *Helv. Chim. Acta*, **33**, 1597 (1950).

(29) G. E. McCasland, *J. Am. Chem. Soc.*, **73**, 2295 (1951).

The final step in the synthesis—replacement of the amino group in XI by a hydroxyl group—was carried out by Posternak[28] by treatment with nitrous acid. Inversion occurred, giving a 10–15% yield of *myo*-inositol; the other products of the reaction could not be identified. A much better yield (71%) was achieved by the nitrous acid deamination of the penta-acetate ester of XI, rather than by deamination of the free inosamine.[30, 31] This method has been utilized[30, 31] for the preparation of *myo*-inositol-*2*-C^{14} from nitromethane-C^{14}.

A different approach has been used by Nakajima and his coworkers[32] in the synthesis of inositols. Their starting materials were the *cis*- and *trans*-3,5-cyclohexadiene-1,2-diols (XIII and XV) ("benzeneglycols") which

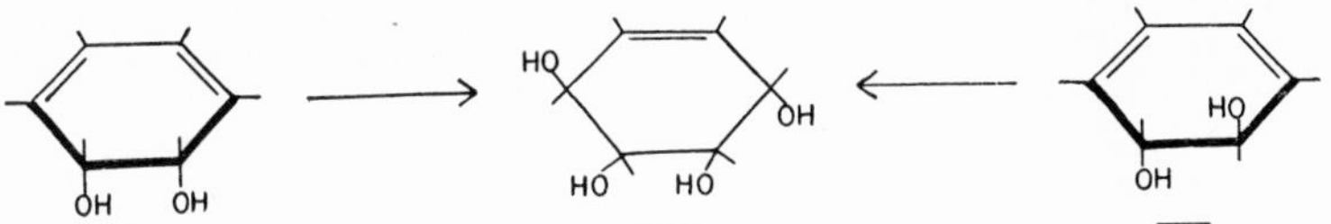

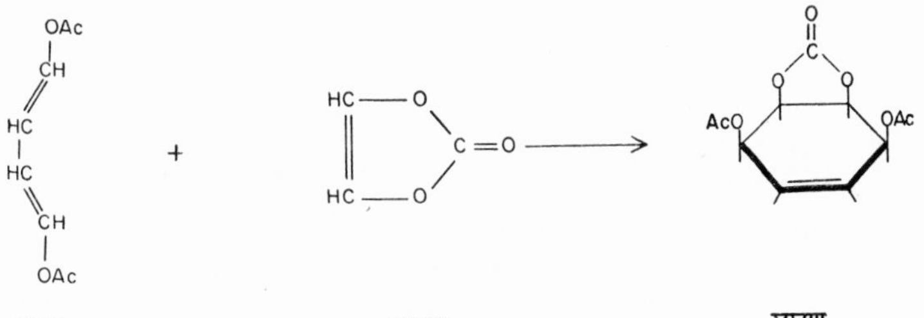

were obtained from α-3,4,5,6-tetrachlorocyclohexene by hydroxylation of the double bond, and subsequent removal of the chlorine atoms by zinc. Hydroxylation of one double bond in these glycols by various methods gave rise to five different 5-cyclohexene-1,2,3,4-tetrols (XIV), all the possible dia-stereomers with exception of the all-*cis* compound being obtained.[32(b),33] Further hydroxylation of each tetrol enabled the Japanese workers to iso-

(30) T. Posternak, W. H. Schopfer and R. Huguenin, *Helv. Chim. Acta*, **40**, 1875 (1957).

(31) L. Anderson and G. I. Drummond, unpublished work.

(32) (a) S. Takei, M. Nakajima and I. Tomida, *Chem. Ber.*, **89**, 263 (1956); M. Naka-jima, I. Tomida, A. Hashizume and S. Takei, *ibid.*, **89**, 2224 (1956); (b) M. Nakajima, I. Tomida and S. Takei, *ibid.*, **92**, 163 (1959).

(33) M. Nakajima, I. Tomida and S. Takei, *Chem. Ber.*, **90**, 246 (1957).

late every inositol except *cis*-inositol.[34] The yields obtained from each tetrol are shown in Table I.

The classical diene synthesis has been used for building the six-membered ring in the preparation of *allo*-inositol by Criegee and Becher.[35] *trans,trans*-Diacetoxybutadiene (XVI) and vinylene carbonate (XVII) condensed at 205–210° to an addition product (XVIII). Hydroxylation of this compound by osmium tetroxide, followed by hydrolysis, gave *allo*-inositol; the bulky osmium tetroxide approaches from the unhindered side of the molecule and the other possible product of the hydroxylation, *cis*-inositol, is not formed.[4] *trans*-Hydroxylation of XVIII would give *epi*-inositol.

TABLE I

Hexa-O-acetylinositols Prepared by cis- *and* trans-*Hydroxylation of Cyclohexenetetrols*[34]

Cyclohexenetetrol	Yields (%) of hexa-O-acetylinositol						
	rac	myo	scyllo	epi	muco	allo	neo
1,4/2,3	59(t)[a]				60(c)	0(c)	
1,3/2,4	44(t)	65(c)	3(t)				
1,2,3/4		3(t)		4(c)		54(t)	20(c)
1,2/3,4	27(t)					45(c)	44(t)
1,2,4/3	69(c)	0(t)		0(c)	15(t)		

[a] Method of hydroxylation: (c) = *cis*, with neutral permanganate; (t) = *trans*, with perbenzoic acid.

2. Reactions

a. Dehydrogenation.—Following the discovery[1] that a pentahydroxy-cyclohexanone (inosose) could be obtained from *myo*-inositol by biological dehydrogenation with *Acetobacter suboxydans*, several workers have given their attention to the selective dehydrogenation of cyclitols. Nearly all the known cyclitols have been tried as substrates for *Acetobacter suboxydans*, an organism which has been widely used for the conversion of open-chain sugar alcohols to ketoses. The standard procedure has been to shake a suspension of washed, resting, bacterial cells in a solution of the cyclitol contained in a Warburg apparatus[36]; most of the oxidations have also been carried out with growing cultures, to provide quantities of the products sufficient for characterization. The results of the early investigations carried out by Magasanik and Chargaff[36] permitted the interesting generali-

(34) M. Nakajima, I. Tomida, N. Kurihara and S. Takei, *Chem. Ber.*, **92,** 173 (1959).

(35) R. Criegee and P. Becher, *Chem. Ber.*, **90,** 2516 (1957).

(36) B. Magasanik and E. Chargaff, *J. Biol. Chem.*, **174,** 173 (1948).

zation that *only axial hydroxyl groups* are oxidized, and this generalization has been confirmed by all subsequent work; for example, *scyllo*-inositol (VII′) is not attacked, *myo*-inositol (V′) gives a monoketone, and *dextro-* or *levo*-inositol (VIII′, IX′) yield diketones.[36] The generalization does not completely describe the observations, however, for the strain of *Acetobacter* used (ATCC 621) did not oxidize every axial hydroxyl group in the cyclitols tested; *epi*-inositol (II′), for example, gives only a (optically active) monoketone. A more complete description of the specificity of the oxidation was offered by Magasanik, Franzl, and Chargaff[37] in the form of rules, which are best understood by reference to projections, as seen from above, of the standard chair-formulas of the cyclitols. In these projections, illustrated by XIX–XXIV, the axial hydroxyl group under discussion is considered

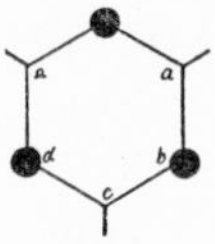

XIX
cis–Inositol

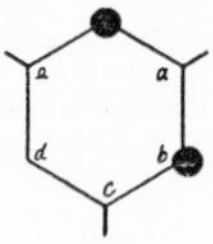

XX
cis–Quercitol

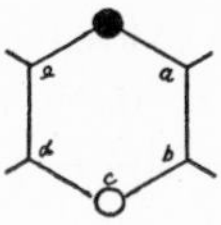

XXI
neo–Inositol

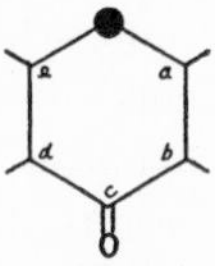

XXII
neo–Inosose

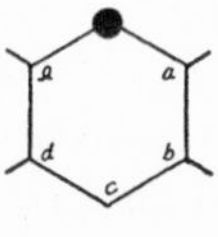

XXIII
neo–Quercitol

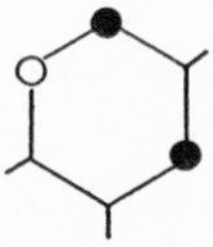

XXIV
allo–Inositol

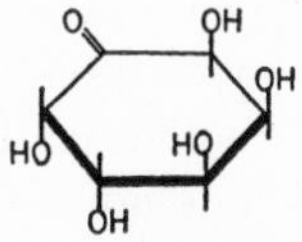

XXV

to point upward, and is represented by a filled circle; axial hydroxyl groups pointing downward are represented by open circles, and equatorial hydroxyl groups by radial lines. The rules (paraphrased) stated that: (1) only axial hydroxyl groups are oxidized; (2) when the cyclitol is oriented as in XIX–XXIV, the carbon atom in (the *meta*) position *d* must carry an equatorial hydroxyl group; and it was suggested that (3) an equatorial hydroxyl group may be required in position *c*.[38] The basis for the rules was the fact that *myo*-inositol, which has equatorial hydroxyl groups at positions *a*, *b*, *c*, *d*, and *e*, is readily oxidized, but that changing the hydroxyl group at position *d* to an axial hydroxyl group, a keto function, or no oxygen function produced compounds unaffected by *Acetobacter*. Similar changes at positions *a*, *b*, and *e* did not prevent oxidation. It was considered

(37) B. Magasanik, R. E. Franzl and E. Chargaff, *J. Am. Chem. Soc.*, **74**, 2618 (1952).

(38) B. Magasanik, in "Essays in Biochemistry," S. Graff, ed., John Wiley & Sons, Inc., New York, N. Y., 1956, p. 181.

that the axial hydroxyl group undergoing dehydrogenation, and the equatorial hydroxyl group at position *d*, represented *points of contact between substrate and enzyme*, and, in view of Ogston's "three-point hypothesis,"[39] it was supposed that an equatorial hydroxyl group might be required at position *c* as a third contact point.

The study of additional cyclitols has led to conflicting conclusions about the specificity rules 2 and 3. Posternak and coworkers[40] have tested not only the inositols and quercitols but also most of the vicinal cyclohexanetetrols, -triols, and -diols, as well as a number of other cyclic alcohols, as substrates for the Delft (Kluyver and De Leeuw) strain of *A. suboxydans*. They find that resting cells of this strain consume one atom of oxygen per axial hydroxyl group in the substrate. Inositols with three axial hydroxyl groups (*cis*, *allo*, and *muco*) appeared to be converted to hexahydroxybenzene, which is further oxidized non-enzymically. Although there are differences in the rates of oxidation of the successive axial hydroxyl groups in cyclitols having more than one such group, Posternak believes that his results do not support rules 2 and 3, even as expressions of steric requirements for maximal rate.

On the other hand, Anderson and coworkers,[41, 42] using *A. suboxydans* ATCC 621, have largely confirmed the results of Magasanik and coworkers. Most of the cyclitols were found to conform to the rules, but some exceptions were noted. *cis*-Inositol (XIX) and *cis*-quercitol (deoxy-*cis*-inositol, XX), which do not satisfy rule 2, are oxidized to monoketones, though very slowly. *neo*-Inositol (XXI), *neo*-inosose (*myo*-inosose-5, XXII), and *neo*-quercitol (5-deoxy-*myo*-inositol, XXIII), which have, respectively, an axial hydroxyl group, a keto group, and no oxygen function at position *c*, are oxidized, but more slowly than cyclitols which satisfy rule 3. Some inosamines and inositol methyl ethers which satisfy the rules are oxidized, but others are not. On the basis of these results, a *modified* third rule was formulated,[42] namely: "The dehydrogenation of an axial hydroxyl in a higher cyclitol [five or six functional groups] proceeds best when there is an equatorial hydroxyl in the *para* position, and when there is a choice, the axial hydroxyl satisfying this rule is attacked preferentially." For example, *allo*-inositol—in which only one hydroxyl group satisfies all three rules (see XXIV)—is dehydrogenated largely to the inosose XXV. A small

(39) A. G. Ogston, *Nature*, **162**, 963 (1948).

(40) T. Posternak, A. Rapin and A. L. Haenni, *Helv. Chim. Acta*, **40**, 1594 (1957); T. Posternak and D. Reymond, *ibid.*, **36**, 260 (1953).

(41) L. Anderson, K. Tomita, P. Kussi and S. Kirkwood, *J. Biol. Chem.*, **204**, 769 (1953).

(42) L. Anderson, R. Takeda, S. J. Angyal and D. J. McHugh, *Arch. Biochem. Biophys.*, **78**, 518 (1958).

amount of diketone is formed as a result of attack at hydroxyl groups which conform only to rules 1 and 2.

It is clear that the two strains of *A. suboxydans* differ in the degree of selectivity with which they oxidize axial hydroxyl groups in cyclitols. However, both strains can be used in growing cultures to prepare (from cyclitols) mono- and di-ketones by the selective oxidation of one, or two, hydroxyl groups. As suggested by Anderson and coworkers,[42] the rules are a useful guide for predicting which positions will be oxidized.

Further progress on the problem of the stereochemical specificity of cyclitol oxidation by *A. suboxydans* will depend on the isolation of the enzyme or enzymes involved. Cell-free preparations capable of oxidizing *myo*-inositol have been obtained,[43, 44] but these have not been further purified. The enzyme is apparently a true dehydrogenase, since it can couple with diaphorase.[44]

Cyclitol dehydrogenases have also been detected in some strains of *Aerobacter aerogenes*[45] and in *Mycobacterium tuberculosis* BCG.[46] The *Aerobacter* enzyme has been fairly extensively studied,[45, 47] and it is considered to function in the fermentation of inositol by this organism.[38] *Pseudomonas beijerinckii* is distinguished by its ability to oxidize *myo*-inositol and *levo*-inositol to the tetrahydroxyquinone stage,[48] and *Propionibacterium pentosaceum* effects a dismutation of *myo*-inositol in which hexahydroxybenzene appears to be the oxidized product.[49]

Cyclitols (in neutral to slightly acidic solution) are smoothly dehydrogenated to inososes over platinum catalysts in the presence of air or oxygen. Interestingly, the reaction[50–52] resembles oxidation by *A. suboxydans*, in that only axial hydroxyl groups are attacked. It differs from the bacterial oxidation, however, in that it stops, in most cases, after one hydroxyl group has been oxidized, even if other axial hydroxyl groups are available in the molecule.

(43) R. E. Franzl and E. Chargaff, *Nature*, **168**, 955 (1951).

(44) F. C. Charalampous and P. Abrahams, *J. Biol. Chem.*, **225**, 575 (1957).

(45) J. M. Goldstone and B. Magasanik, *Federation Proc.*, **13**, 218 (1954).

(46) L. Ottey and F. Bernheim, *Enzymologia*, **17**, 279 (1956).

(47) J. Larner, W. T. Jackson, D. J. Graves and J. R. Stamer, *Arch. Biochem. Biophys.*, **60**, 352 (1956).

(48) A. J. Kluyver, T. Hof and A. G. J. Boezaardt, *Enzymologia*, **7**, 257 (1939).

(49) W. A. Volk and D. Pennington, *J. Bacteriol.*, **64**, 347 (1952).

(50) K. Heyns and H. Paulsen, *Chem. Ber.*, **86**, 833 (1953). For a review, see *idem*, *Angew. Chem.*, **69**, 600 (1957).

(51)(a) L. Anderson and G. G. Post, *Abstracts Papers Am. Chem. Soc.*, **134**, 12D (1958); (b) G. G. Post (with L. Anderson), M. S. Thesis, University of Wisconsin, 1957.

(52) M. Pitman (with S. J. Angyal), M. Sc. Thesis, University of New South Wales, Sydney, 1957.

With pinitol and quebrachitol, the reaction is highly selective for one of the two axial hydroxyl groups in each compound (see formulas LXIII → LXVII, and LXV → LXIX, p. 170).[51] This selectivity shows the steric effect of the methyl group. Nevertheless, the platinum-catalyzed dehydrogenation (in contrast to the action of *Acetobacter*) is not easily inhibited by substitution in the cyclitol molecule; even the hindered axial hydroxyl groups in dambonitol (LXXVII) and in *O*-isopropylidenequebrachitol (LXVI, see p. 172) can be oxidized.[52, 53]

Since, in the dehydrogenation, whether by platinum or by *Acetobacter*, a carbon-bound hydrogen atom is removed, the selectivity for axial hydroxyl groups is readily explained. Only when the carbon atom carries the hydroxyl group in the axial position is the carbon-bound hydrogen atom in the (more readily accessible) equatorial position.

b. *Acetonation.*—Acetonation has been the crucial step in (a) determining the configuration of *myo*-inositol and the positions of the methyl groups in several inositol methyl ethers, and (b) the synthesis of new inositols. After a number of unsuccessful attempts to form various cyclic acetals,[1] Dangschat[54] succeeded in acetonating *myo*-inositol by the use of a very large excess of acetone containing 10 % of acetic acid and 10 % of zinc chloride. Only a preliminary account of the reaction was published, and difficulties were experienced by other workers who tried to repeat it. Anderson and Wallis[18] reported that they were unable to carry out the reaction, and a procedure given in detail by Angyal and Macdonald[6] was later found to be unreliable and was modified.[55] Acetic acid may be omitted from the reaction mixture without deleterious effects; but it is advantageous to increase quite substantially the proportion of zinc chloride to as much as 40 g. per 100 ml. of acetone. The zinc chloride acts not only as a dehydrating agent and as a "Lewis acid," but also enhances the solubility of inositol in acetone, presumably by the formation of a complex. The resistance of *myo*-inositol to acetonation is probably attributable to the presence of three contiguous, *cis* hydroxyl groups; the central axial group is hindered by its two equatorial neighbors in the movement—necessary for formation of the acetal ring—toward the equatorial region.[56]

In contrast to the behavior of *myo*-inositol, other cyclitols and cyclitol methyl ethers are acetonated with ease, provided that they contain two contiguous, *cis*-hydroxyl groups. No reaction occurs with the (all-*trans*)

(53) L. Anderson and G. G. Post, *Abstracts Papers Am. Chem. Soc.*, **134**, 13D (1958).
(54) G. Dangschat, *Naturwissenschaften*, **30**, 146 (1942).
(55) S. J. Angyal, P. T. Gilham and C. G. Macdonald, *J. Chem. Soc.*, 1417 (1957).
(56) S. J. Angyal and D. J. McHugh, *J. Chem. Soc.*, 1423 (1957).

scyllo-inositol and *scyllo*-quercitol. Quebrachitol,[6, 57] sequoyitol,[58] bornesitol,[59] *proto*-quercitol,[6] and *vibo*-quercitol[60] form monoisopropylidene acetals; pinitol,[6, 61] *levo*-inositol,[6] and *dextro*-inositol,[62] having two pairs of *cis*-hydroxyl groups, give diisopropylidene acetals. Some of these derivatives will be discussed under the individual cyclitols. *epi*-Inositol gives two diisopropylidene derivatives[6]: one consumes one mole of periodate per mole and therefore has structure XXVI; the other is not attacked by periodate and hence is the 1,2:4,5-di-*O*-isopropylidene acetal (XXVII).

Surprisingly, the active inositols and *epi*-inositol yield tri-*O*-isopropylidene acetals as well as di-*O*-isopropylidene compounds. The third isopro-

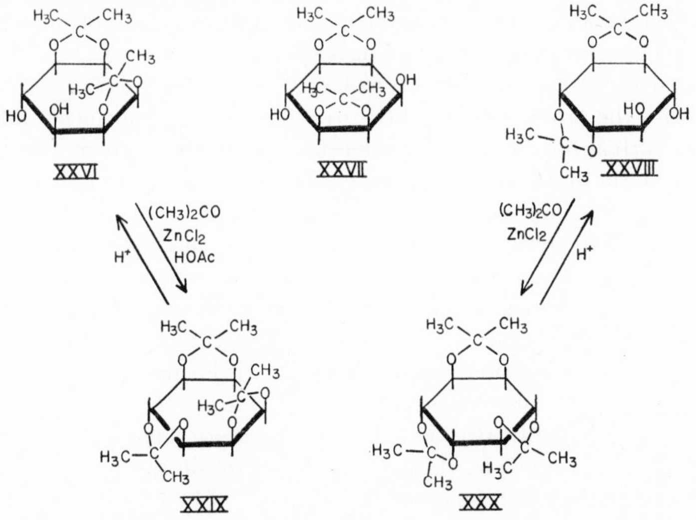

pylidene group, which is introduced more slowly, is also hydrolyzed off faster than the others; partial hydrolysis of the tri-*O*-isopropylidene compounds gives di-*O*-isopropylidene-*levo*(or *dextro*)-inositol (XXVIII) and 1,2:3,4-di-*O*-isopropylidene-*epi*-inositol (XXVI), hence the triacetals have the 1,2:3,4:5,6-tri-*O*-isopropylidene structures XXIX and XXX, respectively. In these compounds, one pair of *trans*-hydroxyl groups has

(57) T. Posternak, *Helv. Chim. Acta*, **35**, 50 (1952).

(58) L. Anderson, E. S. DeLuca, A. Bieder and G. G. Post, *J. Am. Chem. Soc.*, **79**, 1171 (1957).

(59) S. Bien and D. Ginsburg, *J. Chem. Soc.*, 3189 (1958).

(60) T. Posternak, *Helv. Chim. Acta*, **33**, 350 (1950).

(61) A. B. Anderson, D. L. MacDonald and H. O. L. Fischer, *J. Am. Chem. Soc.*, **74**, 1479 (1952).

(62) C. E. Ballou and H. O. L. Fischer, *J. Am. Chem. Soc.*, **75**, 3673 (1953).

been acetonated. Such an unusual reaction occurs only with cyclitol derivatives which *already* contain two *cis*-isopropylidene groups; it has been explained[6] as being due to the distortion of the chair form of the cyclohexane ring by the attachment of the other isopropylidene groups. Such distortion facilitates the closer approach of the two *trans*-hydroxyl groups to each other.

The only other compound which has been successfully used for forming an acetal with a cyclitol is benzaldehyde, which yields a di-*O*-benzylidene acetal with *levo*-inositol.[63]

c. Periodate Oxidation.—The reaction of inositols with sodium metaperiodate and periodic acid is "anomalous." Consumption of six moles of periodate per mole would be expected, with the formation of an equivalent number of moles of formic acid. Instead, it was observed[64, 65] that, under the usual conditions, about 6.7 moles of the reagent were consumed per mole, with the production of a little over 5 moles of formic acid and 0.8–0.9 mole of carbon dioxide. The reaction has been discussed in Fletcher's review[1]; but the figures quoted above differ somewhat from those reported earlier, and the mechanism previously suggested[66] for the course of the reaction has now been discounted.[64, 67] The presence of glyoxylic acid was demonstrated[64, 67] amongst the products of the oxidation of *myo*-inositol with *insufficient* periodate; and it appears that the glycolic acid previously isolated[66] from the reaction mixture was an artifact, probably produced by a Cannizzaro reaction from glyoxylic acid during the process of isolation. Glyoxylic acid is oxidized by periodate to carbon dioxide and formic acid,[68] hence, undoubtedly, it is the intermediate responsible for the production of carbon dioxide. Its formation from inositol is, however, complex. The mechanism recently suggested by Fleury and Le Dizet,[64] which involves the simultaneous attack of two molecules of periodate on one of inositol, is highly improbable. Schwarz[67] has discussed the possible mechanisms: his discussion will be extended here in an attempt to give a clear picture of the periodate oxidation.

The first step in the oxidation of a cyclitol is the formation of a hexodialdose (XXXV); this can either react with more periodate in its straight-chain form or rearrange first to a cyclic form. The latter change clearly occurs in the oxidation of dambonitol[69] (1,3-di-*O*-methyl-*myo*-inositol, XXXI), in which only about 0.2 mole of the formic acid produced is found in

(63) E. A. Shneour and C. E. Ballou, *J. Am. Chem. Soc.*, **80**, 3960 (1958).

(64) P. Fleury and L. Le Dizet, *Bull. soc. chim. biol.*, **37**, 1099 (1955).

(65) A. M. Stephen, *J. Chem. Soc.*, 738 (1952).

(66) P. Fleury, G. Poirot and J. Fiévet, *Compt. rend.*, **220**, 664 (1945).

(67) J. C. P. Schwarz, *Chem. & Ind.* (London), 1388 (1955).

(68) P. Fleury and G. Bon-Bernatets, *J. pharm. chim.*, [8] **23**, 85 (1936).

(69) A. K. Kiang and K. H. Loke, *J. Chem. Soc.*, 480 (1956).

$$
\begin{array}{ccccc}
& \text{HC=O} & \text{HCOH} & & \text{HC=O} \\
& \text{HOCH} & \text{HOCH} & & \text{HCOMe} \\
\text{XXXI} \rightarrow & \text{HCOMe} \rightleftharpoons & \text{HCOMe} & \rightarrow & \text{HCO—CO—H} \\
& \text{HCOH} & \text{HCO———} & & \text{HCOMe} \\
& \text{HCOMe} & \text{HCOMe} & & \text{HC=O} \\
& \text{HC=O} & \text{HC=O} & & \\
& \text{XXXII} & \text{XXXIII} & & \text{XXXIV}
\end{array}
$$

$$
\begin{array}{cccc}
\text{HC=O} & \text{CHOH} & & \\
\text{CHOH} & \text{CHOH} & 2\,\text{HCO}_2\text{H} & \\
\text{CHOH} \rightleftharpoons & \text{CHOH} \rightarrow & + & \\
\text{CHOH} & \text{CHOH} & \text{HC=O} & \text{HC=O} \\
\text{CHOH} & \text{CHO———} & \text{HCO—CO—H} \rightarrow & \text{HOCO—CO—H} \\
\text{HC=O} & \text{HC=O} & \text{HC=O} & \text{HC=O} \\
\text{XXXV} & \text{XXXVI} & \text{XXXVII} &
\end{array}
$$

$$
\begin{array}{ccccc}
& \text{HC=O} & \text{HC=O} & \text{HCOH} & \text{HCO}_2\text{H} \\
3 & \text{HC=O} & 2\ \text{CHOH} \rightleftharpoons & \text{COH} \rightarrow & + \\
\downarrow & & \text{HC=O} & \text{HC=O} & \text{CO}_2\text{H} \rightarrow \begin{array}{c}\text{CO}_2 \\ + \\ \text{HCO}_2\text{H}\end{array} \\
6\ \text{HCO}_2\text{H} & \text{XXXVIII} & \text{XXXIX} & \text{HC=O} &
\end{array}
$$

the free form, the rest being bound as an ester. The formate ester (**XXXIV**) must be derived from the furanose form **XXXIII** of the dialdose.[70, 71] The dialdose **XXXII** therefore reacts, to the extent of at least 80%, in its cyclic form. On the other hand, in the oxidation of the isomeric lirio-dendritol[72] (1,5-di-*O*-methyl-*myo*-inositol, **LXXVIII**) about 80% of the formic acid is found in the free state: the reaction proceeds mainly by oxidation of the open-chain dialdose.[73]

(70) The pyranose form, also present in equilibrium, is not oxidized by periodate and has, therefore, no influence on the course of the reaction.

(71) Production of formate esters in the periodate oxidation of the cyclic forms of carbohydrates is now well established (see Ref. 74; D-glucose itself reacts in this manner [C. Schöpf and H. Wild, *Chem. Ber.*, **87**, 1571 (1954); S. A. Warsi and W. J. Whelan, *Chem. & Ind.* (London), 71 (1958); F. S. H. Head, *ibid.*, 360 (1958)].

(72) S. J. Angyal and V. Bender, unpublished work.

(73) This difference between the oxidation of the two dimethyl ethers is probably caused by the different stabilities of the respective furanosides: the one from dambonitol (*altro*) has all its groups *trans* to each other, whereas in the one from liriodendritol (*ido*), the bulky C5-C6 group is *cis* to the methoxyl group on C3.

If the dialdose XXXV derived from an inositol reacts in its hemiacetal form XXXVI, it will be degraded to the formate ester of tartronaldehyde (XXXVII). The typical reaction[74] of β-dicarbonyl compounds, "over-oxidation," will then give one mole of glyoxylic acid per mole, and thence one mole of carbon dioxide.

On the other hand, since acyclic polyhydroxy compounds react very quickly with periodate,[75] the dialdose may be degraded before it can cyclize. Splitting between C3 and C4 will give two moles of tartronaldehyde (XXXVIII) per mole, whereas splitting of other bonds—since glycols are attacked faster than hydroxy aldehydes[76]—will yield three moles of glyoxal per mole, and ultimately six moles of formic acid. Tartronaldehyde probably reacts in the (tautomeric) reductone form XXXIX, which is known[67, 77] to be oxidized to glyoxylic acid. If about 40 % of compound XXXV is split between C3 and C4, the stoichiometry of the inositol oxidation is accounted for.

Some choice between the two possible mechanisms can be made by studying the periodate oxidation of pinitol,[65] sequoyitol,[78] and *proto*-quercitol.[79] If a methylene (deoxy) or an *O*-methyl group should occur at C3 or C4 of the hexodialdose, the rapid periodate oxidation of the cyclic form XXXVI would end after the consumption of only 2 or 3 moles of periodate per mole, respectively, and would then continue only at the very slow rate governed by the hydrolysis of the formate ester. The above compounds give hexodialdoses of this nature, but they rapidly consume some four moles of periodate per mole. This indicates that the major path of the reaction is *not* the one by way of cyclic intermediates; this conclusion is probably valid for the inositols, too.

Malonaldehyde has been identified by Fleury and coworkers as a product of the rapid stage of the oxidation of (+)-*proto*-quercitol.[79] It is slowly oxidized, with the consumption of another four moles of periodate per mole, to formic acid and carbon dioxide.

The rate of the initial fission of an inositol is considerably increased by the accumulation of *cis*-hydroxyl groups. Thus, whereas *myo*-inositol reacts about twice as fast as the *scyllo* isomer, the reactions of *epi*- and *cis*-inositol are about 200 times as fast.[56]

(74) See, for example, J. M. Bobbitt, *Advances in Carbohydrate Chem.*, **11**, 4 (1956).

(75) P. Fleury, J. Courtois and A. Bieder, *Bull. soc. chim. France*, 118 (1952).

(76) J. W. Pratt, N. K. Richtmyer and C. S. Hudson, *J. Am. Chem. Soc.*, **74**, 2200 (1952).

(77) See also Ref. 74, p. 9.

(78) N. V. Riggs, *J. Chem. Soc.*, 3199 (1949).

(79) P. Fleury, J. Courtois, W. C. Hamman and L. Le Dizet, *Bull. soc. chim. France*, 1307 (1955); P. Fleury, J. Courtois and W. C. Hamman, *Compt. rend.*, **240**, 543 (1955).

Barker and Shaw[80] have recently shown that compounds which contain a cis-cis-1,2,3-triol system, in a six-membered ring, form relatively stable complexes with the periodate ion at a pH of about 7. Steric considerations suggest that the axial–equatorial–axial conformation is required. As expected, one mole of neo-inositol forms a complex with two moles of periodate, but rac-, muco-, and myo-inositols form no such complexes. Although myo-inositol has a cis-cis-1,2,3-triol system, the conformation XL required

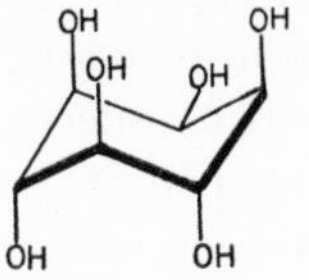

XL

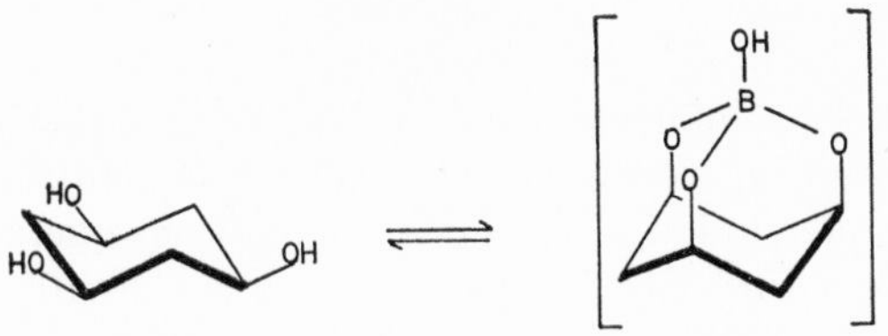

XLI   XLII

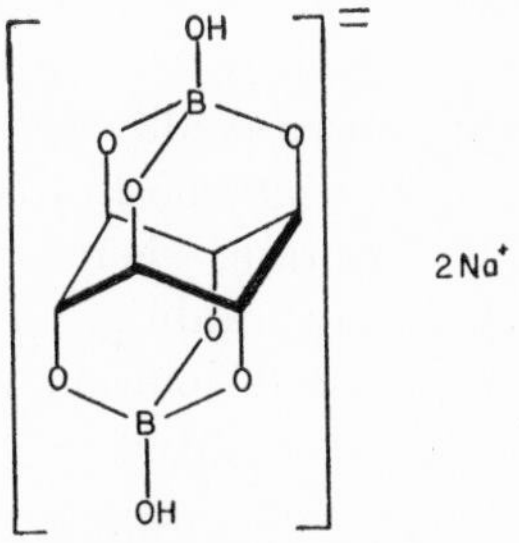

2 Na⁺

XLIII

for complex formation is very unfavorable, because it involves three axial hydroxyl groups on the same side of the ring.

d. Borate Complexes.—The cyclitols form complexes with borate ions, as shown by their electrophoretic mobility in borate buffers. The zone electrophoresis[81] of most of the cyclitols has been studied,[56, 82, 83] and M_G values

(80) G. R. Barker and D. F. Shaw, Proc. Chem. Soc., 259 (1957); J. Chem. Soc., 584 (1959); G. R. Barker, J. Chem. Soc., in press.

(81) A. B. Foster, Advances in Carbohydrate Chem., 12, 81 (1957).

(82) A. B. Foster and M. Stacey, Chem. & Ind. (London), 279 (1953).

(83) A. B. Foster, Chem. & Ind. (London), 591 (1953).

(mobility relative to that of D-glucose) have been published. These studies have led to the discovery of a novel type of borate complex. In many cyclic polyhydroxy compounds, including some cyclitols, complexing involves a cis-1,2-glycol grouping; but cyclitols from which such groupings are absent show good mobility if they have three cis-hydroxyl groups at C1, C3, and C5. Angyal and McHugh[56] therefore postulated the formation of "tridentate" complexes of the type XLII; their formation involves a change from the more stable chair form XLI, in which the three hydroxyl groups are equatorial, to the chair form in which they are axial.

From the change of pH caused by successive additions of cyclitols to a borate solution, the equilibrium constants of complex formation have been calculated[56]; they show that the complexes are formed from cyclitol and borate in a 1:1 ratio. The stability of the tridentate borates depends on the steric disposition of the *free* hydroxyl groups in the complex: the more of these in *axial* positions, the less stable the complex. This is illustrated by the values of the equilibrium constant in the following two series which are arranged by decreasing number of free axial hydroxyl groups in the complex: scyllo-quercitol, 5.0; epi-quercitol, 310; cis-quercitol, 7900; myo-inositol, 25; epi-inositol, 700; and cis-inositol, 1.1×10^6. When the constitution of a cyclitol allows the formation of both the tridentate and the classical, cis-1,2 type of complex, the former predominates.

Only one tridentate complex of a cyclitol has so far been isolated: the disodium salt of scyllo-inositol diborate (XLIII). This unusual compound, which was first obtained fortuitously from scyllo-inosose by treatment with sodium borohydride,[84] crystallizes readily from an aqueous solution of its components. The behavior of scyllo-inositol is remarkable in that the cyclitol reacts only slowly with borate, whereas all other polyhydric alcohols react practically instantaneously. Addition of scyllo-inositol causes no immediate drop in the pH of a borate solution, and it was reported that this cyclitol has no electrophoretic mobility[56, 82]; but it was found to migrate at a rate corresponding to a di-anion after being heated with a borate solution.[84] Presumably, the slow formation of the diborate is attributable to the requirement that the high-energy monoborate, having three axial hydroxyl groups on one side of the ring, must be an intermediate in the reaction.

e. *Reactions of Tosyl Esters.*—Although sulfonyl derivatives of carbohydrates have been studied extensively,[85] sulfonic esters of the cyclitols were not known until the development of acetonation of members of this group had made partially substituted inositols readily available. A number

(84) A. Weissbach, *J. Org. Chem.*, **23**, 329 (1958).
(85) R. S. Tipson, *Advances in Carbohydrate Chem.*, **8**, 107 (1953).

of O-sulfonylinositols have been recently prepared and utilized as intermediates in epoxide formation, in solvolysis, and in elimination reactions.

A compound containing a sulfonyloxy group adjacent and *trans*-situated to a free hydroxyl group is converted to an epoxide by the action of bases.[85a] The application to cyclitols of this well-known reaction will be discussed in Section III, 2 (see p. 181).

The solvolysis of sulfonic esters, a much studied reaction, has not been applied in carbohydrate chemistry, presumably because most sugars are not stable enough to withstand the long heating required. Tosyl derivatives of inositols can, however, be solvolyzed in good yield. For example, 3-O-tosyl-*levo*-inositol (5-O-tosyl-*levo*-inositol) (XLIV)—prepared from di-O-isopropylidene-*levo*-inositol (XXVIII) by tosylation and subsequent removal of the isopropylidene groups—affords *allo*-inositol when refluxed for

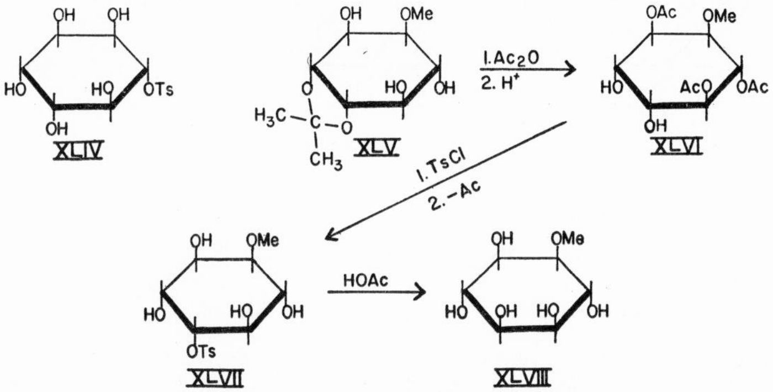

40 hours in 95 % acetic acid.[86] Under the same conditions, 1-O-methyl-*muco*-inositol (XLVIII) is formed[52] from 2-O-methyl-5-O-tosyl-*levo*-inositol (1-O-methyl-4-O-tosyl-*levo*-inositol) (XLVII). The latter compound was prepared from O-isopropylidenequebrachitol (XLV) by the following steps: acetylation, deacetonation to tri-O-acetylquebrachitol (XLVI), tosylation, and deacetylation. In the tosylation, the equatorial hydroxyl group reacts in preference to the axial one.

In these cases, solvolysis occurs with complete inversion, and only one inositol is formed. This seems to be the *normal* course of the reaction. In two instances, however, those of 1-O-tosyl- and 6-O-tosyl-*epi*-inositol, *two* inositols are formed, one by inversion and the other by retention of the configuration.[52] An insufficient number of examples of solvolyses has yet been accumulated, to allow predictions about the stereochemical outcome of the reaction.

(85a) See S. Peat, *Advances in Carbohydrate Chem.*, **2**, 37 (1946).

(86) P. T. Gilham (with S. J. Angyal), Ph.D. Thesis, University of New South Wales, Sydney, 1956.

It is well established in carbohydrate chemistry[85] that two adjacent tosyloxy groups are removed by iodide ion, with the formation of a double bond, but only if one of the groups is primary. In the cyclitol field, however, this limitation does not apply, presumably because the greater stability of the cyclitols permits performing the reaction at a higher temperature, at which the secondary groups also react. The temperature can be lowered, and the yield improved, by using the (more reactive) p-nitrophenylsulfonyl group instead of the customary tosyl group, as suggested, in a general way, by Tipson.[85] Thus, the cyclohexenetetrol L was obtained[4] from 3,4-di-O-tosyl-levo-inositol (5,6-di-O-tosyl-levo-inositol) (XLIX), and the all-cis-tetrol LII from 1,6-di-O-(p-nitrophenylsulfonyl)-epi-inositol (LI).

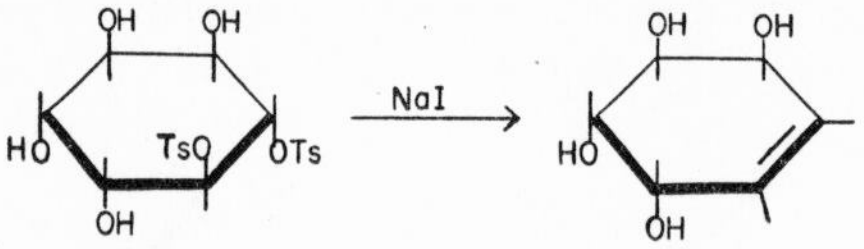

3. Analysis

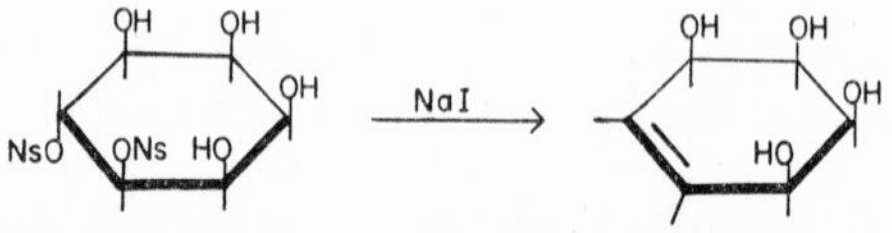

a. Qualitative Analysis.—The classical method for identifying inositols is the Scherer test, of which many modifications have been described.[2(a), 87] This test depends on the oxidation of the cyclitol with nitric acid, and the formation of colored, alkaline-earth salts of the resulting hydroxyquinones. In recent years, it has been largely supplanted by paper chromatography, which has the advantage of greater sensitivity and which also serves in identifying individual cyclitols.

myo-Inositol has a characteristic R_F value in many of the solvent systems regularly used for the paper chromatography of sugars and alditols, and it is often identified in natural materials through the use of such systems. The most generally useful solvent for separating mixtures of cyclitols on paper is acetone containing 5 to 20 vol.-% of water.[88] Other solvents are useful in particular cases. Tables of R_F values have been published for the following systems: acetone–water,[89, 90] phenol–water,[89, 90] collidine–water,[89]

(87) P. Fleury and P. Balatre, "Les Inositols," Masson, Paris, 1947.
(88) C. E. Ballou and A. B. Anderson, J. Am. Chem. Soc., 75, 648 (1953).
(89) T. Posternak, D. Reymond and W. Haerdi, Helv. Chim. Acta, 38, 191 (1955).
(90) S. J. Angyal, D. J. McHugh and P. T. Gilham, J. Chem. Soc., 1432 (1957).

butanol–acetic acid–water,[89, 90] and ethanol–water–concentrated ammonia.[90]

The usual sugar-reagents do not serve to detect cyclitol spots (except those of inososes). Ammoniacal silver nitrate has been widely used, but the best results[90] are obtained with separate solutions of silver nitrate in acetone and sodium hydroxide in ethanol.[91] The Scherer test has been adapted for use on paper chromatograms,[91a] and other reagents are useful in certain instances.[89, 90]

Electrophoresis on borate-buffered paper is potentially useful for the detection of cyclitols. So far, however, the principal application of this technique in the cyclitol field has been to studies on configuration and on the nature of cyclitol–borate complexes (see p. 153).

b. *Column Chromatography.*—Gram quantities of mixtures of cyclitols can be very effectively resolved on columns of cellulose powder, with acetone–water mixtures as the developing solvents.[55, 58] The availability of this technique has made possible the ready solution of a number of problems (in cyclitol chemistry) which otherwise would have been very difficult; for example, the separation of the mixtures resulting from the hydrogenation of hexahydroxybenzene (see p. 141), and the preparation of truly pure samples of the naturally occurring cyclitol methyl ethers.[42, 55] Chromatography on the borate form of a strong-base, anion-exchange resin has been used for purifying *myo*-inositol,[44] and the sucess of the procedure would seem to warrant further exploration as a method for resolving mixtures of cyclitols.

c. *Quantitative Analysis.*—Almost all the work on the quantitative analysis of cyclitols has actually dealt with *myo*-inositol. This is a result of the long-standing interest in the biochemistry of this cyclitol.

Prior to 1941, *myo*-inositol was often determined by isolation, as such or as the hexaacetate.[87] The isolated inositol was weighed, or was oxidized to carbon dioxide (which was measured in a gas buret).[92] In 1941, Woolley[93] published his microbiological method, in which the yeast *Saccharomyces cerevisiae* was used as a test organism. Soon afterward, there appeared an improved procedure, using *Saccharomyces carlsbergensis*,[94, 95] and an additional method based on the discovery of an "inositol-less" mutant of the common bread-mold, *Neurospora crassa*.[95, 96] Hundreds of types of foods,

(91) E. F. L. J. Anet and T. M. Reynolds, *Nature*, **174**, 930 (1954).

(91a) Y. Nagai and Y. Kimura, *Nature*, **181**, 1730 (1958).

(92) J. Needham, *Biochem. J.*, **17**, 422, 431 (1923).

(93) D. W. Woolley, *J. Biol. Chem.*, **140**, 453 (1941).

(94) L. Atkin, A. S. Schultz, W. L. Williams and C. N. Frey, *Ind. Eng. Chem. Anal. Ed.*, **15**, 141 (1943).

(95) E. E. Snell, in "Vitamin Methods," P. György, ed., Academic Press Inc., New York, N. Y., 1950, Vol. 1, p. 327.

(96) G. W. Beadle, *J. Biol. Chem.*, **156**, 683 (1944).

foodstuffs, and plant and animal tissues have been assayed for *myo*-inositol by means of one or other of these methods. A number of other microbiological assays have been devised, but they have not found wide use. The carefully worked-out procedure of Northam and Norris[97] would seem to merit further consideration.

The microbiological methods are all quite specific for free *myo*-inositol,[98] and they can therefore be used for differential determination of free and bound inositol, as is often desired. But, because they are somewhat tedious, and not satisfactorily precise, many efforts to develop chemical methods have been made. The periodate reaction is the basis for most of these, although use of this reaction for the *quantitative* assay of cyclitols poses certain problems; periodate reacts with almost all carbohydrates, and the reaction with cyclitols is, under the usual conditions, not stoichiometric (see p. 150).

In the method of Platt and Glock,[99] an acetone extract of tissue is used, and fermentable sugars are removed by fermentation with yeast. A correction for glycerol present is made possible by carrying out the oxidation at high dilution and low temperature (8°), the reaction with *myo*-inositol then being slow. It is claimed that, under these conditions, good stoichiometry prevails, but the time required (48 hr.) is excessive. A different approach was taken by Fleury and Recoules,[100] who attempted to take advantage of the "anomaly" in the periodate oxidation of cyclitols. Their method is based on the measurement, in a Warburg apparatus, of the carbon dioxide evolved during the reaction. Since carbon dioxide is not produced in the periodate oxidation of other carbohydrates, the presence of other carbohydrates causes no interference.

Recently, it has been reported[101] that *myo*-inositol reacts rapidly and stoichiometrically with periodate at 50–65°. If the excess periodate is determined spectrophotometrically,[102] a sensitive and convenient micromethod results (range 2–70 μg.). That this method will become the one of choice for *myo*-inositol seems probable. It should be applicable to the other inositols, and, perhaps, with some modifications, to inositol methyl ethers, quercitols, etc. Most interfering substances are effectively removed by vigorous treatment with hot, concentrated hydrochloric acid,[101(a)] sulfuric acid,[103] or barium hydroxide,[101(b)] followed by an ion-exchange purification.

(97) B. E. Northam and F. W. Norris, *J. Gen. Microbiol.*, **7**, 245 (1952).

(98) W. H. Schopfer, *Bull. soc. chim. biol.*, **33**, 1113 (1951).

(99) B. S. Platt and G. E. Glock, *Biochem. J.*, **37**, 709 (1943).

(100) P. Fleury and A. Recoules, *Bull. soc. chim. biol.*, **31**, 256 (1949).

(101) (a) F. N. LeBaron, J. Folch and E. E. Rothleder, *Federation Proc.*, **16**, 209 (1957); (b) B. W. Agranoff, R. M. Bradley and R. O. Brady, *J. Biol. Chem.*, **233**, 1077 (1958).

(102) J. S. Dixon and D. Lipkin, *Anal. Chem.*, **26**, 1092 (1954).

(103) J. W. Halliday and L. Anderson, *J. Biol. Chem.*, **217**, 797 (1955).

These treatments convert to ionic substances, and remove, nearly all constituents of natural materials; the acid treatments release any inositol present as phosphate, or combined in phospholipids, glycosides, etc. Glycerol remains in the deionized sample, but it can be oxidized separately, or be removed by heat decomposition or by repeatedly evaporating the solution to dryness. Such polyhydric alcohols of greater chain length as erythritol and mannitol, when present, would still interfere. However, corrections can be made for these compounds by determining the formaldehyde which they form on periodate oxidation, or they may be removed by chromatography on filter paper. The micro-periodate method is well suited to the analysis of samples eluted from filter paper, provided that care is exercised to remove the tiny particles of cellulose which are usually found in such eluates.

A colorimetric method for determining *myo*-inositol has been described.[104] The color is developed with the phosphomolybdotungstic acid reagent of Folin and Denis, after oxidation of the inositol with bromine. Enzymic methods, based on the inositol dehydrogenases of *Acetobacter suboxydans*[44] and *Aerobacter aerogenes*,[105] have also been used. These methods could be employed with any cyclitol readily attacked by the respective enzyme systems (see pp. 144 and 147).

4. *The Individual Inositols*

The recent reviews by Dangschat[2(d)] and Ballou[2(e)] have dealt extensively with cyclitols and related compounds in plants and micro-organisms. The emphasis in the following paragraphs is, therefore, on those aspects of the chemistry and biochemistry of the individual inositols which have not been discussed elsewhere. In particular, reports of the occurrence of cyclitols in plants are only included here if they are necessary for further discussion or if they are too recent to have been included in Dangschat's tables.

a. myo-*Inositol.*—Of all the cyclitols, *myo*-inositol has the widest occurrence, and it is the only cyclitol that is a standard item of commerce. It is the parent substance of many naturally occurring cyclitol derivatives, and the raw material for the chemical synthesis of other cyclitols. It has thus been the most thoroughly studied, and, by virtue of its role as the "typical" cyclitol, its reactions, and the structures and reactions of its derivatives, have been rather extensively discussed in other Sections of this article.

A detailed list of the natural materials in which *myo*-inositol has been detected is presented by Fleury and Balatre,[87] and additional reports of its natural occurrence continue to appear. It is clear that *myo*-inositol is one of the most ubiquitous of organic compounds. Insofar as the authors are aware, no plant or animal tissue which has been examined by an ade-

(104) P. Balatre and M. Traisnel, *Bull. soc. pharm. Lille*, 28 (1955).

(105) A. Weissbach, *Biochim. et Biophys. Acta*, **27**, 608 (1958).

quate method has been found to *lack* this substance,[105a] and, in view of the wealth of positive data, it may be assumed *to be present in nearly all living cells*. There is thus little point in tabulating additional sources; worthy of note, however, is the observation that no less than 20 % of the solids in the seminal-vesicle secretion from boars is *myo*-inositol.[106]

The considerable biochemical interest which attaches to *myo*-inositol has made necessary the devising of ways for isolating it from all kinds of biological material. The older procedures[87] often involved cumbersome precipitations with heavy metals. In the improved methods which have more recently been described,[44, 103] most of the constituents of the tissue (except the polyhydric alcohols) are converted to ionic substances by heating with strong acid and are then removed with ion-exchange resins. The inositol is crystallized from the effluent, after concentration.

myo-Inositol appears to be the only cyclitol which has any general physiological importance. Many investigators have studied its biochemistry, and the principal aspects which have received attention have been: excretion of *myo*-inositol in the urine (inosituria); *myo*-inositol as a growth factor for microorganisms, and as a vitamin and lipotropic agent for animals; metabolic conversion of *myo*-inositol to D-glucose and its possible biosynthesis from D-glucose; bacterial oxidation of *myo*-inositol; and metabolic incorporation of the cyclitol into phospholipids. These items are briefly reviewed in the following paragraphs. Some aspects of the biochemistry of *myo*-inositol have also been reviewed elsewhere.[2(e), 2(f)]

Clinical inosituria was first observed in 1858, shortly after *myo*-inositol had been discovered.[107] It is a usual concomitant of diabetes mellitus and an extended debate has been waged as to whether inosituria is associated with the glucosuria (D-glucose excretion), characteristic of this disease or with the polyuria (excessive urine volume). The debate was apparently resolved in favor of the former hypothesis by the results of careful studies by Daughaday and coworkers.[108] These workers found that, in both humans and rats, the reabsorption of *myo*-inositol in the kidney is inhibited by high loads of D-glucose.

myo-Inositol has been considered to be a growth factor for yeasts, since Eastcott[109] found that it is a component of the Bios I complex. Although a requirement for *myo*-inositol is by no means universal among yeasts and

(105a) Although several species of bacteria which have been examined contain *myo*-inositol, *Escherichia coli* does not [D. W. Woolley, *J. Exptl. Med.*, **75**, 277 (1942)].

(106) T. Mann, *Proc. Roy. Soc.* (London), **B142**, 21 (1954).

(107) H. Vohl, *Arch. physiol. Heilk.*, **17** (new ser., **2**), 410 (1858).

(108) W. H. Daughaday, J. Larner and E. Houghton, *J. Clin. Invest.*, **33**, 326, 1075 (1954).

(109) E. V. Eastcott, *J. Phys. Chem.*, **32**, 1094 (1928).

related organisms, extensive studies, admirably summarized by Schopfer,[98] have revealed a large number of species and strains which respond to this compound.[110] The requirement for *myo*-inositol is seldom absolute, that is, *some* growth takes place without this cyclitol. A number of inositol-requiring mutants of the common bread-mold *Neurospora crassa* have been induced by artificial means.

Several other cyclitols have been found capable of replacing *myo*-inositol as a growth factor for various microorganisms, but the observed activities are much lower than that of *myo*-inositol.[98] The numerical values which are reported should in any case be regarded as tentative, in view of the fact that *myo*-inositol is a persistent impurity in many cyclitol preparations (see p. 157).

In some organisms, *myo*-inositol reverses the toxicity of the insecticidally active *gamma* (*muco*) isomer of hexachlorocyclohexane. In other organisms, the effect cannot be observed, and the notion that *gamma*-hexachlorocyclohexane is an inositol antimetabolite has thus been vigorously disputed.[98] All the discrepant observations can be reconciled, according to Fuller and coworkers,[110a] if one considers that the insecticide interferes only with the utilization of *exogenously supplied* inositol. It has also been claimed that streptomycin is an antimetabolite of inositol lipids, but efforts to substantiate this claim have not been fully successful.[98]

True competitive antagonists of *myo*-inositol have recently been found in the cyclitol series.[111]

Of 27 cyclitols tested in an extensive survey, three had anti-(*myo*-inositol) activity in the yeast *Schizosaccharomyces pombe*, and 15 were active in inositol-less *Neurospora crassa*.[112] The best anti-inositols are the ethylene oxide derivative CXXX (see p.187) and its homologs (which are derived from *scyllo*-inosose by treatment with the appropriate diazoalkane[1]), and isomytilitol (see p. 188) and its derivatives (obtained from CXXX or CXXX' by ring-opening reactions[1]). When the ratio of isomytilitol to *myo*-inositol (in the medium) is adjusted to permit limited growth, the antagonist is incorporated into the phospholipids of the *Neurospora*.[113]

The discovery by Woolley[114] that *myo*-inositol cures the alopecia (loss of hair) suffered by mice existing on a certain experimental diet seemed to

(110) To Schopfer's list may be added the fungus *Diplocarpon rosae* [H. S. Shirakawa, *Am. J. Botany*, **42**, 379 (1955)].

(110a) R. C. Fuller, R. W. Barratt and E. L. Tatum, *J. Biol. Chem.*, **186**, 823 (1950).

(111) W. H. Schopfer and T. Posternak, *Chimia* (Switz.), **7**, 90 (1953).

(112) W. H. Schopfer and T. Posternak, *Schweiz. Z. allgem. Pathol. u. Bakteriol.*, **19**, 647 (1956).

(113) T. Posternak and W. H. Schopfer, *Bull. soc. chim. biol.*, **39**, 1037 (1957).

(114) D. W. Woolley, *J. Biol. Chem.*, **139**, 29 (1941).

place this cyclitol on the list of animal vitamins. In the years immediately following Woolley's discovery, other workers reported that the compound has various beneficial effects in the diets of other species, and, in particular, it was reported that myo-inositol is a lipotropic agent[115] (that is, a substance which prevents or cures fatty infiltration of the liver).

Controversy has attended both of these claims, but it has been established that myo-inositol *does* have lipotropic activity when it is added to a fat-free diet which is low in other lipotropic agents (for example, choline, or methionine).[116] Even here, the inositol does *not* completely prevent the development of a fatty liver; this effect can be produced with choline, with which myo-inositol has a supplementary effect. The fatty livers produced (in rats) by the diet mentioned are characteristically high in cholesterol esters. The designation "biotin fatty liver" for this condition is a misnomer.[117]

The complete elucidation of the components of the B-complex of vitamins, and advances in the art of compounding diets from crystalline components, have made possible more definite tests of the supposed role of myo-inositol as a vitamin. It has been shown that this cyclitol has *no beneficial effect*, when it is added to otherwise adequate diets, on the growth of rats[118] and guinea pigs.[119, 120] Most probably, many of the conditions which were earlier observed to respond to myo-inositol were really deficiencies of *other* vitamins, and the action of the inositol was to make available increased quantities of these (through its effect on the intestinal microflora). The interesting recent claim[121] that myo-inositol in large doses can substitute for L-ascorbic acid in the diet of the guinea pig could not be substantiated.[120]

Despite the negative results of feeding experiments, it is clear that animals require myo-inositol for the synthesis of phospholipids (see p. 175), and, perhaps, for other purposes. Indeed, myo-inositol is necessary for the propagation, in culture, of 19 out of 20 lines of normal and malignant human and mouse tissues.[122] It thus appears likely that only certain animal

(115) G. Gavin and E. W. McHenry, *J. Biol. Chem.*, **139**, 485 (1941).

(116) C. H. Best, C. C. Lucas, J. M. Patterson and J. H. Ridout, *Biochem. J.*, **48**, 448, 452 (1951).

(117) C. H. Best, C. C. Lucas, J. M. Patterson and J. H. Ridout, *Biochem. J.*, **40**, 368 (1946).

(118) M. H. McCormick, P. N. Harris and C. A. Anderson, *J. Nutrition*, **52**, 337 (1954).

(119) M. E. Reid, *Proc. Soc. Exptl. Biol. Med.*, **85**, 547 (1954).

(120) L. Anderson, R. H. Coots and J. W. Halliday, *J. Nutrition*, **64**, 167 (1958).

(121) G. Oggioni, *Boll. soc. ital. biol. sper.*, **29**, 1421 (1953); *Chem. Abstracts*, **48**, 5309 (1954) and others cited in Ref. 120.

(122) H. Eagle, V. I. Oyama, M. Levy and A. E. Freeman, *J. Biol. Chem.*, **226**, 191 (1957).

organs can synthesize *myo*-inositol, and that these supply the compound to the other tissues of the body. Alternatively, there may be a small dietary requirement which has still escaped detection (the control diets used, even in recent experiments, apparently contain about 0.5 mg. of *myo*-inositol per 100 g.), or the intestinal microflora may be the source of supply.[113] With regard to the first possibility, it is known that carbon-14 (administered as D-glucose) is incorporated into *myo*-inositol by rats and embryonic chicks[103, 123]; the evidence strongly points to the rat's own tissues as the site of synthesis, and no other possibility exists for the chick embryo. It has not been shown, however, whether the species concerned can synthesize their full daily requirements of the compound.

The demonstrated biosynthesis of *myo*-inositol from D-glucose is not necessarily to be regarded as evidence for the long-postulated direct interconversion of the two compounds, since the D-glucose may have been degraded to small fragments before its carbon atoms entered the inositol. The reverse conversion (*myo*-inositol → D-glucose) has been demonstrated in the rat by means of deuterated *myo*-inositol,[19, 124] and by means of[125, 126] *myo*-inositol uniformly labeled with C^{14}, and considerable evidence about the mechanism of this conversion is available. *myo*-Inositol-*2*-H^2 (*myo*-inositol-*2*-*d*) is known to give D-glucose-*6*-H^2 in the rat, and *myo*-inositol-*6*-H^2 (*myo*-inositol-*6*-*d*) and *myo*-inositol-*4,6*-H^2_2 give[127] D-glucose-*1,3*-H^2_2. *myo*-Inositol-*2*-C^{14} gives[128] D-glucose-*1,6*-C^{14}_2. It is thus clear that the conversion is not merely a direct ring-cleavage,[129] as had been postulated because of the occurrence of the D-glucose configuration in the *myo*-inositol molecule (see formula LIII). If such were the case, *myo*-inositol labeled at C2 would give D-glucose labeled at C5, and that labeled at C6 would give D-glucose labeled at C1 only.

myo-Inositol is cleaved *in vitro* (by a rat-kidney preparation) to DL-glucuronic acid,[130] and when inositol-*2*-C^{14} is used as the substrate, the carbon-14 appears (as expected) at C5 in both enantiomorphs of the prod-

(123) W. H. Daughaday, J. Larner and C. Hartnett, *J. Biol. Chem.*, **212**, 869 (1955).

(124) Stetten and Stetten considered their material—deuterated by prolonged treatment with deuterium oxide in the presence of platinum—randomly labeled, but it now appears[52] that it was deuterated at C2 only.

(125) E. A. Moscatelli and J. Larner, *Arch. Biochem. Biophys.*, **80**, 26 (1959).

(126) H. Herken, D. Maibauer and F. Weygand, *Z. Naturforsch.*, **12b**, 598 (1957).

(127) T. Posternak, W. H. Schopfer and D. Reymond, *Helv. Chim. Acta*, **38**, 1283 (1955); T. Posternak, W. H. Schopfer, D. Reymond and C. Lark, *ibid.*, **41**, 235 (1958). The numbering used refers to formula LIII. Rigorous nomenclature would require the monodeuterated compound to be called *myo*-inositol-*4*-H^2.

(128) L. Anderson and R. H. Coots, *Biochim. et Biophys. Acta*, **28**, 666 (1958).

(129) H. O. L. Fischer, *Harvey Lectures*, Ser. **40**, 156 (1944–5).

(130) F. C. Charalampous and C. Lyras, *J. Biol. Chem.*, **228**, 1 (1957).

uct.[131] Labeled D-glucuronic acid (LIV) has been identified in the urine of rats which have received labeled *myo*-inositol,[128, 132] and it is thus possible that cleavage to D-glucuronic acid is an important pathway for the *in*

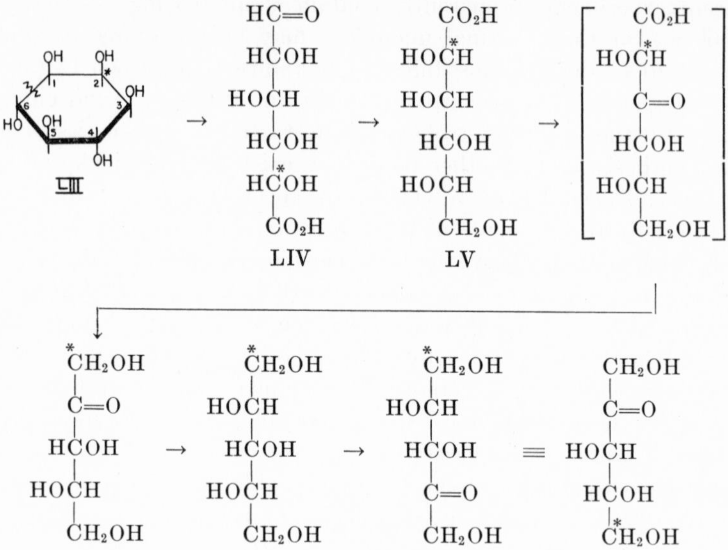

LIII   LIV   LV

LVI

vivo catabolism of *myo*-inositol. If this is so, the formation of D-glucose would involve the known metabolic reactions LIV → LVI, by which D-glucuronic acid is converted to D-*threo*-pentulose (D-xylulose, LVI). By this scheme, *myo*-inositol-6-H^2 (*myo*-inositol-6-d) would give D-*threo*-pentulose-1-H^2, and *myo*-inositol-2-C^{14} would give D-*threo*-pentulose-5-C^{14}. 1-Labeled pentose is known to form 1,3-labeled D-glucose by way of the pentose cycle,[133] and 5-labeled pentose should, by the same cycle, give 1,6-labeled D-glucose. The reactions LIII → LVI, plus the pentose cycle, thus explain fairly well the label distributions observed in D-glucose formed from specifically labeled inositols.[127, 128, 134]

However, there is evidence that the scheme LIII → LVI does not represent the only pathway for catabolism of *myo*-inositol in animals. Label from administered *myo*-inositol appears only slowly in glycogen,[128] but it

(131) F. C. Charalampous, S. Bumiller and S. Graham, *J. Am. Chem. Soc.*, **80**, 2022 (1958).

(132) J. J. Burns, N. Trousof, C. Evans, N. Papadopoulos and B. Agranoff, *Biochim. et Biophys. Acta*, **33**, 215 (1959).

(133) H. H. Hiatt, *J. Biol. Chem.*, **224**, 851 (1957).

(134) *myo*-Inositol-4,6-$H^2{}_2$ (*myo*-inositol-4,6-d_2) gives the same label pattern as inositol-6-H^2 (inositol-6-d), indicating that the deuterium at C4 is lost in metabolism (see Ref. 127).

appears immediately in respiratory carbon dioxide.[31, 125, 126] Also, the addition of the supposed intermediates LIV and LV to certain kidney preparations which can convert labeled inositol to $C^{14}O_2$ does not[135] "trap" the carbon-14.

The role, if any, of L-glucuronic acid in the metabolism of *myo*-inositol *in vivo* is unknown, since this acid has not been found in Nature nor been used in metabolic studies. Apparently, however, the D and L enantiomorphs of glucuronic acid are formed from *myo*-inositol by separate enzymes.[131]

The biosynthesis of *myo*-inositol in a yeast (*Torulopsis utilis*) has been studied with formate-C^{14}, acetate-*2*-C^{14}, formaldehyde-C^{14}, and D-glucose (variously labeled).[136] The small molecules are the best precursors for inositol, and, indeed, it appears that, when the cyclitol is formed from D-glucose, the sugar is fragmented before incorporation, instead of being cyclized directly.

In addition to the limited oxidations described earlier (see p. 144), the fermentation of *myo*-inositol to two-carbon and three-carbon compounds, and its complete oxidation to carbon dioxide plus water, can be performed by a number of micro-organisms. Detailed studies have been carried out with only one organism, *Aerobacter aerogenes*. In the presence of arsenite, this bacterium ferments *myo*-inositol according to the following equation.[137]

$$C_6H_{12}O_6 \quad \rightarrow \quad C_3H_6O_3 + C_2H_5OH + CO_2$$
$$\textit{myo-Inositol} \qquad \text{Lactic acid}$$

The process differs from the fermentation of D-glucose by the same organism. The initial reaction is believed to be a dehydrogenation to an inosose,[137] and the next step may be a dehydration.[45]

The expected incorporation of *myo*-inositol into phospholipids has been observed *in vivo*[31,125] and in kidney preparations *in vitro*,[138] and some progress has been made toward understanding the enzymic mechanism involved.[101(b),138,139] It appears that the inositol is neither phosphorylated nor converted to a coenzyme prior to incorporation. Hokin and Hokin[140] have made the interesting observation that the turnover of *myo*-inositol in the monophosphoinositide of brain and pancreas slices is stimulated by acetylcholine. The effects of various drugs on this turnover have been studied by other workers. It has been postulated that the decomposition and resynthesis of inositol phosphatide is a part of the membrane-transport process.[140]

(135) K. E. Richardson and B. Axelrod, *Biochim. et Biophys. Acta*, **32**, 265 (1959).
(136) F. C. Charalampous, *J. Biol. Chem.*, **225**, 595 (1957).
(137) B. Magasanik, *J. Biol. Chem.*, **205**, 1019 (1953).
(138) B. W. Agranoff, R. M. Bradley and R. O. Brady, *Biochim. et Biophys. Acta*, **25**, 445 (1957).
(139) H. Paulus and E. P. Kennedy, *J. Am. Chem. Soc.*, **80**, 6689 (1958).
(140) L. E. Hokin and M. R. Hokin, *J. Biol. Chem.*, **233**, 805, 818 (1958).

b. dextro-Inositol and levo-*Inositol.*—As had previously been suspected,[1] Müller's *iso*-inositol was found to be identical with *rac*-inositol.[141,142]

The structures of the di-*O*-isopropylidene acetals of *dextro*-inositol and *levo*-inositol were determined by lead tetraacetate oxidation, and the results of these degradations confirmed the configurations previously assigned to the two active inositols.[1] The *dextro* compound gave[61] the di-*O*-isopropylidene acetal of D-*manno*-hexodialdose (LVII), which was reduced by sodium

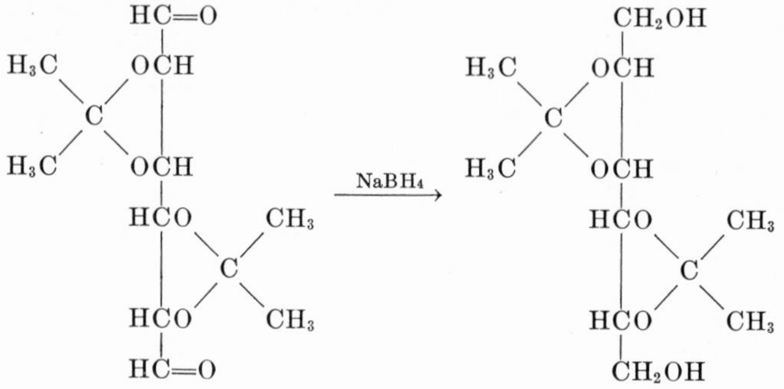

borohydride to 2,3:4,5-di-*O*-isopropylidene-D-mannitol (LVIII). From *levo*-inositol, the L-hexodialdose was obtained,[143] and it was reduced by the Meerwein–Ponndorf reaction to di-*O*-isopropylidene-L-mannitol. By carrying out the oxidation with periodate and the reduction with sodium borohydride, without isolation of the intermediates, L-mannitol, previously a rather inaccessible substance, may be readily obtained.

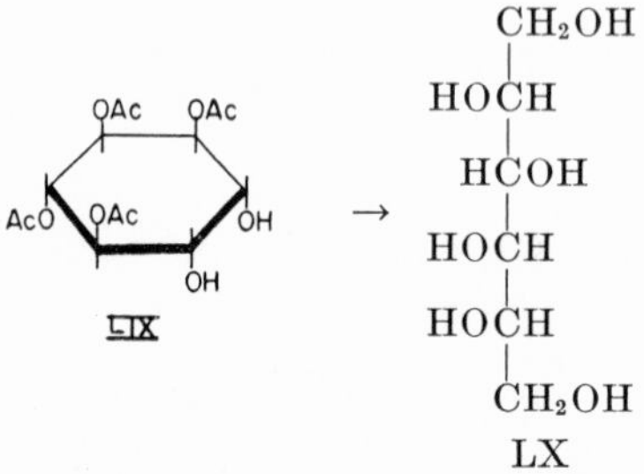

The structure of the mono-*O*-isopropylidene acetal of *dextro*-inositol was determined in a similar way.[144] It was acetylated and then deacetonated, and treatment of the resulting *dextro*-inositol tetraacetate (LIX) with lead

(141) H. G. Fletcher, Jr., and G. R. Findlay, *J. Am. Chem. Soc.*, **70**, 4050 (1948).

(142) T. Posternak, *Helv. Chim. Acta*, **31**, 2242 (1948).

(143) S. J. Angyal, C. G. Macdonald and N. K. Matheson, *J. Chem. Soc.*, 3321 (1953).

(144) C. E. Ballou and H. O. L. Fischer, *Abstracts Papers Am. Chem. Soc.*, **125**, 9D (1954).

tetraacetate and then with sodium borohydride gave a derivative of L-glucitol (LX).

c. scyllo-*Inositol.*—scyllo-Inositol has been found in the urines of several mammals, including that of man,[145] and in *Calycanthus occidentalis* and *Chimonanthus fragrans.*[146] It is an interesting question whether the substance in urine is derived from the animal's diet or whether it arises metabolically. However, the fact that excretion of *scyllo*-inositol can be induced by feeding large doses of *myo*-inositol[147] argues for the latter explanation.

d. allo-*Inositol and* muco-*Inositol.*—These two inositols were originally prepared from conduritol, a naturally occurring cyclohexenetetrol which is difficult to obtain in quantity.[1] Newer methods allow their synthesis from the readily available inositols.

allo-Inositol is best prepared by solvolysis of 3-O-tosyl-*levo*-inositol (see p. 155). It is also obtained by the *cis*-hydroxylation[4] of cyclohexene-1,2/3,4-tetrol (L; see p. 156) with silver chlorate in the presence of catalytic amounts of osmium tetroxide.

muco-Inositol can be prepared from quebrachitol: the steps described on p. 155 lead to 1-O-methyl-*muco*-inositol (XLVIII) which can be demethylated with hydriodic acid. Another preparation[148] starts from 1,2-O-isopropylidene-*myo*-inositol and involves the following steps.

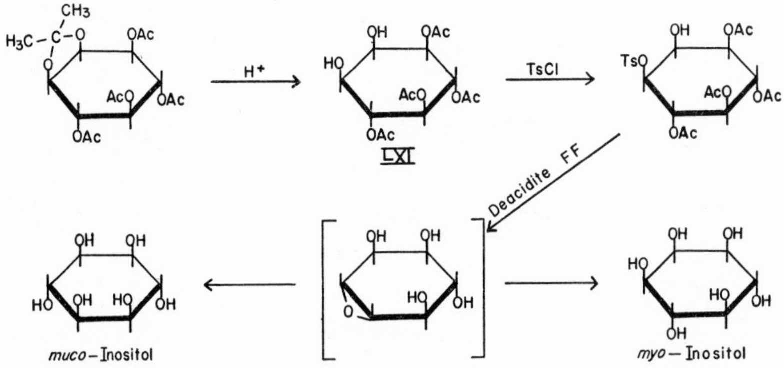

In the tosylation of LXI, only the equatorial hydroxyl group reacts readily; introduction of a second tosyl group (onto the axial oxygen atom) is very difficult. Detosylation is carried out with a strong-base ion-exchange resin to minimize epoxide migration (see p. 182); if alkali is used, *rac*-inositol is the main product.

(145) P. Fleury, J. Courtois and A. L. Jouannet, *Bull. soc. chim. biol.*, **33**, 1885 (1951); P. Malangeau, *ibid.*, **38**, 729 (1956).

(146) V. Plouvier, *Compt. rend.*, **242**, 2389 (1956).

(147) C. Helleu, *Bull. soc. chim. biol.*, **39**, 633 (1957).

(148) S. J. Angyal and J. Curtin, unpublished work.

e. neo-*Inositol*.—*neo*-Inositol was synthesized by Angyal and Matheson[149] from di-*O*-isopropylidene-*levo*-inositol by tosylation, detosylation to (+)-1,2-anhydro-3,4:5,6-di-*O*-isopropylidene-*allo*-inositol (LXII), and hy-

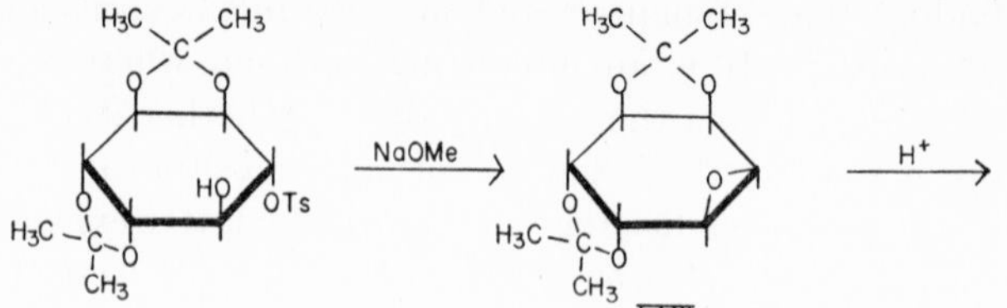

drolysis. These reactions establish the configuration of *neo*-inositol as IV. This cyclitol is remarkable for its low solubility in water (about 0.1 g. in 100 ml. at room temperature).

f. cis-*Inositol*.—*cis*-Inositol was, apparently, first obtained in the hydrogenation of tetrahydroxyquinone over Raney nickel,[18] but, at that time, its configuration could not be ascertained. By the time it was again isolated,[21] from the mixture produced by the low-pressure hydrogenation of tetrahydroxyquinone over palladium (see p. 141), all the *other* diastereomers were already known, and the all-*cis* configuration was allotted to the new inositol. This assignment was confirmed by its dehydrogenation, both by *Acetobacter* and by air in the presence of platinum, to *cis*-inosose (X; see p. 146) which can be reduced, by means of sodium amalgam, to *epi*-inositol. *cis*-Inositol has recently been obtained[52] by the solvolysis of 6-*O*-tosyl-*epi*-inositol, a reaction which also proves its configuration.

In the hydrogenation of tetrahydroxyquinone in presence of the usual palladium catalyst, the yield of *cis*-inositol is small (about 4%), but it can be increased to 20% by the use of a palladium catalyst precipitated on charcoal.[21]

At the time of its first preparation, it was suggested that *cis*-inositol might be the only known compound with three axial oxygen atoms attached to one side of the cyclohexane ring. However, there are two natural compounds which—if the structures at present allocated to them are correct—contain the same arrangement, namely, ouabagenin[150] and lycoctonin.[151]

(149) S. J. Angyal and N. K. Matheson, *J. Am. Chem. Soc.*, **77**, 4343 (1955).

(150) G. Volpp and C. Tamm, *Helv. Chim. Acta*, **40**, 1860 (1957).

(151) M. Przybylska and L. Marion, *Can. J. Chem.*, **34**, 185 (1956); O. E. Edwards, L. Marion and D. K. R. Stewart, *ibid.*, **34**, 1315 (1956).

5. Methyl Ethers of the Inositols

A number of inositol methyl ethers have been known for many years,[1] namely, (+)-pinitol (*dextro*-inositol methyl ether), (−)-quebrachitol (*levo*-inositol methyl ether), (+)-bornesitol and sequoyitol (*myo*-inositol methyl ethers), and dambonitol (*myo*-inositol dimethyl ether). Four new, naturally-occurring inositol methyl ethers have recently been reported. Three of these are ethers of *myo*-inositol, namely, (−)-bornesitol from a number of *Lathyrus* species, from many species of *Leguminaceae*, *Rhamnaceae*, and *Borraginaceae*,[152] and from *Lithospermum ruderale* L.[59]; (+)-ononitol from *Ononis natrix* L. and several other plants,[152(a),153] and (−)-liriodendritol, a dimethyl ether, from the leaves of the Virginia tulip-tree (*Liriodendron*).[154] The fourth is (−)-pinitol, the methyl ether of *levo*-inositol enantiomorphous with the long-known *dextro*-inositol derivative, from *Artemisia dracunculus*.[155] In addition, new sources have been found for two long-known, but hitherto rare, *myo*-inositol methyl ethers, namely, dambonitol, which occurs in the latex sera (yield, 2–2.5%) of *Dyera lowii*[156] (Borneo) and *Dyera costulata* (Malaya)[157]; and (+)-bornesitol, obtained in 3.5% yield from opepe wood (*Sarcocephalus diderrichii*, West Africa).[158] A. B. Anderson and his colleagues[159] have carried out extensive investigations on the isolation of (+)-pinitol from Western sugar-pine on the pilot-plant scale, and crude quebrachitol has now been made available commercially.[160]

Some of the inositol methyl ethers appear to be widely spread in Nature. Many new occurrences (not tabulated by Dangschat[2(d)]) have been reported for (+)-pinitol,[146,153,161,162] quebrachitol,[153,162] and sequoyitol.[153,162] It is interesting that pinitol and sequoyitol frequently occur in the same plants.

As a result of recent work by several investigators, the constitutions of all these methyl ethers are now established. Formulas LXV and LXIII were postulated for (−)-quebrachitol[6,57] and (+)-pinitol,[6,61] respectively, on the basis of their behavior on acetonation. (−)-Quebrachitol gives a

(152) (a) V. Plouvier, *Compt. rend.*, **241**, 983 (1955); (b) **247**, 2190 (1958).

(153) V. Plouvier, *Compt. rend.*, **247**, 2423 (1958).

(154) V. Plouvier, *Compt. rend.*, **241**, 765 (1955).

(155) V. Plouvier, *Compt. rend.*, **243**, 1913 (1956).

(156) Common names: dyera tree or jelutong. The latex is used in the manufacture of chewing gum.

(157) A. J. Comollo and A. K. Kiang, *J. Chem. Soc.*, 3319 (1953).

(158) F. E. King and L. Jurd, *J. Chem. Soc.*, 1192 (1953).

(159) A. B. Anderson, *Ind. Eng. Chem.*, **45**, 593 (1953).

(160) From the Plantation Division, U. S. Rubber Co., Rockefeller Center, New York, N. Y.

(161) S. Gottlieb and F. E. Brauns, *J. Am. Chem. Soc.*, **73**, 5880 (1951); M. Nilsson, *Acta Chem. Scand.*, **10**, 413 (1956).

(162) V. Plouvier, *Compt. rend.*, **232**, 1239 (1951); **234**, 362 (1952); **241**, 1838 (1955); **245**, 2377 (1957).

mono-O-isopropylidene acetal which consumes one molar equivalent of periodate per mole, whereas (+)-pinitol gives a di-O-isopropylidene acetal. If
it is assumed that acetonation takes place only at pairs of vicinal cis-hydroxyl groups (see p. 148), the isopropylidene acetals must be LXVI and
LXIV, and the parent ethers must be LXV and LXIII. The constitutions

of (+)-pinitol and its isopropylidene acetal were confirmed by methylating
the latter to LXVIII and converting this to the bis(methylamide) of di-O-
methyl-D-threaric acid[61]; and, further, by the synthesis of the enantiomorphs of LXIV and LXVIII from di-O-isopropylidene-levo-inositol
(XXVIII), for which an independent proof of structure is available (see p.
166).[143]

Additional proof of the proposed formula for (−)-quebrachitol was furnished by the synthesis of 1-O-methyl-levo-inositol (2-O-methyl-levo-inositol)

(LXXV) by an unequivocal method.[149] (−)-Quebrachitol differs from LXXV and from the enantiomorph of (+)-pinitol. Since each optically-active inositol can give rise to only three monomethyl ethers,[163] (−)-quebrachitol must be 2-O-methyl-*levo*-inositol (1-O-methyl-*levo*-inositol) (LXV).

The remaining naturally-occurring O-methylinositols are derivatives of *myo*-inositol, which can theoretically give rise to six monomethyl ethers. Two of these, the 2-methyl (LXXII) and the 5-methyl ether (LXXI), must be *meso* compounds. The other four must be optically active and constitute two racemic pairs (one enantiomorph of each is shown as LXXIII and LXXIV); they are, therefore, designated (+)- and (−)-1- and (+)- and (−)-4-O-methyl-*myo*-inositol, by the principle of lowest numbering.

Sequoyitol, which is optically inactive, was presumed to be one of the *meso* forms, and this presumption was eventually verified by the finding that the infrared spectrum of its pentaacetate differs from those of the (optically active) bornesitol pentaacetate and ononitol pentaacetate.[55] Many unsuccessful attempts were made to decide between the two possibilities (LXXI and LXXII) by indirect means,[78,83] by synthesis,[164] and by degradation.[58] Proof that sequoyitol is actually 5-O-methyl-*myo*-inositol (LXXI) was finally obtained by synthesizing it from (+)-pinitol.[58] The only *myo*-inositol methyl ethers which could be derived from pinitol by the inversion of one of its hydroxyl groups are LXXI and LXXIV; formula LXXIV is excluded because it must be optically active. The synthesis of sequoyitol from (+)-1,2-anhydro-*neo*-inositol (see p. 183) confirms the formula LXXI.[7,165]

The methoxyl group of the bornesitols was considered to be at C1 (LXXIII and enantiomorph) from the electrophoretic mobility of (+)-bornesitol in borate buffer.[82] This postulate received further support when (±)-bornesitol was obtained by the partial demethylation[55] of dambonitol (LXXVII). Racemic bornesitol was also synthesized by the methylation of 1,3,4,5,6-penta-O-acetyl-*myo*-inositol, but the constitution is not proved by this reaction, since it involves the migration of an acetyl group (from C1 to C2).[164] Final proof that the methoxyl group is at C1 was obtained by the degradation of 2,3-O-isopropylidene-(−)-bornesitol to a derivative of ribitol.[59]

(163) Positions 1 and 6, 2 and 5, and 3 and 4 (2 and 3, 1 and 4, and 5 and 6 in the Fletcher–Anderson–Lardy system) are sterically equivalent in *dextro*- and *levo*-inositol.

(164) L. Anderson and A. M. Landel, *J. Am. Chem. Soc.*, **76**, 6130 (1954).

(165) The designation "sequoyitol R" was applied[2(d)] to a compound contained in a sample of the cyclitol from *Macrozamia riedlei*[78] because this material, unlike sequoyitol, did not show electrophoretic migration in borate buffer.[83] "Sequoyitol R" is a misnomer, however; the non-migrating material was actually[55] the glucoside macrozamin.

An unequivocal synthesis of the racemate of LXXIV was achieved by treating 5,6-anhydro-*allo*-inositol with sodium methoxide[7] (see p. 183). The pentaacetate of LXXIV has the same infrared spectrum as the pentaacetate of (+)-ononitol, and hence the ononitols are the 4-O-methyl-*myo*-inositols.

The assignment of formula LXXIII to (−)-bornesitol results from its successful synthesis from quebrachitol (LXV).[53] The structure of the inosose LXIX was established by the periodate oxidation of its phenylhydrazone and of the O-methyl-*vibo*-quercitol derived from it. Similarly, (+)-ononitol was obtained by catalytically oxidizing O-isopropylidenequebrachitol (LXVI), reducing the resulting inosose (LXX), and removing the isopropylidene group by hydrolysis.[53] It follows that (+)-ononitol is LXXIV. As 2-O-methyl-*myo*-inositol has been synthesized,[55,166] all of the possible *myo*-inositol monomethyl ethers are known [(−)-ononitol has only been obtained as the racemate].

Periodate oxidation was used for studying the position of the methyl groups in dambonitol. The first results were interpreted as indicating a *para* arrangement[157] (through failure to detect formic acid, see p. 150), but later investigation showed that the methyl groups must be *meta* to each other.[69] As dambonitol is optically inactive, it was assumed to be *meso*, leaving only C1 and C3 or C4 and C6 as possibilities for location of the methoxyl groups. The 1,3-dimethyl ether (LXXVII) was indicated as the structure by the lack of electrophoretic mobility of dambonitol in borate buffer, and by its synthesis by the methylation of (±)-1,4,5,6-tetra-O-acetyl-*myo*-inositol (LXXVI) (a reaction which is accompanied by acetyl migration).[55] The partial demethylation of dambonitol to (±)-bornesitol was then used as evidence for assigning formula LXXIII to the latter; however, as mentioned above, the formulas assigned the bornesitols now rest on independent evidence. The relating of the bornesitols to dambonitol by partial demethylation is now the best proof for assigning formula LXXVII to the latter. It is of interest that (+)-bornesitol occurs naturally with dambonitol, and it is, presumably, an intermediate in its biosynthesis.[55]

Like dambonitol, liriodendritol consumes two moles of periodate per mole, with the formation of one mole of formic acid; hence the two methoxyl groups must be *meta* to each other. Partial demethylation gives (−)-bornesitol; (−)-liriodendritol is, therefore, 1,5-di-O-methyl-*myo*-inositol (LXXVIII).[72]

Mixtures of methyl ethers result from the treatment of *myo*-inositol with dimethyl sulfate and alkali. Although none of these mixtures have been adequately characterized, pure (or seemingly pure) compounds which have been isolated from them include the monomethyl ether[166] (later identified

(166) E. G. Griffin and J. M. Nelson, *J. Am. Chem. Soc.*, **37**, 1552 (1915).

as racemic bornesitol),[55,164] 2-O-methyl-*myo*-inositol,[55] sequoyitol,[55] and a di-O-methyl-,[166] a penta-O-methyl-,[167] and hexa-O-methyl-*myo*-inositol.[167]

In addition to the methyl ethers of *dextro-*, *levo-*, and *myo*-inositol which have been discussed in the preceding paragraphs, methyl ethers of most of the other inositols are now known. These compounds have been incidentally obtained in the course of other investigations—by the reduction of inososes formed from known ethers, by the inversion of tosyl esters of known ethers, and by opening the epoxide rings of anhydroinositols with methoxide ion. The individual compounds are listed in Tables II–X, pp. 192–203.

6. *Inositol Phosphates and Inositol Phosphatides*

myo-Inositol occurs to a considerable extent in Nature in the form of phosphate esters.[168] Prominent among these phosphates are (a) the hexaphosphoric ester (phytic acid) in plants, and (b) the inositol-containing phospholipids (inositol phosphatides or phosphoinositides) which are found in plants, animals, and micro-organisms, and which comprise 2 to 9% of the total phosphatides of animal tissues.

On hydrolysis of the *phosphatides*, *myo*-inositol monophosphate—and, from a brain phosphatide, a diphosphate—is obtained; but, these products have, in most cases, not been adequately characterized, and it is not yet known whether all phospholipids contain the same *myo*-inositol phosphate. It has been shown[169,170] that the phosphate obtained by hydrolysis of liver phosphatide[171] or soybean phosphatide[172] is a mixture of *myo*-inositol 1- and 2-phosphates. A *myo*-inositol phosphate, of unknown constitution, was isolated[173] from liver without previous hydrolysis; apparently it occurs in the free state.

myo-Inositol can give rise to six different monophosphates: two *meso* forms and four optically-active derivatives. Partial hydrolysis of phytic acid by acid,[174] by alkali,[175] or enzymically[176] gives *myo*-inositol monophosphate, besides higher phosphates. Contrary to an earlier report,[177] the *same*

(167) J. C. McGowan, *J. Soc. Chem. Ind.* (London), **66**, 446 (1947).
(168) None of the other inositols has been found in combination with phosphate.
(169) (a) T. Posternak, *Helv. Chim. Acta*, **41**, 1891 (1958); (b) **42**, 390 (1959).
(170) F. L. Pizer and C. E. Ballou, *J. Am. Chem. Soc.*, **81**, 915 (1959).
(171) J. M. McKibbin, *J. Biol. Chem.*, **220**, 537 (1956).
(172) E. Klenk and R. Sakai, *Z. physiol. Chem., Hoppe-Seyler's*, **258**, 33 (1939).
(173) G. Hübscher and J. N. Hawthorne, *Biochem. J.*, **67**, 523 (1957).
(174) J. Courtois and M. Masson, *Bull. soc. chim. biol.*, **32**, 314 (1950).
(175) A. Desjobert, *Bull. soc. chim. biol.*, **36**, 1293 (1954).
(176) S. Posternak and T. Posternak, *Helv. Chim. Acta*, **12**, 1165 (1929).
(177) P. Fleury, A. Desjobert and J. Lecocq, *Bull. soc. chim. biol.*, **36**, 1301 (1954).
(177a) D. M. Brown and G. E. Hall, *J. Chem. Soc.*, 357 (1959).

phosphate is obtained by the various methods of hydrolysis[169,170,177a]; it is identical with *myo*-inositol 2-phosphate, synthesized[178] by phosphorylation of 1,3,4,5,6-penta-*O*-acetyl-*myo*-inositol. Apparently, the axial phosphate group in phytic acid is hydrolyzed more slowly than the other phosphate groups (by each method of hydrolysis). This phosphate has a lower activity as a growth factor for cells in tissue culture[122] than the one obtained by the hydrolysis of liver phosphoinositide (see below).[171]

myo-Inositol 5-phosphate has recently been synthesized from 1,2,3,4,6-penta-*O*-acetyl-*myo*-inositol.[179]

To obtain model compounds for the study of inositol phosphates, Kilgour and Ballou[180] treated di-*O*-isopropylidenepinitol (LXIV) and di-*O*-isopropylidene-*levo*-inositol (XXVIII) with diphenyl phosphorochloridate. For the latter, the result was surprising: instead of the expected mono- or di-phosphate, a cyclic phosphate (LXXIX) was obtained. In it, the phosphate group is attached to two *trans*-hydroxyl groups, like the third isopropylidene group in tri-*O*-isopropylidene-*levo*-inositol (see p. 149). This

LXXIX   **LXXX**

appears to be the first instance of the isolation of a cyclic phosphate from a phosphorylation reaction. Hydrolysis of the cyclic phosphate gives *levo*-inositol 3-phosphate (*levo*-inositol 5-phosphate).

The reaction of 1,4,5,6-tetra-*O*-acetyl-*myo*-inositol (LXXVI) with diphenyl phosphorochloridate also gave[169,170] a cyclic phosphate which was, however, not isolated; its hydrolysis yielded a mixture of the 2-phosphate with another phosphate which must be the (±)-1-phosphate. A similar mixture was obtained by heating either phosphate with dilute acid, owing to phosphate migration. Acid hydrolysis of the liver phosphoinositide—a process that would be expected[170,177a] to occur by the intermediate formation of a cyclic phosphate—also produced a mixture of the 1- and 2-phosphates; in this case, the former was shown to be optically active.[170] Since *myo*-inositol 2-phosphate is a *meso* compound it cannot give rise to an active derivative by phosphate migration; it appears, therefore, that, in the phosphoinositide of the liver, the phosphate group is attached to one of the enantiomeric 1-positions of *myo*-inositol.

(178) B. M. Iselin, *J. Am. Chem. Soc.*, **71**, 3822 (1949).
(179) S. J. Angyal, unpublished work.
(180) G. L. Kilgour and C. E. Ballou, *J. Am. Chem. Soc.*, **80**, 3956 (1958).

The *inositol phosphatides* or phosphoinositides are a rather heterogeneous group of substances having, in common, *myo*-inositol, phosphoric acid, glycerol, and fatty acids among their constituents. They have been admirably reviewed,[181] and hence only a short discussion will be given here. The first evidence for the occurrence of inositol phosphatides was obtained by R. J. Anderson[182] who, in 1930, showed that *myo*-inositol is a constituent of a phosphatide from tubercle bacillus, and he followed this work by the isolation of one hydrolysis product containing *myo*-inositol, D-mannose (two molecular proportions), and phosphoric acid,[183] and another one consisting of one mole of *myo*-inositol, one mole of glycerol, and two moles of phosphoric acid.[184] Other workers reported the isolation of inositol phosphatides from soybean,[185] brain,[186] peanut (groundnut),[186a] and many other sources.[181] On hydrolysis, these phosphatides give *myo*-inositol phosphate and glycerol phosphate, and those which were adequately investigated were found to contain *myo*-inositol and glycerol in equimolecular amounts. The presence of various sugars and of amines has been reported in some cases, but, owing to the great difficulties of separating and purifying the phosphatides, it is not clear whether they all were constituents or were merely impurities. Only in recent years, by the use of countercurrent extraction and of chromatographic techniques, have apparently pure inositol phosphatides been isolated.

The simplest type of phosphoinositide is represented by the phosphatide isolated from horse liver or dog liver by McKibbin.[171] This consists only of glycerol, *myo*-inositol, phosphoric acid, and fatty acids; it probably has structure LXXX. Similar inositides, differing only in the nature of the fatty acids, have been isolated from wheat germ,[187] beef heart, [188] and beef liver.[189] That the major portion of the fatty acids is attached to glycerol, not to *myo*-inositol, was shown by the isolation of a diglyceride on mild hydrolysis.[189]

More complex inositides probably embody LXXX as a structural unit. Thus, a lipid which, apparently, has this structure has been isolated from peas,[190] but the isolators believe that it is actually an artifact which arises

(181) J. Folch and F. N. LeBaron, *Can. J. Biochem. and Physiol.*, **34**, 305 (1956).

(182) R. J. Anderson, *J. Am. Chem. Soc.*, **52**, 1607 (1930).

(183) R. J. Anderson, W. C. Lothrop and M. M. Creighton, *J. Biol. Chem.*, **125**, 299 (1938).

(184) G. I. de Sütö-Nagy and R. J. Anderson, *J. Biol. Chem.*, **171**, 749, 761 (1947).

(185) D. W. Woolley, *J. Biol. Chem.*, **147**, 581 (1943).

(186) J. Folch, *J. Biol. Chem.*, **177**, 497, 505 (1949).

(186a) T. Malkin and A. G. Poole, *J. Chem. Soc.*, 3470 (1953).

(187) M. J. Morelec-Coulon and M. Faure, *Bull. soc. chim. biol.*, **39**, 947 (1957).

(188) M. Faure and M. J. Morelec-Coulon, *Compt. rend.*, **238**, 411 (1954).

(189) D. J. Hanahan and J. N. Olley, *J. Biol. Chem.*, **231**, 813 (1958).

(190) A. C. Wagenknecht and H. E. Carter, *Federation Proc.*, **16**, 266 (1957); A. C. Wagenknecht and L. M. Lewin, *ibid.*, **17**, 329 (1958).

by enzymic action during the storage of the seeds. Similarly, Okuhara and Nakayama[191] claim to have isolated a substance of structure LXXX from soybean lipid; this may represent a degradation product of the more complex phosphatide indicated by Woolley's earlier findings.[185] Tubercle bacillus yields a phosphatide, one mole of which contains, in addition to the constituents of LXXX, two moles of D-mannose, probably attached to the *myo*-inositol moiety.[192] Moreover, the peanut (groundnut) yields a phosphoinositide, one mole of which contains two moles of phosphate, one of ethanolamine, one of D-galactose, and two moles of L-arabinose, the D-galactose residue and one L-arabinose residue being present as a disaccharide.[186a]

The phosphoinositide isolated from brain cephalin by Folch[186] gives a *myo*-inositol diphosphate on hydrolysis; the two phosphate groups in the hydrolysis product are *meta* to each other, as is shown by the consumption of two molar equivalents of periodate with the formation of one mole of formic acid per mole. This phosphatide contains only one mole of fatty acid for each mole of inositol and glycerol, and it appears to differ considerably from the monophosphoinositides. Another particularly interesting inositol phospholipid is that isolated from corn and other seeds.[193] It contains the long-chain hydroxyamine phytosphingosine (instead of glycerol); three sugars, namely, L-arabinose, D-galactose, and D-mannose; and D-glucosamine and a hexuronic acid.

The structure of none of these phosphoinositides is fully known, but it is apparent that their study has reached a stage at which important results can be expected within the next few years.

7. Galactinol

Although *myo*-inositol appears to be bound to sugars in several phospholipids, only one pure inositol glycoside has thus far been described, namely, galactinol,[194] isolated from the sugar beet (*Beta vulgaris*). It is hydrolyzed by melibiase to D-galactose and *myo*-inositol. Complete methylation, followed by hydrolysis, gives 2,3,4,6-tetra-*O*-methyl-D-galactose and a penta-*O*-methyl-*myo*-inositol.[195] The position of the free hydroxyl group in the latter was determined by oxidation to a penta-*O*-methylinosose, which was

(191) E. Okuhara and T. Nakayama, *J. Biol. Chem.*, **215**, 295 (1955).

(192) (a) E. Vilkas and E. Lederer, *Bull. soc. chim. biol.*, **38**, 111 (1956); (b) E. Vilkas, *Compt. rend.*, **245**, 588 (1957).

(193) H. E. Carter, R. H. Gigg, J. H. Law, T. Nakayama and E. J. Weber, *J. Biol. Chem.*, **233**, 1309 (1958).

(194) R. J. Brown and R. F. Serro, *J. Am. Chem. Soc.*, **75**, 1040 (1953).

(195) E. A. Kabat, D. L. MacDonald, C. E. Ballou and H. O. L. Fischer, *J. Am. Chem. Soc.*, **75**, 4507 (1953).

converted by reduction and demethylation to *levo*-inositol. Galactinol is, therefore, a 1-*O*-α-D-galactopyranosyl-*myo*-inositol (LXXXI).

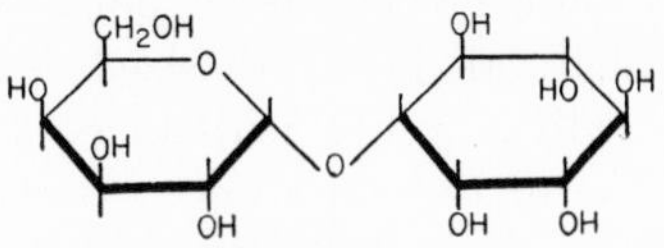

LXXXI

Galactinol

An additional glycoside of *myo*-inositol, not so well characterized as galactinol, is manninositose[183,192(b)] from the phosphatides of the tubercle bacillus (see p. 175).

III. Compounds Related to the Inositols

1. *Inososes*

The best known of the inososes (pentahydroxycyclohexanones) are (±)-*epi*-inosose [(±)-*epi*-inosose-2, LXXXIV] and *scyllo*-inosose (*myo*-inosose-2, LXXXII).[196] These are obtained from *myo*-inositol by moderated oxida-

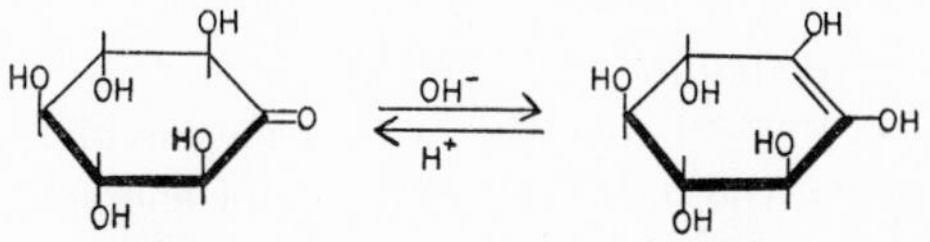

LXXXII   LXXXIII

scyllo—Inosose

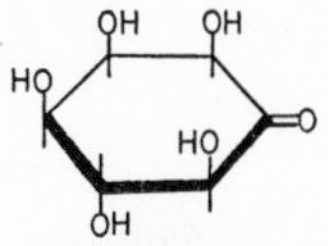

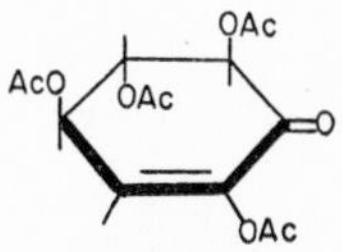

LXXXIV   LXXXV

epi—Inosose

tion with nitric acid, and by oxidation with *Acetobacter* or by catalytic aerial oxidation, respectively. Standardized directions for preparing them have appeared in *Biochemical Preparations*.[197]

The moderated oxidation, with nitric acid, of inositols other than *myo*-inositol has not been explored, probably because of the poor yields, but

(196) See Fletcher's review (Ref. 1, p. 62), where they are named *epi-meso*-inosose and *scyllo-meso*-inosose, respectively.

(197) T. Posternak, *Biochem. Preparations*, **2,** 57 (1952).

Acetobacter oxidation and catalytic aerial oxidation are synthetic methods of general applicability (see p. 144). The fact that only axial hydroxyl groups are oxidized, by both procedures, is not a severe limitation on the number of inososes which can be synthesized, since, for every possible inosose, there is theoretically a cyclitol with an axial hydroxyl group. Where selective oxidation of one of two, or three, axial hydroxyl groups in the parent cyclitol is necessary, suitably substituted derivatives may be required (for example, LXVI; see p. 172). The two methods complement each other rather well; the metal-catalyzed dehydrogenation is useful for obtaining monoketones from cyclitols (for example, *neo-* and *levo-*inositol) which give diketones with *Acetobacter*. Where both methods give the same product, the aerial oxidation is probably the method of choice for small quantities (1–10 g.). The *Acetobacter* method is preferable for work on a larger scale.

A noteworthy attribute of the inososes is their ability to reduce alkaline copper and similar reagents at room temperature. It was suggested[198,199] that this property could be explained by the hypothesis that the inososes exist in solution in the *keto* form, and this seems to be the case with LXXXII and LXXXIV, which show typical carbonyl absorption at 275–285 mμ in neutral solution.[200] However, the reduction of Tillmans' reagent (2,6-dichlorophenolindophenol) by alkaline (but not by neutral) solutions of *epi*-inosose and *scyllo*-inosose,[50,202,203] together with other evidence, suggests that, under these conditions, the inososes form salts of enediols of the type LXXXIII. Enediol formation would be a better explanation of the strong copper-reducing power of the inososes, and would also explain the fact that these compounds consume two equivalents of iodine per mole under the Willstätter–Schudel conditions.[198,204,204a] *epi*-Inosose has been converted into a crystalline compound which may be[203] a stereoisomer of the enediol LXXXIII.

Posternak[204] observed that the pentaacetate and pentabenzoate (and also the pentapropionate[205]) of *scyllo*-inosose occur in two interconvertible forms; the higher-melting forms are obtained by crystallization from solvents con-

(198) T. Posternak, *Helv. Chim. Acta*, **19**, 1333 (1936).

(199) T. Posternak, *Helv. Chim. Acta*, **29**, 1991 (1946).

(200) *vibo*-Inosose (*myo*-inosose-1, XCIV) loses its carbonyl absorption on standing in solution, apparently through dimerization (see Ref. 201).

(201) B. Magasanik and E. Chargaff, *J. Biol. Chem.*, **175**, 929 (1948).

(202) D. H. Couch and W. W. Pigman, *Anal. Chem.*, **24**, 1364 (1952).

(203) H. von Euler and A. Glaser, *Arkiv Kemi*, **8**, 61 (1955).

(204) T. Posternak, *Helv. Chim. Acta*, **24**, 1045 (1941).

(204a) It has been found (L. Anderson and G. G. Post, unpublished results) that exact stoichiometry in this reaction is obtained only under narrowly defined conditions which differ greatly for individual inososes.

(205) S. J. Angyal and N. K. Matheson, *J. Chem. Soc.*, 3349 (1950).

taining mineral acid or zinc chloride, and the lower-melting ones by crystallization from pure solvents. This observation puzzled cyclitol chemists for a number of years, and could not be traced either to ordinary dimorphism or to tautomerism.[205] It has now been found that the two "forms" are really identical, as judged by melting points determined in Pyrex capillary-tubes and on the Maquenne block, by x-ray powder diagrams, and by infrared spectra.[206] The low melting point of the one "form" in soft glass is actually the solid-state threshold temperature of the facile, alkali-catalyzed elimination of one mole of acid per mole, to give the unsaturated ketone LXXXV.[207] If traces of acid are present, or soft glass is avoided, the compound shows its true melting point.

Reactions of the carbonyl group of inososes include the addition of diazoalkanes, dithioacetal formation, reduction, hydrogenolysis, and phenylhydrazone formation. The epoxide CXXX′, which is formed from *scyllo*-inosose pentaacetate and diazomethane, is the starting material for a considerable series of seven-carbon derivatives.[1] Some of the newer compounds of this group are discussed on pages 187 and 188.

LXXXVI LXXXVII LXXXVIII LXXXIX

XC XCI XCII + 3 HCO_2H XCIII + 2 HCO_2H

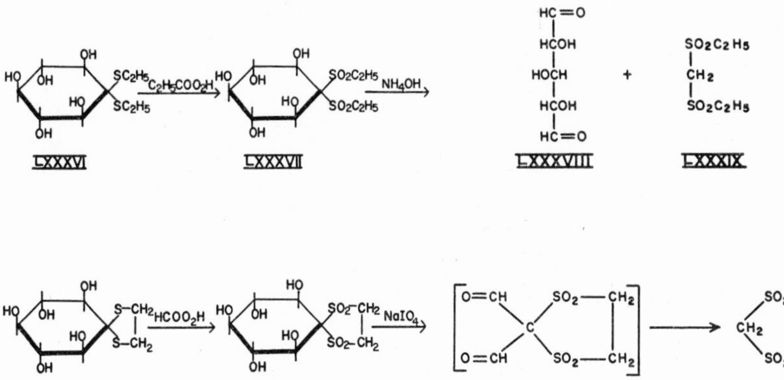

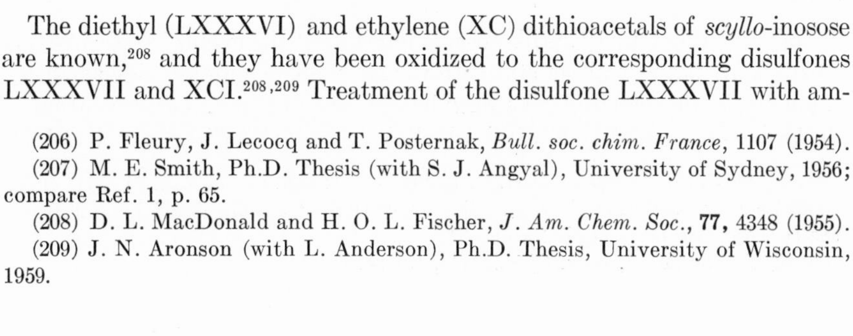

The diethyl (LXXXVI) and ethylene (XC) dithioacetals of *scyllo*-inosose are known,[208] and they have been oxidized to the corresponding disulfones LXXXVII and XCI.[208,209] Treatment of the disulfone LXXXVII with am-

(206) P. Fleury, J. Lecocq and T. Posternak, *Bull. soc. chim. France*, 1107 (1954).

(207) M. E. Smith, Ph.D. Thesis (with S. J. Angyal), University of Sydney, 1956; compare Ref. 1, p. 65.

(208) D. L. MacDonald and H. O. L. Fischer, *J. Am. Chem. Soc.*, **77**, 4348 (1955).

(209) J. N. Aronson (with L. Anderson), Ph.D. Thesis, University of Wisconsin, 1959.

monia ("sulfone degradation"[210]) causes cleavage of the cyclitol ring on *both* sides of the erstwhile carbonyl carbon atom, liberating bis(ethylsulfonyl)-methane (LXXXIX) and *xylo*-pentodialdose (LXXXVIII).[208] Single cleavage, leading to an open-chain product having all of the original carbon atoms, has been effected on the disulfone XCI.[209] The periodate oxidation of XCI follows a novel course: four molar equivalents of oxidant are consumed per mole, but five molar equivalents of formic acid are produced and the ethylene disulfone (XCIII) of formaldehyde is liberated.[209] Presumably, the dialdehyde XCII is formed as an intermediate and is then hydrolyzed.

The reduction of inososes is a method much used for the preparation of new cyclitols. Catalytic hydrogenation in neutral, aqueous solution yields predominantly the isomer with the newly formed hydroxyl group in the axial position,[210a] whereas the product from a reduction by sodium amalgam usually contains considerable quantities of both the possible epimers.[211] Recently, sodium borohydride has been used for reducing inososes[52,53,211]; in some cases, but not in others, it provides more of the equatorial isomer than does sodium amalgam.

Posternak found that hydrogenation of *scyllo*-inosose over platinum catalyst in a strongly acidic solution (for example, 5% sulfuric acid) brings about removal of the carbonyl oxygen atom, to yield *scyllo*-quercitol (CXLIV).[204] This reaction is a general one for the preparation of quercitols. However, it has recently been found[51] that, when a hydroxyl group adjacent to the keto group is axial, the results are more complex; the epimeric inositols (related to the inosose) and the expected quercitol are formed and, in addition, the tetrol derived from the inosose by loss of both the carbonyl oxygen atom and the axial hydroxyl group. The reaction is illustrated with (+)-*vibo*-inosose [(+)-*myo*-inosose-1, XCIV].

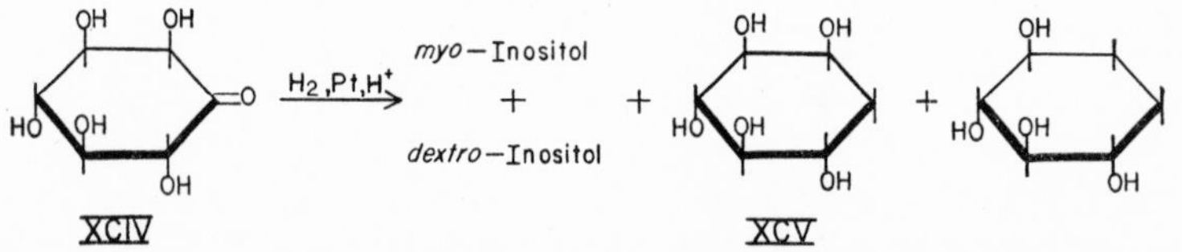

Only one diketone (2,5-diketo-*myo*-inositol) of the cyclitol series has been isolated in the crystalline state. However, there is ample evidence that a number of other cyclitol diketones have been obtained. Thus, solutions of *dextro*-inositol and *levo*-inositol which have been oxidized by *Acetobacter*

(210) D. L. MacDonald and H. O. L. Fischer, *J. Am. Chem. Soc.*, **74**, 2087 (1952).

(210a) When a hydroxyl group adjacent to the keto group is axial, a mixture of the two possible products is formed.[201]

(211) D. Reymond, *Helv. Chim. Acta*, **40**, 492 (1957).

readily furnish typical osazones (XCVI) on treatment with phenylhydrazine in the cold.[36] This finding shows that the oxidation products of *dextro*-inositol and *levo*-inositol are *ortho*-diketones.

The oxidation of (+)-*epi*-inosose by *Acetobacter* [only the (+)-form is affected] would be expected to give a *meta*-diketone (see p. 144), and, in fact, oxidized solutions of (±)-*epi*-inosose are acidic, as would be expected (since 1,3-diketones enolize readily).[36]

Cyclitol osazones consume the expected amount of periodate (three molar equivalents per mole), but the presumed product, 2,3-bis(phenylhydrazono)succindialdehyde (XCVII), cyclizes to the pyrazole XCVIII.[212] The

XCVI   XCVII   XCVIII

osazone XCVI has been converted to the osotriazole, but the yield was very poor.[209]

The biochemistry of the inososes has been but little investigated. Aside from their supposed function as intermediates in the bacterial catabolism of *myo*-inositol, three of them [*scyllo*-inosose, (±)-*epi*-inosose, and (+)-*vibo*-inosose] have been found to stimulate the growth of several *myo*-inositol-requiring organisms, although not as well as does *myo*-inositol itself.[213]

2. Anhydroinositols

1,3-Anhydro and 1,4-anhydroinositols are not known, but 1,2-anhydroinositols are readily prepared by two methods: (a) the action of bases on tosyl derivatives in which an adjacent hydroxyl group is *trans*-situated, and (b) treatment of cyclohexenetetrols with peracids. The former method has been used by Angyal and coworkers,[7, 149] the latter by Nakajima and coworkers.[34] As a result of their work, six out of the ten possible diastereomeric anhydrides are now known. On p. 168, the preparation of (+)-1,2-anhydro-3,4:5,6-di-O-isopropylidene-*allo*-inositol (LXII) from the monotosyl derivative of di-O-isopropylidene-*levo*-inositol has already been mentioned; careful, acidic hydrolysis of LXII gives (+)-1,2-anhydro-*allo*-inositol (XCIX), the most readily available of the anhydroinositols.[7] Similarly, the diisopropylidene acetal of 1-O-tosyl-*epi*-inositol gives 5,6-anhydro-*allo*-inositol (CIII).[7] The *trans*-1,2-di-O-tosyl compounds react in

(212) B. Magasanik and E. Chargaff, *J. Am. Chem. Soc.*, **70**, 1928 (1948).

(213) W. H. Schopfer and T. Posternak, *Schweiz. Z. allgem. Pathol. u. Bakteriol.*, **19**, 654 (1956).

the same way, albeit only at a higher temperature: from the diisopropyl-idene acetal of 1,6-di-O-tosyl-*epi*-inositol, 1,2-anhydro-*cis*-inositol (CVII) was obtained. Conduritol (CVIII) and peroxybenzoic acid give 2,3-an-hydro-*allo*-inositol (CIX).[7] These compounds are useful intermediates,

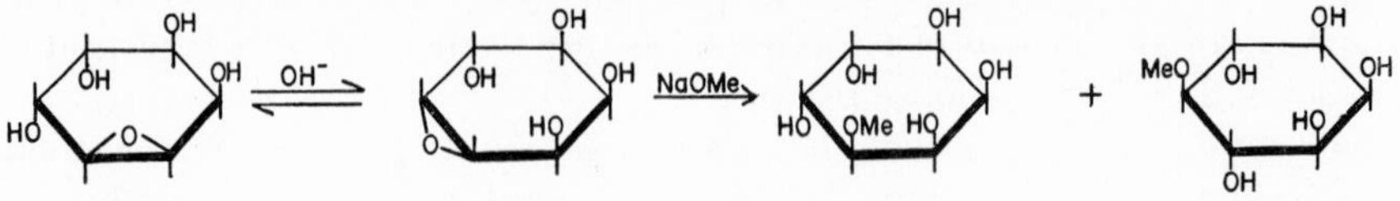

because they yield inositols on acidic or basic hydrolysis, inositol methyl ethers with sodium methoxide,[7] and inosamines with ammonia.[214]

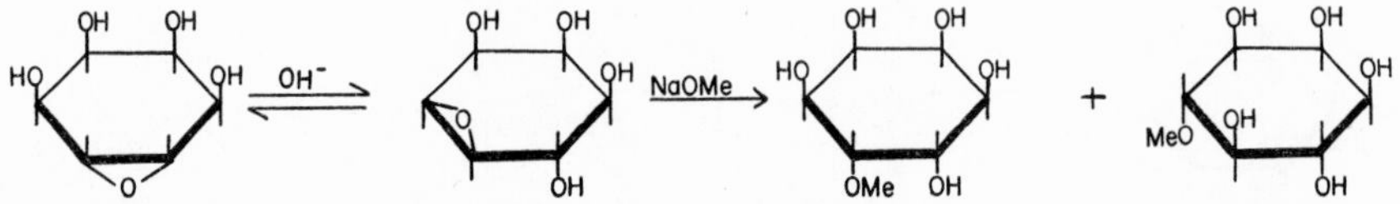

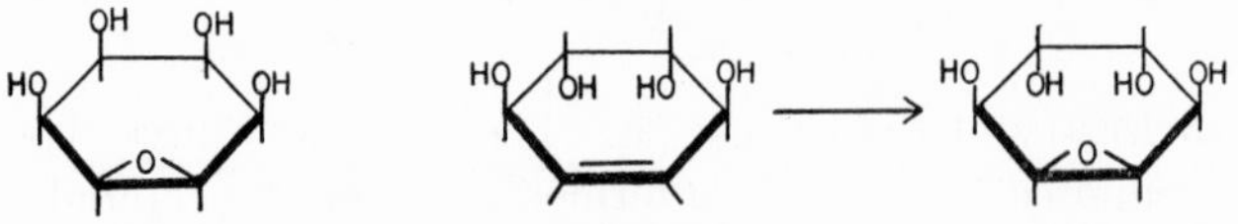

The anhydroinositols have provided an opportunity for studying the phe-nomenon[7] of "epoxide migration," that is, opening of an epoxide ring by rearward attack by an adjacent *trans*-situated hydroxyl group, with forma-tion of another epoxide ring. Occurrence of this rearrangement has often been postulated in carbohydrate chemistry,[215] but no clear-cut example has previously been described. All anhydroinositols in which there is a *trans*-hydroxyl group adjacent to the epoxide ring undergo epoxide migration in alkaline solution at room temperature. For example, 1,2-anhydro-*allo*-inosi-tol (XCIX) rearranges to 1,2-anhydro-*neo*-inositol (C). The reaction is reversible, and the position of the equilibrium is in accordance with confor-mational considerations, the isomer with the fewer axial hydroxyl groups being the more stable. Of the two anhydrides, XCIX has two axial hydroxyl groups, but compound C has only one; in the equilibrium mixture, they were found[7] in the ratio of 1:9.

The epoxide ring of a given anhydroinositol can open in two ways. The predominant direction of ring-opening can be predicted, since it depends

(214) G. R. Allen, Jr., *J. Am. Chem. Soc.*, **79**, 1167 (1957).
(215) For discussions, see F. H. Newth, *J. Chem. Soc.*, 441 (1956), and Ref. 85a.

only on conformational effects[216]: of the two possible isomers, the one with the larger number of axial groups is formed predominantly. Approximately equal amounts of *levo-* and *neo*-inositol (each having two axial hydroxyl groups) are formed from 1,2-anhydro-*allo*-inositol (see p. 181), but compound C, on treatment with sodium methoxide, gives mainly (+)-1-*O*-methyl-*allo*-inositol (CI) and only small amounts of sequoyitol (CII).[7] Similarly, the treatment of CIII yields, by way of the rearranged anhydride CIV, much (±)-5-*O*-methyl-*allo*-inositol (CV) and a little (±)-ononitol (CVI).[7] These are unambiguous syntheses of ononitol and sequoyitol (see p. 169).

3. *Inosamines*

The term "inosamine," which was suggested by Carter and coworkers[217] as a designation for the monoamino-monodeoxy-inositols, is used here in the original sense and *also* as a generic name for all cyclitols which bear amino groups. For specific reference to the diamino compounds, the term "inosadiamine" is used.[218] The configurational prefixes which designate the individual inositols are used in naming inosamines of corresponding configuration; and when, as is usually the case, two or more inosamines can be derived from a given inositol, a number is attached as a suffix to indicate the position(s) of the amino group(s).[5] Such systematic names as "2-amino-2-deoxy-*myo*-inositol" are also employed. The numbering is the same as for the inositols (see p. 137). According to theory, 32 inosamines (monoamines) (8 *meso* forms and 12 DL pairs) and 90 inosadiamines (18 *meso* forms and 36 DL pairs) may be derived from the 9 inositols.

Four antibiotic substances (or families of antibiotic substances)—the streptomycins, the neomycins, hygromycin A, and the kanamycins—yield inosamines, along with sugars and other fragments, on hydrolysis. No other natural sources of inosamines are known at present. The best known of the natural inosamines is streptamine, which is obtained by the alkaline hydrolysis of the diguanidine streptidine, itself a primary hydrolysis product of the streptomycins. Lemieux and Wolfrom[219] have reviewed the early work on the structure of streptomycin A, work which established the glycosidic nature of this antibiotic substance and showed that streptamine is a *meta*-inosadiamine of *meso*-configuration.

The subsequent elucidation of the configuration of streptamine, for which

(216) S. J. Angyal, *Chem. & Ind.* (London), 1230 (1954).

(217) H. E. Carter, R. K. Clark, Jr., B. Lytle and G. E. McCasland, *J. Biol. Chem.*, **175**, 683 (1948).

(218) M. L. Wolfrom, J. Radell, R. M. Husband and G. E. McCasland, *J. Am. Chem. Soc.*, **79**, 160 (1957).

(219) R. U. Lemieux and M. L. Wolfrom, *Advances in Carbohydrate Chem.*, **3**, 337 (1948).

eight formulas had to be considered, resulted from the efforts of several investigators. The *trans* disposition of the three contiguous hydroxyl groups was established by oxidizing tetra-O-methylstreptamine (CXI) to di-O-methyl-DL-threaric acid (CXII).[220,221] Later, the all-*trans* (*scyllo*) formula CX was postulated on the basis of a brilliant application of the nitrometh-

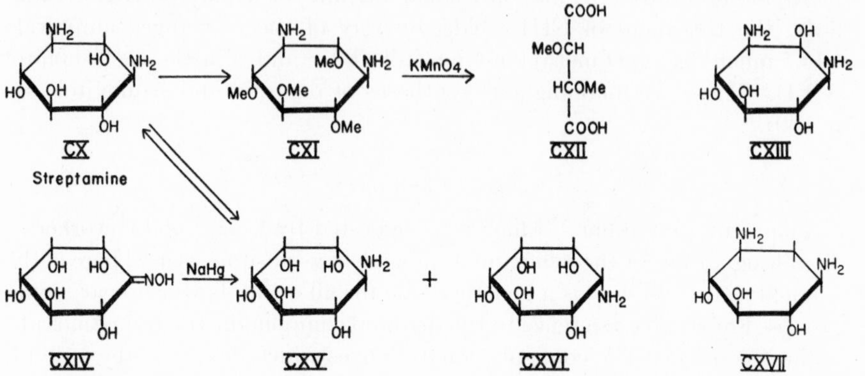

ane synthesis (see p. 142),[222] which actually limited the possible formulas to two (namely, CX and CXIII). The key to the full confirmation of formula CX was a fortuitously obtained N-acetyl-tri-O-acetyl derivative of streptamine which, on monodeamination and acetylation,[221] gave the hexaacetate of one of the inosamines which can be derived from ($\pm$)-*epi*-inosose oxime (CXIV) by reduction.[223] If it is assumed that no hydroxyl or acetoxyl group is inverted in either process, streptamine must have the formula CX, and the deamination must proceed with inversion in order to give an inosamine derivable from CXIV; moreover, this inosamine must have the *myo*-configuration CXV.[223] Heyns and Paulsen[223a] have completed the cycle of interconversions by synthesizing streptamine from CXV.

The neomycins[224] and the kanamycins[225,226] yield the same inosadiamine

(220) O. Wintersteiner and A. Klingsberg, *J. Am. Chem. Soc.*, **70**, 885 (1948).

(221) O. Wintersteiner and A. Klingsberg, *J. Am. Chem. Soc.*, **73**, 2917 (1951).

(222) M. L. Wolfrom, S. M. Olin and W. J. Polglase, *J. Am. Chem. Soc.*, **72**, 1724 (1950).

(223) H. Straube-Rieke, H. A. Lardy and L. Anderson, *J. Am. Chem. Soc.*, **75**, 694 (1953).

(223a) K. Heyns and H. Paulsen, *Chem. Ber.*, **89**, 1152 (1956).

(224) (a) F. A. Kuehl, Jr., M. N. Bishop and K. Folkers, *J. Am. Chem. Soc.*, **73**, 881 (1951); (b) J. R. Dyer, Ph.D. Thesis (with H. E. Carter), University of Illinois, 1954.

(225) M. J. Cron, D. L. Johnson, F. M. Palermiti, Y. Perron, H. D. Taylor, D. F. Whitehead and I. R. Hooper, *J. Am. Chem. Soc.*, **80**, 752 (1958).

(226) H. Schmitz, O. B. Fardig, F. A. O'Herron, M. A. Rousche and I. R. Hooper, *J. Am. Chem. Soc.*, **80**, 2911 (1958).

on hydrolysis. This amine is a 1,5-diamino-2,3,4-trihydroxycyclohexane and hence a quercitol derivative, and its amino groups are known to be *cis*.[224(a)] The *N*,*N'*-dibenzoyl derivatives of this amine and of streptamine are oxidized by periodate at comparable rates, and neither derivative undergoes acyl migration in ethanolic hydrogen chloride.[224(b)] On the basis of these facts, the all-*trans* configuration CXVII, and the name "deoxystreptamine" have been proposed.

An inosamine having a single amino group is obtained by the hydrolysis of hygromycin A. To this amine was assigned the configuration of *neo*-inosamine-2 (CXIX) on the basis of evidence that it is a *meso* compound, has its amino group *cis* to a neighboring hydroxyl group, has vicinal *cis*-hydroxyl groups, and is deaminated (see below) to afford *myo*-inositol.[227,228] The synthesis of the amine by the catalytic hydrogenation of the phenylhydrazone of *neo*-inosose (CXVIII) confirms the configurational assignment (see below).[229]

CXVIII CXIX CXX

CXXI CXXII CXXIII

CXXIV CXXV CXXVI

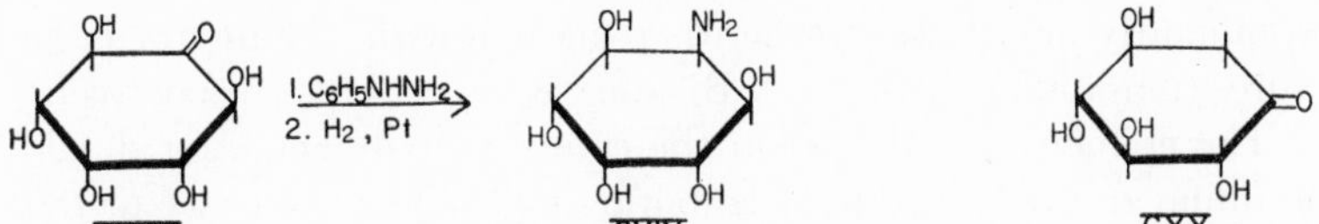

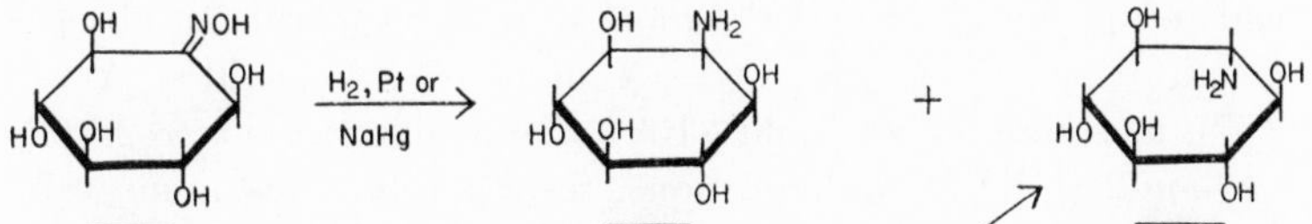

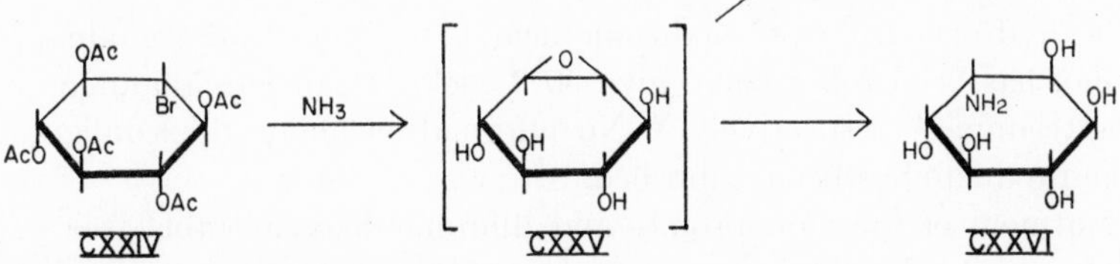

The discovery that inosamines are component parts of the molecules of antibiotic substances stimulated attempts to find synthetic routes to these compounds. The natural inosamines do not have antibiotic activity, once they are released by hydrolysis, and the hope that some inosamines or their

(227) J. B. Patrick, R. P. Williams, C. W. Waller and B. L. Hutchings, *J. Am. Chem. Soc.*, **78**, 2652 (1956).

(228) R. L. Mann and D. O. Woolf, *J. Am. Chem. Soc.*, **79**, 120 (1957).

(229) G. R. Allen, Jr., *J. Am. Chem. Soc.*, **78**, 5691 (1956).

simple derivatives might prove to be useful chemotherapeutic agents,[230,231] has so far not been realized. However, it is worthy of note that several inosamine derivatives have anti-(myo-inositol) activity in inositol-less *Neurospora crassa* (see p. 161).[112]

Three inosamines were obtained in the course of efforts to synthesize *myo*-inositol by the nitro-sugar cyclization (see p. 142). However, the methods which have been the most productive of new inosamines are those which are well known as means of preparing amino sugars and aminopolyhydric alcohols, namely, reduction of imine derivatives of carbonyl compounds (in this case, inososes) and ammonolysis of halohydrins and epoxides.

In each of these procedures, two inosamines (or more, from dihalohydrins) may be formed from a given starting-material. The proportions of the epimeric inosamines obtained from the oxime or phenylhydrazone of an inosose vary with the method of reduction employed. In the catalytic hydrogenation of the oximes of *scyllo*-inosose (CXXI) and (±)-*epi*-inosose (CXIV), one amine (inosamine "SA" and inosamine "EA," respectively) is formed predominantly in each case, whereas reduction with sodium amalgam gives mixtures (inosamines "SA" + "SB" and "EA" + "EB," respectively).[28,223, 230,232] The epimers resulting from the catalytic hydrogenation should have their amino groups *cis* to the neighboring hydroxyl groups (see p. 180), and this supposition was verified by comparing the rates of certain reactions of the pairs of epimers. On the basis of their more rapid reaction with periodate and lead tetraacetate[28,223] and the more rapid acyl migration observed for their acetates (pentaacetates, $O \rightarrow N$ in base[232]; N-acetates, $N \rightarrow O$ in acid,[29,223]), inosamines "SA" and "EA" were assigned the *myo*-2 (CXXII) and (±)-*epi*-2 (CXVI) configurations, respectively. Inosamine "SB" and "EB" are, therefore, *scyllo*-inosamine (CXXIII) and (±)-*myo*-inosamine-4 (CXV), respectively.

The hydrogenation of rhodizonic acid 1,4-diimine and triaminophloroglucinol has been reported to give 50% yields of an inosadiamine and an "inosatriamine," respectively.[233] No information about the configurations of the products has been published.

Treatment of the monobromo- and dibromo-deoxyinositols (see p. 188) and their acetates with ammonia at elevated temperatures gives inosamines, presumably by way of epoxide intermediates. The pentaacetate of bromodeoxy-*scyllo*-inositol (CXXIV) gives, on ammonolysis in dioxane solution, *scyllo*-inosamine and (presumably) *rac*-inosamine-1 (*rac*-inosamine-2,

(230) E. L. May and E. Mosettig, *J. Org. Chem.*, **14,** 1137 (1949).
(231) H. G. Latham, E. L. May and E. Mosettig, *J. Am. Chem. Soc.*, **74,** 2684 (1952).
(232) L. Anderson and H. A. Lardy, *J. Am. Chem. Soc.*, **72,** 3141 (1950).
(233) G. Quadbeck and E. Röhm, *Chem. Ber.*, **89,** 1645 (1956).

CXXVI).[218] Similarly, inosadiamines have been obtained from the two available dibromodideoxyinositols, but, in spite of the fact that this reaction has been studied in three different laboratories,[218,234,235] the exact number and nature of these products is still obscure.

Only one example is available of the use of a preformed "true" anhydroinositol for inosamine synthesis: (+)-1,2-anhydro-3,4:5,6-di-*O*-isopropylidene-*allo*-inositol (CXXVII) yields (+)-*neo*-inosamine-1 (CXXVIII) and *levo*-inosamine-3 (*levo*-inosamine-5, CXXIX) on ammonolysis and hydrolysis.[214] However, the epoxide CXXX and its pentaacetate CXXX′ (see below) have been treated with ammonia and with a variety of primary and

CXXVII CXXVIII CXXIX

CXXX CXXX′ CXXXI CXXXII CXXXIII CXXXIV CXXXV

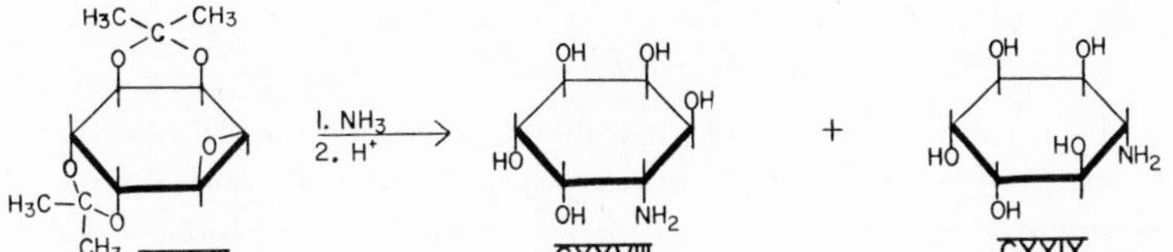

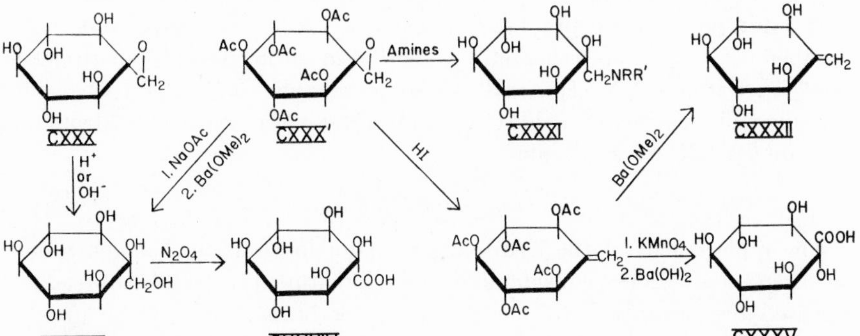

secondary amines.[28,236] As might be expected, ring opening takes place at the primary carbon atom, to give aminoisomytilitol derivatives (CXXXI). When the pentaacetate CXXX′ is used as the starting material, the products are *N*-acetylated as a result of base-catalyzed $O \rightarrow N$ acyl migration.

The nitrous acid deamination of *scyllo*-inosamine (CXXIII) and *myo*-inosamine-2 (CXXII),[28] as well as that of *neo*-inosamine-2 (see above), has been studied. Much reducing material is formed from CXXII and CXXIII, and the deoxyinosose CXX has been demonstrated[28] among the deamination

(234) A. E. O. Menzel, M. Moore and O. Wintersteiner, *J. Am. Chem. Soc.*, **71**, 1268 (1949).

(235) E. H. Flynn (with H. E. Carter), Ph.D. Thesis, University of Illinois, 1949.

(236) E. L. May and E. Mosettig, *J. Org. Chem.*, **16**, 1471 (1951).

products of CXXII. The formation of the deoxyinosose might be expected
from the well-known tendency of 1,2-aminoalcohols to give ketones on deamination.

In the deamination of an inosamine, small proportions of inositol are
formed by simple replacement of the amino group, and, in the three cases
just mentioned, this replacement seems to take place predominantly, if not
exclusively, by inversion of configuration. However, the amino groups of
levo-inosamine-1 (*levo*-inosamine-2) and *myo*-inosamine-1 are apparently
replaced with retention.[236a] Configurations should, thus, not be assigned
to inosamines on the basis of the inositols which they give in this reaction,
unless corroborating evidence is available.

4. C-Methylinositols

Besides the previously described mytilitol and isomytilitol,[1] one new C-
methyl-inositol is known; it is laminitol, which has been isolated from the
algae *Laminaria cloustoni*, *Fucus spiralis*, *Desmarestia aculeata*, *Porphyra
umbilicalis* and *Gelidum cartilagineum*.[237] Its configuration is now known.[237a]
Mytilitol has been found in a new source, the tunicate *Cionia intestinalis*.[238]

In addition to those previously reported,[1] Posternak[239] has prepared a
number of compounds related to C-methyl-inositols, such as methylene-
scyllo-quercitol (CXXXII), *scyllo*-inositolcarboxylic acid (CXXXV), and
myo-inositol-2-carboxylic acid (CXXXIV). These were synthesized from the
epoxide CXXX' as shown above.

5. Deoxyhalogenoinositols

The replacement of the hydroxyl groups of inositols by halogen atoms
has been the subject of considerable study. Treatment of the inositols at an
elevated temperature with acetyl chloride or bromide, or of the inositol
acetates with hydrogen halides in acetic acid solution, gives mixtures from
which mono- and di-halogenated deoxyinositols have been isolated.[166,234,
235,240] Some of these have, in recent times, been further investigated by
McCasland.[241] The positions of the halogen atoms and the configurations
of the hydroxyl groups are readily ascertained by catalytic hydrogenolysis,
which removes the halogen atoms and yields a quercitol or a cyclohexane-

(236a) G. G. Post (with L. Anderson), Ph.D. Thesis, University of Wisconsin, 1959.

(237) B. Lindberg and J. M. McPherson, *Acta Chem. Scand.*, **8**, 1875 (1954); H.
Bouveng and B. Lindberg, *ibid.*, **9**, 168 (1955); B. Lindberg, *ibid.*, **9**, 1097, 1323 (1955).

(237a) B. Lindberg and B. Wickberg, *Arkiv Kemi*, **13**, 447 (1959). See Addendum,
p. 191.

(238) D. Ackerman and R. Janka, *Z. physiol. Chem., Hoppe-Seyler's*, **296**, 283
(1954).

(239) T. Posternak and D. Reymond, *Helv. Chim. Acta*, **36**, 1370 (1953).

(240) H. Müller, *J. Chem. Soc.*, **101**, 2383 (1912).

(241) G. E. McCasland and E. C. Horswill, *J. Am. Chem. Soc.*, **75**, 4020 (1953).

tetrol. In this way, it was found[241] that the two monobromo compounds obtained from *myo*-inositol are derivatives of *scyllo*- and *vibo*-quercitol, respectively. The configuration of the halogen atom is not so readily determined, but present evidence indicates that the two compounds are bromodeoxy-*scyllo*-inositol (CXXXVI, R = H) and 1-bromo-1-deoxy-*rac*-

CXXXVI   CXXXVII   CXXXVIII

nositol (2-bromo-2-deoxy-*rac*-inositol, CXXXVIII, R = H). On treatment with alkali, both halogen derivatives give *rac*-inositol through an intermediate epoxide.

The mechanism of the halogenation is not clearly understood, but it is of interest that the same two bromo compounds were obtained from *myo*-inositol, *scyllo*-inositol, or the active inositols. Presumably, participation by neighboring acetoxy groups takes place and a common intermediate is involved. *epi*-Inositol gives mainly one monobromo compound, of unknown configuration.[242]

Under more vigorous reaction-conditions, two dibromo compounds were obtained from *myo*-inositol; these were also formed from CXXXVIII, but not from CXXXVI. One of these has the two bromine atoms in *meta*-, the other in *para*-positions; their configurations are, however, still unknown.[243]

On treatment with zinc in acetic acid, a bromodeoxyinositol pentaacetate gives the tetraacetate of a cyclohexenetetrol.[241,242] From CXXXVI and from CXXXVIII (R = Ac), the same 1,3/2,4-tetrol (CXXXVII) was obtained in good yield.

IV. The Quercitols

Besides the dextrorotatory quercitol of the acorn[1]—which has been known for a hundred years and which had its configuration determined by Posternak[1] in 1932—one other cyclohexanepentol has been found in Nature. Power and Tutin,[244] who first isolated it from the leaves of *Gymnema sylvestre*, a milkweed, named it a *"levo*-rotatory quercitol," although it is *not* the enantiomorph of the dextrorotatory quercitol. The same quercitol was also isolated from *Viburnum tinus* by Hérissey and Poirot,[245] who named it "viburnitol," but, owing to an error in an optical rotation reported by

(242) G. E. McCasland and J. M. Reeves, *J. Am. Chem. Soc.*, **77**, 1812 (1955).
(243) G. E. McCasland and E. C. Horswill, *J. Am. Chem. Soc.*, **76**, 2373 (1954).
(244) F. B. Power and F. Tutin, *J. Chem. Soc.*, **85**, 624 (1904).
(245) H. Hérissey and G. Poirot, *Compt. rend.*, **203**, 466 (1936); *J. pharm. chim.*, [8] **26**, 385 (1937).

Power and Tutin,[244] its identity was not established until years later.[246] (−)-Viburnitol has also been found in *Stephania hernandifolia*, an Australian plant,[247] and in *Menispermum canadense*.[146]

Other quercitols have been synthesized by catalytic hydrogenolysis of the corresponding inososes (see p. 180). All the known quercitols are shown, with their names, in formulas CXXXIX–CXLIV; according to Angyal and Macdonald's proposals,[6] the quercitol of acorn is called (+)-*proto*-quercitol, and natural viburnitol is named (−)-*vibo*-quercitol; the corresponding Fletcher–Anderson–Lardy names are (+)-1-deoxy-*muco*-inositol and (−)-1-deoxy-*myo*-inositol. Synthesis of the four as-yet-unknown diastereomers should not present serious difficulties.

The configuration of (−)-*vibo*-quercitol was established by Posternak.[60] Oxidation by permanganate gave the metasacharinic acid CXLV, also obtained earlier (by the same reaction) from *proto*-quercitol[1]; and epimerization of one hydroxyl group, by *Acetobacter* oxidation followed by reduction gave *scyllo*-quercitol (CXLIV). These reactions establish the configuration CXLIII; it was confirmed by the formation of a monoisopropylidene acetal (CXLVI) which consumes two equivalents of periodate per mole and, hence, has a *cis* pair of hydroxyl groups adjacent to the methylene group.

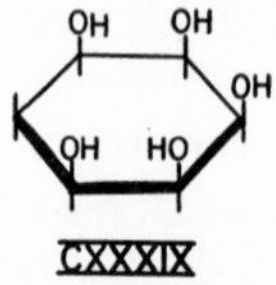

CXXXIX
cis-Quercitol

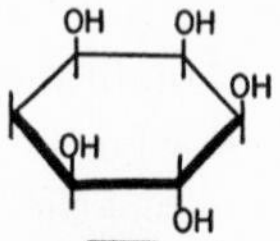

CXL
(−)-*epi*-Quercitol

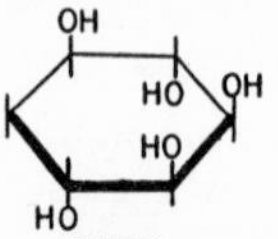

CXLI
(+)-*proto*-Quercitol

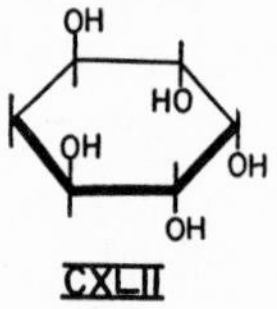

CXLII
neo-Quercitol

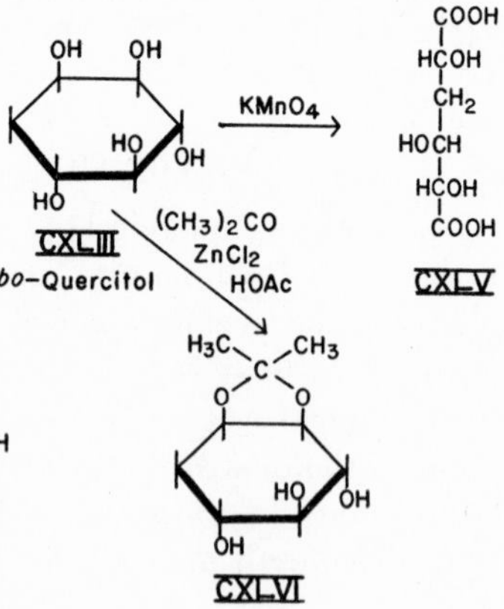

CXLIII
(−)-*vibo*-Quercitol

CXLV

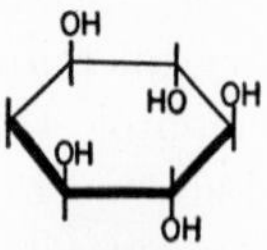

CXLIV
scyllo-Quercitol

CXLVI

---

(246) T. Posternak and W. H. Schopfer, *Helv. Chim. Acta*, **33**, 343 (1950).

(247) J. Ewing, G. K. Hughes and E. Ritchie, *Australian J. Sci. Research*, **3A**, 514 (1950).

Finally, the enantiomorph, $(+)$-*vibo*-quercitol, was synthesized[248] by hydrogenation of the corresponding inosose in acid solution (XCIV → XCV; see p. 180).

V. PHYSICAL CONSTANTS OF THE CYCLITOLS AND THEIR DERIVATIVES

Tables II to X give the melting points and, where applicable, the optical rotations of the inositols, inososes, inosamines, and quercitols, and of all of their known O-substituted derivatives. Anhydroinositols, although not substitution products in the strict sense, are included, as are the carbonyl-functional derivatives of the inososes. Halogen- and nitro-substituted cyclitols, and the C-methyl-inositols and their derivatives, are not included; most of these compounds are referred to in the text. The derivatives are arranged in the following order: salts (inosamines) or functional derivatives (inososes), carboxylic esters, borates, nitrates, sulfonic esters, phosphates, glycosides, acetals (and Schiff bases), ethers (and N-alkyl derivatives), and anhydrides.

The abbreviations and symbols used in the Tables are: Ac, acetyl; Bz, benzoyl; Ms, methylsulfonyl; Ns, *p*-nitrophenylsulfonyl; Ts, *p*-tolylsulfonyl; Bzd, benzylidene; Ipd, isopropylidene; Et, ethyl; Me, methyl; Ph, phenyl; -O-, anhydro; d. 338, decomposes (without melting) at 338°; 153 d., melts at 153° with decomposition; $\{^{166}_{177}$, compound is dimorphous, with melting points at 166° and 177°; amorph., amorphous; cryst., crystalline; trans. 192, transition in crystal form at 192°; ±, racemic; and active, asymmetric, but [α]D not recorded.

The first reference to the literature deals, in each instance, with the first isolation or synthesis; other references are to improved methods of preparation or to physical constants differing considerably from those given in the first reference. Where a compound has been described more than once, before 1930, a reference to Beilstein is given.

(248) T. Posternak, *Helv. Chim. Acta*, **33**, 1594 (1950).

ADDENDUM

Laminitol was shown[237a] to be a 4-C-methyl-*myo*-inositol by: (1) the epimerization of one of its hydroxyl groups, by catalytic oxidation followed by reduction with sodium amalgam, to give mytilitol, which has the *scyllo*-configuration[1]; and (2) the pyrolysis of its hexaacetate to a methylene compound, and oxidation of the latter, first with potassium permanganate, then lead tetraacetate, to an *epi*-inosose pentaacetate. A decision between the two enantiomorphous formulas corresponding to 4-C-methyl-*myo*-inositol will be possible when enough of the inosose pentaacetate is available to allow the determination of its optical rotation.

TABLE II

Derivatives of myo-Inositol

Positions are numbered according to one, either, or both, of the following formulas, as indicated in the *formula* column.

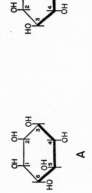

A 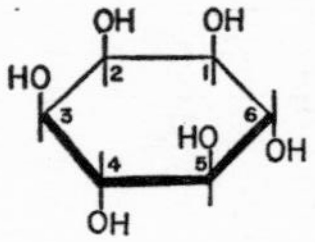   B

(Abbreviations are defined on p. 191)

	Substituents					Formula	Melting point, °C.	$[\alpha]_D$, °	Rotation solvent	References
1	2	3	4	5	6					
—	—	—	—	—	—	either	225	meso		249, 250

ISOTOPICALLY LABELED *myo*-INOSITOLS [a]

1	2	3	4	5	6	Formula				References
—	C^{14}	—	—	—	—	either				30
—	C^{14}	—	C^{14}	C^{14}	—	B				209
C^{14}	C^{14}	C^{14}	C^{14}	C^{14}	C^{14}	either				24, 125
—	H^2	—	H^2	—	—	B				127
—	H^2	—	H^2	—	—	either				127
—	—	—	—	—	H^2	either				127
—	H^3	H^3	—	—	—					140
H^3	H^3	H^3	H^3	H^3	H^3					101b

METAL COMPLEXES [b]

	Melting point, °C.	References
Barium complex, $C_6H_{12}O_6 \cdot BaO$		251
Copper complex, $C_6H_{14}Cu_3O_{10}$		252
Zinc complex, $C_{12}H_{37}N_3O_{18}Zn_4$ (?)	cryst.	253

O-SUBSTITUTED DERIVATIVES

						M.P., °C	±	References
Triacetate								
Ac	—	Ac	Ac	Ac	both	71		254
Ac	—	Ac	Ac	—	either	142–143	meso	54, 55
Ac	Ac	Ac	Ac	Ac	either	{ 166–168, 177–179	meso	204, 178, 255
Ac	Ac	Ac	(c)	Ac	either	177–178	meso	256
Ac	Ac	Ac	Ac	Ac	either	216–217	meso	249
Ac	(d)	Ac	Ac	Ac	either	177	meso	255
Ac					either	{ 202–202.5, 227–232	meso	255
2-*p*-Aminobenzoate								
Ac	(e)	Ac	Ac		either	249–254	meso	255
					either	201–203	meso	255
Pentaanisate						251		166
Hexaanisate					either	225	meso	166
Pentabenzoate						269		166
Hexabenzoate					either	258	meso	257
Hexa-(*p*-bromobenzoate)					either	264	meso	258
Hexabutyrate					either	94–95	meso	259, 260
Hexacarbethoxy ester					either	131–135	meso	261
Pentacinnamate						271		166
Hexacinnamate					either	199	meso	166
2-(2-Hydroxy-4-aminobenzoate)					either	153–155 d.	meso	255
Hexaisobutyrate					either	181	meso	259
Hexaisovalerate					either	151	meso	249
Hexanicotinate					either	254.5–255	meso	262
Hexa-(*m*-nitrobenzoate)					either	217	meso	166
Ac	(f)	Ac	Ac	Ac	either	233–235	meso	255
Hexa-(*p*-nitrobenzoate)					either	310–315	meso	263
Hexa-(3,5-dinitrobenzoate)					either	86	meso	259
Hexapalmitate					either	83	meso	249
Hexapropionate					either	115–116	meso	259, 260
Hexavalerate					either	63	meso	259

TABLE II—Continued

Substituents						Formula	Melting point, °C.	[α]$_D$, °	Rotation solvent	References
1	2	3	4	5	6					
Trinitrate							cryst.	meso		264
NO_2	NO_2	NO_2	NO_2	NO_2	NO_2	either	128–129	meso		249, 87, 265
Ts	—	Ac	Ac	Ac	Ac	both	195–197	±		86
Ts	Ac	Ac	Ac	Ac	Ac	both	151	±		86
Ac	Ts	Ac	—	Ts	Ac	either	219–220	meso		179
—	—	Ac	Ac	Ts	—	either	200.5	meso		256
Ac	Ac	Ac	—	Ac	Ac	either	224–225	meso		256
Ts	Ts	Ac	Ac	Ac	—	both	173	±		86
PO_3H_2	—	—	—	—	—	?	^{g}	−9.8	H_2O (pH 2)	170
$PO_3^{\ominus\ominus}$	—	—	—	—	—	?	197–210	+3.4	H_2O	170
$PO_3^{\ominus\ominus}$ bis(cyclohexylammonium) salt						both	210–215 d.	±		169(b), 170
—	PO_3H_2	—	—	—	—	either	195–197 d.	meso		176, 178, 266
bis(cyclohexylammonium) salt	$PO_3H^{\ominus}$					either	203–205	meso		177a
mono(cyclohexylammonium) salt	$PO_3^{\ominus\ominus}$					either	244–247 d.	meso		177a
monobrucine salt							198–210	meso		170
bis(cyclohexylammonium) salt	$PO_3^{\ominus\ominus}$					either	211–213	meso		177a
Ac	PO_3H_2	Ac	Ac	Ac	Ac	either	233–234	meso		178
Ac	PO_3Ph_2	Ac	—	Ac	—	either	192–193	meso		178
bis(cyclohexylammonium) salt				$PO_3^{\ominus\ominus}$	—	either	209–211	meso		25
Ac	Ac	Ac	Ac	PO_3H_2	Ac	either	229 d.	meso		25
Ac	Ac	Ac	Ac	PO_3Ph_2	Ac	either	168	meso		25

Compound					Form	M.p., °C	[α]	Solvent	Ref.
Phosphate, dibrucine salt	—	—	—	—		172–175	±		171
Phosphate, dibrucine salt					both	236			172
—PO₂⊖	—	—	—	—		amorph.			169(a)
barium salt						130–140 d.			170
cyclohexylammonium salt						"		H₂O	176
Diphosphate						"	−6	H₂O	176
—, sodium salt						amorph.	−11[h]		176
—, monobarium salt						amorph.			186
meta-Diphosphate						"	−8	H₂O	176
Triphosphate						"	−22[h]	H₂O	176
—, sodium salt						amorph.			176
—, sesquibarium salt						"	−4	H₂O	176
Tetraphosphate						"	−8[h]	H₂O	176
—, sodium salt						amorph.			176
—, dibarium salt						sirup	meso		249
Hexaphosphate[i]					both	220–222	+136[k]	H₂O	194
1-α-D-Galactopyranoside[j]	(l)	Me	Me	Me	Me	A	96.5–98	+119	H₂O	195
		Me	Me	Me	Me	A	>215 d.	+74	H₂O	267, 183
Dimannoside[m]						112	+49	MeOH	183
Dimannoside, dodecaacetate[m]						137–139	+53	MeOH	192(b)
Dimannoside, dodecaacetate[o]						182–183	±		54, 6
—Ipd—	—	Ac	Ac	—	both	123–124	±		54, 55
—Ipd—	Ac	Ac	Ac		both	b.p.₁ 169–170	±		268
Hexa-O-allyl-					either	128			166
Mono-O-ethyl-, pentaacetate						212			166
Di-O-ethyl-						212			166
Di-O-ethyl-, tetraacetate[n]						212			166

TABLE II—Continued

Substituents						Formula	Melting point, °C.	[α]D, °	Rotation solvent	References
1	2	3	4	5	6					
Me	—	—	—	—	—	A	201–202	+31	H_2O	249, 158
Me	Ac	Ac	Ac	Ac	Ac	A	138–139, 157	+12	Me_2CO	158
Me	Bz	Bz	Bz	Bz	Bz	A	125–126	active		158
1-O-Methyl-, pentapropionate						A	47–48	active		158
Me	Ac	Ac	Ac	Ac	Ac	B	203–204	−32	H_2O	152(a), 53
Me	Ac	Ac	Ac	Ac	Ac	B	142, 157	−11	$CHCl_3$	152(a)
Me	—Ipd—		—	—	—	B	60–62	active		59
Me	—Ipd—		Ac	Ac	Ac	B	112–114	+9	$CHCl_3$	59
Me	—	—Ipd—		—	—	B	158–159	active		59
Me	—	—Ipd—		Ac	Ac	B	138–139	active		59
1-O-Methyldi-O-isopropylidene-						both	174	±		166, 164
1-O-Methyldi-O-isopropylidene-, monoacetate						both	204	±		166, 164
						either	141, 154–154.5, 96[p]	meso		55
						either	212	meso		55
—	Me	Ac	Ac	Ac	Ac	B	235–236	+6.6	H_2O	152(a), 236a
—	Me	Ac	Me	Ac	Ac	B	172	−12	$CHCl_3$	152(a), 236a
Ac[q]	Me	Ac	Me	Ac	Ac	both	122, 131	±		7
Ac	Ac	Ac	Me	Me	Ac	either	129–130	meso		269, 58
Ac[r]	Ac	Ac	Ac	Me	Ac	either	243	meso		269, 58
—Ipd—		Ac	Ac	Me	Ac	both	203–203.5, 115–116	±		58

(Left-margin bracket label: *Bornesitols and derivatives*)

Compound	Substituents (ring positions)	Config.	M.P. (°C)	$[\alpha]$	Solvent	References
—Ipd—	Me, Ac	both	171–172	±		58
—Ipd—	Me, Ac	both	{ 100–101 / 107–108	±		58
Me	Me	both	162–163	±		55
[s]Me	Me, Me	either	210	meso		249, 157, 55
Me / Ac	Ac, Me, Ac	either	202	meso		249, 55
Me / Bz	Bz, Me, Bz	either	250	meso		270
[t]Me		B	224		H$_2$O	154
Me / Ac	Me, Ac	B	139	−25		154
Di-O-methyl-			sirup	−24	CHCl$_3$	166
Di-O-methyl-, tetraacetate[n]	Me, Me		223			166
Penta-O-methyl-	Me, Me	A	117–117.5	−4	H$_2$O	195
Penta-O-methyl-, monoacetate[n]	Me, Me		50–51			254
Penta-O-methyl-, monobenzoate	Me, Me		101			167
Me	Me, Me		132–133			254
Me	Me, Me	either	b.p.$_{757}$, 272	meso		167
Hexakis-O-(2,4-dinitrophenyl)-		either	d. 338–340	meso		271
—O—		both	154–155	±		34

[a] Symbols indicate positions of labeled carbon ring atoms or carbon-bound hydrogen isotopes. [b] A number of metal complexes of myo-inositol have been reported (see Ref. 87). Only those of apparently well defined composition are listed here. [c] (2-acetoxy-4-aminobenzoyl)- [d] (2-acetoxy-4-nitrobenzoyl)- [e] p-aminobenzoyl- [f] p-nitrobenzoyl- [g] Not isolated. [h] Calculated on the basis of free acid. [i] Salts of the hexaphosphate, and of some other (ill-defined) myo-inositol phosphates, are listed in Beilstein (See Ref. 249). [j] Galactinol. [k] For the dihydrate. [l] tetra-O-methyl-α-D-galactopyranosyl- [m] Manninositose. It is not known whether the second and mannose residue is attached directly to the inositol or to the first mannose residue. [n] Acetate of the preceding compound. [o] May be identical with the preceding compound. [p] Hydrate, 1.5 H$_2$O (?). [q] Ononitol. [r] Sequoyitol. [s] Dambonitol. [t] Liriodendritol.

REFERENCES FOR TABLE II

(249) F. K. Beilstein, "Handbuch der organischen Chemie," 4th Edition, Vol. VI, pp. 1192–1198; Suppl. I, Vol. VI, pp. 587–592; Suppl. II, Vol. VI, pp. 1157–1161.

(250) Corn Products Sales Co., "i-Inositol," 1947, p. 3.

(251) A. Girard, Compt. rend., 67, 820 (1868).

(252) T. Lieser and R. Ebert, Ann., 532, 89 (1937).

(253) A. Windaus, Ber., 40, 799 (1907).

(254) G. E. McCasland and S. Boutsicaris, J. Am. Chem. Soc., 75, 3845 (1953).

(255) E. L. May, J. Org. Chem., 17, 286 (1952).

(256) S. J. Angyal and J. Murdoch, unpublished work.

(257) Ref. 249, Vol. IX, p. 146; Suppl. I, Vol. IX, p. 79.

(258) S. Odén, Arkiv Kemi, Mineral. Geol., 7, No. 15, 1 (1918).

(259) F. A. Hoglan and E. Bartow, Ind. Eng. Chem., 31, 749 (1939).

(260) J. Erdos and M. C. Gómez, Ciencia (Mex.), 15, 101 (1955); Chem. Abstracts, 50, 16683 (1956).

(261) B. Moldavskiĭ, Ukrain. Khem. Zhur., 1, 408 (1925); Chem. Abstracts, 20, 2831 (1926).

(262) C. O. Badgett and C. F. Woodward, J. Am. Chem. Soc., 69, 2907 (1947).

(263) C. Siebenmann and R. J. Schnitzer, J. Am. Chem. Soc., 65, 2126 (1943).

(264) H. Vohl, Ber., 7, 106 (1874).

(265) H. Ficheroulle and A. Kovache, Mém. poudres, 32, 133 (1950); Chem. Abstracts, 48, 4454 (1954).

(266) M. H. McCormick and H. E. Carter, Biochem. Preparations, 2, 65 (1952).

(267) R. J. Anderson and E. G. Roberts, J. Am. Chem. Soc., 52, 5023 (1930).

(268) P. L. Nichols, Jr., and E. Yanovsky, J. Am. Chem. Soc., 67, 46 (1945).

(269) E. C. Sherrard and E. F. Kurth, J. Am. Chem. Soc., 51, 3139 (1929).

(270) L. Maquenne, Ann. chim. et phys., [6] 12, 566 (1887).

(271) M. L. Wolfrom, B. O. Juliano, M. S. Toy and A. Chaney, J. Am. Chem. Soc., 81, 1446 (1959).

TABLE III

Derivatives of dextro-*Inositol*[a]

(Abbreviations are defined on p. 191)

Substituents[b]						Melting point, °C.	[α]D,°	Rotation solvent	References
1(2)	2(1)	3(5)	4(6)	5(4)	6(3)				
—	—	—	—	—	—	247–248	+65	H₂O	249
[c] Ac	Ac	Ac	Ac	—	—	amorph.			144, 271a
Ac	Ac	Ac	Ac	Ac	Ac	amorph.	+9.8	EtOH	249
Bz	Bz	Bz	Bz	Bz	Bz	253			272
—Ipd—		—	—	—	—	152–153	+96	H₂O	62
—Ipd—		Ac	Ac	Ac	Ac	amorph.			144, 271a
—Ipd—		—	—	—Ipd—		149–151	+4.8	EtOH	62
—Ipd—		—Ipd—		—Ipd—		213–214	−36	CHCl₃	62
—	—	Me	—	—	—	186	+65	H₂O	249, 159
Ac	Ac	Me	Ac	Ac	Ac	98–99	+11	EtOH	166, 273, 159
3-O-Methyl-, pentaanisate (5-O-Methyl-, pentaanisate)						101	0.0		166
Bz	Bz	Me	Bz	Bz	Bz	97	+32		166
3-O-Methyl-, pentacinnamate (5-O-Methyl-, pentacinnamate)						105	+41		166
—	—	Me	Ts	—	—	193 d.	−1	C₅H₅N	149
Ac	Ac	Me	Ts	Ac	Ac	153	−18	CHCl₃	149
—	—	Me	PO₃⊖⊖	—	—				
bis(cyclohexylammonium) salt						>250	+20	H₂O	180
—Ipd—		Me	—	—Ipd—		103–104	−22	H₂O	6
						104.5–106	−45	CHCl₃	61
—Ipd—		Me	Ts	—Ipd—		90	+53	EtOH	149
—Ipd—		Me	PO₃⊖⊖	—Ipd—					
bis(cyclohexylammonium) salt						177–177.5	+2.0	EtOH	180
—Ipd—		Me	PO₃Ph₂	—Ipd—		69	+45	EtOH	180
—	—	Me	Me	—	—	191–193	+73	H₂O	61
Ac	Ac	Me	Me	Ac	Ac	102.5–103.5	−1.4	CHCl₃	61
—Ipd—		Me	Me	—Ipd—		88–90	−44	CHCl₃	61

(Left margin bracket, rows from "— — Me —" downward: dextro-Pinitol and derivatives)

[a] See also *rac*-inositol, Table VII. [b] Numbering as in formula VIII [Fletcher–Anderson–Lardy numbers (p. 137) in parentheses]. [c] Derived from the 1,2-O-isopropylidene-, tetraacetate. Change of numbering (but not shift of groups) takes place on removal of the isopropylidene group.

(271a) C. E. Ballou, personal communication.

(272) L. Maquenne, *Compt. rend.,* **109,** 968 (1889); *Ann. chim. et phys.,* [6] **22,** 264 (1891).

(273) D. C. Pease, M. J. Reider and R. C. Elderfield, *J. Org. Chem.,* **5,** 198 (1940).

TABLE IV

Derivatives of levo-*Inositol*[a]

(Abbreviations are defined on p. 191)

1(2)	2(1)	3(5)	4(6)	5(4)	6(3)	Melting point, °C.	$[\alpha]_D,°$	Rotation solvent	References
—	—	—	—	—	—	247	−64	H_2O	249, 87
Ac	Ac	Ac	Ac	Ac	Ac	amorph.	−10	H_2O	249
Bz	Bz	Bz	Bz	Bz	Bz	252	−62	$(CH_2Cl)_2$	274, 195
—	—	Ns	Ns	—	—	d. >170			4
—	—	Ts	—	—	—	124–126 d.	−30	H_2O	86, 179
[c] —	—	Ac	Ts	—	—	192 d.			86
Ac	Ac	Ac	Ts	Ac	Ac	152–153			86
—	—	Ts	Ts	—	—	185–186	−28	C_5H_5N	149
Ac	Ac	Ts	Ts	Ac	Ac	$\begin{cases} 138\text{–}139 \\ 158 \end{cases}$	+17	$CHCl_3$	4
—	—	$PO_3^{\ominus\ominus}$	—	—	—				
bis(cyclohexylammonium) salt						250	−26	H_2O	180
Hexaphosphate						[d]	−5.2	H_2O	275
—, barium salt						amorph.			275
—Bzd—		—	—	—Bzd—		158–159.5	+6.0	$CHCl_3$	63
—Ipd—		—	—	—	—	157.5–158			6
—Ipd—		—	—	—Ipd—		153	−4.7	EtOH	6
—Ipd—	Ac	Ac	—Ipd—			129	−116	$CHCl_3$	6
—Ipd—	Ms	Ms	—Ipd—			260	−120	$CHCl_3$	4
—Ipd—	Ns	Ns	—Ipd—			171–172	−62	$CHCl_3$	4
—Ipd—	Ac	Ts	—Ipd—			144	−114	$CHCl_3$	149
—Ipd—	Ts	Ts	—Ipd—			$\begin{cases} 146\text{–}147 \\ 161\text{–}162 \end{cases}$	−80	$CHCl_3$	149
—Ipd—	$PO_3^{\ominus\,\ominus}$	—	—Ipd—						
bis(cyclohexylammonium) salt						>250	−2.2	H_2O	180
—Ipd—	PO_3Et_2	—	—Ipd—			135	−50	EtOH	180
—Ipd—	—$PO_2^{\ominus}$—	—Ipd—							
cyclohexylammonium salt						>250	+17	H_2O	180
—Ipd—	—PO_2Ph—	—Ipd—				105–115			180
—Ipd—	—Ipd—	—Ipd—				213–214	+38	$CHCl_3$	6
Me	—	—	—	—	—	207	−58	H_2O	149
Me	Ac	Ac	Ac	Ac	Ac	111	−31	EtOH	149
—	Me	—	—	—	—	190–191	−80	H_2O	249
Ac	Me	Ac	Ac	—	—	129–130	−76	$CHCl_3$	52, 179
Ac	Me	Ac	Ac	Ac	Ac	91, 94–95	−17	$CHCl_3$	249
2-O-Methyl-, pentaisovalerate (1-O-Methyl-, pentaisovalerate)						liq.			276
2-O-Methyl-, pentalaurate (1-O-Methyl-, pentalaurate)						32			276
2-O-Methyl-, pentapalmitate (1-O-Methyl-, pentapalmitate)						58			276
2-O-Methyl-, pentaphosphate (1-O-Methyl-, pentaphosphate)						[d]	−23	H_2O	275
—, barium salt						amorph.			275
—	Me	—	—	Ts	—	172–173 d.	−50	EtOH	52, 179
Ac	Me	Ac	Ac	Ts	Ac	142–143	−43	$CHCl_3$	52, 179
—	Me	—	—	—Ipd—		135–137	−89	H_2O	57, 6

Substituents[b]

Quebrachitol and derivatives

TABLE IV—*Continued*

Substituents[b]						Melting point, °C.	$[\alpha]_D$,°	Rotation solvent	References
1(2)	2(1)	3(5)	4(6)	5(4)	6(3)				
[e] —	—	Me	—	—	—	186	−65	H_2O	155, 42
—Ipd—		Me	—	—Ipd—		102–104	+45	$CHCl_3$	143
—	—	Me	Me	—	—	191–192	−73	H_2O	42
—Ipd—		Me	Me	—Ipd—		88–89			143

[a] See also *rac*-inositol, Table VII. [b] Numbering as in formula IX [Fletcher–Anderson–Lardy numbers (p. 137) in parentheses]. [c] Acetyl derivative of the previous compound. Change in numbering (but not shift of groups) takes place if only one of the two positions is substituted. [d] Not isolated. [e] *levo*-Pinitol.

(274) L. Maquenne and C. Tanret, *Compt. rend.*, **110**, 86 (1890).
(275) A. Contardi, *Ann. chim. appl.*, **14**, 281 (1924).
(276) T. G. Levi, *Gazz. chim. ital.*, **59**, 550 (1929).

TABLE V
Derivatives of epi-*Inositol (Formula II, p. 137)*[a]
(Abbreviations are defined on p. 191)

Substituents						Melting point, °C.	References
1	2	3	4	5	6		
—	—	—	—	—	—	303–304 d.	198, 6
Ac	—	Ac	Ac	Ac	Ac	153–154	198
Ac	Ac	Ac	Ac	Ac	Ac	188	198
2-*p*-Aminobenzoate						214–223	255
Ac	([b])	Ac	Ac	Ac	Ac	198–202	255
Bz	Bz	Bz	Bz	Bz	Bz	224	198
Ac	([c])	Ac	Ac	Ac	Ac	{ 95, 156–158	255
Ac	Ac	Ac	Ac	Ns	Ns	190	4
Ts	—	—	—	—	—	227 d.	7
[d] Ts	—	—	—	—	Ac	193	86
Ts	Ac	Ac	Ac	Ac	Ac	152–153	86
Ac	Ac	Ac	Ac	Ac	Ts	227	52
[d] Ts	—	—	—	—	Ts	190	86
—Ipd—		—Ipd—		—	—	181	6, 4
—Ipd—		—Ipd—		Ac	Ac	138	6
—Ipd—		—Ipd—		Ns	Ns	145	4
—Ipd—		—Ipd—		Ts	Ac	182	7
—Ipd—		—Ipd—		Ts	Ts	208–209	7
—Ipd—		—	—Ipd—		—	181	6
—Ipd—		Ac	—Ipd—		Ac	201–203	6
—Ipd—		—Ipd—		—Ipd—		{ 121, 127–128	6
Ac	Ac	Ac	Ac	Ac	Me	171–172	52
—Ipd—		—Ipd—		—	Me	104–105	52

[a] No optically active derivatives of *epi*-inositol have been prepared. All asymmetrically substituted compounds listed in this Table are racemic. [b] *p*-aminobenzoyl-. [c] *p*-nitrobenzoyl-. [d] Derived from the corresponding 5,6-di-*O*-acylated 1,2:3,4-di-*O*-isopropylidene-*epi*-inositols. Change of numbering (but not shift of groups) takes place on removal of the isopropylidene groups.

TABLE VI

Derivatives of allo-*Inositol*

(Abbreviations are defined on p. 191)

Substituents						Formula	Melting point, °C.	$[\alpha]_D,°$	Rotation solvent	References
1	2	3	4	5	6					
—	—	—	—	—	—	III	d. *ca.* 320	meso		277, 86
Ac	Ac	Ac	Ac	Ac	Ac		144	meso		7, 4
Bz	Bz	Bz	Bz	Bz	Bz		196	meso		35
Me	—	—	—	—	—		sirup	active		86
Me	Ac	Ac	Ac	Ac	Ac	[a]	145–146	−8.5	CHCl₃	86
Me	Ac	Ac	Ac	Ac	Ac	CI	145–146	+9	CHCl₃	7
Ac	Ac	Ac	Ac	Me	Ac		124	±		7
—O—		—	—	—	—	XCIX	d. *ca.* 200	+153	H₂O	7
—O—		—	—	—	—	XCIX	175–176 / 186–189	±		34
—O—		—Ipd—		—Ipd—		LXII	108–109	+14	MeOH	149
—	—O—		—	—	—	CIX	112 / 130	meso		278, 34 / 279
Me	—O—		Ac	Ac	Ac	[b]	76	−64	CHCl₃	149
—	—	—	—	—O—		CIII	120–122 / 148–150	meso		7
—Ipd—		—Ipd—		—O—			97–98	meso		7

[a] Acetate of previous compound; enantiomorph of CI. [b] See III; clockwise numbering.

(277) G. Dangschat and H. O. L. Fischer, *Naturwissenschaften*, **27,** 756 (1939).

(278) C. Schöpf, W. Arnold and C. H. Schwietzer, *Ann.*, **558,** 123 (1947).

(279) C. Schöpf and A. Schmetterling, *Angew. Chem.*, **64,** 591 (1952).

TABLE VII

Other Inositols and Their Derivatives

Compound	Melting point, °C.	References
cis-Inositol (I)	377 d.	21
hexaacetate	208	21
hexabenzoate	252	21
—, 1,2-anhydro- (CVII)	59–60	7
—, 1,2-anhydro-3,4:5,6-di-*O*-isopropylidene-	142–143	7
muco-Inositol (VI)	d. 285–290	277
hexaacetate	177–178	34
neo-Inositol (IV)	315 d.	149
hexaacetate	253	149
—, 1,2-anhydro-(C)[a]	154	7
rac-Inositol (VIII + IX)	252–253	249, 240, 142, 141
hexaacetate	112	249, 240, 142, 141
tetrabenzoate	213	240
hexabenzoate	217	274, 141
—, 3-*O*-methyl-, pentaacetate[b] (5-*O*-methyl-,[c] penta-acetate)	125	7
scyllo-Inositol (VII)	352	249, 204
pentaacetate	211–213	255
hexaacetate	301	249
diborate, disodium salt		84
dihydrogen phosphate	212–214 d.	178
—, penta-*O*-acetyl-, dihydrogen phosphate	252–253 d.	178
—, *O*-methyl-	239–242 d.	42
—, *O*-methyl-, pentaacetate	⎰trans. 172–175⎱ ⎱192–194⎰	42
—, 1,3-di-*O*-methyl-	⎰trans. 140–145⎱ ⎱155–156⎰	52

[a] $[\alpha]_D$ + 113° (H₂O). [b] *rac*-Pinitol pentaacetate. [c] Fletcher–Anderson–Lardy numbering.

TABLE VIII

Inososes and Their Derivatives

(Abbreviations are defined on p. 191)

Compound[a]	Melting point, °C.[b]	[α]D,°	Rotation solvent	References
cis-Inosose (X)	179–180 d.	meso		21, 42
phenylhydrazone	d. 150–160	meso		21
epi-Inosose (epi-Inosose-2) (enantiomorph of LXXXIV)	198 d.	−4.5	H₂O	199, 36
phenylhydrazone	d. ca. 200	active		199
pentabenzoate	134–136	active		199
epi-Inosose (epi-Inosose-2) (LXXXIV)	198–200 d.	±		198, 197
(2,4-dinitrophenyl)hydrazone	270[e]	±		198
oxime	150–151 d.	±		230
phenylhydrazone	d. 185–194	±		197
	220–222 d.[c]			198
semicarbazone	207 d.	±		198
thiosemicarbazone	197–198 d.	±		230
pentaacetate	106–108	±		198, 197
pentabenzoate	144			198
neo-Inosose (myo-Inosose-5) (CXVIII)	218–220 d.	meso		229
phenylhydrazone	201–204 d.	meso		229
scyllo-Inosose (myo-Inosose-2) (LXXXII)	200 d.	meso		280, 197
bis(ethyl sulfone) (LXXXVII)	d. 196–198	meso		208
ethylene dithioacetal (XC)	263–265 d.	meso		208
ethylene disulfone (XCI)	d. >225	meso		209
diethyl dithioacetal (LXXXVI)	185.5–186.5	meso		208
penta-O-acetyl-	180.5–182	meso		208
oxime	d. 140	meso		281
sodium salt	138–139 d.	meso		281
hexa-O-acetyl-	111–112	meso		281
phenylhydrazone	184	meso		204, 197

Compound	M.p.	meso/active	Rotation	Solvent	References
penta-O-acetyl-	112–113	meso			205
thiosemicarbazone	194.5–196 d.	meso			231
pentaacetate	211–212^d	meso			204, 197, 206
pentabenzoate	286^d	meso			204
pentapropionate	162^d	meso			205
—, 2-O-methyl- (myo-Inosose-2, 1-O-methyl-)	^e	active			42
—,	^e	active			236a
—, 4-O-methyl- (myo-Inosose-2, 5-O-methyl-)	162–163	meso			236a
—, 2,6-di-O-methyl- (myo-Inosose-2, 1,3-di-O-methyl-)	120	meso			52
—, 3-amino-3-deoxy- (myo-Inosose-2, 4-amino-4-deoxy-), hydrochloride	d. 145–149	±			223a
—, 3-(benzyloxycarbonylamino)-3-deoxy- [myo-Inosose-2, 4-(benzyloxycarbonylamino)-4-deoxy-]	d. 172–176	±			223a
(2,4-dinitrophenyl)hydrazone	cryst.	±			223a
oxime	135–137 d.	±	–24	H_2O	223a
talo-Inosose (allo-Inosose-1) (XXV)	141–142	±			42
—	^e				52
vibo-Inosose (myo-Inosose-1)^o hemihydrate (XCIV)	138–139	active	+20	H_2O	201
phenylhydrazone	196–197 d.		–55	$EtOH–C_5H_5N$	201
—, 5-O-methyl- (myo-Inosose-1, 5-O-methyl-) (LXVII)	153–154		+25	H_2O	236a
phenylhydrazone	139–140		–71	$EtOH–C_5H_5N$	236a
vibo-Inosose (myo-Inosose-1) (enantiomorph of XCIV)	138–139	active	–17	H_2O	51
phenylhydrazone	196–197^d	active			51
—, 3-O-methyl- (myo-Inosose-1, 3-O-methyl-) (LXIX)	156–157	active	–43		51
(2,4-dinitrophenyl)hydrazone	232 d.	active			51
phenylhydrazone	175–176 d.	active			51
—, 5-O-methyl- (myo-Inosose-1, 5-O-methyl-) (enantiomorph of LXVII)	^e	active		H_2O	42
—, 2,3-O-isopropylidene-6-O-methyl-(myo-Inosose-1, 2,3-O-isopropylidene-6-O-methyl-) (LXX)	^e	active			53, 236a
3-Deoxy-1-keto-cis-inositol (3-Deoxy-cis-inosose)	^e	active			42
4-Deoxy-2-keto-epi-inositol (4-Deoxy-epi-inosose-2)	^e	active			37
2-Deoxy-1-keto-myo-inositol (2-Deoxy-myo-inosose-1)	^e	active			60
—^f	^e	±			248
—					28

TABLE VIII—Continued

Compound^a	Melting point, °C.^b	[α]D, °	Rotation solvent	References
3-Deoxy-2-keto-1-O-methyl-myo-inositol (3-Deoxy-1-O-methyl-myo-inosose-2)	^e	active		236a
5-Deoxy-2-keto-myo-inositol (5-Deoxy-myo-inosose-2)	^e	meso		42
2,5-Diketo-epi-inositol	^e	±		52
1,2-Diketo-myo-inositol, bis(phenylhydrazone) (XCVI)	217 d.	−250 → −222^h	EtOH–C₅H₅N	36
—,—^f	217 d.	+240 → +214^h	EtOH–C₅H₅N	36
1,2-Diketo-myo-inositol, bis[(2,4-dinitrophenyl)hydrazone] (?)	193–195	±		282
bis(phenylhydrazone)^i	205 d.	±		281, 36
phenylosotriazole	278–282 d.	±		209
tetra-O-acetyl-	194–195	±		209
2,5-Diketo-myo-inositol	d. 170–180	meso		42
bis(phenylhydrazone)	d. 175–180	meso		42
2,3-Diketo-4-deoxy-epi-inositol, bis(phenylhydrazone)	210–212 d.	→ −55^h	EtOH–C₅H₅N	248
—,—^f	210–212 d.	+105 → +62^h	EtOH–C₅H₅N	244(?), 283, 60
—,—^f	208–209 d.	±		28

^a Listing is in the order: inososes, deoxyinososes (deoxyketoinositols), diketoinositols, and deoxydiketoinositols. The listing of the individual inososes in each group is alphabetical by configurational prefix. The first name given is the Angyal name; the Fletcher–Anderson–Lardy name follows in parentheses. The keto group has the number 1 in the Angyal system, and the direction of numbering around the ring is such as to give the lowest numbers to the larger number of cis-hydroxyl groups. In the Fletcher–Anderson–Lardy system, inososes are numbered as for the inositol which is indicated by the configurational prefix. The reader is referred to section I.1 and the papers there cited for further details. ^b The melting points of inososes vary with the methods used to determine them, and are not reliable indexes of purity. ^c Maquenne block. ^d See p. 178 concerning the so-called "lower-melting forms." ^e Originally called "d-inosose." ^h Mutarotation may be due to decomposition. ^i scyllo-Inosose phenylosazone.

(280) A. J. Kluyver and A. G. J. Boezaardt, Rec. trav. chim., 58, 956 (1939).

(281) H. E. Carter, C. Belinskey, R. K. Clark, Jr., E. H. Flynn, B. Lytle, G. E. McCasland and M. Robbins, J. Biol. Chem., 174, 415 (1948).

(282) E. I. Fulmer and L. A. Underkofler, Iowa State Coll. J. Sci., 21, 256 (1947).

(283) B. Magasanik and E. Chargaff, J. Biol. Chem., 175, 939 (1948).

TABLE IX

Inosamines and Their Derivatives

(Abbreviations are defined on p. 191)

Compound[a]	Melting point, °C.	$[\alpha]_D,°$	Rotation solvent	References
Inosamine I[b], hydrochloride	d. 230			26
Inosamine II[b], hydrochloride	265–270 d.			27
hexaacetate	{trans. 215 / 233–234			29
—, di-O-isopropylidene-, p-tolyl-sulfonate	d. 225			26
epi-Inosamine-2 (CXVI)	204–208 d.	±		230
hydrochloride	234–236 d.	±		217, 230
picrate	174–176	±		230
—, N-acetyl-	205–206 d.	±		217, 230
hexaacetate	192–194[e]	±		217, 230
—, di-N-methyl-, hydrochloride	{188–191 / 223–225 d.	±		230
—, di-N-methyl-, picrate	182–184	±		230
—, N-ureido-	208 d.	±		230
levo-Inosamine-1 (levo-Inosamine-2)	d. 200–205	−64	H_2O	236a
hexaacetate	111–112	active		236a
levo-Inosamine-3 (levo-Inosamine-5) (CXXIX)	amorph.	−60	H_2O	214
—, N-acetyl-	232–234 d.	−70	H_2O	214
—, N-acetyl-1,2:5,6-di-O-isopropylidene- (levo-Inosamine-5, N-acetyl-1,2:3,4-di-O-isopropylidene-)	141–142	−39	H_2O	214
—, N,O⁴-diacetyl-1,2:5,6-di-O-isopropylidene- (levo-Inosamine-5, N,O⁶-diacetyl-1,2:3,4-di-O-isopropylidene-)	131–148	active		214
myo-Inosamine-1	d. 200–205	+3.8	H_2O	236a
hexaacetate	206–207	active		236a
myo-Inosamine-2 (CXXII)	278 d.	meso		217, 28, 284
hydrochloride	{trans. 192 / 235–237	meso		217
—, N-acetyl-	246–248 d.	meso		217
—, penta-O-acetyl-	189	meso		284
hydrochloride	220 d.	meso		232
—, N-acetyl-1,4,5,6-tetra-O-acetyl-	245–247	±		284
—, N-acetyltetra-O-acetyl- (isomer)	225–230			284
hexaacetate	{240–242 / 255	meso		217, 28
—, N-acetyltetra-O-acetyl-O-p-bromophenylsulfonyl-	226			284
—, N-acetyl-1-O-methylsulfonyl-	208 d.	±		284

TABLE IX—*Continued*

Compound[a]	Melting point, °C.	[α]D,°	Rotation solvent	References
—, N-acetyl-1,4,5,6-tetra-O-acetyl-3-O-methylsulfonyl-	239	±		284
—, N-acetyltetra-O-acetyl-O-methylsulfonyl-(isomer)	213–214			284
—, N-acetyl-1,4,5,6-tetra-O-acetyl-3-O-(2-naphthylsulfonyl)-	223–224	±		284
—, N-acetyltetra-O-acetyl-O-(2-naphthylsulfonyl)- (isomer)	228–229			284
—, N-acetyl-1,4,5,6-tetra-O-acetyl-3-O-p-tolylsulfonyl-	214–216	±		284
—, N-acetyltetra-O-acetyl-O-p-tolylsulfonyl- (isomer)	207–209			284
—, N-salicylidene-	243–244 d.	meso		232
—, N-(O-acetylsalicylidene)-penta-O-acetyl-	243–244	meso		232
—, di-N-methyl-, hydrochloride	218–220	meso		231
—, di-N-methylpenta-O-acetyl-	132–133	meso		285
picrate	252	meso		285
—, tri-N-methylpenta-O-acetyl-, iodide	255–257	meso		285
myo-Inosamine-4 (CXV)	210–250 d.	±		223
—, N-acetyl-	270–271 d.	±		223
—, penta-O-acetyl-, hydrochloride	223–225	±		223
hexaacetate	237–239	±		221, 223
N-benzyloxycarbonyl-	213–215	±		223a
N-benzyloxycarbonyl-penta-O-acetyl-	152	±		223a
—, N-salicylidene-	219–221	±		223
—, N-(O-acetylsalicylidene)-penta-O-acetyl-	trans. 156–158 / 181–182	±		223
—, 2-keto-, and derivatives—see under scyllo-*inosose*, Table VIII				
neo-Inosamine-1 (CXXVIII)	265–267 d.	+8	H_2O	214
—, N-acetyl-	266–268 d.	−65	H_2O	214
hexaacetate	267.5–269.5	−5	H_2O	214
—, N-benzyloxycarbonyl-	235–236.5	active		214
—, N,O²-carbonyl-	amorph.	active		214
—, N-acetyl-2,3:4,5-di-O-isopropylidene-	145–147	−173	H_2O	214
—, N,O⁶-diacetyl-2,3:4,5-di-O-isopropylidene-	amorph.	active		214
—, N-acetyl-2,3:5,6-di-O-isopropylidene-	201.5–203.5	−76	H_2O	214
neo-Inosamine-2 (CXIX)	238–240 d.	meso		227, 229
d-camphorsulfonate	230–232	active		227
hydrochloride	215–216c / 114–115c	meso		227, 228

TABLE IX—*Continued*

Compound[a]	Melting point, °C.	$[\alpha]_D,°$	Rotation solvent	References
—, N-acetyl-	238–242	meso		228
—, penta-O-acetyl-, hydrochloride	185–187	meso		229
hexaacetate	277.5–278.5	meso		227, 229
—, N,O^1-carbonyl-	203–205	±		227
—, N-(α-methyl-3,4-dihydroxycin-namoyl)-	251–252	meso		228, 229
—, N-(α-methyl-3,4-dipropionoxy-cinnamoyl)-penta-O-acetyl-	157–160	meso		229
—, N,N-phthaloyl-	255–261 d.	meso		227
—, N,O^1-thiocarbonyl-	245	±		227
—, N-benzylidene-	209–211 d.	meso		229
penta-O-acetyl-	217–219	meso		229
—, 4,5-O-isopropylidene-N,N-phthaloyl-	210–212	±		227
rac-Inosamine-1 (rac-Inosamine-2) (?), hexaacetate[d]	157			218
scyllo-Inosamine (XI, CXXIII)	>300	meso		26, 232
hydrochloride	d. > 260	meso		217
—, N-acetyl-	289–291 d.	meso		217, 232
—, penta-O-acetyl-, hydrochloride	270 d.	meso		232
hexaacetate	288[c] 299–301[c,e]	meso		217, 28
—, N-salicylidene-	264.5–265.5	meso		232
—, N-(O-acetylsalicylidene)-penta-O-acetyl-	206–206.5	meso		232
—, di-N-methyl-, hydrochloride	222–223	meso		285
penta-O-acetyl-	213–214	meso		285
—, tri-N-methylpenta-O-acetyl-, picrate	193–194	meso		285
Inosadiamine,[b] di-N-acetyl-	269			234
Inosadiamine[b] hexaacetate	170–173			218
Inosadiamine[b] hexaacetate (isomer)	298–303			218
meta-Inosadiamine[b] hexaacetate	350–355			222
scyllo-Inosadiamine-1,3—see Strep-tamine (next entry)				
Streptamine (systematic name: scyllo-inosadiamine-1,3) (CX)	>290	meso		286
Streptamines, deoxy- —see Deoxy-streptamines, below				
Streptamine, dihydrochloride	245–255 d.	meso		286
dihydriodide	d. > 280	meso		286
di-p-(p-hydroxyphenylazo)ben-zenesulfonate	d. 270–300	meso		286
dipicrate	>300	meso		286
sulfate	d. ca. 340	meso		287, 286
—, di-N-acetyl-	283–284	meso		286
—, N-acetyltri-O-acetyl-, hydro-chloride	d. > 300	±		221

TABLE IX—*Continued*

Compound[a]	Melting point, °C.	[α]D,°	Rotation solvent	References
—, tetra-*O*-acetyl-, dihydrochloride	260 d.	meso		232
hexaacetate	{trans. 240–250 342–345	meso		287, 286
—, di-*N*-amidino- —see *Streptidine*, below				
—, di-*N*-benzoyl-	293–295	meso		287, 286
hexabenzoate	350–351	meso		287, 286
—, di-*N*-carbamyl- (also called *strepturea*)	d. 290–300	meso		288, 286
—, di-*N*-benzyloxycarbonyl-	249–250	meso		221
tetra-*O*-acetyl-	232–233	meso		221, 223a
tetra-*O*-benzoyl-	241–242	meso		221
—, di-*N*-benzylidene-	222–228 d.	meso		286
tetra-*O*-acetyl-	247.5–248.5	meso		232
—, tetra-*N*-methyl-, dihydrochloride	275–276	meso		285
tetra-*O*-acetyl-	190–200	meso		285
—, tetra-*O*-methyl- (CXI)	83–84	meso		221
hemihydrate	52–54	meso		221
dihydrochloride	>300	meso		221
dipicrate	238–239 d.	meso		221
—, di-*N*-acetyltetra-*O*-methyl-	>300	meso		221
—, di-*N*-methyltri-*N′*-methyltetra-*O*-acetyl-, dipicrate	212–214	±		285
—, di-*N*-(2,4-dinitrophenyl)-	315–317 d.	meso		218
Streptidine (di-*N*-amidino derivative of streptamine)[f]	cryst.	meso		288
2-Deoxystreptamine (see text, p. 185) (CXVII)		meso		224(a)
dihydrobromide	263–267 d.	meso		224(b)
dihydrochloride		meso		224(a)
—, di-*N*-acetyl-		meso		225
—, di-*N*-benzoyl-	313–313.5 d.	meso		224
pentabenzoate		meso		224(a)
4-Deoxystreptamine, di-*N*-benzoyl-	287–289	−4	HOAc–H₂O	290
pentabenzoate	298–299	˙active		290

[a] Listing is in the order: (mono)inosamines, inosadiamines, and deoxyinosadiamines. Within these groups, the individual inosamines appear in alphabetical order according to their configurational prefixes. Fletcher–Anderson–Lardy names are shown in parentheses when they differ from Angyal names (see pp. 138 and 183). [b] Configuration unknown. [c] In capillary tube and on Kofler block, respectively. [d] Parent inosamine, formula CXXVI. [e] Shows two transitions in crystal form.

[f] Many derivatives of streptidine have been prepared. Descriptions of the syntheses and physical constants are given in Refs. 287, 289, 290 and 290a.

(284) G. I. Drummond and L. Anderson, *J. Am. Chem. Soc.*, **78**, 1750 (1956).

(285) G. F. Holland, R. C. Durant, S. L. Friess and B. Witkop, *J. Am. Chem. Soc.*, **80**, 6031 (1958).

TABLE X

Quercitols and Their Derivatives

(Abbreviations are defined on p. 191)

Compound[a]	Formula	Melting point, °C.	[α]D,°	Rotation solvent	References
Quercitol, configuration unknown		d. 230–240			21
pentaacetate		115–117			21
cis-Quercitol (Deoxy-cis-inositol)	CXXXIX	235–240 d.	meso		21
pentaacetate		165.5	meso		21
epi-Quercitol (2-Deoxy-epi-inositol)	CXL	194	−5.4	H₂O	37
pentaacetate		121	active		42
epi-Quercitol (2-Deoxy-epi-inositol)	CXL	206–208	±		230
		214–215			37
pentaacetate		{123–124.5 / 142–143	±		230
		113–115			37
neo-Quercitol (5-Deoxy-myo-inositol)	CXLII	238–239 d.	meso		42
pentaacetate		182	meso		42
proto-Quercitol (1-Deoxy-muco-inositol)	CXLI	232, 235	+26, +24	H₂O	291
pentaacetate		amorph.	active		291
pentabenzoate		155	+61	EtOAc	292
—, 3,4-O-isopropylidene- (1-Deoxy-muco-inositol, 4,5-O-isopropylidene-)		159	+74	EtOH	6
scyllo-Quercitol (2-Deoxy-myo-inositol)	CXLIV	233–235	meso		204
pentaacetate		190	meso		204
—, 3-O-methyl- (2-Deoxy-myo-inositol, 5-O-methyl-)		215	meso		236a
tetraacetate		184–185	meso		236a
vibo-Quercitol (1-Deoxy-myo-inositol)	CXLIII	180–181	−50ᶜ	H₂O	244, 245, 51(b)
pentaacetate		124–125	−22	CHCl₃	244, 247
pentabenzoate		158.5	−79	CHCl₃	244, 247
—, 1,2-O-isopropylidene-, 3,4,5-triacetate (3-Deoxy-myo-inositol, 1,2-O-isopropylidene-, 4,5,6-triacetate)	b	{104–105 / 118–120	−66	EtOAc	60
—, 2-O-methyl- (3-Deoxy-myo-inositol, 1-O-methyl-)		148–149	−71	H₂O	51(b)
vibo-Quercitol (1-Deoxy-myo-inositol)	XCV	180–181	+50ᶜ	H₂O	248
pentaacetate		126	active		248

TABLE X—*Continued*

Compound[a]	Formula	Melting point, °C.	[α]D,°	Rotation solvent	Refer- ences
—, 4-O-methyl- (1-Deoxy-*myo*-inositol, 5-O-methyl-)		[d]	active		236a
vibo-Quercitol (1-Deoxy-*myo*-inositol)	XCV + CXLIII	161–163	±		248, 28
pentaacetate		{64 {113–114	±		248, 28

[a] Quercitols are listed alphabetically according to their configurational prefixes. The names are given in the Angyal system, followed by the Fletcher–Anderson–Lardy names in parentheses. In the Angyal system, the positions are so numbered as to give the lowest numbers to the larger number of *cis*-hydroxyl groups, the methylene carbon atom being numbered 6. Numbering in the Fletcher–Anderson–Lardy system is as for the inositol indicated by the configurational prefix. The reader is referred to section I.1 and the papers there cited for further details. [b] Free hydroxy compound, formula CXLVI. [c] For the monohydrate. [d] Not isolated.

(286) R. L. Peck, C. E. Hoffhine, Jr., E. W. Peel, R. P. Graber, F. W. Holly, R. Mozingo and K. Folkers, *J. Am. Chem. Soc.*, **68**, 776 (1946).

(287) H. E. Carter, R. K. Clark, Jr., S. R. Dickman, Y. H. Loo, J. S. Meek, P. S. Skell, W. A. Strong, J. T. Alberi, Q. R. Bartz, S. B. Binkley, H. M. Crooks, Jr., I. R. Hooper and M. C. Rebstock, *Science*, **103**, 53 (1946).

(288) J. Fried, G. A. Boyack and O. Wintersteiner, *J. Biol. Chem.*, **162**, 391 (1946).

(289) R. L. Peck, R. P. Graber, A. Walti, E. W. Peel, C. E. Hoffhine, Jr., and K. Folkers, *J. Am. Chem. Soc.*, **68**, 29 (1946).

(290) F. A. Kuehl, Jr., R. L. Peck, C. E. Hoffhine, Jr., and K. Folkers, *J. Am. Chem. Soc.*, **70**, 2325 (1948).

(290a) R. L. Peck, F. A. Kuehl, Jr., C. E. Hoffhine, Jr., E. W. Peel and K. Folkers, *J. Am. Chem. Soc.*, **70**, 2321 (1948).

(291) Ref. 249, Vol. VI, pp. 1186–1188; Suppl. I, Vol. VI, p. 584; Suppl. II, Vol. VI, p. 1151.

(292) K. H. Bauer and H. Moll, *Arch. Pharm.*, **280**, 37 (1942).

ASPECTS OF THE CHEMISTRY OF THE AMINO SUGARS

By A. B. Foster and D. Horton

Department of Chemistry, The University of Birmingham, England
Sebright School, Wolverley, Worcestershire, England

I. Introduction

Seven years have elapsed since the general chemistry of the amino sugars was last reviewed in this Series.[1] During the interval, interest in this field of organic chemistry has been stimulated to a remarkable degree and the discovery of a range of new amino sugars of differing types has been witnessed. It is most noticeable that such primitive forms of life as fungi and bacteria synthesize, for reasons yet unknown, complex substances possessed of remarkable chemical and biological properties. Many of these "chemical curiosities" have antibiotic properties, and it is within this general group that many of the new amino sugars have been found.

Since 1952, particular[2-6] and general[7, 8] developments in the chemistry and biochemistry of the amino sugars have been the subjects of reviews which should be regarded as complementary to the present Chapter.

II. Chemical Syntheses of 2-Amino-2-deoxy-aldoses

An account of the methods of synthesis of amino sugars has been given in an earlier Volume of this Series[1]; attention is devoted in this Section to methods recently developed. Several general methods have been employed for the synthesis of 2-amino-2-deoxy-aldoses; these respectively involve direct amination of suitable sugar derivatives, interconversion of sugar series, and ascent or descent of a series with or without concomitant amination or molecular rearrangements.

1. Syntheses Involving Addition of Hydrogen Cyanide

The Fischer–Leuchs synthesis of 2-amino-2-deoxy-D-gluconic acid[9] (by hydrolysis of the corresponding nitrile, produced on addition of hydrogen

(1) A. B. Foster and M. Stacey, *Advances in Carbohydrate Chem.*, **7**, 247 (1952).

(2) R. Kuhn, *Angew. Chem.*, **69**, 23 (1957).

(3) A. B. Foster and A. J. Huggard, *Advances in Carbohydrate Chem.*, **10**, 335 (1955).

(4) R. L. Whistler and E. J. Olson, *Advances in Carbohydrate Chem.*, **12**, 299 (1957).

(5) F. Zilliken and M. W. Whitehouse, *Advances in Carbohydrate Chem.*, **13**, 237 (1958).

(6) R. W. Jeanloz, *Advances in Carbohydrate Chem.*, **13**, 189 (1958).

(7) H. H. Baer, *Fortschr. chem. Forsch.*, **3**, 822 (1958).

(8) P. W. Kent and M. W. Whitehouse, "Biochemistry of the Aminosugars," Butterworths, London, 1955.

(9) E. Fischer and H. Leuchs, *Ber.*, **36**, 24 (1903)

cyanide to D-arabinosylamine) is of great historical interest, but it is not a practicable synthetic route to the 2-amino-2-deoxy-aldoses since a satisfactory procedure for the reduction of the amino-substituted aldonic acids to the corresponding aldoses is still lacking. Recently, Kuhn and coworkers[10] have shown that hemihydrogenation and subsequent acidic hydrolysis of carbohydrate α-amino nitriles yields the corresponding aldoses. (An improved synthesis of N-alkylamino nitriles had been reported by Wolfrom and coworkers.[10a]) The procedure appears to be generally applicable, and aryl substituents on the amino group are hydrogenolyzed during the reaction.[11] The reaction stops at the aldose stage since there is no tendency for the cyclic sugars to be reduced under noble-metal catalysis. The reaction sequences are as follows.

$$\begin{array}{c}\text{C}\!\equiv\!\text{N}\\|\\\text{HCNH}_2\\|\end{array} \xrightarrow{\;\text{H}_2\ (1\ \text{mol.})/\text{H}_2\text{O}/\text{Pt}\;} \begin{array}{c}\text{CHOH}\\|\\\text{HCNH}_2\\|\end{array}\ \text{O}$$

Amino nitriles

$$\begin{array}{c}\text{C}\!\equiv\!\text{N}\\|\\\text{HCNHR}\\|\end{array} \xrightarrow{\;\text{H}_2\ (1\ \text{mol.})/\text{H}_2\text{O}\;} \begin{array}{c}\text{CHOH}\\|\\\text{HCNHR}\\|\end{array}\ \text{O}$$

Alkylamino   R = alkyl or
nitriles   —CH₂—CO₂Et
[Et ester is hydrolyzed
during reaction]

$$\begin{array}{c}\text{C}\!\equiv\!\text{N}\\|\\\text{HCNH}\!-\!\text{CH}_2\!-\!\text{C}_6\text{H}_5\\|\end{array} \xrightarrow{\;\text{H}_2\ (2\ \text{mols.})/\text{H}_2\text{O}\;} \begin{array}{c}\text{CHOH}\\|\\\text{HCNH}_2\\|\end{array}\ \text{O}\ +\ \text{C}_6\text{H}_5\!-\!\text{CH}_3$$

Benzylamino nitriles

$$\begin{array}{c}\text{C}\!\equiv\!\text{N}\\|\\\text{HCNH}\!-\!\text{C}_6\text{H}_5\\|\end{array} \xrightarrow{\;\text{H}_2\ (3\ \text{mols.})/\text{H}_2\text{O}\;} \begin{array}{c}\text{CHOH}\\|\\\text{HCNH}_2\\|\end{array}\ \text{O}\ +$$

Arylamino nitriles

An N-alkyl group is not removed under the reaction conditions, and an N-substituted 2-amino-2-deoxy-aldose is formed. Under the same reaction conditions, an N-benzyl group is cleaved (with the uptake of a further mole of hydrogen per mole), to give the free 2-amino-2-deoxy-aldose and toluene;

(10) R. Kuhn and W. Kirschenlohr, *Angew. Chem.*, **67**, 786 (1955).

(10a) M. L. Wolfrom, A. Thompson and I. R. Hooper, *J. Am. Chem. Soc.*, **68**, 2343 (1946).

(11) R. Kuhn and W. Kirschenlohr, *Ann.*, **600**, 115 (1956).

an N-phenyl group is likewise eliminated, this time with *two* moles of hydrogen per mole, the aryl group being reduced to cyclohexanone.

The addition of hydrogen cyanide to aldosylamines gives a mixture of the two epimeric α-amino nitriles, and synthesis of a pair of epimeric hexosamines can thus be achieved from one pentose. Several of the theoretically possible hexosamines have now been synthesized in this way[11-14] (see Table I), and the first example of a 2-amino-2-deoxy-heptose has been synthesized from N-benzyl-D-galactosylamine.[11] Since the procedure involves reaction conditions under which glycosidic linkages are, in general, unaffected, it can be used for the synthesis of oligosaccharides having a 2-amino group on the terminal reducing residue; the method has been successfully employed in the synthesis of N-acetyl-lactosamine [2-acetamido-2-deoxy-4-O-(β-D-galactopyranosyl)-D-glucose] using 3-O-(β-D-galactopyranosyl)-D-arabinose as the starting material.[15]

Certain exceptions to this general scheme have been noted in which the normal hydrogenation of the nitrile group has not taken place. In these cases, a hydrolytic reaction has occurred, with the formation of an aldonic acid instead of the expected aldose.[12] The "anomalous" reaction occurs when the nitrile exists in the (isomeric) iminolactone form; for example, compound I is hydrolyzed directly, before hydrogenation can take place. This isomerism of the aldononitriles was established by Papadakis and Cohen,[16] and the cyclic structure I was postulated by Wolfrom and co-workers.[10a]

$$
\begin{array}{l}
\text{HN=C} \longrightarrow \\
\quad | \\
\text{H}\overset{|}{\text{C}}\text{NHCH}_2\text{Ph} \\
\text{HO}\overset{|}{\text{C}}\text{H} \\
\text{HO}\overset{|}{\text{C}}\text{H} \\
\text{H}\overset{|}{\text{C}}\text{O} \longrightarrow \\
\quad | \\
\text{CH}_2\text{OH}
\end{array}
$$

I

It is not known whether the cyclization of hexose derivatives takes place with the C4- or the C5-hydroxyl group; work on model compounds suggests that both the furanoid and the pyranoid rings are possible. Iminolactone formation is theoretically possible for any 4- or 5-hydroxy nitrile,

(12) R. Kuhn and W. Kirschenlohr, *Ann.*, **600**, 126 (1956).

(13) R. Kuhn and W. Bister, *Ann.*, **602**, 217 (1957).

(14) R. Kuhn and H. Fischer, *Ann.*, **612**, 65 (1958).

(15) R. Kuhn and W. Kirschenlohr, *Ann.*, **600**, 135 (1956).

(16) P. E. Papadakis and H. J. Cohen, *J. Am. Chem. Soc.*, **60**, 765 (1938); P. E. Papadakis, *ibid.*, **64**, 1950 (1942).

and the cyclic structure can be detected by infrared spectroscopy; all such cyclic derivatives studied are hydrolyzed readily, to give carboxylic acids, and they cannot be hydrogenated to give aldose derivatives.[17, 18] The only carbohydrate α-amino nitrile derivative so far encountered which exhibits this behavior is 2-benzylamino-2-deoxy-D-galactononitrile (I), which gives 2-amino-2-deoxy-D-galactonic acid under the hydrogenation conditions, consuming only the one mole of hydrogen per mole required for scission of the benzyl group. Free 2-amino-2-deoxy-D-galactononitrile and its N-phenyl derivative behave normally and are hydrogenated to give 2-amino-2-deoxy-D-galactose.[12]

It appears probable that the aldimine II, initially formed by hydrogenation of the nitrile group, is itself in the stabilized, cyclic-hemiacetal form as a 1,2-diamino-1,2-dideoxy derivative (III), the 1-amino group of which is subsequently hydrolyzed to yield the cyclic 2-amino-2-deoxy sugar (IV) directly.[10, 10a]

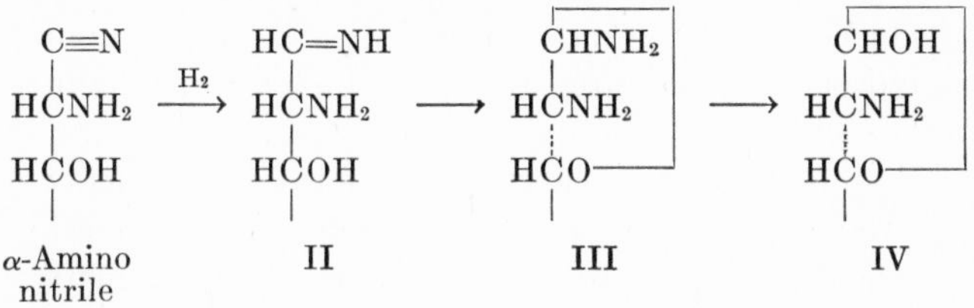

α-Amino nitrile   II   III   IV

The amino nitrile synthesis is particularly useful for the preparation of 2-amino-2-deoxy derivatives of rare sugars which would be difficult to obtain as intermediates in a synthesis involving amination alone. Thus, 2-amino-2-deoxy-L-glucose and 2-amino-2-deoxy-L-mannose can be prepared in good yield from the readily available L-arabinose.[11, 13]

2. Direct Amination Reactions

a. Syntheses Involving Change of Configuration.—Many sugar epoxides react with ammonia to give two isomeric amino sugars according to the following general reaction-sequence.

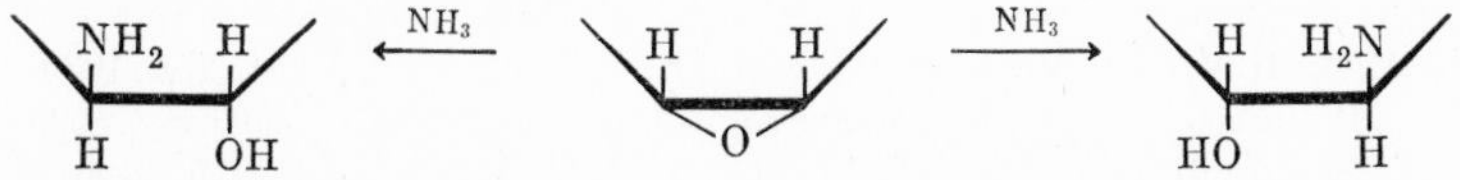

The new groups formed in these reactions are *trans*-related, and the proportion of each isomer formed depends on the structure and stereochemistry of the parent sugar epoxide. When attached to rigid, six-membered

(17) R. Kuhn and D. Weiser, *Ann.*, **600,** 144 (1956).
(18) R. Kuhn and D. Weiser, *Ann.*, **602,** 208 (1957).

ring-systems, epoxides tend to open so that the new groups formed are in axial positions (the Fürst–Plattner rule[19]). Thus, the action of methanolic ammonia on methyl 2,3-anhydro-4,6-O-benzylidene-α-D-allopyranoside yields methyl 2-amino-4,6-O-benzylidene-2-deoxy-α-D-altropyranoside predominantly; the 3-amino-3-deoxy-D-glucose derivative is produced simultaneously to a very small extent.[20] Under similar conditions, methyl 2,3-anhydro-4,6-O-benzylidene-α-D-mannopyranoside yields methyl 3-amino-4,6-O-benzylidene-3-deoxy-α-D-altropyranoside, with the 2-amino-2-deoxy-D-glucose derivative as the minor product. This reaction provided the first constitutional synthesis of 2-amino-2-deoxy-D-glucose.[21] Control of the direction of epoxide-ring opening in sugar derivatives by ammonia and other reagents may be accomplished by limiting the flexibility of the pyranoid ring—by fusing on to it a second ring (a benzylidene acetal group in the reaction noted above) or by 1,6-anhydro ring formation. Thus, treatment of 1,6:2,3-dianhydro-β-D-talopyranose with aqueous ammonia yields 2-amino-1,6-anhydro-2-deoxy-β-D-galactopyranose as the major reaction product. Acidic hydrolysis of this compound yields 2-amino-2-deoxy-D-galactose hydrochloride; the reaction was employed in the first constitutional synthesis of the amino sugar.[22] If a substituted amine is used, an N-substituted amino sugar derivative is formed. For instance, variation of the above synthesis of 2-amino-2-deoxy-D-altrose by using methylamine or guanidine instead of ammonia results in the formation of 2-methylamino or 2-guanidino derivatives.[23]

Other examples of related reactions have been summarized,[24] and the cleavage of sugar epoxide derivatives with ammonia has been discussed in detail.[25]

b. *Interconversion of Sugar Series*—Baker and coworkers,[26, 27] in extending the work of Winstein and colleagues,[28] showed that the *trans*-amino alcohols, arising from the action of ammonia on sugar epoxide derivatives, can be converted to the *cis* configuration by solvolysis of the N-acetyl-O-

(19) A. Fürst and P. A. Plattner, *Intern. Congr. Pure and Appl. Chem., 13th Congr.*, 409 (1951); *J. Colloid Sci.*, Suppl. No. 1 (1954).

(20) A. B. Foster, M. Stacey and S. V. Vardheim, *Nature*, **180**, 247 (1957); *Acta Chem. Scand.*, **12**, 1605 (1958).

(21) W. N. Haworth, W. H. G. Lake and S. Peat, *J. Chem. Soc.*, 271 (1939).

(22) S. P. James, F. Smith, M. Stacey and L. F. Wiggins, *J. Chem. Soc.*, 625 (1946).

(23) S. N. Danilov and I. S. Lyshanskiĭ, *Zhur. Obshcheĭ Khim.*, **25**, 2106 (1955).

(24) W. G. Overend and G. Vaughan, *Chem. & Ind.* (London), 995 (1955).

(25) F. Shafizadeh, *Advances in Carbohydrate Chem.*, **13**, 9 (1958).

(26) B. R. Baker and R. E. Schaub, *J. Am. Chem. Soc.*, **75**, 3864 (1953).

(27) B. R. Baker, R. E. Schaub, J. P. Joseph and J. H. Williams, *J. Am. Chem. Soc.*, **76**, 4044 (1954).

(28) S. Winstein and R. Boschan, *J. Am. Chem. Soc.*, **72**, 4669 (1950) and earlier related papers. *See also*, G. E. McCasland, R. K. Clark, Jr., and H. E. Carter, *ibid.*, **71**, 637 (1949).

tosyl (or N-acetyl-O-mesyl) compounds, as in the following reaction sequence.

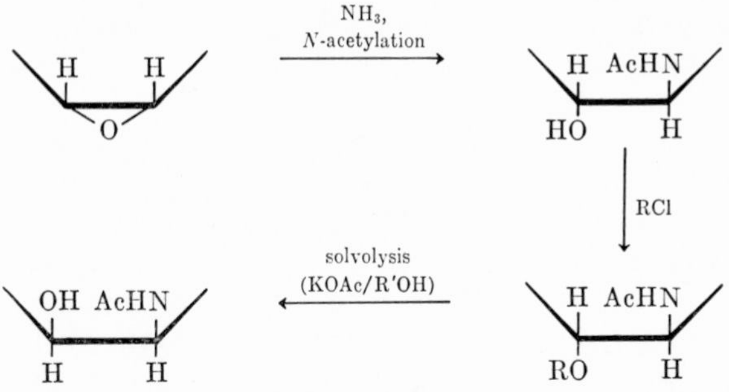

where R = p-tolylsulfonyl or methylsulfonyl.

Baker's original work concerned the synthesis of 3-amino-3-deoxy-D-ribose, a component residue of the antibiotic puromycin.[29] Two independent syntheses were achieved, starting from L-arabinose and D-xylose, respectively. The main steps in the reaction schemes are outlined in the following reaction sequences.

(1) *From* L-*Arabinose*.[29]

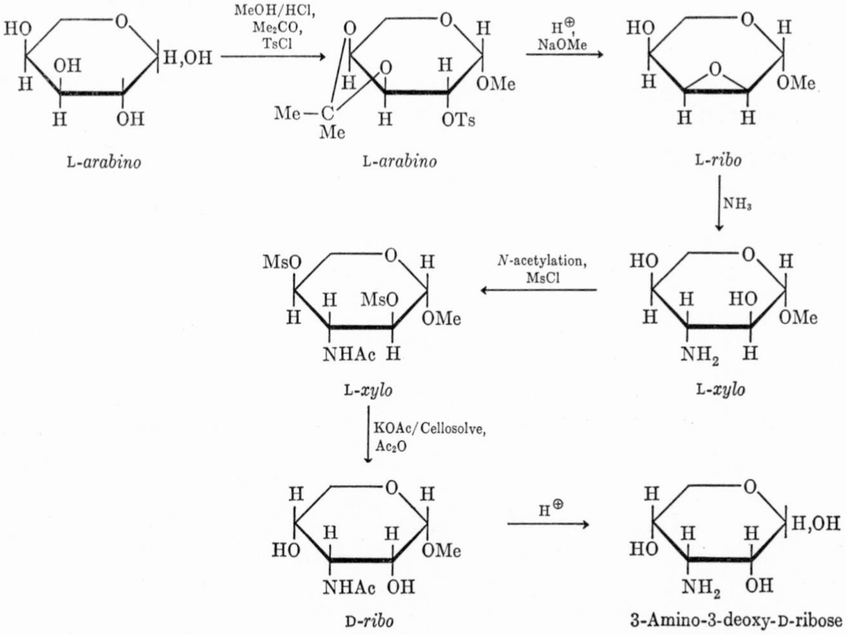

(29) B. R. Baker and R. E. Schaub, *J. Org. Chem.*, **19**, 646 (1954).

(2) *From* D-*Xylose.*[30]

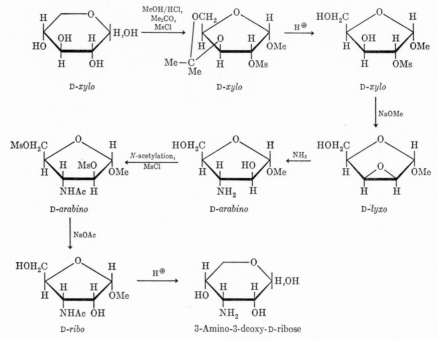

Subsequently Jeanloz[31] was able to convert 2-amino-2-deoxy-D-glucose into 2-amino-2-deoxy-D-allose (VI) by solvolysis of the 3-methylsulfonyl ester of methyl 2-acetamido-4,6-O-benzylidene-2-deoxy-α-D-glucopyranoside (V).

Similarly, 2-amino-2-deoxy-D-galactose was converted into 2-amino-2-deoxy-D-gulose by solvolysis of methyl 2-acetamido-2-deoxy-3-O-mesyl-α-D-galactopyranoside.[32]

This method appears to be of general application for the synthesis of amino sugars with the *cis* configuration of hydroxyl groups vicinal to amino groups. The synthesis of all of the theoretically possible 2-amino-2-deoxy-,

(30) B. R. Baker, R. E. Schaub and J. H. Williams, *J. Am. Chem. Soc.*, **77,** 7 (1955).
(31) R. W. Jeanloz, *J. Am. Chem. Soc.*, **79,** 2591 (1957).
(32) Z. Tarasiejska and R. W. Jeanloz, *J. Am. Chem. Soc.*, **79,** 2660 (1957).

3-amino-3-deoxy-, and 4-amino-4-deoxy-hexoses and -pentoses is feasible, using a combination of the general methods 2(a) and 2(b), provided that the appropriate nitrogen-free sugar derivatives are available.

3. *Intramolecular Rearrangements*

The rearrangement of aldosylamines ("*N*-glycosides") to form 1-amino-1-deoxy-ketoses (the Amadori "rearrangement," enolization of an imino aldehyde) is well known[33] and has permitted the preparation of numerous 1-amino-1-deoxyketose derivatives.[7] A recent variation of this synthesis involves the rearrangement of a ketosylamine to give a mixture of the two epimeric 2-amino-2-deoxy-aldoses. Thus, a D-fructosylamine derivative (VII) gives rise to a mixture of derivatives of 2-amino-2-deoxy-D-glucose (VIII) and 2-amino-2-deoxy-D-mannose (IX). 2-Amino-2-deoxy-D-glucose has been so synthesized[33a] from benzyl-*N*-(D-fructosyl)amine.

VIII   VII   IX

Several *N*-alkoxycarbonyl derivatives of 2-amino-2-deoxy-D-glucose have been prepared in this way by reacting D-fructose with the appropriate amino acid.[34] The rearrangement is catalyzed by ammonium chloride, and the epimer with the D-*gluco* configuration is formed preferentially. Such derivatives, when formed from optically active amino acids, are diastereoisomers, separable by chromatography; this observation has been used for the resolution of DL-alanine, since the rearrangement can be reversed, and the amino acid can be recovered by alkaline treatment.

Free amino sugars can be synthesized by the rearrangement of ketosylamines which carry no *N*-substituent.[35] The rearrangement is catalyzed by weak organic acids, and takes place concurrently with a similarly acid-catalyzed, hydrolytic cleavage of the ketosylamine. It is found that strong acids catalyze the hydrolysis and that weak acids (for example, benzoic and succinic acids) catalyze the rearrangement. Of the four ketohexosylamines studied by Heyns and coworkers, D-*lyxo*-hexulosylamine (D-tagatosylamine) was rearranged the most readily, to give 2-amino-2-deoxy-D-galactose plus a little 2-amino-2-deoxy-D-talose, whereas D-*arabino*-hexulosylamine (D-fructosylamine) and D-*ribo*-hexulosylamine (D-psicosylamine) rearranged

(33) J. E. Hodge, *Advances in Carbohydrate Chem.*, **10**, 169 (1955).
(33a) J. F. Carson, *J. Am. Chem. Soc.*, **78**, 3728 (1956).
(34) K. Heyns, H. Breuer and H. Paulsen, *Chem. Ber.*, **90**, 1374 (1957).
(35) K. Heyns, H. Paulsen, R. Eichstedt and M. Rolle, *Chem. Ber.*, **90**, 2039 (1957).

less readily, the former giving mainly 2-amino-2-deoxy-D-glucose plus a little 2-amino-2-deoxy-D-mannose, the latter giving 2-amino-2-deoxy-D-allose and 2-amino-2-deoxy-D-altrose in the ratio of 2 to 1. The remaining ketosylamine, L-*xylo*-hexulosylamine (L-sorbosylamine) was *least* readily rearranged, but it gave an equimolar mixture of 2-amino-2-deoxy-L-gulose and 2-amino-2-deoxy-L-idose. The formation of two amino sugars from a pentulosylamine has also been reported.[35]

Six of the eight hexosamines above were identified as crystalline derivatives or by chromatographic properties. The remaining epimeric pair, 2-amino-2-deoxy-L-gulose and 2-amino-2-deoxy-L-idose, were isolated and were differentiated by comparison of the specific rotations of the corresponding 2-amino-2-deoxyhexonic acids and their sodium salts (Levene's salt rule[36]). In addition, the specific rotation recorded for 2-amino-2-deoxy-L-gulose ($+ 17.8°$ in water) is in excellent agreement with the value ($- 17.9°$ in water) reported by Jeanloz[32] for the D analog prepared by a different synthetic route.

The mechanism of the rearrangement is believed to involve protonation of the ring oxygen atom of the ketosylamine (X) to give XI, with subsequent formation of a carbonium cation (XII) which rearranges and loses a proton by electron transfer. The *aldehydo* form of the 2-amino-2-deoxy sugar (XIII a or b) so obtained cyclizes to give the amino sugar (XIV a

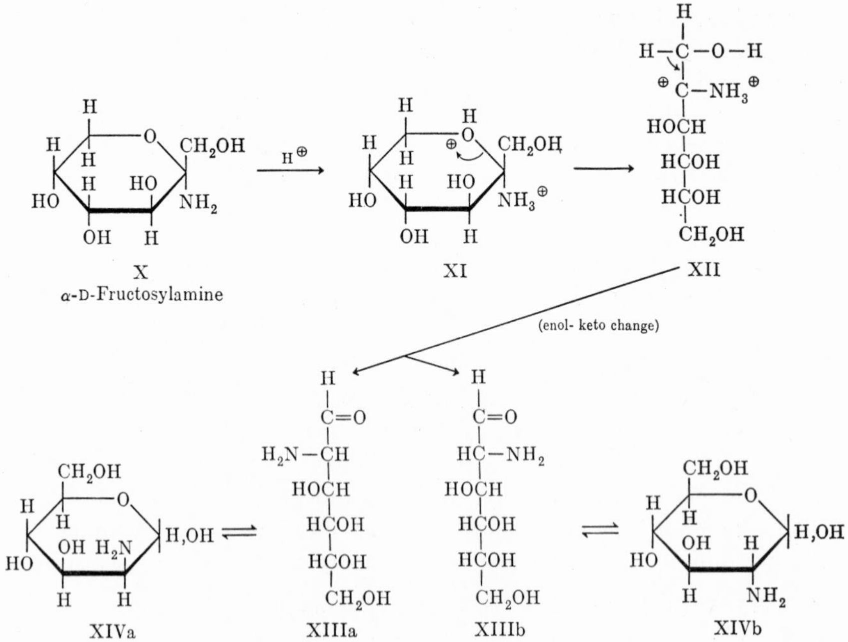

(36) P. A. Levene, *J. Biol. Chem.*, **63,** 95 (1925).

or b). During the transition stage (XII), epimerization is possible, with the formation of both epimeric amino sugars.

The Heyns synthesis of amino sugars is of particular theoretical interest since it is believed that the biosynthesis of amino sugars takes place in a related manner which involves the 6-phosphates.[34, 37] Considerable difficulty attends the isolation of the products, and over-all yields are often low.

4. Descent of Series; Miscellaneous

It is possible to degrade 2-amino-2-deoxyhexoses to 2-amino-2-deoxy-pentoses by means of chain-shortening reactions from the nonreducing end of the molecule. Thus, Wolfrom and Anno[38] converted ethyl 2-acetamido-2-deoxy-1-thio-α-D-glucofuranoside (XV) into 2-amino-2-deoxy-α-D-xylose hydrochloride (XVI) by sequential application of periodate oxidation, borohydride reduction, and hydrolysis, as in the following reaction scheme.

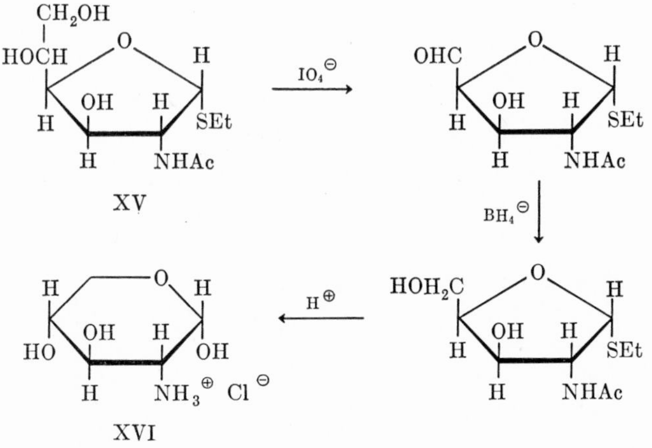

Analogous reactions cleaved ethyl 2-acetamido-2-deoxy-1-thio-α-D-galactofuranoside (ethyl 2-acetamido-2-deoxy-1-thio-D-*glycero*-β-L-*arabino*-hexofuranoside) to 2-amino-2-deoxy-β-L-arabinose hydrochloride.[38a]

Reductive cleavage of hydrazino sugars leads to their amino analogs. Thus, methyl 3,4-O-isopropylidene-2-O-*p*-tolylsulfonyl-β-L-arabinopyranoside was converted through the hydrazino derivative, with Walden inversion,[38a, 38b] to 2-amino-2-deoxy-α-L-ribose hydrochloride.[38c] The D and

(37) L. F. Leloir and C. E. Cardini, *Biochim. et Biophys. Acta*, **20**, 33 (1956).

(38) M. L. Wolfrom and K. Anno, *J. Am. Chem. Soc.*, **75**, 1038 (1953).

(38a) M. L. Wolfrom and Z. Yosizawa, *J. Am. Chem. Soc.*, **81**, 3474, 3477 (1959).

(38b) R. U. Lemieux and P. Chu, *J. Am. Chem. Soc.*, **80**, 4745 (1958).

(38c) M. L. Wolfrom, F. Shafizadeh and R. K. Armstrong, *J. Am. Chem. Soc.*, **80**, 4885 (1958).

DL forms were also synthesized[38d] and α-D-lyxosamine (2-amino-2-deoxy-α-D-lyxose) hydrochloride was synthesized[38d] in an analogous manner from 3,5-O-isopropylidene-2-O-p-tolylsulfonyl-α,β-D-xylofuranoside.

Direct alkaline epimerization of the 2-amino-2-deoxyaldoses may become a useful reaction, since a ketose cannot be formed.[38e]

A new synthesis of a 3-amino sugar was reported by Baer and Fischer[38f] through a double aldolization between nitromethane and the derivative obtained by the action of periodate ion on methyl α-D-glucopyranoside.

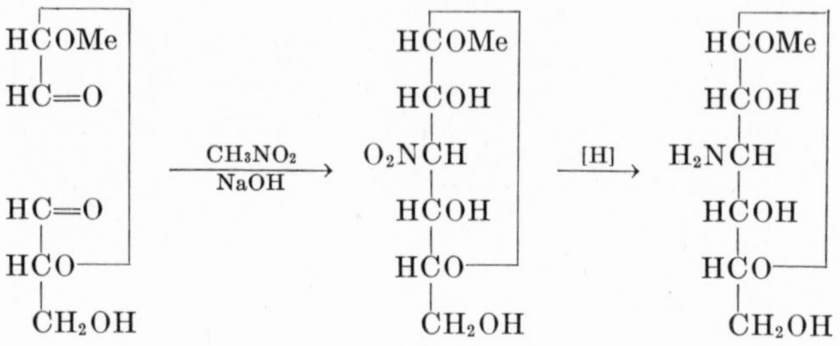

$$
\begin{array}{ccc}
\text{HCOMe} & \text{HCOMe} & \text{HCOMe} \\
\text{HC}{=}\text{O} & \text{HCOH} & \text{HCOH} \\
\xrightarrow[\text{NaOH}]{\text{CH}_3\text{NO}_2} & \text{O}_2\text{NCH} & \xrightarrow{\text{[H]}} \quad \text{H}_2\text{NCH} \\
\text{HC}{=}\text{O} & \text{HCOH} & \text{HCOH} \\
\text{HCO} & \text{HCO} & \text{HCO} \\
\text{CH}_2\text{OH} & \text{CH}_2\text{OH} & \text{CH}_2\text{OH}
\end{array}
$$

Table I records the 2-amino-2-deoxy sugars which have been synthesized to date.

III. Amino Sugars from Natural Products

Both 2-amino-2-deoxy-D-glucose and 2-amino-2-deoxy-D-galactose occur as components of mucopolysaccharides which are widely varied in their structure and their distribution in Nature.[1] Until a few years ago, these hexosamines were the only naturally occurring amino sugars recognized, but a variety of other amino sugars have recently been discovered, especially in bacteria and the lower fungi, and in particular as components of their soluble metabolites. The new amino sugars may be classified as: (i) the 2-amino-2-deoxy sugars, (ii) the 3-amino-3-deoxy sugars and related compounds, and (iii) the nonulosaminic acids (neuraminic acids). The latter group of substances has recently been reviewed.[5]

1. 2-Amino-2-deoxy-aldoses

Of the sixteen theoretically possible 2-amino-2-deoxyaldohexoses, derivatives of six have so far been found in natural products; these have the D-

(38d) M. L. Wolfrom, F. Shafizadeh, R. K. Armstrong and T. M. Shen Han, *J. Am. Chem. Soc.*, **81**, 3716 (1959).

(38e) R. Kuhn and R. Brossmer, Ref. 54.

(38f) H. H. Baer and H. O. L. Fischer, *Proc. Natl. Acad. Sci. U. S.*, **44**, 991 (1958).

TABLE I
Synthetic 2-Amino-2-deoxy Sugars

2-Amino-2-deoxy derivative of	Mode of synthesis[a]	Melting point, °C.	Hydrochloride		References
			$[\alpha]_D$, degrees	Rotation solvent	
D-Allose	C, D	sirup	+29	H_2O	31,[b] 38g
D-Altrose	B, D	sirup	−14	CH_3-OH	20,[c] 23,[c] 38g[b]
D-Glucose	A, B, D, E	dec.	+72.5 (equil.)	H_2O	9, 13, 21, 35, 39,[b] 40, 41, 42[c]
L-Glucose	D	sirup	−70.3	H_2O	11
D-Mannose	A, D	180	−5	HCl, 5%	13,[b] 43
L-Mannose	D	177	+4.7	HCl, 5%	13
D-Galactose	A, B, D, E	182	+80 (equil.)	H_2O	12, 22, 35, 44, 45[b]
D-Talose	D, E	151–153	−5.7 (equil.)	H_2O	12, 14,[b] 35
D-Gulose	C, D	170 (dec.)	−17.9 (equil.)	H_2O	32,[b] 46, 46a
L-Gulose	E	164 (dec.)	+17.8 (equil.)	H_2O	35,[b] 46a
D-Idose	D	—	+1	H_2O	46[c], 46b
L-Idose	E	amorph.	−4.8	H_2O	35
β-L-Arabinose	F	153–155 (dec.)	+174 → +115	H_2O	38a
α-D-Lyxose	G	148–155 (dec.)	+54 → −36	H_2O	38d
α-D-Ribose	G	144–149 (dec.)	+14.1 → −2.75	H_2O	38d
α-L-Ribose	G	142–148 (dec.)	−15.6 → +6.7	H_2O	38c
DL-Ribose	G	169–170	—		38d
α-D-Xylose	F	165–167 (dec.)	+80 → +40	H_2O	38

[a] Mode of synthesis: A. cyanohydrin, by way of 2-amino-2-deoxy-aldonic acid; B. scission of sugar derivative epoxide with ammonia; C. interconversion of hexosamine series; D. hemihydrogenation of α-amino nitrile[46b]; E. rearrangement of ketosylamine; F. Removal of last carbon atom of hexosamine; G. Hydrazinolysis (with inversion) of 2-O-tosyl-pentose. [b] Physical constants taken from this reference. [c] Derivatives (only) isolated.

(38g) R. Kuhn and H. Fischer, Ann., **617,** 88 (1958).

(39) J. C. Irvine and J. C. Earl, J. Chem. Soc., **121,** 2370, 2376 (1922).

(40) G. J. Robertson, W. H. Myers and W. E. Tetlow, Nature, **142,** 1076 (1938).

(41) K. Heyns and K.-H. Meinecke, Chem. Ber., **86,** 1453 (1953).

(42) K. Heyns, H. Paulsen and H. Breuer, Angew. Chem., **68,** 334 (1956).

(43) P. A. Levene, J. Biol. Chem., **39,** 69 (1919).

(44) P. A. Levene, J. Biol. Chem., **31,** 609 (1917).

(45) P. A. Levene, J. Biol. Chem., **57,** 337 (1923).

(46) R. Kuhn, W. Kirschenlohr and W. Bister, Angew. Chem., **69,** 60 (1957).

(46a) R. Kuhn and W. Bister, Ann., **617,** 92 (1958).

(46b) R. Kuhn, W. Bister and H. Fischer, Ann., **617,** 109 (1958).

gluco,[1] D-*galacto*,[1] L-*gluco*,[47] D-*gulo*,[48] *talo*,[49] and D-*manno*[50] configurations, respectively. The occurrence of 2-amino-2-deoxy-D-glucose and its D-galactose analog is well documented[1, 8] and need not be considered here. 2-Amino-2-deoxy-L-glucose occurs as the *N*-methyl derivative in antibiotic substances of the streptomycin group, and its properties have been fully described.[13, 47, 51]

2-Amino-2-deoxy-D-gulose. Hydrolysis of the *Streptomyces* antibiotic substances streptothricin and streptolin B yields, amongst other compounds, a hexosamine hydrochloride.[48] Designation of this compound as 2-amino-2-deoxy-D-gulose rested on the following evidence: (1) oxidative deamination[52] with ninhydrin yielded xylose; (2) D-*xylo*-hexose phenylosazone was obtained by reaction with phenylhydrazine; (3) the amino sugar gave on acid treatment a 1,6-anhydride which had a [M]D +88° closely similar to that of 1,6-anhydro-β-D-gulopyranose (+82°) and widely different from that (−103°) of 1,6-anhydro-β-D-idopyranose. The physical constants of the hexosamine agree with those[46b] of 2-amino-2-deoxy-D-gulose synthesized from D-arabinose by the amino nitrile method (see p. 215). This is the first example of a naturally occurring sugar having the *gulo* configuration.

2-Amino-2-deoxytalose. The presence of a new amino sugar (together with 2-amino-2-deoxy-D-galactose) in the hydrolyzate of chondroitinsulfate from tracheal cartilage has been reported.[49, 53] Ninhydrin degradation[52] of the amino sugar gave lyxose (identified by chromatography and zone electrophoresis), thereby indicating the parent amino sugar to be 2-amino-2-deoxytalose. The chromatographic constants[49] of the amino sugar and of its *N*-acetyl amide are in good agreement with those reported for the synthetic compound.[14] The specific rotation of the natural 2-amino-2-deoxytalose has not been reported, so that assignment to the D or L series *cannot yet be made.* It is possible that the 2-amino-2-deoxytalose arises as an artifact during the isolation procedure, since it has not been detected in association with 2-amino-2-deoxy-D-galactose isolated, by a *different* procedure, from tracheal cartilage.[49]

2-Amino-2-deoxy-D-mannose. Enzymic degradation of *N*-acetylneuraminic acid (sialic acid) yields 2-amino-2-deoxy-D-mannose,[50] identical with

(47) F. A. Kuehl, Jr., E. H. Flynn, F. W. Holly, R. Mozingo and K. Folkers, *J. Am. Chem. Soc.*, **69**, 3032 (1947).

(48) E. E. van Tamelen, J. R. Dyer, H. E. Carter, J. V. Pierce and E. E. Daniels, *J. Am. Chem. Soc.*, **78**, 4817 (1956).

(49) M. J. Crumpton, *Nature*, **180**, 605 (1957).

(50) D. G. Comb and S. Roseman, *J. Am. Chem. Soc.*, **80**, 497 (1958).

(51) R. U. Lemieux and M. L. Wolfrom, *Advances in Carbohydrate Chem.*, **3**, 337 (1948).

(52) P. J. Stoffyn and R. W. Jeanloz, *Arch. Biochem. Biophys.*, **52**, 373 (1954).

(53) H. Muir, *Biochem. J.*, **62**, 26P (1956); **65**, 33P (1957).

the long known, synthetic product.[13, 44] 2-Acetamido-2-deoxy-D-mannose, but not the D-glucose analog can be incorporated enzymically, in the presence of pyruvic acid, into N-acetylneuraminic acid by an enzyme from *Clostridium perfringens*. Since 2-acetamido-2-deoxy-D-mannose can undergo a reversible epimerization with 2-amino-2-deoxy-D-glucose, under mildly alkaline conditions,[54] it is believed that the 2-amino-2-deoxy-D-glucose hitherto reported as a constituent of N-acetylneuraminic acid arises, in fact, as *an artifact* during the isolation procedure.

Muramic acid has been isolated[55, 56] by ion-exchange resin chromatography of the hydrolyzates of bacterial cell-walls and spore peptides of *Bacillus megatherium*, *B. subtilis*, *B. cereus*, and *Micrococcus lysodeikticus*. It has been suggested that the cell walls of certain bacteria consist of a chitin-like polysaccharide composed of muramic acid units and containing peptide cross-linkages.[57] Muramic acid has been shown[58] to be a nine-carbon amino sugar derivative having a free carboxyl group.

On the basis of (1) its behavior in the Elson–Morgan test, (2) its pattern of periodate oxidation, and (3) its oxidative deamination,[52] which gave a substituted pentose, muramic acid was shown to be a 3-substituted 2-amino-2-deoxyhexose. Release of propionic acid on treatment of muramic acid with hydriodic acid plus phosphorus indicated the substituent to be an O-(2-carboxyethyl) group. Synthesis[59] has proved muramic acid to be 2-amino-3-O-(2-carboxyethyl)-2-deoxy-D-glucose. Reaction of the 3-O-sodio derivative of methyl 2-acetamido-4,6-O-benzylidene-2-deoxy-α-D-glucopyranoside (XVII) with triethyl DL-2-iodo-orthopropionate (XVIII) gave the substituted derivative XIX, which yielded 2-amino-3-O-(2-carboxyethyl)-2-deoxy-D-glucose (XX) on acidic hydrolysis. The configuration of the asymmetric carbon atom of the lactic acid moiety is still not decided.

2-Amino-2-deoxy-D-fucose(?). Hydrolysis of the specific lipopolysaccharide of a strain of *Chromobacterium violaceum* yields,[60] together with 2-amino-2-deoxy-D-glucose, an amino sugar believed to be 2-amino-2,6-dideoxy-D-galactose (2-amino-2-deoxy-D-fucose),[61, 62] although the epimeric structure 2-amino-2,6-dideoxy-D-talose has not been completely ruled out. The new amino sugar occurs in the polysaccharide moiety of the lipopolysaccharide, whereas all of the 2-amino-2-deoxy-D-glucose occurs in the lipid fraction.

(54) R. Kuhn and R. Brossmer, *Ann.*, **616**, 221 (1958).
(55) R. E. Strange and J. F. Powell, *Biochem. J.*, **58**, 80 (1954).
(56) R. E. Strange and F. A. Dark, *Nature*, **177**, 186 (1956).
(57) E. Work, *Nature*, **179**, 841 (1957).
(58) R. E. Strange, *Biochem. J.*, **64**, 23P (1956).
(59) L. H. Kent, *Biochem. J.*, **67**, 5P (1957).
(60) M. J. Crumpton and D. A. L. Davies, *Biochem. J.*, **64**, 22P (1956).
(61) D. A. L. Davies, *Nature*, **180**, 1129 (1957).
(62) D. A. L. Davies, *Biochem. J.*, **69**, 25P (1958).

XVII   XVIII   XIX, R = CHMeC(OEt)$_3$

XX, R = CHMeCO$_2$H

The amino sugar gives a reaction similar to that of 2-amino-2-deoxy-D-glucose in the Elson–Morgan test.

Other 2-amino-2-deoxy sugars have been reported. Thus, acidic hydrolysis of the *Vi* antigen, the major immunogenic component of *Salmonella typhosus* and several other micro-organisms, gives rise principally to an aminodeoxyhexuronic acid[63] having reactions very similar to those of synthetic 2-amino-2-deoxy-D-glucuronic acid.[64] It has a high stability toward acids, in contrast to the uronic acids (which are readily decarboxylated).[65]

A diaminodideoxyhexose of unknown structure constitutes the hexose moiety of a pentose hexoside (disaccharide) called neobiosamine which may be isolated[66] from the antibiotic substances neomycin B and neomycin C.

2. 3-Amino-3-deoxy Sugars

Recent chemical studies on the soluble metabolites of the lower fungi and bacteria have revealed that 3-amino-3-deoxy sugars are often components thereof. Several closely related amino sugars have been reported. The stereochemistry of 3-amino-3-deoxy-D-ribose and 3-amino-3-deoxy-D-glucose[66a] have now been fully elucidated, and skeletal structures have been assigned (see Table II, p. 231) to the others, generally on the basis of periodate oxidation patterns.

The 3-amino-3-deoxy-β-D-ribosyl residue occurs in puromycin (Stylo-

(63) W. R. Clark, J. McLaughlin and M. E. Webster, *J. Biol. Chem.*, **230,** 81 (1958).

(64) K. Heyns and H. Paulsen, *Chem. Ber.*, **88,** 188 (1955).

(65) K. U. Lefèvre and B. Tollens, *Ber.*, **40,** 4513 (1907).

(66) K. L. Rinehart, P. W. K. Woo, A. D. Argondelis and A. M. Giesbrecht, *J. Am. Chem. Soc.*, **79,** 4567 (1957).

(66a) M. J. Cron, D. L. Evans, F. M. Palermiti, D. F. Whitehead, I. R. Hooper, P. Chu and R. U. Lemieux, *J. Am. Chem. Soc.*, **80,** 4741 (1958).

mycin) as the N-(O-methyl-L-tyrosinyl)amide; in the furanose form, this is linked to position 9 of 6-dimethylaminopurine. Puromycin is produced by *Streptococcus alboniger*[67, 68]; it is active against a wide range of micro-

Puromycin

6-Dimethylamino-9-[3-(p-methoxy-L-phenylalanylamino)-β-D-ribofuranosyl]purine

organisms (in particular, against trypanosomes), and some of this activity is retained in synthetic analogs where the N-acyl group is either absent or replaced by other amino acid residues.[69-71] 3-Amino-3-deoxy-D-ribose has been synthesized[29, 30] by methods involving (a) scission of 2,3-epoxide derivatives of pentoses by ammonia, and (b) interconversion of sugar series by solvolysis of methylsulfonyl esters (see p. 218). During the course of the syntheses, 3-amino-3-deoxy-D-arabinose and 3-acetamido-3-deoxy-L-xylose were also isolated.

3-Amino-3-deoxy-D-glucose has been recognized[72] as a component of the antibiotic substance Kanamycin elaborated by *Streptomyces kanamyceticus*. The antibiotic substance also contains a 6-amino-6-deoxy-D-glucose residue as part of its structure. Synthetic derivatives of 3-amino-3-deoxy-D-glucose have long been known[73]; they were obtained by the action of ammonia on derivatives of methyl 2,3-anhydro-α-D-allopyranoside. The amino sugar obtained after the action of ammonia[73] and hydrazine (followed by reduction)[74] on 1,2:5,6-di-O-isopropylidene-3-O-tosyl-D-glucose, earlier thought to have the D-*gluco* configuration, has in fact the D-*allo* configuration.[75]

Graded, acidic hydrolysis of 2-acetamido-2-deoxy-1,2:5,6-di-O-iso-

(67) C. W. Waller, P. W. Fryth, B. L. Hutchings and J. H. Williams, *J. Am. Chem. Soc.*, **75**, 2025 (1953).

(68) B. R. Baker, R. E. Schaub and J. P. Joseph, *J. Org. Chem.*, **19**, 638 (1954).

(69) B. R. Baker, J. P. Joseph and J. H. Williams, *J. Am. Chem. Soc.*, **77**, 1 (1955).

(70) B. R. Baker, R. E. Schaub, J. P. Joseph and J. H. Williams, *J. Am. Chem. Soc.*, **77**, 12 (1955).

(71) B. R. Baker and R. E. Schaub, *J. Am. Chem. Soc.*, **77**, 2396, 5900 (1955).

(72) M. J. Cron, O. B. Fardig, D. L. Johnson, D. F. Whitehead, I. R. Hooper and R. U. Lemieux, *J. Am. Chem. Soc.*, **80**, 2342 (1958).

(73) S. Peat and L. F. Wiggins, *J. Chem. Soc.*, 1810 (1938).

(74) K. Freudenberg, O. Burkhart and E. Braun, *Ber.*, **59**, 714 (1926).

(75) See Ref. 38b.

propylidene-α-D-allofuranose removes the 5,6-isopropylidene group. Subjection of the product to periodate oxidation, followed by reduction with sodium borohydride and acidic hydrolysis, yields 3-amino-3-deoxy-D-ribose. An alternative synthesis of the D-ribose derivative is thus provided, and the D-*allo* configuration of the hexose precursor is proved.

Desosamine (XXI) has been isolated from erythromycin[76] and shown to be identical with *picrocin*, the 3-dimethylamino sugar isolated from the antibiotic substances picromycin,[77] narbomycin,[78] and methymycin.[79]

Structure allocation[76, 80] is based on the pattern of periodate oxidation, which shows a rapid initial uptake of 1 mole of oxidant per mole (indicative of a glycol grouping) to give a 2-deoxy-2-dimethylaminopentose (picrocinin, XXII). The latter sugar slowly reacts with a further mole of periodate per mole, forming dimethylamine and crotonaldehyde (XXIV), the latter being derived from aldol (XXIII) by dehydration.

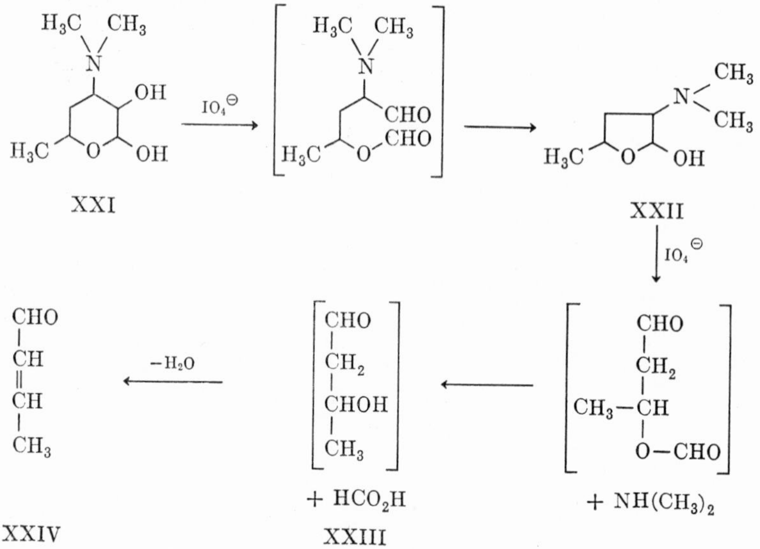

Further evidence for the location of the dimethylamino group at C3 of desosamine was afforded by its high alkali lability. This property appears

(76) E. H. Flynn, M. V. Sigal, P. F. Wiley and K. Gerzon, *J. Am. Chem. Soc.*, **76**, 3121 (1954).

(77) H. Brockmann, *Angew. Chem.*, **65**, 257 (1953).

(78) R. Corbaz, L. Ettlinger, E. Gäumann, W. Keller, F. Kradolfer, E. Kyburz, L. Neipp, V. Prelog, R. Reusser and H. Zähner, *Helv. Chim. Acta*, **38**, 935 (1955).

(79) C. Djerassi, A. Bowers, R. Hodges and B. Riniker, *J. Am. Chem. Soc.*, **78**, 1733 (1956).

(80) H. Brockmann, H.-B. König and R. Oster, *Chem. Ber.*, **87**, 856 (1954).

to be general for 3-amino-3-deoxy sugars; 2-amino-2-deoxy sugars are much more stable toward alkali. It may be inferred that desosamine exists in the pyranoid ring-form, since its infrared absorption spectrum indicates a

TABLE II

3-Amino-3-deoxy Sugars from Natural Products

Name	Structure	Source	Reference
3-Amino-3-deoxy-D-ribose	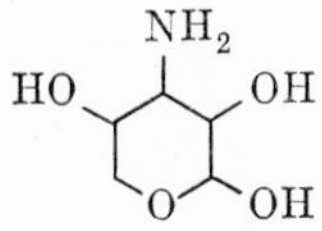 NH₂ HO OH O OH	puromycin (Stylomycin)	67, 68
Amosamine	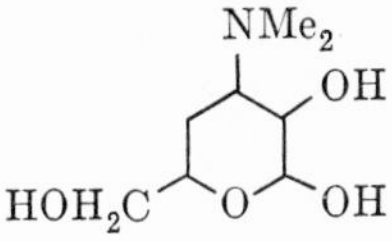 NMe₂ OH HOH₂C O OH	amicetin (Allomycin, Sacromycin)	85
Mycosamine	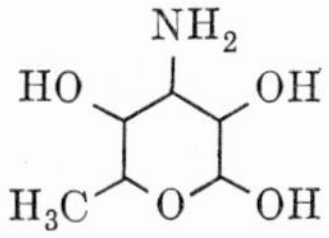 NH₂ HO OH H₃C O OH	nystatin (Fungicidin), amphotericin B	86
Mycaminose (3,6-dideoxy-3-dimethylamino-D-altrose)	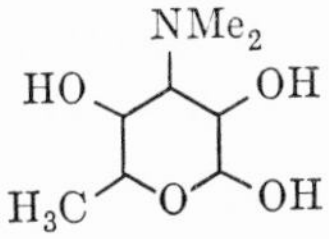 NMe₂ HO OH H₃C O OH	carbomycin (Magnamycin)	83, 84, 84a
Desosamine (picrocin)	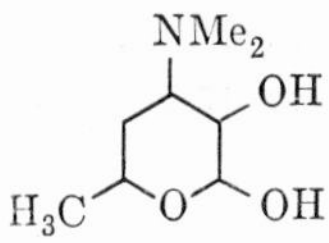 NMe₂ OH H₃C O OH	erythromycin (Erythrocin, Ilotycin) narbomycin picromycin methymycin	76 78 77 79
Rhodosamine	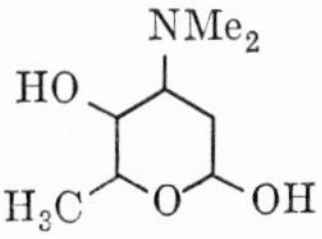 NMe₂ HO H₃C O OH	rhodomycin	82

cyclic structure which differs from that of the deoxy(dimethylamino)pentose picrocinin (XXII) in which a pyranose ring *cannot* be formed. The stereochemistry of desosamine is unknown.

Rhodosamine[81, 82] is obtained by acid hydrolysis of rhodomycin (produced

(81) H. Brockmann and I. Borchers, *Chem. Ber.*, **86,** 261 (1953).
(82) H. Brockmann and E. Spöhler, *Naturwissenschaften*, **42,** 154 (1955).

by *Streptomyces purpurascens*). It is isomeric with desosamine, and shows a similar high lability toward alkali but differs in its periodate oxidation pattern. Oxidant is consumed, to yield, ultimately, acetaldehyde. Rhodosamine is believed to be a 2,3,6-trideoxy-3-dimethylamino-hexose (see Table II).

Mycaminose has been found as a component of carbomycin (Magnamycin)[83] and, structurally, it resembles desosamine[84] (see Table II). On periodate oxidation, one carbon atom is split out, to yield a seven-carbon amino sugar; the results of subsequent reaction with the oxidant indicated the presence of a hydroxyl group at C4. Alkaline deamination of the seven-carbon sugar proceeded at a rate similar to that of 2-amino-2-deoxy-D-glucose, whereas mycaminose itself reacted far more rapidly; this indicates the dimethylamino group to be at C3. Mycaminose is believed to be 3,6-dideoxy-3-dimethylamino-β-D-altrose.[84a]

Amosamine,[85] isolated from the antibiotic substance amicetin produced by *Streptomyces vinaceus-drappus*, was shown, by methods similar to those used for other dimethylamino sugars in the series (namely, by periodate oxidation and by study of the rate of alkaline hydrolysis), to have the structure given in Table II.

Mycosamine differs from most of the other amino sugars isolated from antibiotic substances in not being *N*-methylated.[86] The tetraacetate XXVI of mycosamine (XXV) can be isolated by acetolysis of nystatin or of the antifungal antibiotic substance amphotericin B, and it yields the acetamido derivative XXVII on catalytic deacetylation.

The structure XXV for the parent amino sugar was inferred from the behavior of the *N*-acetyl amide XXVII and of the methyl *N*-ethylamino glycoside (XXX) on periodate oxidation. The former gave the 2-acetamido-2-deoxypentose (XXIX) by way of the dialdehyde XXVIII, the latter gave XXXI plus ethylamine. Since periodate oxidation of methyl 6-deoxy-α-D-glucoside *also* gives XXXI, it may be inferred that mycosamine belongs to the D series. The steric configurations at C2, C3, and C4 are still unknown.

3. *Diamino Sugar*

Sharon and Jeanloz[86a] describe the isolation of a crystalline 4-acetamido-2-amino-2,4,6-trideoxyhexose hydrochloride from *Bacillus subtilis*.

(83) F. A. Hochstein and K. Murai, *J. Am. Chem. Soc.*, **76**, 5080 (1954).

(84) F. A. Hochstein and P. P. Regna, *J. Am. Chem. Soc.*, **77**, 3353 (1955).

(84a) R. B. Woodward, *Angew. Chem.*, **69**, 50 (1957).

(85) C. L. Stevens, R. L. Gasser, T. K. Mukherjee and T. H. Haskell, *J. Am. Chem. Soc.*, **78**, 6212 (1956).

(86) D. L. Walters, J. D. Dutcher and O. Wintersteiner, *J. Am. Chem. Soc.*, **79**, 5076 (1957).

(86a) N. Sharon and R. W. Jeanloz, *Biochim. et Biophys. Acta*, **31**, 277 (1959).

IV. General Chemistry of 2-Amino-2-deoxy-d-glucose

1. *Acyl Derivatives*

a. Esters and Amides.—According to the conditions employed, peracylation or *N*-acylation of amino sugars may be achieved. Partially acylated derivatives of 2-amino-2-deoxy-d-glucose are often useful intermediates in synthesis, and certain of them play a part in metabolic processes.

Peracylation can be achieved by treatment of the amino sugar with the appropriate acid anhydride or chloride in pyridine at room temperature[87] or with the acid anhydride and the sodium salt of the acid at a higher temperature[88]; the resulting product is usually a mixture of the α and β anomers

(87) Y. Inouye, K. Onodera, S. Kitaoka and S. Hirano, *J. Am. Chem. Soc.*, **78**, 4722 (1956).

(88) P. A. Levene, "Hexosamines and Mucoproteins," Longmans, Green and Co., London, 1925, p. 15.

of the 1,3,4,6-tetra-*O*-acyl-2-acylamido-2-deoxy-D-glucose. De-*O*-acylation of the latter compounds is possible by the Zemplén–Pacsu method[89] or with methanolic ammonia, and it provides a convenient route to *N*-acyl derivatives. The incursion of side reactions under these de-*O*-acylating conditions is possible.[90] The amide linkage is also stable under the conditions used for reductive detosylation (sodium amalgam–methanol), so that tosyl groups may be removed without hydrolysis of the substituent on the nitrogen atom.[91]

Improved methods of *N*-acetylation have superseded the earlier procedure (silver acetate–acetic anhydride[92]), and some of these methods may be used as general procedures for the preparation of *N*-acyl derivatives. Prior to its acylation, the amino sugar hydrochloride is converted to the free base by the use of an ion-exchange resin,[93] sodium acetate,[15] or sodium bicarbonate.[7] With an equimolar proportion of the acyl anhydride, selective *N*-acylation takes place. Ketene may also be used[15, 94, 95] for the preparation of *N*-acetyl amides (after neutralization of hydrochloric acid with a base). A general procedure for the preparation of acylamido sugar derivatives[87, 96] involves, for example, the preparation of a supersaturated, methanolic solution of 2-amino-2-deoxy-D-glucose by treatment of the hydrochloride with sodium methoxide in methanol. Addition of a slight excess of an acid anhydride yields the corresponding amide. A range of fatty-acid amides of 2-amino-2-deoxy-D-glucose has been prepared in this manner, thereby extending earlier work[97] on stearoyl amides of 2-amino-2-deoxy-D-glucose; these amides have a potential importance as model compounds for bacterial lipopolysaccharides. Related peracylated derivatives were prepared by reacting fatty acid chlorides with 2-amino-2-deoxy-D-glucose in pyridine solution. Esters and amides of 2-amino-2-deoxy-D-glucose and of the mycolic acids isolated from *Mycobacterium tuberculosis* have been described.[98, 99] The acid chlorides of the mycolic acids were reacted with partially substituted derivatives of 2-amino-2-deoxy-D-glucose, giving rise to mycolanoyl

(89) G. Zemplén and E. Pacsu, *Ber.*, **62**, 1613 (1929).

(90) T. White, *J. Chem. Soc.*, 1498 (1938).

(91) R. W. Jeanloz, *J. Am. Chem. Soc.*, **76**, 555 (1954).

(92) T. White, *J. Chem. Soc.*, 428 (1940).

(93) S. Roseman and J. Ludowieg, *J. Am. Chem. Soc.*, **76**, 301 (1954).

(94) A. Neuberger and R. P. Rivers, *J. Chem. Soc.*, 122 (1939).

(95) G. Quadbeck, *Angew. Chem.*, **68**, 361 (1956).

(96) Y. Inouye, K. Onodera, S. Kitaoka and T. Kirii, *Bull. Inst. Chem. Research Kyoto Univ.*, **33**, 270 (1955); *Chem. Abstracts*, **50**, 10656 (1956).

(97) A. S. Jones, M. A. G. Kaye and M. Stacey, *J. Chem. Soc.*, 5016 (1952).

(98) J. Asselineau, H. Bloch and E. Lederer, *Biochim. et Biophys. Acta*, **15**, 136 (1954).

(99) J. Asselineau and E. Lederer, *Bull. soc. chim. France*, 1232 (1955).

amides. N-Acylation proceeded normally, but O-acylation was generally restricted to the C6-hydroxyl group.

2-Acetamido-2-deoxy-D-glucose derivatives generally crystallize as the α anomer and mutarotate in polar solvents to a mixture of the two anomers, but the pure β anomer may be prepared by acylation of 2-amino-2-deoxy-β-D-glucose at a low temperature with the acid anhydrides in N,N-dimethylformamide solution.[100] Mutarotation in this solvent is very slow, and the reaction product may be removed long before mutarotational equilibrium has been established.

It has been known for some time that N-acetyl derivatives of amino sugars may be obtained enzymically.[101-103] Synthetic N-acyl derivatives obtained by using aromatic acids[104] act as competitive inhibitors for hexokinase.

The reaction of phthalic anhydride with 1,3,4,6-tetra-O-acetyl-2-amino-2-deoxy-D-glucose leads to the formation of the expected N-phthaloyl amide or "phthalamic acid." Furthermore, intramolecular condensation occurs, presumably by way of a mixed anhydride intermediate, on treating this with ethyl chloroformate, thereby forming an N,N-phthaloyl imide, 1,3,4,6-tetra-O-acetyl-2-deoxy-2-phthalimido-D-glucose.[105, 106] The 2-amino-2-deoxy-D-glucose derivative can be regenerated by the action of hydrazine.[69, 107]

The reactions of partially acylated derivatives of 2-amino-2-deoxy-D-glucose are complicated by the possibility of migration of acyl residues. Ammonolysis of 1,3,4,6-tetra-O-acetyl-2-amino-2-deoxy-D-glucose leads to the formation of 2-acetamido-2-deoxy-D-glucose,[90] one of the O-acetyl groups migrating to the amino group. It has recently been demonstrated[108, 109] that a similar, alkali-catalyzed, acyl migration in methyl 3,4,6-tri-O-acetyl-2-amino-2-deoxy-β-D-glucoside (XXXII) proceeds intramolecularly from C3 to C2, by way of a cyclic intermediate XXXIII. Under very mild conditions, scission of the 4- and 6-O-acetyl groups does not take place, and methyl 2-acetamido-4,6-di-O-acetyl-2-deoxy-β-D-glucoside (XXXIV) can

(100) R. Kuhn and F. Haber, *Chem. Ber.*, **86**, 722 (1953).

(101) T. C. Chou and M. Soodak, *J. Biol. Chem.*, **196**, 105 (1952).

(102) H. Tabor, A. H. Mehler and E. R. Stadtman, *J. Biol. Chem.*, **204**, 127 (1953).

(103) J. Katz, I. Lieberman and H. A. Barker, *J. Biol. Chem.*, **200**, 417 (1953).

(104) F. Maley and H. A. Lardy, *J. Biol. Chem.*, **214**, 765 (1955).

(105) B. R. Baker, J. P. Joseph, R. E. Schaub and J. H. Williams, *J. Org. Chem.*, **19**, 1786 (1954).

(106) S. Akiya and T. Osawa, *Yakugaku Zasshi*, **77**, 726 (1957).

(107) H. R. Ing and R. H. F. Manske, *J. Chem. Soc.*, 2348 (1926).

(108) G. Fodor and L. Ötvös, *Acta Chim. Acad. Sci. Hung.*, **5**, 205 (1954); *Chem. Abstracts*, **49**, 13114 (1955).

(109) G. Fodor and L. Ötvös, *Chem. Ber.*, **89**, 701 (1956).

be isolated as its 3-carbanilate ester. Under acidic conditions, the migration is reversed, due to the stabilizing effect of the amine salt thus formed from the free amino group.[109] This facile, reversible migration from C3 to C2 must involve the *C1* chair-conformation (equatorial substituents) of 2-amino-2-deoxy-D-glucose (XXXV), since the (alternative) *1C* conformation (XXXVI) would be unfavored.

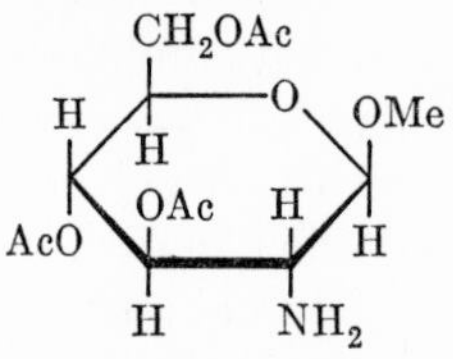

XXXII 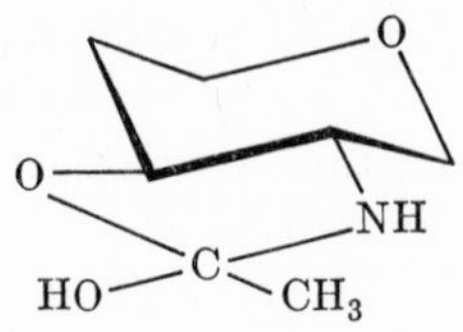   XXXIII 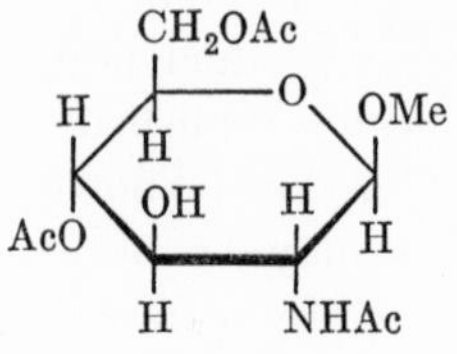   XXXIV

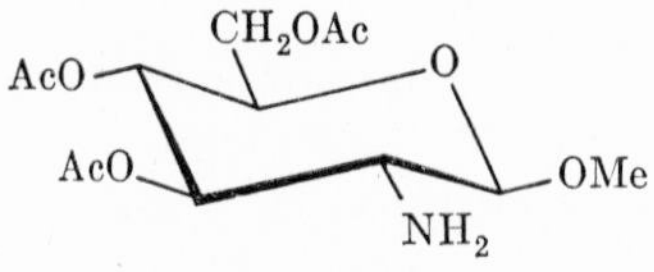

XXXV 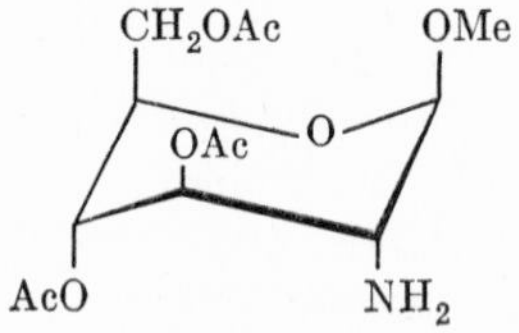   XXXVI

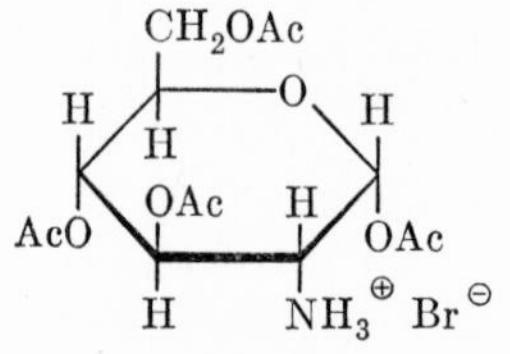

XXXVII 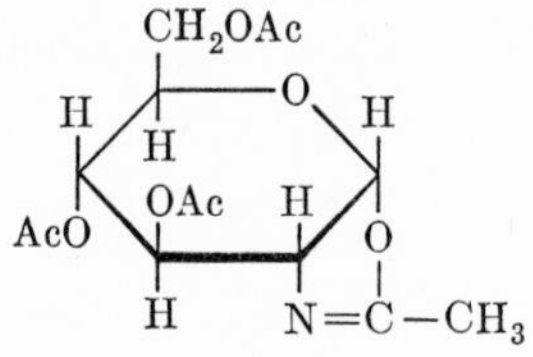   XXXVIII 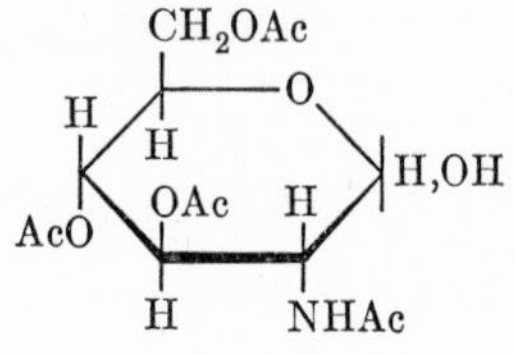   XXXIX

An acyl migration takes place when 1-*O*-acetyl-2-amino-2-deoxy-D-glucose derivatives are treated with weak alkali; the 1-*O*-acetyl group migrates to the amino group, presumably by way of a cyclic intermediate.[110] The rate of migration depends on the nature of the substituents at C3, C4, and C6; methoxylated derivatives rearrange more rapidly than acetoxylated derivatives. and α anomers rearrange faster than β anomers. 1-*O*-Benzoyl groups migrate in a similar manner. The reaction of 1,3,4,6-tetra-*O*-acetyl-2-amino-2-deoxy-α-D-glucose hydrobromide (XXXVII) with alkali, reported[92, 111] to yield an oxazoline derivative (XXXVIII), has been shown to yield, actually, 2-acetamido-3,4,6-tri-*O*-acetyl-2-deoxy-D-glucose

(110) F.-P. van de Kamp and F. Micheel, *Chem. Ber.*, **90**, 2054 (1957).

(111) F. Micheel, F.-P. van de Kamp and H. Wulff, *Chem. Ber.*, **88**, 2011 (1955).

(XXXIX). However, oxazoline derivatives similar to XXXVIII *can* be obtained under other conditions.[112, 113]

The alkali-lability of the esters of 2-amino-2-deoxy-D-glucose is responsible for O-acyl hydrolysis under the conditions of the Morgan–Elson reaction (see p. 264). Although derivatives having a free amino group do not give the reaction, the possibility of $O \rightarrow N$-acyl migration during the alkaline pretreatment must not be overlooked.

The infrared absorption spectra of O- and N-acylated amino sugars show absorption bands characteristic of these groupings and these bands may be of value in structural investigations.[114, 115]

An unusual reaction occurs[116] when methyl 2-(benzyloxycarbonylamino)-2-deoxy-6-O-tosyl-α-D-glucoside (XL) is treated with aqueous, ethanolic alkali solution. The product is methyl 2-amino-3,6-anhydro-2-N,4-O-carbonyl-2-deoxy-α-D-glucoside (XLI). It appears that 3,6-anhydro ring-for-

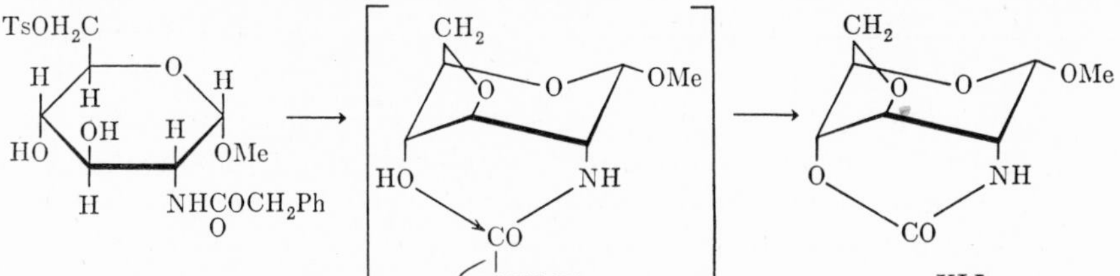

mation occurs first, thereby fixing the molecule in the *1C* conformation and bringing the groups on C2 and C4 into axial positions. This steric arrangement facilitates the nucleophilic displacement of the benzyloxy group by the C4-hydroxyl group.

b. Phosphates.—The importance of 2-amino-2-deoxy-D-glucose 6-phosphate in mucopolysaccharide biosynthesis is well established,[117] and three possible biosynthetic pathways for its formation have been proposed, namely, (i) direct phosphorylation of 2-amino-2-deoxy-D-glucose with adenosinetriphosphoric acid[118-120] in the presence of hexokinase; (ii) interaction of D-fructose 6-phosphate with ammonium ions in the presence of a pig-

(112) F. Micheel, F.-P. van de Kamp and H. Petersen, *Chem. Ber.*, **90**, 521 (1957).
(113) F. Micheel and H. Köchling, *Chem. Ber.*, **90**, 1597 (1957).
(114) S. A. Barker, E. J. Bourne and D. H. Whiffen, *Methods of Biochem. Anal.*, **3**, 213 (1956).
(115) W. Otting, *Ann.*, **612**, 68 (1958).
(116) A. B. Foster, M. Stacey and S. V. Vardheim, *Acta Chem. Scand.*, **13**, 281 (1959).
(117) L. Glaser and D. H. Brown, *Proc. Natl. Acad. Sci. U. S.*, **41**, 253 (1955).
(118) R. P. Harpur and J. H. Quastel, *Nature*, **164**, 693 (1949).
(119) D. H. Brown, *Biochim. et Biophys. Acta*, **7**, 487 (1951).
(120) P. T. Grant and C. Long, *Biochem. J.*, **50**, xx (1952).

kidney enzyme[37]; and (iii) enzymic reaction of D-glucose 6-phosphate with
L-glutamine.[121-123] All three pathways occur under physiological conditions;
the *first* requires the presence of free 2-amino-2-deoxy-D-glucose in the tissues. Since L-glutamine plays an important part in the synthesis of mammalian mucopolysaccharides, the *third* pathway is considered the most
probable. Subsequent stages in the biosynthesis of the mucopolysaccharides
are believed to involve an initial isomerization of 2-amino-2-deoxy-D-glu-
cose 6-phosphate to the 1-phosphate by a phosphoglucomutase,[124, 125] probably catalyzed by traces of the 1,6-diphosphate,[126] followed by the formation of uridine 5-(2-acetamido-2-deoxy-6-O-phospho-D-glucosyl dihydrogen
pyrophosphate),[127] "UDPAG," which appears to be the intermediate from
which hexosamine is transferred[117] to the mucopolysaccharide undergoing
biosynthesis. The anaerobic degradation of 2-amino-2-deoxy-D-glucose in
animal tissues is also believed to involve initial phosphorylation to the 6-
phosphate, which serves as a substrate for further degradation to ammonia
plus D-fructose 6-phosphate, the latter then undergoing normal glycolytic
degradation.[128, 129]

2-Amino-2-deoxy-D-glucose 6-phosphate can be isolated from the mixture of products obtained by the direct phosphorylation of 2-amino-2-deoxy-
D-glucose with metaphosphoric acid in the presence of acetonitrile,[130] but a
more satisfactory synthesis is by the reaction of 2-acetamido-1,3,4-tri-O-
acetyl-2-deoxy-D-glucose with diphenyl phosphorochloridate, with subsequent dephenylation (hydrogenolysis) and deacetylation.[131] 2-Amino-2-
deoxy-D-glucose 6-phosphate has been synthesized[126] by reaction of diphenyl
phosphorochloridate with 2-(p-anisylideneamino)-2-deoxy-D-glucose. Subsequent peracetylation, acidic hydrolysis of the azomethine, dephenylation,
and acid hydrolysis led to the formation of 2-amino-2-deoxy-D-glucose 6-
phosphate; a modified procedure involving acetylation and a final ammonolysis stage led to the formation of 2-acetamido-2-deoxy-D-glucose 6-phos-
phate. This amide was also described by Roseman and coworkers,[132, 133] who

(121) L. F. Leloir and C. E. Cardini, *Biochim. et Biophys. Acta*, **12**, 15 (1953).
(122) D. A. Lowther and H. J. Rogers, *Biochem. J.*, **62**, 304 (1956).
(123) B. M. Pogell and R. M. Gryder, *J. Biol. Chem.*, **228**, 701 (1957).
(124) D. H. Brown, *J. Biol. Chem.*, **204**, 877 (1953).
(125) J. L. Reissig, *J. Biol. Chem.*, **219**, 753 (1956).
(126) F. Maley and H. A. Lardy, *J. Am. Chem. Soc.*, **78**, 1393 (1956).
(127) F. Maley, G. F. Maley and H. A. Lardy, *J. Am. Chem. Soc.*, **78**, 5303 (1956).
(128) J. B. Wolfe, R. Y. Moriata and H. I. Nakada, *Arch. Biochem. Biophys.*, **64**, 480 (1956).
(129) J. B. Wolfe and H. I. Nakada, *Arch. Biochem. Biophys.*, **64**, 489 (1956).
(130) J. M. Anderson and E. E. Percival, *Chem. & Ind.* (London), 1018 (1954).
(131) J. M. Anderson and E. E. Percival, *J. Chem. Soc.*, 814 (1956).
(132) S. Roseman, *Federation Proc.*, **13**, 283 (1954).
(133) J. J. Distler, J. M. Merrick and S. Roseman, *J. Biol. Chem.*, **230**, 497 (1958).

prepared it by chemical acetylation of enzymically synthesized 2-amino-2-deoxy-D-glucose 6-phosphate; enzymic N-acetylation has also been described.[134] 2-Amino-2-deoxy-D-glucose 6-phosphate is more stable toward acidic hydrolysis than D-glucose 6-phosphate; it is broken down slowly in N hydrochloric acid[130] at 100°. The phosphate group has an influence on the chromogen produced in the Elson–Morgan test, causing a bathochromic shift of the normal absorption maximum ($\lambda = 512$ mμ) to $\lambda = 518$ mμ.[131]

Chemical synthesis of 1-phosphate esters of 2-amino-2-deoxy-D-glucose has been described.[37, 127] Reaction of 3,4,6-tri-O-acetyl-2-amino-2-deoxy-α-D-glucosyl bromide hydrobromide (XLII) with triethylammonium diphenyl phosphate gave the 1-(diphenyl phosphate) ester, isolated as its hydrochloride (XLIII). Cleavage of the phenyl groups and subsequent deacetylation gave 2-amino-2-deoxy-D-glucosyl phosphate as the crystalline, dipolar-ionic, monopotassium salt (XLV).

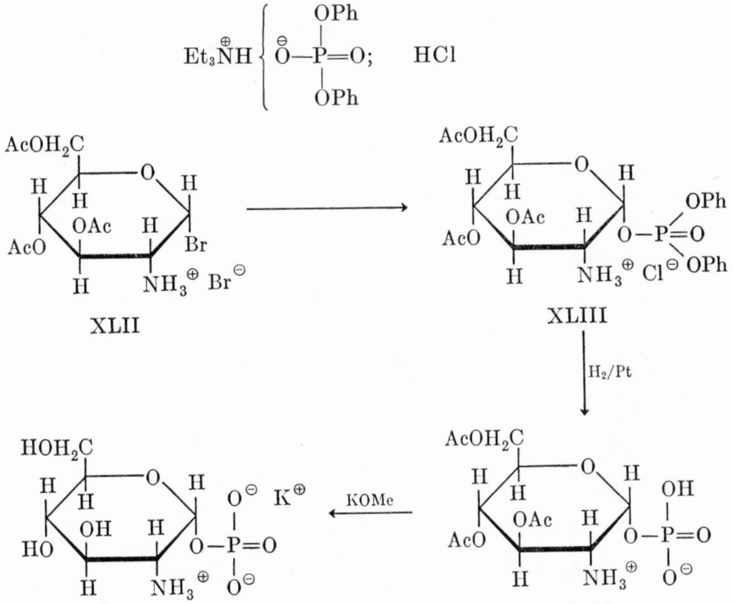

The calcium salt of 2-amino-2-deoxy-D-glucosyl phosphate has been synthesized[37] by the interaction of 2-acetamido-3,4,6-tri-O-acetyl-2-deoxy-α-D-glucosyl chloride with silver orthophosphate, with subsequent partial saponification. On the basis of optical rotation, the derivative has been assigned to the α-D series. 2-Amino-2-deoxy-D-glucosyl phosphate is much less stable than the 6-phosphate toward acidic hydrolysis, but it is markedly more

(134) D. H. Brown, *Biochim. et Biophys. Acta*, **16**, 429 (1955).

stable than the corresponding D-glucosyl ester. The adjacent —$NH_3^\oplus$ center in XLV greatly enhances the acidity of the 1-substituent, in comparison with the 1-phosphate ester of a non-nitrogenous sugar; this is reflected in the higher pK value for the second acid-dissociation of the N-acetyl analog of XLV compared with that of XLV itself. The N-acetyl derivative of XLV was synthesized[127] from the intermediate XLIV by ammonolysis, under which alkaline conditions acetoxyl migration from C3 to C2 is favored before the O-acetyl groups are removed, with the resultant formation of 2-acetamido-2-deoxy-D-glucosyl phosphate. This compound gives no reaction in the Morgan–Elson test, indicating that the 1-phosphate group is not hydrolyzed by the alkaline treatment.

Nucleotide derivatives of 2-amino-2-deoxy-D-glucose have not yet been synthesized chemically, but incubation of 2-amino-2-deoxy-D-glucose 6-phosphate with uridinetriphosphoric acid in the presence of a rat-liver enzyme leads to the formation[127] of uridine 5-(2-acetamido-2-deoxy-6-O-phospho-D-glucosyl dihydrogen pyrophosphate), "UDPAG." Under similar conditions, no nucleotide was synthesized from 2-acetamido-2-deoxy-D-glucose 6-phosphate.

c. Sulfates.—Sulfated derivatives of hexosamines are important, since they occur in such mucopolysaccharides as heparin, chondroitinsulfate, and mucoitinsulfate.[3, 8] Crystalline derivatives have, however, only recently been described.[135] In an extension of earlier work,[136, 137] Wolfrom and co-workers[135] synthesized 2-deoxy-2-sulfoamino-D-glucose, its methyl α-D-glycoside, and its methyl 3,4,6-tri-O-methyl-α-D-glycoside, each being isolated as the sodium salt. These compounds will undoubtedly prove to be valuable as model derivatives for study of the stability of the N-sulfate groups toward acidic and alkaline reagents.[137a] It is believed that the rapid release of sulfate ions from heparin on mild acid hydrolysis is due to the scission of sulfoamido groups. Heparin is unique in the field of mucopolysaccharides in possessing a sulfoamido residue as part of its molecule.

2. Glycosides of 2-Amino-2-deoxy-D-glucose

a. Glycosides—Normal glycoside formation by hexosamines occurs when the amino group is suitably protected. 2-Amino-2-deoxy sugars are not glycosidated by acid–alcohol mixtures, because of the electrostatic, shielding effect of the —$\overset{\oplus}{N}H_3$ group. Cation-exchange resins ($H^\oplus$ form) are particu-

(135) M. L. Wolfrom, R. A. Gibbons and A. J. Huggard, *J. Am. Chem. Soc.*, **79**, 5043 (1957).

(136) K. H. Meyer and D. E. Schwartz, *Helv. Chim. Acta*, **33**, 1651 (1950).

(137) M. L. Wolfrom, T. M. Shen and C. G. Summers, *J. Am. Chem. Soc.*, **75**, 1519 (1953).

(137a) See M. L. Wolfrom, R. A. Gibbons, A. J. Huggard and W. B. Neely, *Abstracts Papers Am. Chem. Soc.*, **130**, 21D (1956).

larly convenient glycosidation catalysts[138] for the production of alkyl 2-acylamido-2-deoxy-D-glucosides directly in alcoholic solution.[139, 140] Refluxing appears to favor α-D glycoside formation, whereas β-D glycosides predominate at lower temperatures.[140] None of the glycosidation methods give either anomer *exclusively*, and chromatographic methods may be necessary for accomplishing purification. Thus, the substance described in the literature as methyl 2-acetamido-2-deoxy-α-D-glucopyranoside[94, 141, 142] has been shown[139] to contain 15 % of the β anomer, which is not removed by repeated recrystallization. The pure α anomer has a molecular rotation of +30,800, very close to that of methyl α-D-glucopyranoside (+30,700); this emphasizes the similarity of structure.

Ethyl 2-acetamido-2-deoxy-β-D-glucopyranoside is one of the few simple glycosides of hexosamines to occur naturally; it acts as a growth factor for *Lactobacillus bifidus* var. Penn.[143] Fusion of 1,3,4,6-tetra-O-acetyl-2-acetamido-2-deoxy-D-glucose with phenols (in the presence of zinc chloride) yields aryl 2-acetamido-2-deoxy-D-glycosides.[144] β-D-Glycosides may be formed (under very mild conditions) by treatment of reducing amino sugars with diazomethane[145] in moist methanol–ether, a procedure which is particularly valuable for "protecting" the reducing end-group of oligosaccharides prior to methylation. The sensitivity of amino sugars to alkali renders difficult the application of normal methods for methylating the reducing center.

A number of very useful indirect methods are available for the preparation of β-D-glycosides. Polyacetate esters of 2-amino-2-deoxy-D-glucosyl bromide can be used,[146] but, for general use, the more stable chlorides are to be preferred, since there is then little tendency for acyl migration[147] and they can yield a wider range of glycosides.[148, 149] Under certain circum-

(138) J. E. Cadotte, F. Smith and D. Spriestersbach, *J. Am. Chem. Soc.*, **74**, 1501 (1952).

(139) R. Kuhn, F. Zilliken and A. Gauhe, *Chem. Ber.*, **86**, 466 (1953).

(140) F. Zilliken, C. S. Rose, G. A. Braun and P. György, *Arch. Biochem. Biophys.*, **54**, 392 (1955).

(141) K. Freudenberg, H. Eich, C. Knoevenagel and W. Westphal, *Ber.*, **73**, 441 (1940).

(142) R. C. G. Moggridge and A. Neuberger, *J. Chem. Soc.*, 745 (1938).

(143) S. Pope, R. M. Tomarelli and P. György, *Arch. Biochem. Biophys.*, **68**, 362 (1957).

(144) S. Fujise and K. Yokoyama, *Nippon Kagaku Zasshi*, **72**, 728 (1951); *Chem. Abstracts*, **46**, 11116 (1952).

(145) R. Kuhn and H. H. Baer, *Chem. Ber.*, **86**, 724 (1953).

(146) R. Kuhn and W. Kirschenlohr, *Chem. Ber.*, **86**, 1331 (1953).

(147) Y. Inouye, K. Onodera, S. Kitaoka and H. Ochai, *J. Am. Chem. Soc.*, **79**, 4218 (1957).

(148) D. H. Leaback and P. G. Walker, *Chem. & Ind.* (London), 1017 (1956).

(149) D. H. Leaback and P. G. Walker, *J. Chem. Soc.*, 4754 (1957).

stances, the corresponding glycosyl fluorides *also* give β-D-glycosides.[150] A wide range of alkyl and aryl 2-benzamido-2-deoxy-β-D-glucopyranosides can be obtained by the action of the appropriate alcohol or phenol on the 4,5-(3,4,6-tri-O-acetyl-2-dehydro-2-deoxy-α-D-glucopyranosyl) fused derivative of 2-phenyl-Δ^1-oxazoline (XLVI) or its hydrobromide,[112, 113, 151, 152]

XLVI

and the procedure has also been applied to the preparation of a crystalline derivative having a DL-serine residue as the aglycon.

Furanoside derivatives of 2-amino-2-deoxy-D-glucose have not been extensively studied, but they are formed from 2-acylamido-2-deoxy-D-glucose derivatives plus alcoholic hydrogen chloride under certain conditions. At room temperature, 2% methanolic hydrogen chloride converts 2-deoxy-2-(2,4-dinitrophenylamino)-D-glucose into a mixture of pyranosides and furanosides, from which methyl 2-deoxy-2-(2,4-dinitrophenylamino)-α-D-glucofuranoside can be isolated.[153] β-D-Furanosides are formed from acyclic dithioacetal derivatives[8, 154] by treatment with mercuric chloride in methanolic solution.

Glycosides of the 2-amino-2-deoxy sugars must be obtained indirectly, using a N-substituted derivative, with subsequent liberation of the amino group. The benzyloxycarbonyl group commonly used may be removed by catalytic hydrogenolysis or with sodium in liquid ammonia[155, 156]; the more drastic conditions often employed in protein chemistry may degrade the hexosamine molecule.[156] The N-(2,4-dinitrophenyl) group can be readily removed, along with O-acetyl groups, by treatment with a basic, ion-exchange resin.[153]

Acidic hydrolysis of 2-acylamino-2-deoxy-D-glucosides is incomplete, owing to the operation of two separate reaction-pathways, one leading to glycoside hydrolysis, the other to hydrolysis of the N-substituent. The product of the second reaction pathway is strongly resistant to further hy-

(150) F. Micheel and E. Michaelis, *Chem. Ber.*, **91**, 188 (1958).
(151) F. Micheel and E. Drescher, *Chem. Ber.*, **91**, 670 (1958).
(152) F. Micheel and H. Köchling, *Chem. Ber.*, **91**, 673 (1958).
(153) P. F. Lloyd and M. Stacey, *Chem. & Ind.* (London), 917 (1955).
(154) P. W. Kent, *Research* (London), **3**, 427 (1950).
(155) A. B. Foster, D. Horton and M. Stacey, *J. Chem. Soc.*, 81 (1957).
(156) A. B. Foster and D. Horton, unpublished results.

drolysis, because of the electrostatic, shielding effect of the $—NH_3^{\oplus}$ group on the glycosidic center.[156, 157] On this account, it is necessary to interpret with care the evidence of hexosamine determinations made on mucopolysaccharide hydrolyzates, since a similar mechanism operating here will lead to low apparent values for the hexosamine content.

b. N-*Substituted Glycosylamines and Relatives* ("N-*Glycosides*")—1-(N-Substituted) derivatives of 2-amino-2-deoxy-D-glucosylamine fall into three main categories, namely: (i) those formed theoretically (and, sometimes, in practice) by condensation of 2-amino-2-deoxy-D-glucose with an amine or ammonia (glycosylamines); (ii) derivatives of 2-amino-2-deoxy-D-glucosyl azides, and (iii) 1-isothiocyanate and related derivatives (1-thioureido and 1-isothioureido compounds).

(i) *Glycosylamines*.[158]—The direct interaction of 2-acetamido-2-deoxy-D-glucose with aromatic amines leads to the formation of N^1-substituted derivatives of 2-acetamido-2-deoxy-D-glucosylamine. In some cases, fusion of the reactants is sufficient[159]; in others, catalysis with ammonium chloride is necessary for reaction to take place.[159] Condensation may also occur in aqueous solution, in the presence of acetic acid.[160] The unsubstituted glycosylamines can also be obtained by catalytic reduction of derivatives of 2-amino-2-deoxy-D-glucosyl azides.[161] Peracetylated glycosylamines result from the interaction of 2-acetamido-3,4,6-tri-O-acetyl-2-deoxy-α-D-glucosyl bromide with aromatic amines,[159] and they may be readily de-O-acetylated. N^1,N^1-Dialkyl derivatives of 2-amino-2-deoxy-D-glucosylamine have also been prepared.[162] In all cases so far encountered in the hexosamine series, the β-D-glycosylamine appears to be preferentially formed.

The 2-amino-2-deoxy glycosylamines closely resemble their non-nitrogenous sugar counterparts; the 1-amino group is very readily hydrolyzed (see p. 217), especially by dilute acid, and the derivatives mutarotate in aqueous media and reduce Fehling solution. The N^1-arylglycosylamines exhibit a similar lack of stability. On the other hand, *acylation* of the 1-amino group confers a considerable measure of stability[41]; for instance, 1,2-bis-(acetamido)-1,2-dideoxy-D-glucose and its 3,4,6-triacetate ester do not mutarotate in aqueous solution (and fail to reduce Fehling solution or to react with the Morgan–Elson reagent).[7] This behavior is in agreement with similar observations for non-nitrogenous derivatives.

(ii) *Glycosyl Azides*.—3,4,6-Tri-O-acetyl-2-amino-2-deoxy-α-D-glucosyl

(157) A. B. Foster, D. Horton and M. Stacey, *Chem. & Ind.* (London), 175 (1956).

(158) G. P. Ellis and J. Honeyman, *Advances in Carbohydrate Chem.*, **10**, 95 (1955).

(159) A. Bertho and D. Koziollek, *Chem. Ber.*, **87**, 934 (1954).

(160) Y. Inouye, K. Onodera and S. Kitaoka, *Bull. Inst. Chem. Research Kyoto Univ.*, **29**, 139 (1955); *Chem. Abstracts*, **50**, 825 (1956).

(161) A. Bertho and A. Révesz, *Ann.*, **581**, 161 (1953).

(162) K. Heyns, R. Eichstedt and K. H. Meinecke, *Chem. Ber.*, **88**, 1551 (1955).

bromide hydrobromide reacts with silver azide to give the β-D-azide.[161] The azide group is stable under the usual conditions of acylation and catalytic de-O-acylation, and a range of derivatives has consequently been prepared.[163] Catalytic reduction of the β-D-azide leads to the formation of a β-D-glycosylamine.[161]

(iii) *Glycosyl Isothiocyanates.*—The interaction of 1,3,4,6-tetra-O-acetyl-2-amino-2-deoxy-α-D-glucose hydrobromide (XLVII) with silver thiocyanate has been shown[164] to give 2-acetamido-3,4,6-tri-O-acetyl-2-deoxy-β-D-glucosyl isothiocyanate (XLVIII). For this reaction,[164] a mechanism has been proposed involving an oxazoline intermediate (L) which results after dehydration of an initially formed 1,2-(orthoacetyl) amide (XLIX). The oxazoline derivative subsequently reacts with the thiocyanate ion at C1, with Walden inversion. This mechanism has been disputed[7] on the grounds of the instability of the oxazoline intermediate, although such derivatives can in fact be isolated (see p. 247).

The isothiocyanate group of compound XLVIII is very reactive and readily undergoes addition reactions with ethanol or with the amino group of ethyl esters of amino acids, giving either a thioethylurethan (LIa) or a substituted thiourea; for instance, the derivative LIb is formed when glycine ethyl ester is employed. If the isothiocyanate derivative is permitted to react with ammonia, there results the thioureido derivative (LIc) which, after de-O-acetylation, undergoes a rearrangement reaction with ethyl bromide, yielding the substituted isothiourea (LII). This compound can itself react with glycine, with the elimination of ethanethiol, forming a guanidine derivative isolable as the 3,4,6-triacetate ester (LIII).

XLVII

XLVIII

c. *1-Thioglycosides.*—The acid-catalyzed "glycosidation" of 2-acetamido-2-deoxy-D-glucose with ethanethiol, under suitable conditions, proceeds only as far as the hemiacetal stage; and, from the reaction products, the anomers of ethyl 2-acetamido-2-deoxy-1-thio-D-glucopyranoside may be isolated.[165] The α anomer of the corresponding D-furanoside can be obtained indirectly by reaction of 2-acetamido-2-deoxy-D-glucose diethyl

(163) F. Micheel and H. Wulff, *Chem. Ber.*, **89**, 1521 (1956).
(164) F. Micheel and W. Lengsfeld, *Chem. Ber.*, **89**, 1246 (1956).
(165) L. Hough and M. I. Taha, *J. Chem. Soc.*, 2042 (1956).

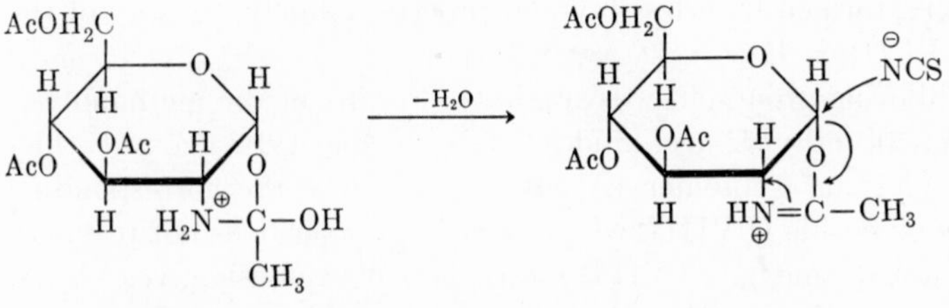

AcOH$_2$C

H H O H
AcO OAc H $\xrightarrow{-\text{H}_2\text{O}}$
H H$_2$N$\overset{\oplus}{-}$C$-$OH
|
CH$_3$

XLIX

AcOH$_2$C

H H O H $\overset{\ominus}{\text{NCS}}$
AcO OAc H O
H HN$\overset{\oplus}{=}$C$-$CH$_3$

L

AcOH$_2$C

H H O NH$-$CS$-$R
AcO OAc H
H H
H NHAc

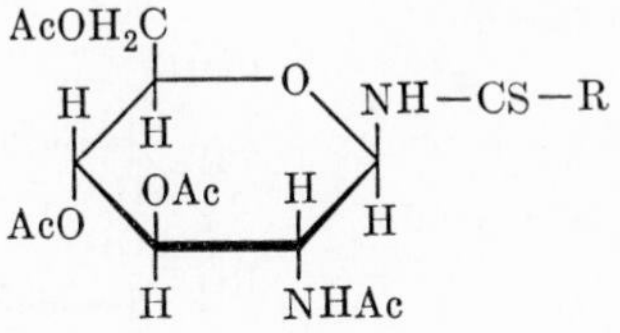

LI

a, R = OEt;
b, R = NHCH$_2$CO$_2$Et;
c, R = NH$_2$

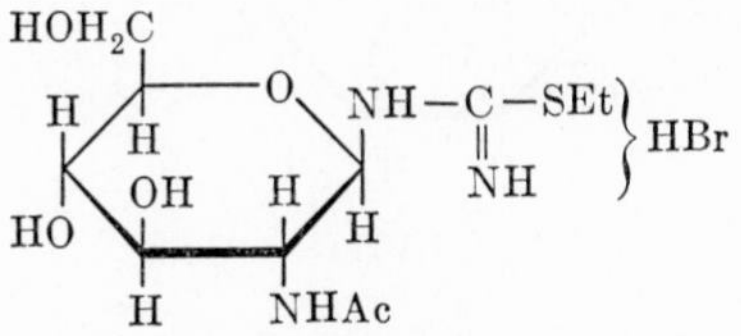

HOH$_2$C

H H O NH$-$C$-$SEt
HO OH H || $\Big\}$ HBr
H H NH
H NHAc

LII

AcOH$_2$C

H H O NH$-$C$-$NH$-$CH$_2$CO$_2$H
AcO OAc H || NH
H H
H NHAc

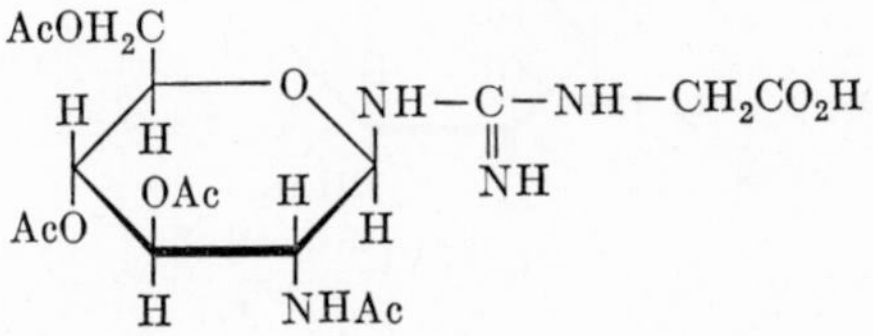

LIII

dithioacetal with mercuric chloride plus mercuric oxide.[166, 167] This furanoside derivative has been used in the synthesis of streptidine[166] and in the
preparation of 2-amino-2-deoxy-D-xylose.[38]

Mercaptolysis of 2-acetamido-1,3,4,6-tetra-O-acetyl-2-deoxy-α-D-glu-
cose (LIV) with ethanethiol plus zinc chloride leads to the formation of
ethyl 2-acetamido-3,4,6-tri-O-acetyl-2-deoxy-1-thio-β-D-glucopyranoside
(LV, R = Ac).[165] It is probable that initial scission of the acetoxy
group at C1 leads to the formation of an oxonium ion (LVI, R = Ac) which
is stabilized as the cyclic carbonium cation LVII by neighboring-group participation. The thioglycoside with the β-D configuration is exclusively
formed from this intermediate. A similar mechanism appears to operate in
favoring the formation of LV (R = H) by acid-catalyzed glycosidation, the

(166) M. L. Wolfrom, S. M. Olin and W. J. Polglase, *J. Am. Chem. Soc.*, **72**, 1724 (1950).

(167) M. L. Wolfrom and K. Anno, *J. Am. Chem. Soc.*, **74**, 6150 (1952).

α-D anomer being formed by a less favored process, namely, by way of the oxonium ion LVI (R = H).

Similar neighboring-group effects explain the results of the methanolysis of the anomers of ethyl 2-acetamido-3,4,6-tri-O-acetyl-2-deoxy-1-thio-D-glucopyranoside; the β anomer LV (R = Ac) gives the corresponding methyl β-D-thioglycoside (LVIII), whereas the α anomer does not react. In the first case, the intermediate LVII can form; it subsequently gives LVIII. In the case of the α anomer, the ethylthio group in the axial position prevents the participation of the neighboring N-acetyl group and inhibits methanolysis.

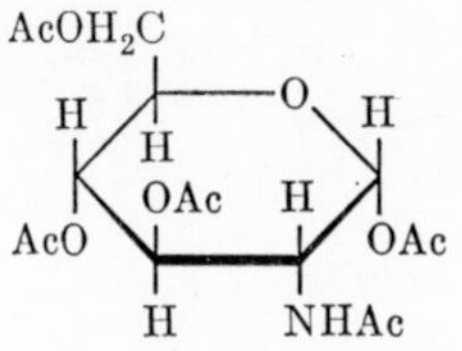

LIV

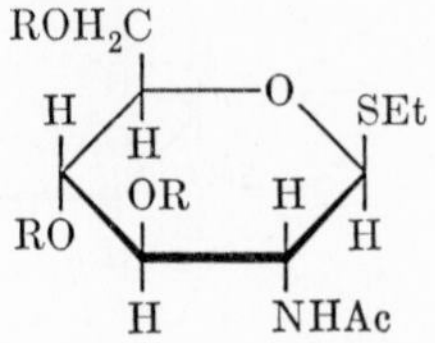

LV

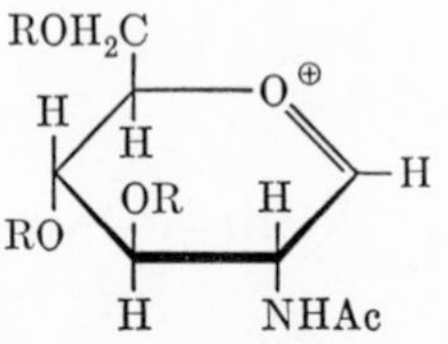

LVI

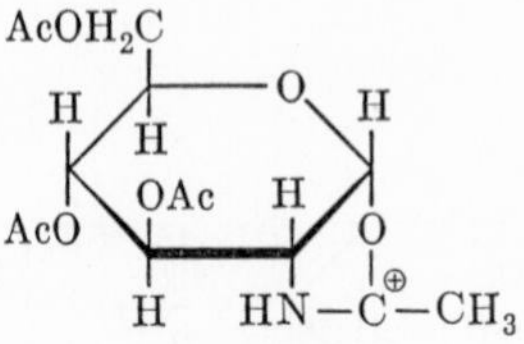

LVII

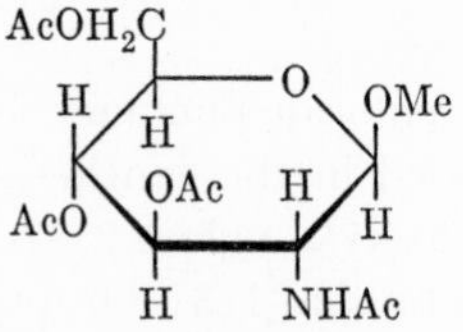

LVIII

3. Glycosyl Halides

Numerous derivatives of 2-amino-2-deoxy-D-glucosyl halides have been reported recently, especially by Micheel and coworkers.[112, 113, 150, 163, 168] Methods of synthesis are similar to those for the analogous non-nitrogeneous sugars, namely, treatment of acylated derivatives with acyl halides,[169] hydrogen halides,[105, 111, 112, 147, 149] or titanic halide.[105]

The relative stabilities of the halides depend to some extent on the other

(168) F. Micheel and E. Drescher, Chem. Ber., **91**, 668 (1958).

(169) J. C. Irvine, D. McNicoll and A. Hynd, J. Chem. Soc., **99**, 250 (1911).

substituents in the hexosamine molecule, but the fluorides are generally the most stable, contrasting with the very reactive bromides; chlorides are intermediate in reactivity. No iodides have as yet been reported.

Under suitable conditions, most D-glycosyl halides react with alcohols to form β-D-glycosides; inversion usually occurs with the bromides and chlorides. D-Glycosyl bromides readily give β-D-glycosides, whereas fluorides react either slowly or not at all. General tendencies in the reaction of derivatives of 2-amino-2-deoxy-D-glucosyl halides become apparent when a number of derivatives are compared, but, since there are also significant differences according to the particular halogen, it is convenient to consider the three groups separately.

a. Bromides.—One of the earliest 1-bromo-1-deoxyhexosamine derivatives to be described was 2-acetamido-3,4,6-tri-O-acetyl-2-deoxy-α-D-glucosyl bromide (LIX),[142] but its properties have been widely misunderstood[105, 142, 148] because attempted purification leads to a rearrangement[111, 147] giving LX, which has been incorrectly described as "acetobromglucosamine"

LIX

LX

(LIX). Under anhydrous conditions, LIX can be isolated[170] and, in the crude state, it yields β-D-glycosides with alcohols in the presence of mercuric cyanide,[146] and can also give 1-amino-1-deoxy derivatives[159] and 1-phosphates,[127] but it readily rearranges to LX on standing, especially in such polar solvents as acetone.[170]

Aryl substituents at N^2 tend to stabilize the 1-bromide center, and a range of poly-O-acetyl-α-D-glycosyl bromides with N-benzoyl,[112] N-tosyl,[163, 171] N-(2,4-dinitrophenyl),[153] and other N-substituents[168] have been prepared, all of which yield glycosides on treatment with alcohols. The N-benzoyl derivative (LXI) readily undergoes an intramolecular rearrangement[112, 113] to give the oxazoline derivative hydrobromide (LXII), from which the free base (LXIII) can be prepared.[113]

The oxazoline derivative LXIII or its hydrobromide (LXII) readily react with alcohols to give β-D-glycosides.[113, 151, 152] Under other conditions, the oxazoline hydrobromide (LXII) isomerizes to LXIV (3,4,6-tri-O-acetyl-2-amino-1-O-benzoyl-2-deoxy-α-D-glucose hydrobromide),[112] the

(170) G. Fodor and L. Ötvös, *Ann.*, **604**, 29 (1957).
(171) A. Neuberger and R. P. Rivers, *Biochem. J.*, **33**, 1580 (1939).

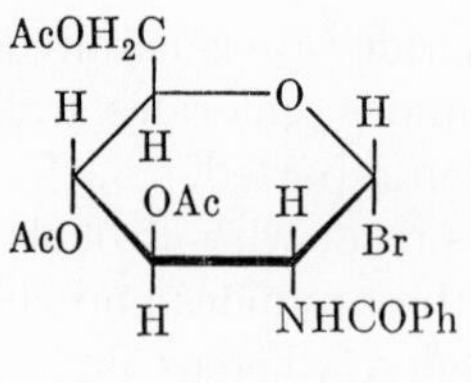

LXI 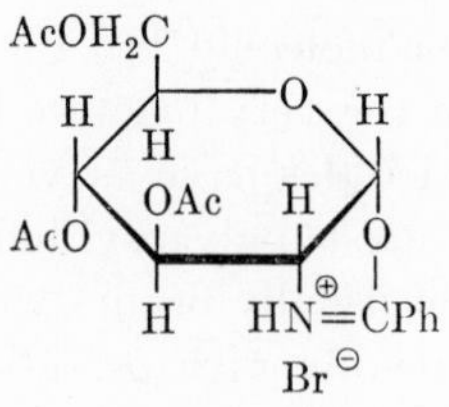   LXII 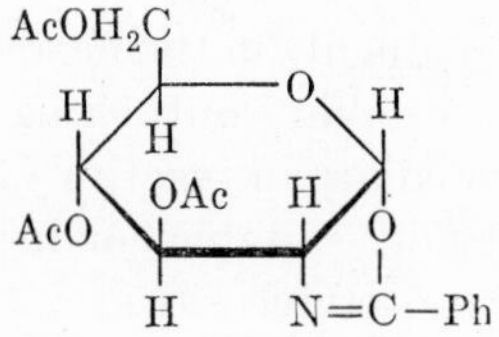   LXIII

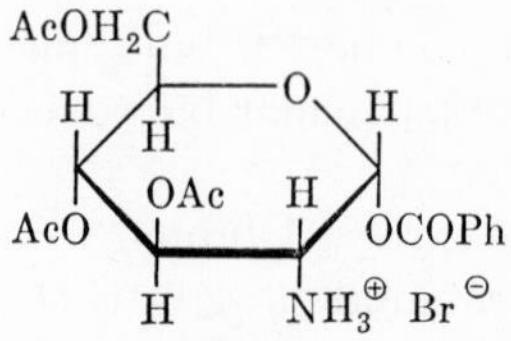

LXIV

over-all reaction LXI → LXIV being analogous to the isomerization LIX → LX.

3,4,6-Tri-O-acetyl-2-amino-2-deoxy-α-D-glucosyl bromide hydrobromide (LXVa)[169, 170] is more stable than the N-acyl analogs, possibly because heterolysis of the C—Br bond with the generation of a carbonium cation proceeds less readily as a result of the presence of the neighboring—$NH_3^{\oplus}$ center. β-D-Glycoside formation proceeds normally with alcohols,[169] and treatment with an equivalent of sodium ethoxide under anhydrous conditions liberates[170] the free base (LXVb).

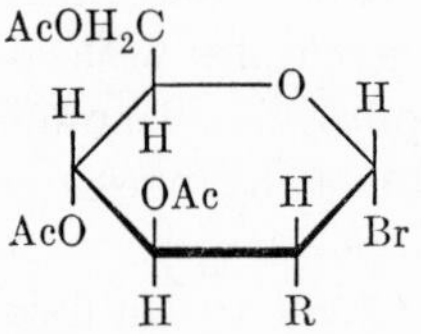

LXVa (R = —$NH_3^{\oplus}$ $Br^{\ominus}$)
LXVb (R = —NH_2)

The highly reactive 2-amino and 1-bromide groups are sterically remote in the "preferred" conformation LXVI, and intramolecular reaction does not occur. The (theoretically possible) ethyleneimine hydrobromide struc-

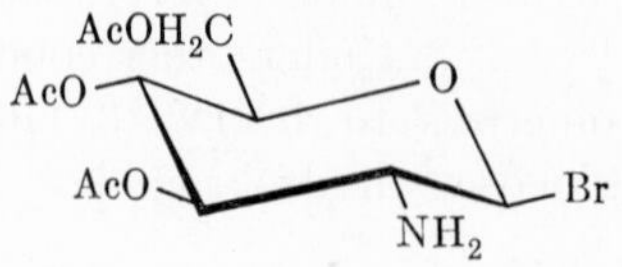

LXVI 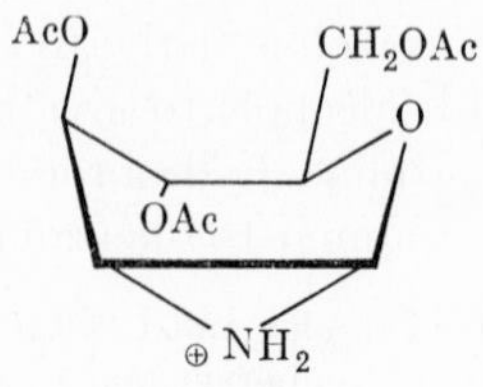   LXVII ture LXVII is improbable, since the derivative does not exhibit salt-like characteristics.

However, it is believed[170] that intermolecular condensation is possible under conditions where a 3-O-acetyl → N-acetyl migration can take place initially, with the resultant formation of a β-D-(1 → 3)-linked polyhexosamine.

b. Chlorides.—2-Acetamido-3,4,6-tri-O-acetyl-2-deoxy-α-D-glucosyl chloride (LXVIII) is a convenient intermediate for β-D-glycoside synthesis[112, 147-149, 172]; its reaction with purine derivatives[105] and its use in the synthesis of 1-phosphates have been recorded.[37] In moist, ethereal solution, a rearrangement analogous to LIX → LX can occur, with the formation of LXIX, but it takes place significantly less readily than with the bromide.[112]

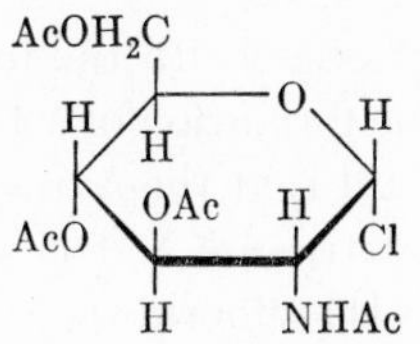

AcOH$_2$C

H H O H
AcO OAc H Cl
H NHAc

LXVIII

AcOH$_2$C

H H O H
AcO OAc H OAc
H NH$_3^\oplus$ Cl$^\ominus$

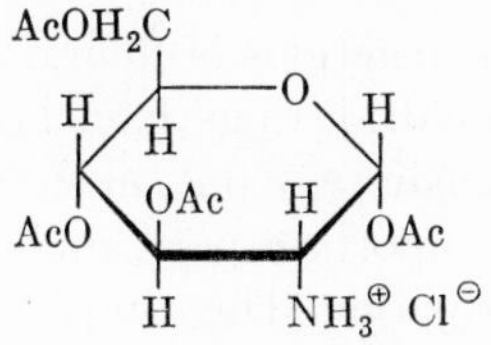

LXIX

3,4,6-Tri-O-acetyl-2-deoxy-2-phthalimido-D-glucosyl chloride was used by Baker and coworkers[105] for the synthesis of 2-amino-2-deoxy-D-glucosyl-purines. The configuration at C1 was not stated, but it is believed that the bulky purine residue enters the molecule in the β-D configuration, regardless of the configuration of the D-glycosyl chloride.

c. Fluorides.—2-Acetamido-3,4,6-tri-O-acetyl-2-deoxy-α-D-glucosyl fluoride (LXX)[163] contrasts with the chloride and bromide in not undergoing a rearrangement of the type LIX → LX.

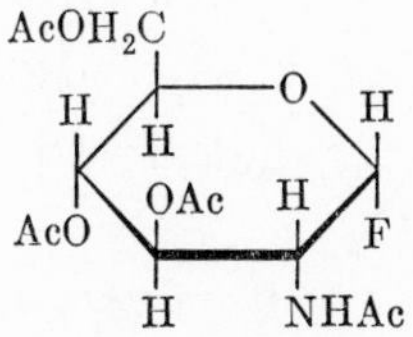

AcOH$_2$C

H H O H
AcO OAc H F
H NHAc

LXX

HOH$_2$C

H H O H
HO OH H F
H NHAc

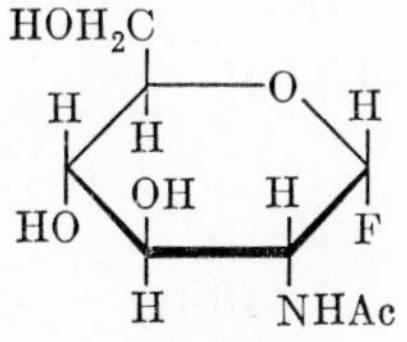

LXXI

The fluoride LXX is extremely stable toward alcohols, and sodium methoxide effects de-O-acetylation to give LXXI (a stable crystalline compound), leaving the fluoride group intact.

The fluoride LXXI is unaffected by aqueous solvents, and it undergoes alkaline hydrolysis, with difficulty, to give 2-acetamido-2-deoxy-D-glucose. 3,4,6-Tri-O-acetyl-2-deoxy-2-(p-tolylsulfonamido)-α-D-glucosyl fluoride

(172) C. J. Morel, *Experientia*, **12**, 419 (1956).

(LXXII) may also be readily de-O-acetylated,[150] in contrast to the corresponding β-D derivative LXXIII. Both fluorides (LXXII and LXXIII) react with excess of hot, methanolic sodium methoxide with the formation of a β-D-1,6-anhydride (LXXVII) as the principal product,[150] together with a smaller quantity of methyl 2-acetamido-2-deoxy-β-D-glucopyranoside (LXXVI).

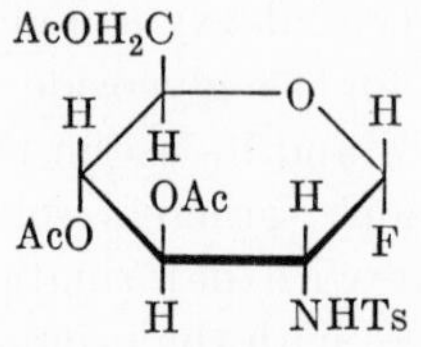

LXXII 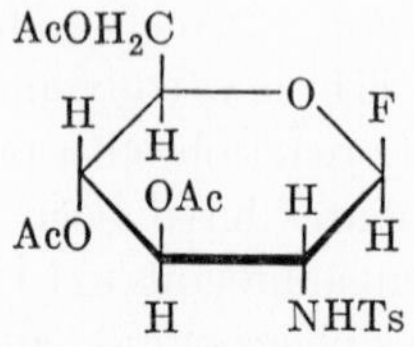   LXXIII

Related reactions of fluorides in the D-glucose series, with the formation of 1,6-anhydride rings, have been explained by the formation of a 1,2-epoxide intermediate,[173] but, in this case, it is considered that the N-tosyl group plays an important part, since the N-acetyl derivative LXX does not form a 1,6-anhydride. The α-D (LXXII) or β-D (LXXIII) fluoride is believed to react with alkali to give the de-O-acetylated carbonium ion LXXIV, which is stabilized by cyclic imine (LXXV) formation. This imine can readily re-form the carbonium ion LXXIV and give a β-D-glycoside LXXVI by intermolecular, *trans* addition, or it may react intramolecularly with the deacetylated C6-hydroxyl group to give the β-D-1,6-anhydride LXXVII.

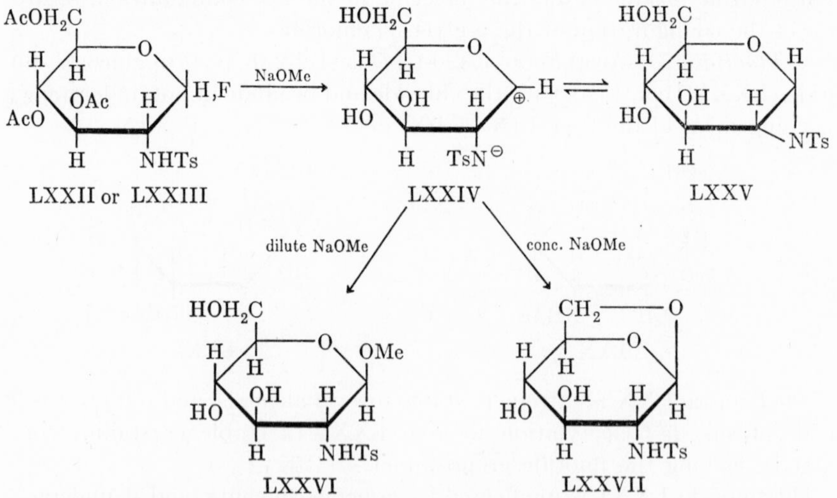

LXXII or LXXIII   LXXIV   LXXV

dilute NaOMe   conc. NaOMe

LXXVI   LXXVII

Anhydride formation is favored by a large excess of alkali, which increases the negativity of the oxygen atom at C6.

(173) F. Micheel, A. Klemer and G. Baum, *Chem. Ber.*, **88**, 475 (1955).

The imino hydrogen atom of the —NHTs group is sufficiently activated for N-methylation to take place on treatment with diazomethane, and the corresponding N-methyl-N-tosyl derivatives can be prepared from LXXII and LXXIII. Both anomers can be de-O-acetylated by the Zemplén-Pacsu[89] method, but the 1-fluoride group is extraordinarily unreactive.[150]

4. *Ethers*

Classical methylation techniques have not been used extensively in constitutional studies on natural oligo- and poly-saccharides in the hexosamine field, mainly because of the one-time lack of most of the theoretically possible methylated derivatives as reference compounds, but the researches of Jeanloz and coworkers[6] have made available a wide range of partially methylated derivatives of 2-amino-2-deoxy-D-glucose, most of them characterized as crystalline N-(2-hydroxy-1-naphthylmethylene) derivatives. Methyl ethers of 2-acetamido-2-deoxy-D-glucose derivatives can be prepared by the usual methods with sodium hydroxide and dimethyl sulfate or with methyl iodide and silver oxide, provided that the terminal reducing group is initially protected by glycosidation. Methylation with the latter reagents can advantageously be effected in N,N-dimethylformamide solution,[174] most derivatives then undergoing practically complete O-methylation in one operation. Partial oxidation of the acetamido group by the silver oxide can be obviated if barium oxide is used instead.[175]

Mild conditions must be used for initial "protection" of the reducing group of an oligosaccharide by glycosidation (to avoid degradation or rearrangement), and the diazomethane method (see p. 241) is satisfactory. Conversion of the reducing moiety to the alditol residue before methylation,[176] either with hydrogen[176] plus a catalyst or with borohydride,[177] may also be convenient. Application of methylation techniques is then feasible.[176] This approach is at present limited by the non-availability of partially methylated derivatives of 2-amino-2-deoxy-D-glucitol.

Triphenylmethyl (trityl) ethers of 2-amino-2-deoxy-D-glucose derivatives are formed with the primary C6-hydroxyl group, and they are useful intermediates in synthesis,[6, 156, 178] being readily removed by hydrogenolysis.

5. N-*Substituted 2-Amino-2-deoxy-*D-*glucose Derivatives*

Simple monoamides have already been discussed (see p. 233).

Schiff bases derived from 2-amino-2-deoxy-D-glucose are useful as char-

(174) R. Kuhn, H. Trischmann and I. Löw, *Angew. Chem.*, **67**, 32 (1955).
(175) R. Kuhn, H. H. Baer and A. Seeliger, *Ann.*, **611**, 236 (1958).
(176) R. Kuhn and H. H. Baer, *Chem. Ber.*, **89**, 504 (1956).
(177) A. B. Foster and D. Horton, *J. Chem. Soc.*, 1890 (1958).
(178) R. Kuhn, H. H. Baer and A. Gauhe, *Chem. Ber.*, **88**, 1713 (1955).

acterization derivatives.[6] They are readily prepared[39, 179, 180] and are stable in neutral or alkaline solution, but are easily decomposed by dilute acid. These derivatives have been superseded by the N-benzyloxycarbonyl amides in synthetic work; the benzyloxycarbonyl group is often more satisfactory as a "blocking group" for the amino group (see p. 242).

N-Alkyl derivatives of 2-amino-2-deoxy-D-glucose are very stable and show the typical properties of aliphatic, secondary amines. They may be prepared by direct alkylation of 2-amino-2-deoxy-D-glucose under vigorous conditions,[181] but, unless the amino group is activated by a strongly electron-attracting substituent (for example, tosyl[150]), reaction is slow. More satisfactory synthetic routes involve the amino nitrile synthesis[13] (see p. 215) or rearrangement of a N-alkyl-ketosylamine[162, 182] (see p. 221).

Ethylene oxide reacts with the amino group of 1,3,4,6-tetra-O-acetyl-2-amino-2-deoxy-β-D-glucose to give a N,N-bis(2-hydroxyethyl) derivative (LXXVIII)[183] which readily affords the corresponding "nitrogen mustard" (LXXIXa) on treatment with thionyl chloride. The hydrochloride of the deacetylated derivative (LXXIXb) was prepared as an antitumor agent; its positive activity is, however, accompanied by a high degree of toxicity.

LXXVIII   LXXIXa

On standing, LXXIXb undergoes a rearrangement, apparently with the formation of an iminium cation (LXXX)—a reaction analogous to the formation of an ethyleneiminium cation from N-alkyl-N,N-bis(2-chloroethyl)-amine.[184] The di-O-mesyl ester (LXXXI) of LXXVIII is remarkably resistant to catalytic de-O-acetylation.

In an extension of the work on the synthesis of N-substituted amino sugars by the amino nitrile method, Kuhn and coworkers[13] have prepared 2-(carboxymethylamino)-2-deoxy-D-glucose (2-deoxy-2-glycino-D-glucose), as the dipolar ion LXXXII, from glycine ethyl ester plus D-arabinose.

Similar derivatives were prepared by Heyns[34] by the rearrangement of

(179) A. Neuberger, *Biochem. J.*, **32**, 1435 (1938).

(180) Z. E. Jolles and W. T. J. Morgan, *Biochem. J.*, **34**, 1183 (1940).

(181) M. L. Wolfrom and A. Thompson, *J. Am. Chem. Soc.*, **69**, 1847 (1947).

(182) K. Heyns and W. Stumme, *Chem. Ber.*, **89**, 2833, 2844 (1956).

(183) S. Vargha, Ö. Fehér and S. Lendvai, *J. Chem. Soc.*, 810 (1957).

(184) W. E. Hanby, G. S. Hartley, E. O. Powell and H. N. Rydon, *J. Chem. Soc.*, 519 (1947).

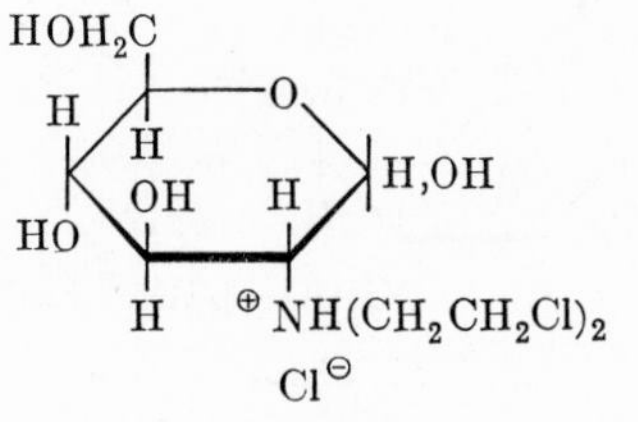

HOH$_2$C ... H,OH ... HO ... H ... $\overset{\oplus}{N}H(CH_2CH_2Cl)_2$ ... Cl$^{\ominus}$

LXXIXb

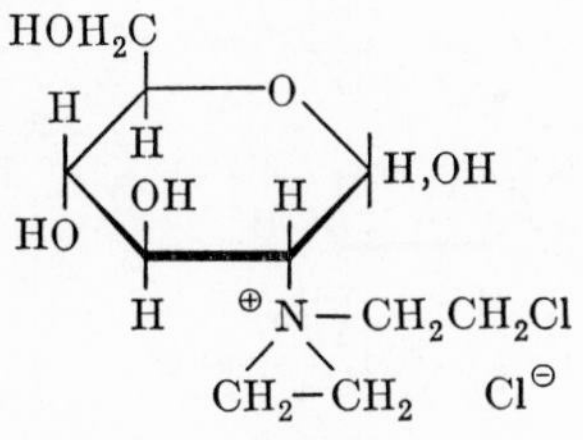

HOH$_2$C ... H,OH ... HO ... H ... $\overset{\oplus}{N}-CH_2CH_2Cl$ ... CH_2-CH_2 ... Cl$^{\ominus}$

LXXX

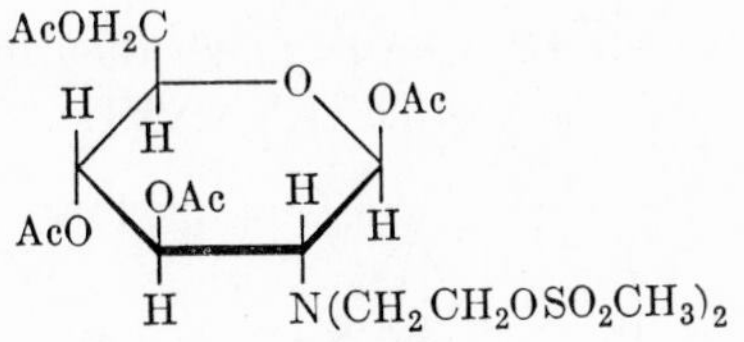

AcOH$_2$C ... OAc ... AcO ... OAc ... H ... H ... N(CH$_2$CH$_2$OSO$_2$CH$_3$)$_2$

LXXXI

HOH$_2$C ... H,OH ... HO ... H ... $\overset{\oplus}{N}H_2CH_2CO_2^{\ominus}$

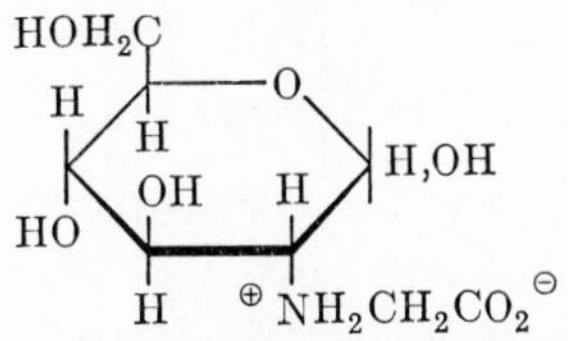

LXXXII

N-substituted ketosylamines prepared from D-fructose plus a range of different amino acids.

The above N-(carboxyalkyl) derivative may be regarded, theoretically, as resulting from the condensation of the C2-hydroxyl group of D-glucose with the amino group of an amino acid. Another type of hexose–amino acid derivative has an amino acid residue linked to the amino group of 2-amino-2-deoxy-D-glucose by a *peptide* linkage. These "glucopeptides" can be readily synthesized by reacting 1,3,4,6-tetra-O-acetyl-2-amino-2-deoxy-β-D-glucose (LXXXIII) with acylamino acid chlorides, with subsequent removal of the blocking groups from the product (LXXXIV)[185, 186]; they are of importance as model compounds for the amino acid–hexosamine complexes found in the mucoproteins.

If, however, acylamino acid azides are used in the synthesis, as is common in peptide chemistry, the reaction proceeds differently. The azide derivative LXXXV undergoes an initial Curtius rearrangement, with the

(185) M. Bergmann and L. Zervas, *Ber.*, **64**, 975 (1931); **65**, 1201 (1932).

(186) D. G. Doherty, E. A. Popenhoe and K. P. Link, *J. Am. Chem. Soc.*, **75**, 3466 (1953).

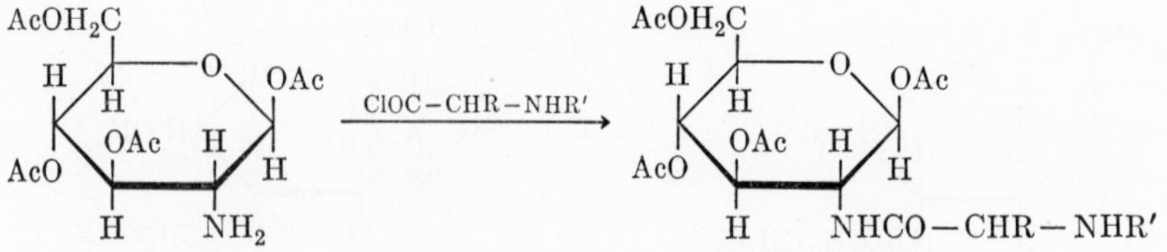

AcOH$_2$C

H $\overset{O}{\diagup}$ OAc $\xrightarrow{\text{ClOC—CHR—NHR'}}$ AcOH$_2$C

H
    OAc   H
AcO   H

H   NH$_2$

LXXXIII

H $\overset{O}{\diagup}$ OAc

H
    OAc   H
AcO   H

H   NHCO—CHR—NHR'

LXXXIV

$$\text{R'NH—CHR—CON}_3 \rightarrow \text{R'NH—CHR—N=C=O}$$
$$\text{LXXXV} \qquad\qquad \text{LXXXVI}$$

formation of an isocyanate (LXXXVI) which then reacts with LXXXIII
to form a 2-deoxy-2-ureido derivative (LXXXVII).[187]

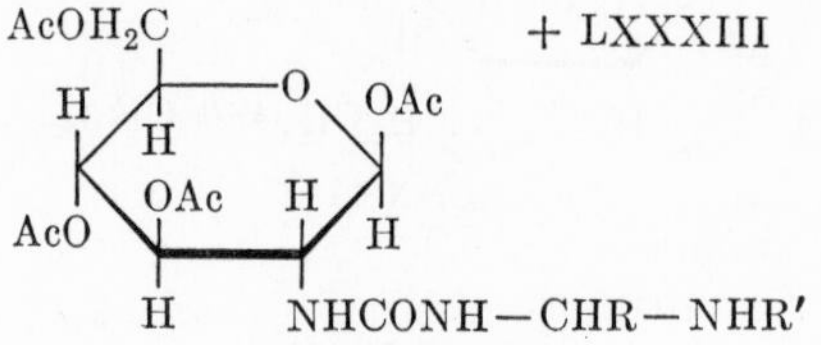

AcOH$_2$C   + LXXXIII

H $\overset{O}{\diagup}$ OAc

H
    OAc   H
AcO   H

H   NHCONH—CHR—NHR'

LXXXVII

Related 2-deoxy-2-ureido-D-glucose derivatives can be obtained by direct
reaction of phenyl isocyanate or silver isocyanate with LXXXIII, the
former giving LXXXVIII, whereas the latter affords the free 2-ureido derivative LXXXIX.[164, 188] This reaction contrasts with the behavior of
LXXXIII with isothiocyanates, which react at C1 (see p. 244).

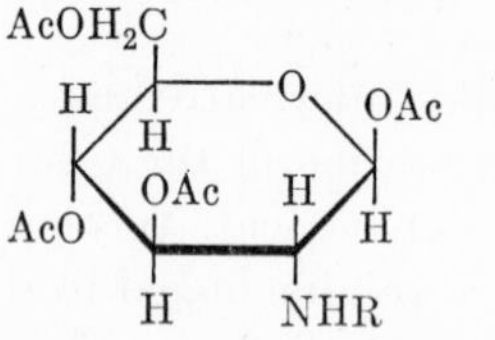

AcOH$_2$C

H $\overset{O}{\diagup}$ OAc

H
    OAc   H
AcO   H

H   NHR

LXXXVIII (R = CO—NH—Ph)
LXXXIX (R = CO—NH$_2$)

2-Deoxy-2-ureido derivatives of D-glucose have been known for many
years,[189, 190] but only recently have their properties been studied in detail.
The acetate esters show a marked resistance to catalytic de-O-acetylation
with sodium methoxide, only the 1-O-acetyl group being removed.[164] This
behavior resembles that of 1,3,4,6-tetra-O-acetyl-2-deoxy-2-{N,N-bis[2-

(187) E. A. Popenhoe, D. G. Doherty and K. P. Link, J. Am. Chem. Soc., 75, 3469
(1953).

(188) W. H. Bromund and R. M. Herbst, J. Org. Chem., 10, 267 (1945).

(189) C. Neuberg and E. Hirschberg, Biochem. Z., 27, 339 (1910).

(190) H. Steudel, Z. physiol. Chem., Hoppe-Seyler's, 33, 224; 34, 371 (1901).

(mesyloxy)ethyl]amino}-β-D-glucose (LXXXI), and of 3,4,6-tri-O-acetyl-2-deoxy-2-tosylamino-β-D-glucosyl fluoride,[163] under similar reaction conditions. Under more vigorous deacetylation conditions (methanolic ammonia) complete de-O-acetylation takes place, compound LXXXIX giving 2-deoxy-2-ureido-D-glucose. The N-(N-phenylaminocarbonyl) derivative LXXXVIII simultaneously eliminates water to give[164] the heterocyclic

XC

compound XC. The same derivative (XC) also results from the direct interaction of 2-amino-2-deoxy-D-glucose with phenyl isocyanate.[190]

The two anomers of 3,4,6-tri-O-acetyl-2-deoxy-2-phenylureido-D-glucose are unusual in *not* undergoing mutarotation in aqueous solution, and it is believed that an intra- or inter-molecular chelation prevents mutarotation.[168] Both anomers react with methyl iodide–silver oxide to form the methyl β-D-glycoside, which is also formed from the corresponding D-glucosyl bromide on treatment with methanol plus mercuric cyanide.

6. *Acyclic Derivatives*

2-Acetamido-2-deoxy-D-glucose *readily* forms a diethyl dithioacetal on reaction with ethanethiol in concentrated hydrochloric acid (see p. 244), whereas the free amino sugar requires fuming hydrochloric acid[167, 191] to drive the reaction. Peracetylation of the diethyl dithioacetal, followed by demercaptalation, yields 2-acetamido-3,4,5,6-tetra-O-acetyl-2-deoxy-*aldehydo*-D-glucose, which resembles other aldehydo sugars in its properties and which is readily decomposed by alkali.[191] Another acyclic derivative, 2-acetamido-3,4,5,6-tetra-O-acetyl-1,2-dideoxy-1-*p*-toluidino-D-glucose, is formed by acetylation of 2-acetamido-1,2-dideoxy-1-*p*-toluidino-D-glucose.[160] Extending earlier work,[192] Hough and Taha[193] have shown that oxidation of 2-amino-2-deoxy-D-glucose diethyl dithioacetal hydrochloride (XCI) with peroxypropionic acid at −10° leads to elimination of ammonium chloride, with the formation of a cyclic disulfone, bis(ethylsulfonyl)methyl 1-deoxy-α-D-arabinopyranoside [that is, 2,6-anhydro-1-deoxy-1,1-bis(ethylsulfonyl)-D-mannitol, XCIV], by the reaction sequence XCI → XCIIa →

(191) M. W. Whitehouse, P. W. Kent and C. A. Pasternak, *J. Chem. Soc.*, 2315 (1954).

(192) D. L. MacDonald and H. O. L. Fischer, *J. Am. Chem. Soc.*, **74**, 2087 (1952).

(193) L. Hough and M. I. Taha, *J. Chem. Soc.*, 3564 (1957).

XCIII → XCIV (which involves an inversion of configuration at C2). Treatment of XCIV with ammonia leads to the formation of D-arabinose (XCV) plus bis(ethylsulfonyl)methane. Oxidation of the N-acetyl analog of XCI results in de-N-acetylation, with the formation of XCII, stabilized as the crystalline peroxypropionate salt XCIIb. Treatment of XCIIb with ammonia gives a mixture of XCIV, D-arabinose (XCV), and bis(ethylsulfo-

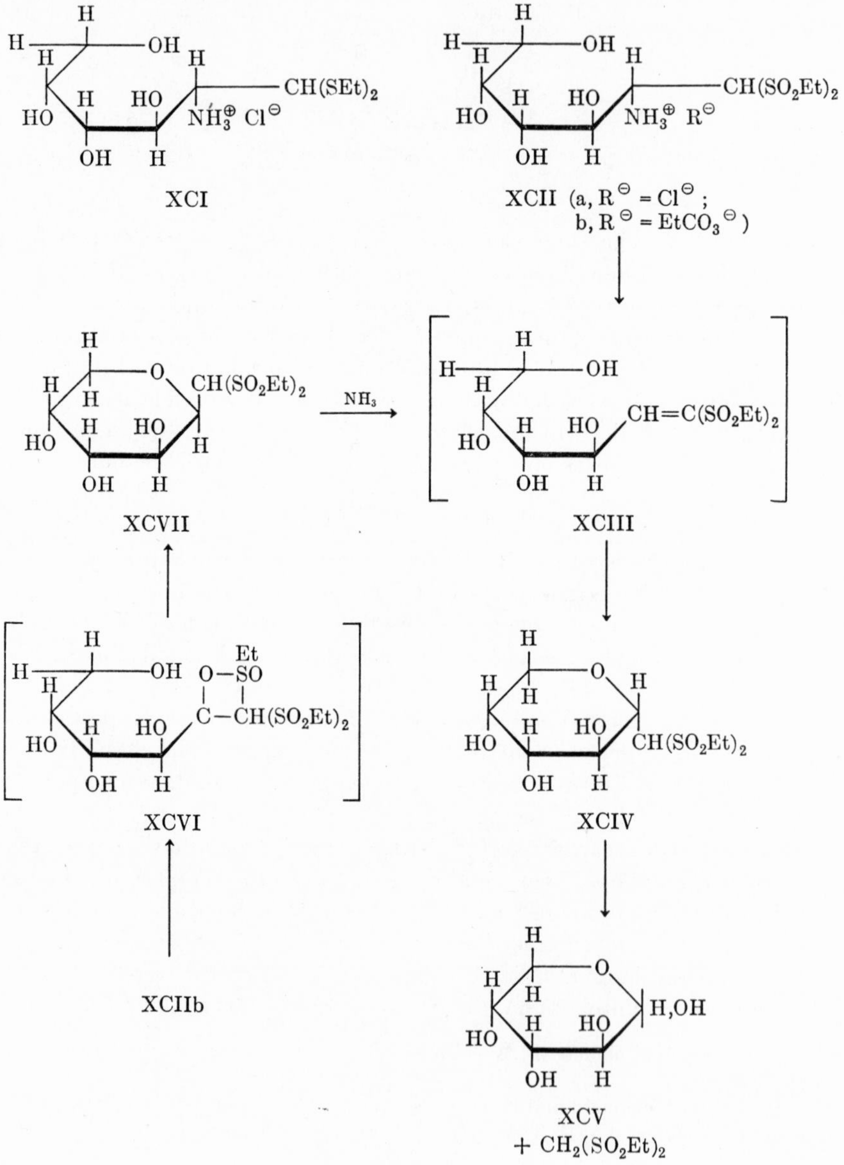

XCI

XCII (a, $R^\ominus = Cl^\ominus$;
b, $R^\ominus = EtCO_3{}^\ominus$)

XCVII

XCIII

XCVI

XCIV

XCIIb

XCV
+ $CH_2(SO_2Et)_2$

nyl)methyl 1-deoxy-β-D-arabinopyranoside (XCVII). It is believed that
XCVII arises from XCIIb as a result of neighboring-group participation,
with inversion to give the intermediate XCVI, which then cyclizes (with a
second inversion) to give a product (XCVII) with the D-*arabino* configuration. Since XCIV (with one axial substituent in the "preferred" conformation) is more stable than XCVII (with two axial substituents), the isomerization XCVII → XCIV readily takes place, by way of the intermediate
XCIII. Prolonged treatment of both XCVII and XCIV thus gives complete conversion to D-arabinose. Substituents in the aldohexose molecule
may stabilize some of the intermediates in the above reactions, and derivatives with the structures of XCII and XCIII have been isolated from the
oxidation products of diethyl dithioacetals, in addition to cyclic products
with the structures XCIV and XCVII. For example, from D-glucose, the
derivative XCVIII can be prepared; this yields XCIX on treatment with
ammonia, followed by acetylation. The same derivative is formed[192] on oxidation of 2-acetamido-3,4,5,6-tetra-O-acetyl-2-deoxy-D-glucose diethyl dithioacetal (C).

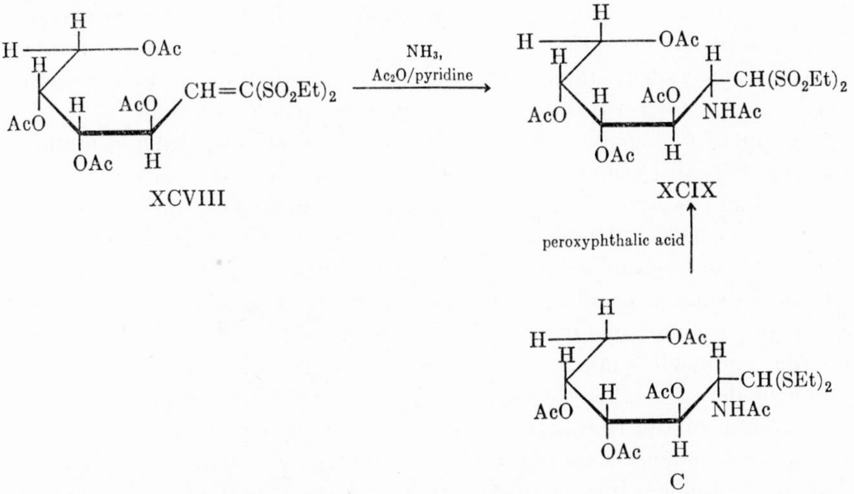

Aminodeoxyalditols have a potential importance in the determination of
amino sugars in oligo- and poly-saccharides, the saccharides being hydrolyzed and the resulting monosaccharides being subsequently reduced to the
alditols. The 2-amino-2-deoxy-D-glucitol thus formed (from saccharides
containing residues of 2-amino-2-deoxy-D-glucose) readily gives the bright
yellow N-(2,4-dinitrophenyl) derivative, which can be easily identified and
isolated by chromatography.[194]

(194) S. Leskowitz and E. A. Kabat, *J. Am. Chem. Soc.*, **76**, 4887 (1954).

Oxidation of 2-amino-2-deoxy-D-glucose, either with mercuric oxide[195] or with oxygen in the presence of platinum oxide catalyst,[196] gives 2-amino-2-deoxy-D-gluconic acid. The molecule is stabilized by dipolar-ion formation[197] ($\Delta H - 11.5 \pm 1$ k.cal./mole) in neutral solution, and contrasts with D-gluconic acid in having no tendency to form a lactone. In acidic solution, or when the amino group is substituted, 1,5-lactone formation takes place readily if the C5-hydroxyl group is free. A 1,4-lactone is formed if the C5-hydroxyl group is substituted and the C4-hydroxyl group is free.

7. *Oxidation and Degradation*

The molecule of 2-amino-2-deoxy-D-glucose is considerably stabilized in aqueous solution as the hydrochloride salt, and it undergoes but little degradation (even at 100°) in 7 N hydrochloric acid, although evaporation in the presence of other sugars or amino acids leads to a considerable loss of hexosamine.[198] Free 2-amino-2-deoxy-D-glucose readily rearranges and becomes degraded in aqueous solution under physiological conditions,[199] resembling, in this respect, D-fructose more than D-glucose. The reaction is complex and, although D-fructosazine and 5-(hydroxymethyl)-2-furaldehyde have been detected amongst the products, the over-all reactions are not yet fully understood. The presence of a N-acetyl group stabilizes the molecule and, under similar conditions, 2-acetamido-2-deoxy-D-glucose undergoes but little autoxidative degradation in aqueous solution.[199]

Treatment of benzyl 2-(N-benzyloxycarbonyl)amino-2-deoxy-α-D-glucopyranoside with oxygen in the presence of platinum oxide catalyst causes oxidation at C6; hydrogenolysis of the substituents yields 2-amino-2-deoxy-D-glucuronic acid.[64] Under similar conditions of oxidation, the N-acetyl derivative is less stable than the N-benzyloxycarbonyl derivative, and complete degradation of the molecule occurs. Glycosides of 2-amino-2-deoxy-D-glucuronic acid are remarkably resistant to acidic hydrolysis, and the free acid itself is much more stable toward mineral acids than are other uronic acids.

Oxidation of the free hexosamines and their N-acetyl derivatives with sodium metaperiodate is not limited to scission of glycol grouping and 1-ol, 2-amine groupings; further oxidation occurs, the extent of which depends on the concentrations, temperature, and pH of the reactants.[200-203] Struc-

(195) H. Pringsheim and G. Ruschmann, *Ber.*, **48**, 680 (1915).

(196) K. Heyns and W. Koch, *Chem. Ber.*, **86**, 110 (1953).

(197) D. B. Hope and P. W. Kent, *J. Chem. Soc.*, 1831 (1955).

(198) F. G. Fischer and H. J. Nebel, *Z. physiol. Chem., Hoppe-Seyler's*, **302**, 10 (1955).

(199) K. Heyns, C.-M. Koch and W. Koch, *Z. physiol. Chem., Hoppe-Seyler's*, **296**, 121 (1954).

(200) R. W. Jeanloz and E. Forchielli, *J. Biol. Chem.*, **188**, 361 (1951).

tural inferences from such oxidation data thus need to be interpreted with care. Glycosides of 2-amino-2-deoxy-D-glucose are also liable to be subject[200] to "overoxidation," although this can be limited by operating under controlled conditions.[156, 200] 2-Acetamido-2-deoxy-D-glucitol derivatives behave normally on periodate oxidation, and 2-acetamido-2-deoxy-D-glucitol itself is degraded to a triose derivative, 2-acetamido-2-deoxy-D-glycerose (CI), resistant to further oxidation, which can be reduced[177] to crystalline 2-acetamido-2-deoxyglyceritol (2-acetamido-1,3-propanediol; CII). The normal behavior of these alditol derivatives on periodate oxidation renders

$$
\begin{array}{cc}
\text{CHO} & \text{CH}_2\text{OH} \\
| & | \\
\text{HC--NHAc} & \text{H--C--NHAc} \\
| & | \\
\text{CH}_2\text{OH} & \text{CH}_2\text{OH} \\
\text{CI} & \text{CII}
\end{array}
$$

them particularly useful in structural studies,[177] as an alternative to the older techniques, such as methylation.

Oxidation of 2-acetamido-2-deoxy-D-glucose derivatives with hypoiodite at 0° proceeds quantitatively, without side reactions, and is satisfactory as a procedure for end-group assay in oligosaccharides containing amino sugar residues.[177] The possibility that (1 → 3)-linked disaccharides may be degraded under the reaction conditions must not be overlooked.

Triketohydrindene hydrate (ninhydrin) degrades 2-amino-2-deoxy-D-glucose to the related pentose (D-arabinose).[204] This degradation appears to be a general reaction of 2-amino-2-deoxy sugars and is the basis of a very useful method developed[52] for the identification of small amounts of amino sugars, by means of which assignment of the amino sugar to a particular epimeric pair may be made.

Deamination of the hexosamine molecule occurs on heating it with alkali,[205] and determination of the ammonia evolved is the basis of one quantitative method for the determination of 2-amino-2-deoxy-D-glucose.[206] Deamination of 2-amino-2-deoxy-D-glucose with nitrous acid leads to the formation of 2,5-anhydro-D-mannose ("chitose"), which can be isolated as the crystalline diphenylhydrazone.[207] Reduction of 2,5-anhydro-D-man-

(201) A. Neuberger, J. Chem. Soc., 47 (1941).

(202) D. Aminoff and W. T. J. Morgan, Biochem. J., 44, xxi (1949).

(203) H. Masamune and Z. Yosizawa, Tôhoku J. Exptl. Med., 55, 43 (1951).

(204) S. Gardell, F. Heijkenskjöld and A. Rochnarlund, Acta Chem. Scand., 4, 970 (1950).

(205) W. T. J. Morgan, Biochem. J., 30, 909 (1936).

(206) M. V. Tracey, Biochem. J., 52, 265 (1952).

(207) S. Akiya and T. Osawa, Yakugaku Zasshi, 74, 1259 (1954); Chem. Abstracts, 49, 14649 (1955); A. B. Grant, New Zealand J. Sci. Technol., 37B, 509 (1956).

nose yields crystalline 2,5-anhydro-D-mannitol,[208] the structure of which has been firmly established.

The molecular environment of the carbonium-cation intermediate in deamination reactions determines the nature of the product.[209] An effective illustration of this fact is found in the variety of reaction patterns observed in the deamination of 2-amino-2-deoxy derivatives of D-glucitol, D-glucose, and D-gluconic acid. In 2-amino-2-deoxy-D-glucose, the ring-oxygen atom is in a sterically favorable position for 2,5-anhydro ring-formation, with Walden inversion to give CIV from the carbonium-ion intermediate CIII.

CIII   CIV

The cation CV, initially formed on deamination of the corresponding alditol, is stabilized by proton ejection, to give the enolic form of 2-deoxy-D-glucose (CVI), which subsequently ketonizes to give CVII.

CV   CVI   CVII

During the deamination of 2-amino-2-deoxy-D-gluconic acid, it is probable that the carboxyl group is involved in a participation reaction with the carbonium cation CVIII from the side of the molecule opposite to the departing diazo group, to give an intermediate CIX with the D-*manno* con-

CVIII   CIX   CX

---

(208) B. C. Bera, A. B. Foster and M. Stacey, *J. Chem. Soc.*, 4531 (1956).

(209) A. B. Foster, *Chem. & Ind.* (London), 627 (1955).

figuration, which subsequently cyclizes with a second inversion at C2, to give 2,5-anhydro-D-gluconic acid (CX). This net retention of configuration resembles the behavior of amino acids on deamination.[210]

Deamination of the methyl 2-amino-2-deoxy-D-glucopyranosides is dependent on the configuration at the glycosidic center, the α anomer apparently reacting more slowly than the β anomer.[211]

V. 2-AMINO-2-DEOXY-D-GALACTOSE

2-Amino-2-deoxy-D-galactose has been less extensively studied than the D-glucose analog, but the two hexosamines exhibit close similarities in most of their reactions. 2-Amino-2-deoxy-D-galactose can be N-acetylated with acetic anhydride in the presence of a basic, ion-exchange resin,[93] and O-acyl derivatives can be formed under the usual conditions. Enzymic synthesis of the N-acetyl derivative is possible by acetyl transfer from acetyl-coenzyme A or acetylphosphate in the presence of a pigeon-liver[101, 102] or a *Clostridium kluyveri*[103] enzyme. 2-Amino-2-deoxy-D-galactosyl phosphate is elaborated by the action of an enzyme (probably galactokinase) from *Saccharomyces fragilis* on a substrate of the hexosamine and adenosinetriphosphoric acid.[212]

2-Acetamido-3,4,6-tri-O-acetyl-2-deoxy-α-D-galactosyl bromide, like the D-*gluco* analog, is unstable,[213] but the corresponding (stable) chloride is readily prepared from 2-acetamido-1,3,4,6-tetra-O-acetyl-2-deoxy-α,β-D-galactose with hydrogen chloride in acetic acid.[214] It readily gives β-D-glycosides with alcohols, and undergoes N-acetyl migration under conditions similar to those for the D-*gluco* analog (LIX → LX), to yield 1,3,4,6-tetra-O-acetyl-2-amino-2-deoxy-D-galactose hydrochloride. p-Nitrophenyl 2-acetamido-2-deoxy-β-D-galactopyranoside, prepared from the corresponding chloride, has been used as a substrate for enzymic studies; β-D-glycosidases from almond emulsin and ram testis were shown to hydrolyze the glycoside, but at only a quarter of the rate of that of the D-*gluco* analog.[215]

The recent researches of Jeanloz[6] have made available most of the (theoretically possible) methylated derivatives of 2-amino-2-deoxy-D-galactose.

The diethyl dithioacetal of 2-amino-2-deoxy-D-galactose (and related acetyl derivatives) has been prepared[191, 216] and it is of potential value as a

(210) P. Brewster, F. Hiron, E. D. Hughes, C. K. Ingold and P. A. D. Rao, *Nature*, **160**, 178 (1950).

(211) A. B. Foster, E. F. Martlew and M. Stacey, *Chem. & Ind.* (London), 825 (1953).

(212) C. E. Cardini and L. F. Leloir, *Arch. Biochem. Biophys.*, **45**, 55 (1953); *J. Biol. Chem.*, **225**, 317 (1957).

(213) M. Stacey, *J. Chem. Soc.*, 272 (1944).

(214) R. Heyworth and D. H. Leaback, *Chem. & Ind.* (London), 1145 (1958).

(215) R. Heyworth, J. Borooah and D. H. Leaback, *Biochem. J.*, **67**, 21P (1957).

(216) M. L. Wolfrom and K. Onodera, *J. Am. Chem. Soc.*, **79**, 4737 (1957).

reference compound for studies on the mercaptolysis of polysaccharides.[51, 217] A related acyclic derivative, 2-acetamido-3,4,5,6-tetra-O-acetyl-1,2-dideoxy-1,1-bis(ethylsulfonyl)-D-galactitol (CXI) is formed in small yield by treatment of bis(ethylsulfonyl)methyl tri-O-acetyl-β-D-lyxopyranoside (CXII) with ammonia, but D-lyxose (CXIII) constitutes the major reaction-product.[218] This observation militates against the idea of the possible formation of the intermediate[192] CXIV from CXII, since CXIV would be expected to give CXI in high yield (by addition of ammonia across the double bond, followed by O-acyl → N-acyl migration, thereby resulting in a stabilization of the molecule and preventing disproportionation). It is believed that CXI arises by virtue of direct nucleophilic attack by ammonia

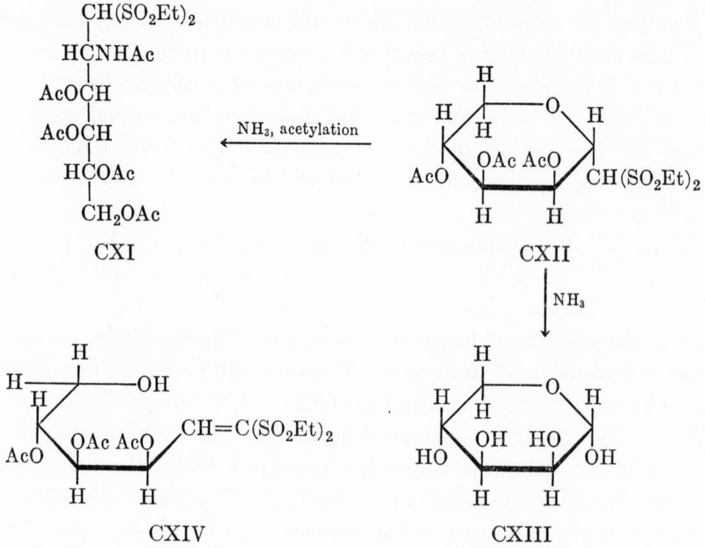

at C2 of CXII, with inversion at C2 and concurrent ring-fission. This derivative either becomes stabilized by O-acyl → N-acyl migration (to give CXI) or disproportionates to form CXIII and bis(ethylsulfonyl)methane. Alternatively, D-lyxose (CXIII) may arise directly by attack by hydroxyl ion at the cationoid C2 of CXII.

Borohydride reduction of 2-acetamido-2-deoxy-D-galactose affords 2-acetamido-2-deoxy-D-galactitol,[219] whereas oxidation of the benzyl 2-(N-benzyloxycarbonyl)amino α-D-glycoside with oxygen in the presence of platinum oxide, followed by hydrogenolysis of the blocking groups, yields

(217) A. N. O'Neill, J. Am. Chem. Soc., 77, 6324 (1955).
(218) L. Hough and T. J. Taylor, J. Chem. Soc., 970 (1956).
(219) W. R. C. Crimmin, J. Chem. Soc., 2838 (1957).

2-amino-2-deoxy-D-galacturonic acid.[220] The former derivative may be of value in structural investigations on mucopolysaccharides,[194] and the latter is important since 2-amino-2-deoxy-hexuronic acids occur naturally.[63]

VI. Detection and Determination of Amino Sugars

1. *Chromatography*

Although the paper-chromatographic behavior of N-acetylhexosamines resembles that of non-nitrogenous sugars and presents no special problems, the separation of the free hexosamines by use of the conventional basic solvents is generally unsatisfactory, resulting in poor separation, "tailing," double spots, and, often, extensive degradation of the hexosamine. Suitable acidic (acetic acid) and basic (pyridine) solvent systems for separation of the free hexosamines have been recommended[198, 221-224]; these permit the separation of 2-amino-2-deoxy-D-glucose and 2-amino-2-deoxy-D-galactose (a) from each other and (b) from uronic acids and amino acids present in tissue hydrolyzates. A quantitative, paper-chromatographic procedure for 5–20 μg. of hexosamines has been developed[198] which uses 2,3,5-triphenyl-2-H-tetrazolium hydroxide or ninhydrin as the detecting reagent. Glycosides of the N-acylated hexosamines do not react with aniline hydrogen phthalate, ammoniacal silver nitrate, or ninhydrin, but they may be detected on paper chromatograms—either by the action of chlorine (followed by treatment with benzidine–potassium iodide[145]) or with a glycol-splitting reagent, for example, sodium periodate–potassium permanganate.[156, 225] Other amino derivatives must be absent before the former reagent may be satisfactorily used. Paper-chromatographic separations based on ninhydrin degradation have already been described (see p. 259).

The use of acidic ion-exchange columns continues to find wide application in the field of amino sugars, both for the resolution of complex hydrolyzates prior to analysis[11, 13, 41, 62, 226-230] and for preparative purposes.[93] Neutral sugar-derivatives are not retained by the column, but free hexosamines

(220) K. Heyns and M. Beck, *Chem. Ber.*, **90**, 2443 (1957).

(221) H. Masamune and Z. Yosizawa, *Tôhoku J. Exptl. Med.*, **59**, 1 (1953).

(222) W. J. Payne and R. J. Kieber, *Arch. Biochem. Biophys.*, **52**, 1 (1954).

(223) R. L. Consden, L. E. Glynn and W. M. Stanier, *Biochem. J.*, **55**, 248 (1953).

(224) F. G. Fischer and H. Dörfel, *Z. physiol. Chem., Hoppe-Seyler's*, **301**, 224 (1955).

(225) R. U. Lemieux and H. F. Bauer, *Anal. Chem.*, **26**, 920 (1954).

(226) S. Gardell, *Acta. Chem. Scand.*, **7**, 207 (1953).

(227) J. E. Eastoe, *Nature*, **173**, 540 (1954).

(228) C. J. M. Rondle and W. T. J. Morgan, *Biochem. J.*, **59**, xiii (1955).

(229) N. Hiyama, H. Masamune and M. Maki, *Tôhoku J. Exptl. Med.*, **55**, 333 (1952).

(230) B. Weissman, P. Sampson and A. Linker, *J. Biol. Chem.*, **208**, 417 (1954).

can be separated from one another, and from amino acids, by graded elution with mineral acid.[62]

2. Colorimetric Methods

A colorimetric method for determination of hexosamines has been proposed[206]; it involves treatment of the hexosamine with alkali, the ammonia evolved being determined with Nessler reagent. Other methods[227, 231] depend on measurement of the color developed on reaction of the hexosamine with ninhydrin, following elution from an ion-exchange column. The analytical procedures most widely used for determination of hexosamines, however, remain those based on the Morgan–Elson[232] and Elson–Morgan[233] methods for N-acylhexosamines and free hexosamines, respectively.

a. *The Morgan–Elson and Elson–Morgan Reactions*—The red color produced by various N-acetylhexosamine derivatives on treating with acidic p-dimethylaminobenzaldehyde, after pretreatment with alkali, is the basis of the *Morgan–Elson* reaction[232] for determining 2-acetamido-2-deoxy-D-glucose and 2-acetamido-2-deoxy-D-galactose. The determination of the free amino sugars in tissue hydrolyzates is rendered possible by initial N-acetylation followed by the usual colorimetric determination[234, 235] (when other sugars and amino acids do not interfere).

In a detailed study of the original methods,[236] it was observed that the presence of borate buffer increases the intensity of the color in the reaction, thus permitting the development of a more sensitive analytical method.[237]

The closely related *Elson–Morgan* reaction for the determination of 2-amino-2-deoxy-D-glucose and 2-amino-2-deoxy-D-galactose involves successive treatment with alkaline 2,4-pentanedione and the Ehrlich reagent to produce a red color. This has received further investigation,[238-240] and the two hexosamines were found to produce similar color intensities. This finding contrasts with their behavior in the Morgan–Elson reaction, where 2-acetamido-2-deoxy-D-galactose produces only 23 % of the color given by 2-acetamido-2-deoxy-D-glucose, and a difference method for the determination of the two hexosamines in the presence of each other can be applied.[235] The observation that, in the presence of borate buffer, the colors given by

(231) S. Moore and W. H. Stein, *J. Biol. Chem.*, **211**, 907 (1954).

(232) W. T. J. Morgan and L. A. Elson, *Biochem. J.*, **28**, 988 (1934).

(233) L. A. Elson and W. T. J. Morgan, *Biochem. J.*, **27**, 1824 (1933).

(234) W. R. Smithies, *Biochem. J.*, **53**, xxix (1953).

(235) S. Roseman and I. Daffner, *Anal. Chem.*, **28**, 1743 (1956).

(236) D. Aminoff, W. T. J. Morgan and W. M. Watkins, *Biochem. J.*, **51**, 379 (1952).

(237) J. L. Reissig, J. L. Strominger and L. F. Leloir, *J. Biol. Chem.*, **217**, 959 (1955).

(238) R. Belcher, A. J. Nutten and C. M. Sambrook, *Analyst.*, **79**, 201 (1954).

(239) C. J. M. Rondle and W. T. J. Morgan, *Biochem. J.*, **61**, 586 (1955).

(240) J. P. Johnston, A. G. Ogston and J. E. Stanier, *Analyst*, **76**, 88 (1951).

the two hexosamines are diminished to 75% and 50%, respectively, has resulted in another difference-method for their determination.[241] Non-nitrogenous sugars and amino acids do not interfere in the Elson–Morgan estimation *singly*, but high values are often obtained when compounds of both kinds are present.[242, 243]

The nature of the chromogens formed during the alkaline treatment of N-acetylhexosamines in the Morgan–Elson test have been variously described as pyrrolines, oxazolines (formed by intramolecular reaction), or pyrazines (produced by intermolecular condensation),[8] but no crystalline derivatives were isolated in the early work. It was observed[244] that *at least two* compounds are formed when 2-acetamido-2-deoxy-D-glucose is treated with hot, dilute sodium carbonate solution, but the use of chromatographic techniques[245, 246] has shown at least three chromogens to be formed. Two of the products, Chromogens I and II, correspond to anhydro-2-acetamido-2-deoxy-D-glucose derivatives, and Chromogen III corresponds to a dianhydro derivative. Although the sirupy Chromogen I is the major product of alkaline treatment under the usual conditions (0.05 N sodium carbonate at 100°), further heating of 2-acetamido-2-deoxy-D-glucose, either directly or in a number of high-boiling solvents, gives crystalline Chromogen III as the chief product. It appears that Chromogen I (which is initially formed by heat treatment, together with a little Chromogen II) gives Chromogen III by dehydration on further heating. The alkali seems merely to accelerate the reaction.

All three chromogens are optically active, and their infrared absorption spectra indicate that they all possess an exocyclic —NH—CO— linkage. This observation rules out the possibility of a pyrrolidine, an oxazoline, or a pyrazine structure; and high-vacuum distillation of the chromogen mixture yields a crystalline, optically inactive, Ehrlich-positive product identified as 3-acetamidofuran (CXX). The formation of the furan ring is explained in terms of dehydration of an initially formed furanoid derivative CXV to form Chromogen I or II in the first instance, followed by loss of a second molecule of water from a molecule of Chromogen I, to give Chromogen III (CXIX).

Chromogens I and III were found to contain, respectively, one and two double bonds; the hydrogenated derivatives gave no reaction with the Ehrlich reagent. Chromogen III was formulated as 3-acetamido-5-(1,2-dihydroxyethyl)furan (CXIX), and was found to be identical with the syn-

(241) M. V. Tracey, *Biochim. et Biophys. Acta*, **17**, 159 (1955).
(242) J. Immers and E. Vasseur, *Acta Chem. Scand.*, **6**, 363 (1952).
(243) N. F. Boas, *J. Biol. Chem.*, **204**, 553 (1953).
(244) P. G. Stanley, *Australian J. Exptl. Biol. Med. Sci.*, **31**, 187 (1953).
(245) R. Kuhn and G. Krüger, *Chem. Ber.*, **89**, 1473 (1956).
(246) R. Kuhn and G. Krüger, *Chem. Ber.*, **90**, 264 (1957).

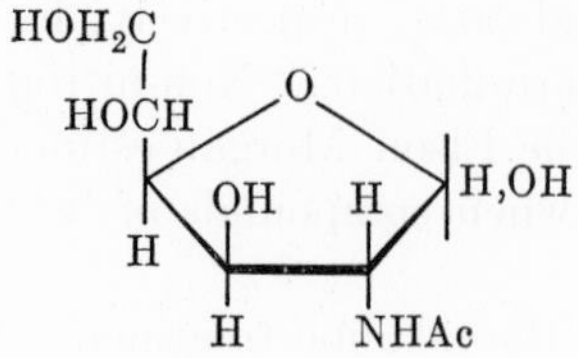

thetically prepared compound. Since, with the exception of that at C5, all asymmetric centers in the hexosamine are destroyed, it is seen that 2-acetamido-2-deoxy-D-galactose should give the same chromogen; this has been shown experimentally to be the case. The structures of Chromogens I and II have not been assigned with certainty, but the structures CXVII and CXVIII seem the most probable, with CXVI as a further possibility.

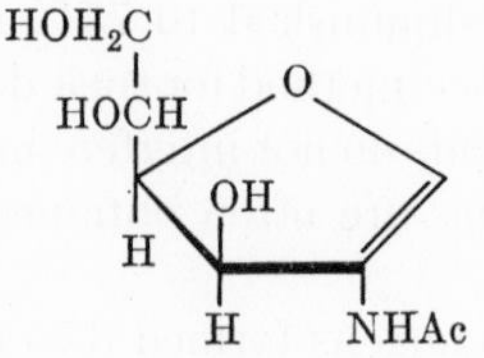

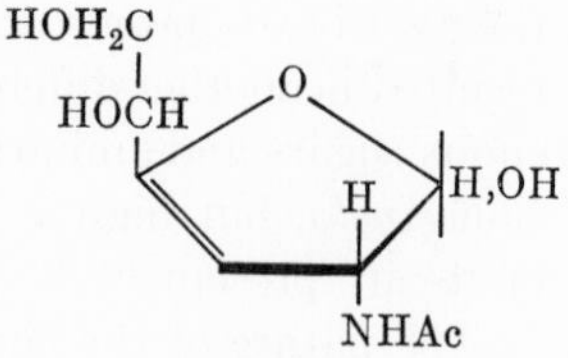

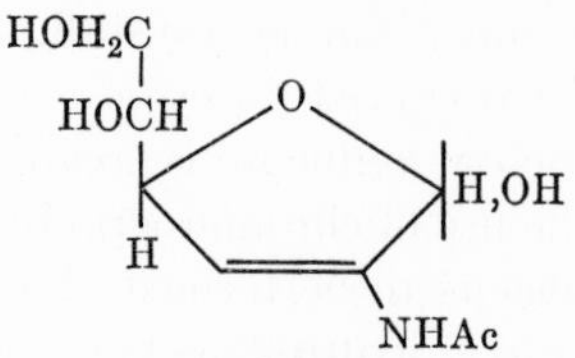

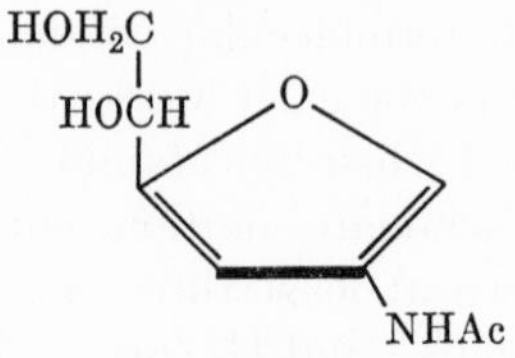

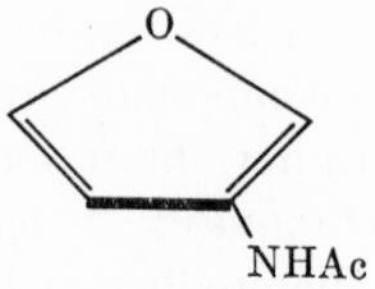

Since the course of chromogen formation involves 2-acetamido-2-deoxy-D-glucofuranose or 2-acetamido-2-deoxy-D-galactofuranose as an intermediate, the failure of alkali-stable glycopyranosides to respond to the test is understandable. An alkali-stable 4-O-substituent will likewise prevent furanose formation; it has been observed that (a) methylated derivatives of 2-acetamido-2-deoxy-D-glucose which contain a C4-methoxy group[177, 247] and (b) certain 4-O-substituted 2-acetamido-2-deoxy-D-*gluco* oligosaccharides respond weakly, if at all, to the Morgan–Elson test.[248] The presence of substituents at C6 has but little influence on chromogen formation,[177, 247, 248] and such compounds as 2-acetamido-2,6-dideoxy-L-mannose[7] and 2-acetamido-2-deoxy-D-xylose[38] also react in the test. The nature of the N-substituent is not critical, since chromogen formation also takes place with N-benzoyl, N-formyl, N-(ethoxycarbonyl), N-trimethylacetyl, N-p-tolylsulfonyl, N-methyl, and N-isopropyl derivatives, and with compounds in which the acetamido group has been replaced by a ureido or an amino acid residue. 3-Acetamido-3-deoxy- and 6-acetamido-6-deoxy-hexoses do not react in this test.[191]

In contrast to the non-reaction of 4-O-substituted 2-acetamido-2-deoxy sugars, 3-O-substituted derivatives react *far more readily* (to give Chromo-

(247) R. W. Jeanloz and M. Trémège, *Federation Proc.*, **15**, 282 (1956).
(248) R. Kuhn, A. Gauhe and H. H. Baer, *Chem. Ber.*, **87**, 1138 (1954).

gen I) than does the parent N-acetylated hexosamine.[248, 249] The 3-O-substituent is eliminated in the reaction, giving high colorimetric values in the test (as compared with the value given by 2-acetamido-2-deoxy-D-glucose).[247] One of the steps in the formation of Chromogen I involves the formation of a double bond between C3 and either C4 or C2, with elimination of water (or, in the case of a 3-methyl ether, of methanol). Similarly, a saccharide is eliminated from a $(1 \rightarrow 3)$-linked oligosaccharide, and acetic acid is eliminated from a 3-acetate ester. It is believed that elimination of methanol, acetic acid, or a saccharide from the molecule takes place more readily than elimination of water. An instance of the facile elimination of the 3-O-substituent is observed when 2-acetamido-1,3,4,6-tetra-O-acetyl-2-deoxy-D-glucose is treated with cold, methanolic barium methoxide; Chromogen I is formed readily, but some of the acetyl derivative is saponified and the resultant 2-acetamido-2-deoxy-D-glucose reacts only slowly to give Chromogen I. A striking example of the influence of a 3-O-substituent in promoting chromogen formation is afforded by a comparison of the behavior of the two disaccharides 2-acetamido-2-deoxy-6-O-(β-D-galactopyranosyl)-D-glucose and 2-acetamido-2-deoxy-3-O-(β-D-galactopyranosyl)-D-glucose (lacto-N-biose I) on treatment with dilute sodium carbonate solution.[248] The $(1 \rightarrow 6)$-linked disaccharide gives a D-galactopyranosyl derivative of Chromogen I under the usual conditions (0.05 N sodium carbonate at 100° for 3–4 min.), whereas the $(1 \rightarrow 3)$ isomer gives Chromogen I itself (with elimination of D-galactose), the reaction taking place with great readiness; a few minutes at room temperature in the presence of a trace of alkali is sufficient for this to occur. The fact that many mucopolysaccharides give a positive Morgan–Elson test although they contain pyranosidically linked 2-amino-2-deoxy-D-glucose may be rationalized in terms of the reactions studied by Kenner and coworkers.[250, 251] It was shown that 3-O-alkyl- or 3-O-glycosyl-hexoses readily eliminate the 3-O-substituent on treatment with cold, dilute alkali, giving a saccharinic acid derivative. 4-O-Substituted aldoses, on the other hand, must first give the corresponding ketoses (by a Lobry de Bruyn–Alberda van Ekenstein rearrangement) before elimination of the 4-O-substituent and formation of an isosaccharinic acid derivative can take place, and this requires more vigorous conditions. Under conditions leading to almost complete elimination of a 4-O-substituent, 2-O-substituted derivatives have been shown to be virtually unaffected.[252-254]

(249) R. Kuhn, H. H. Baer and A. Gauhe, *Chem. Ber.*, **87**, 1553 (1954).

(250) J. Kenner, *Chem. & Ind.* (London), 727 (1955).

(251) J. Kenner and G. N. Richards, *J. Chem. Soc.*, 3019 (1957), and earlier papers in this series.

(252) R. Kuhn, H. H. Baer and A. Gauhe, *Chem. Ber.*, **88**, 1135 (1955).

(253) R. Kuhn, H. H. Baer and A. Gauhe, *Ann.*, **611**, 242 (1958).

(254) R. L. Whistler and W. M. Corbett, *J. Am. Chem. Soc.*, **77**, 3822 (1955).

Thus, the conventional alkaline treatment (in the Morgan–Elson test) of an oligosaccharide containing amino sugar residues will allow degradation of the molecule from the reducing end-group, the rate depending on the nature of the linkage between the penultimate glycosyl residue and the terminal group. $(1 \rightarrow 3)$-Linkages will undergo rapid scission, $(1 \rightarrow 4)$-linkages will be cleaved more slowly, and $(1 \rightarrow 2)$-linkages will be resistant. Chromogen formation can take place whenever a 2-acetamido-2-deoxyhexose residue is the terminal reducing group, provided that it is not linked $(1 \rightarrow 4)$ to the penultimate group. Chromogen formation will take place particularly readily, however, if this linkage is $(1 \rightarrow 3)$.

Whilst there appears to be limited scope at present for the utilization of these observations in determinations of polysaccharide structures, they can be of value when the Morgan–Elson test is applied to oligosaccharides containing amino sugar residues, as the work on the oligosaccharides from human milk[2] has shown. Obviously, no simple relation exists between a positive test and the presence of free 2-acetamido-2-deoxyhexose, but much information may be culled by a consideration of all the factors outlined above.

Much less is known about the nature of the chromogens formed on heating 2-amino-2-deoxy-D-glucose with alkaline 2,4-pentanedione (the Elson–Morgan test),[233] but it is believed that they differ significantly from those formed in the Morgan–Elson test; the red compounds finally produced have different ultraviolet absorption maxima. In this reaction, much appears to depend upon the procedure used in (a) the reaction with the 2,4-pentanedione, (b) the conditions of treatment with the Ehrlich reagent, and (c) the wavelength at which the red coloration is measured. Under Nilsson's conditions,[255] maximal absorption takes place at $> \lambda 530$ mμ, but, under the conditions of Belcher and coworkers,[238] the maximal absorption is at 512 mμ. These observations would suggest that a different chromogen predominates under each set of conditions.

In a recent investigation,[256] it was found that the steam-volatile chromogen earlier mentioned by Schloss[257] is 2-methylpyrrole; it was formed in about 10 % yield under conditions similar to those of Nilsson; and it was found to be intensely chromogenic, giving $\lambda_{max} = 544$ mμ with the Ehrlich reagent. A second chromogen, not volatile in steam, was isolated and found to be 3-acetyl-2-methylpyrrole, but it had less than 1 % of the chromogenic activity of 2-methylpyrrole having $\lambda_{max} = 570$ mμ and was thus considered to be insignificant in estimates of total production of color. Earlier work by Gottschalk[258]—which had indicated that a component (on paper chro-

(255) J. Nilsson, *Biochem. Z.*, **285**, 386 (1936).
(256) J. W. Cornforth and M. E. Firth, *J. Chem. Soc.*, 1091 (1958).
(257) B. Schloss, *Anal. Chem.*, **23**, 1321 (1951).
(258) A. Gottschalk, Personal communication quoted in Ref. 256.

matograms) corresponding to 3-acetyl-2-methylpyrrole is the major chromogen—had not taken into account the volatility of 2-methylpyrrole; this had presumably escaped *before* treatment with the Ehrlich reagent. The mechanism proposed by Cornforth and Firth[256] for the formation of 2-methylpyrrole involves initial formation of 3-acetyl-2-methyl-5-(tetrahydroxybutyl)pyrrole (CXXI)[259] by condensation of 2-amino-2-deoxy-D-glucose with 2,4-pentanedione, followed by loss of the 3-acetyl group from an intermediate (CXXII), to form the pyrrole-ring compound (CXXIII), the tetrahydroxybutyl group being lost at some stage by a reverse aldol reaction.

where R = $(CHOH)_3$—CH_2OH

CXXI   CXXII   CXXIII

Under different analytical conditions,[238] with maximal absorption of the colored complex appearing at 512 mμ, it would appear that a *different* chromogen plays the significant role. A chromogen giving a color absorbing at this wavelength was reported by Schloss[257] and by Anastassiadis and Common[260]; the latter authors showed that its formation is inhibited by an excess of 2,4-pentanedione, but its nature is unknown.

Substitition at the hydroxyl group of C4 or C6 with a methyl group has little effect on the behavior of 2-amino-2-deoxy-D-glucose in the Elson–Morgan test,[157] although a 6-phosphate substituent causes a shift in the absorption maximum of the colored complex (see p. 239). Substitution with a 3-O-methyl group causes an increase in the color intensity, together with[157] a shift in the absorption maximum from 512 mμ to 503 mμ. Other chromogens have been reported[258] on the basis of chromatographic evidence, but no pure compounds have been isolated.

The isolation and characterization of 2-methylpyrrole and 3-acetyl-2-methylpyrrole as chromogens in the Elson–Morgan reaction has represented a major advance in our understanding of the reactions involved, but it clearly does not contribute a complete account of the situation.

VII. Oligosaccharides Containing Amino Sugars

The oligosaccharides containing amino sugar residues have received considerable attention during the last few years, and numerous compounds of this type are now known (see Table III). Degradation of certain polysaccha-

(259) H. Pauly and E. Ludwig, *Z. physiol. Chem., Hoppe-Seyler's*, **121,** 176 (1922).

(260) P. A. Anastassiadis and R. H. Common, *Can. J. Chem.*, **31,** 1093 (1953).

rides has yielded nitrogenous di- and oligo-saccharides. In addition, there are naturally occurring oligosaccharides, and some success has been achieved in their chemical synthesis. Several nitrogenous disaccharides have been synthesized enzymically. Chemical identification and definitive proof of structure of these disaccharides has been achieved, mainly by the application of classical techniques, but also by supplementary, newer methods.

Di- and oligo-saccharides containing amino sugar residues may be conveniently divided into at least three categories: those containing (1) residues of amino sugars only, (2) non-nitrogenous residues *and* amino sugar residues, and (3) uronic acid residues *and* amino sugar residues.

1. *Saccharides Containing Amino Sugar Residues Only*

Controlled degradation of chitin has been effected by the following sequence.[261] The saccharide mixture may be separated by carbon–Celite

$$\text{Chitin} \xrightarrow[\text{(de-}N\text{-acetylation)}]{\text{KOH}} \text{chitosan} \xrightarrow{\text{H}^{\oplus}} \text{chitosaccharides}$$

$$\Big\downarrow \text{(selective acetylation)}$$

$$N\text{-acetylchitosaccharides}$$

chromatography. Alternatively, the saccharide mixture obtained by acidic hydrolysis of chitosan may be separated by elution (with acid) from Dowex-50 cation-exchange resin.[262]

2-Acetamido-4-O-(2-acetamido-2-deoxy-β-D-glucopyranosyl)-2-deoxy-D-glucose ("di-*N*-acetylchitobiose"), which has been known since 1931,[263, 264] has only recently been obtained crystalline.[265] Chitosan, its saccharide fragments, and the glycosides of 2-amino-2-deoxy-D-glucose exhibit a marked resistance to acidic hydrolysis (see p. 243). Enzymic cleavage to the di-*N*-acetylchitobiose occurs readily on treatment with the "β-acetylglucosaminidase" from *Aspergillus oryzae*[266] and, under certain conditions, the disaccharide can take part in transferase (transglycosylation) reactions.[267]

Controlled fragmentation of chitin yields, in addition to di-*N*-acetylchitobiose, a range of saccharides containing β-D-(1 → 4)-linked 2-acetamido-2-deoxy-D-glucose residues.[261]

(261) S. A. Barker, A. B. Foster, M. Stacey and J. M. Webber, *Chem. & Ind.* (London), 208 (1957); *J. Chem. Soc.*, 2218 (1958).

(262) S. T. Horowitz, H. J. Blumenthal, K. Seppala and S. Roseman, *Federation Proc.*, **14**, 229 (1955); S. T. Horowitz, H. J. Blumenthal and S. Roseman, *J. Am. Chem. Soc.*, **79**, 5046 (1957).

(263) M. Bergmann and L. Zervas, *Ber.*, **64**, 2436 (1931).

(264) L. Zechmeister and G. Tóth, *Ber.*, **64**, 2028 (1931); **65**, 161 (1932).

(265) F. Zilliken, G. A. Braun, C. S. Rose and P. György, *J. Am. Chem. Soc.*, **77**, 1296 (1955).

(266) R. Kuhn and H. Tiedemann, *Chem. Ber.*, **87**, 1141 (1954).

(267) J. M. Webber, Ph. D. Thesis, University of Birmingham, Engl. (1957).

A definitive chemical synthesis of a disaccharide containing *two* hexosamine residues remains to be achieved, but acidic reversion of 2-acetamido-2-deoxy-D-glucose at room temperature leads to the formation of a saccharide mixture containing two disaccharides which have been shown to be *2-acetamido-6-O-(2-acetamido-2-deoxy-α-* and *β-D-glucopyranosyl)-2-deoxy-D-glucose*, respectively.[177] The $-NH_3^{\oplus}$ grouping of 2-amino-2-deoxy-D-glucose in acidic solution inhibits formation of oligosaccharides by reversion, but, since the uncharged *N*-acetyl derivative is hydrolyzed very slowly at room temperature, reversion *can* take place. The β-D-linked disaccharide has a growth-factor effect for *Lactobacillus bifidus* var. *Penn.* which is about 50% of that of *N*-acetyl-lactosamine (see p. 274), whereas the α anomer is inactive. The reversion technique may be of general application in the preparation of (1 → 6)-linked disaccharides.[268, 269]

2. Saccharides Containing Residues of Amino Sugars and of Neutral, Non-nitrogenous Sugars

Several disaccharides containing one residue of an amino sugar have been synthesized by definitive chemical methods in connection with the study of the oligosaccharides from human milk. Others have only been prepared, as noted, by degradation of natural oligosaccharides.

The presence of nitrogen-containing saccharides in human milk has been known for 25 years,[270] but only in the last few years has the importance of their growth-promoting ability *in vivo* for certain strains of *Lactobacillus bifidus* been realized and investigated.[2, 271] This microorganism is an important member of the intestinal flora of infants, and it is responsible for conferring immunity against certain enteric infections.[272] The recent investigations have added valuable new techniques to the chemistry of amino sugars. Chromatography of the natural saccharide mixture revealed the series of oligosaccharides shown in Table III. Higher saccharides are also present.[252, 272a-275] The results of total hydrolysis of the saccharide mixture indicate that residues of D-glucose, D-galactose, 6-deoxy-L-galactose, and 2-amino-2-deoxy-D-glucose are the only structural units present.[276] The

(268) A. Thompson, K. Anno, M. L. Wolfrom and M. Inatome, *J. Am. Chem. Soc.*, **76**, 1309 (1954).

(269) C. N. Turton, A. Bebbington, S. Dixon and E. Pacsu, *J. Am. Chem. Soc.*, **77**, 2565 (1955).

(270) M. Polonovski and A. Lespagnol, *Bull. soc. chim. biol.*, **15**, 320 (1933).

(271) R. Kuhn, *Angew. Chem.*, **64**, 493 (1952); *Bull. soc. chim. biol.*, **40**, 297 (1958).

(272) E. Walch, *Deut. med. Wochschr.*, **81**, 661 (1956).

(272a) F. H. Malpress and F. E. Hytten, *Nature*, **180**, 1201 (1957).

(273) R. Kuhn, H. H. Baer and A. Gauhe, *Chem. Ber.*, **89**, 2514 (1956).

(274) R. Kuhn, A. Gauhe and H. H. Baer, *Chem. Ber.*, **86**, 827 (1953).

(275) R. Kuhn, A. Gauhe and H. H. Baer, *Chem. Ber.*, **87**, 289 (1954).

(276) A. Gauhe, P. György, J. R. E. Hoover, R. Kuhn, C. S. Rose, H. W. Ruelius and F. Zilliken, *Arch. Biochem. Biophys.*, **48**, 214 (1954).

trisaccharide "fucosyl-lactose" does not contain[252, 277] an amino sugar residue, but "lacto-N-tetraose," the first of these oligosaccharides to be isolated pure, contains two D-galactose residues, one D-glucose residue, and a
2-acetamido-2-deoxy-D-glucose residue.[274] Evidence for the structure was
obtained by hydrolysis of the permethylated "lacto-N-tetraitol" followed
by comparison of the resulting methylated monosaccharides with known
derivatives.[176]

TABLE III

Oligosaccharides of Human Milk

Oligosaccharide	Amount in mixture, %	$R_{lact.}$
Fucosyl-lactose	10	0.73
Lacto-N-tetraose	15	0.36
Lacto-N-fucopentaose I	8	0.27
Lacto-N-fucopentaose II	4	0.19
Lacto-N-difucohexaose	7	0.11

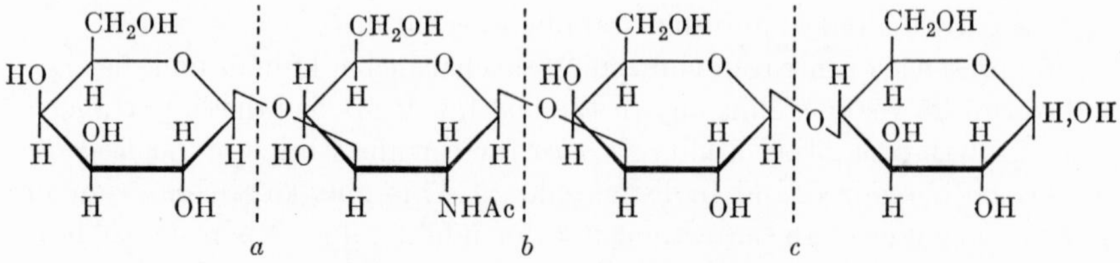

"Lacto-N-tetraose"

Further evidence was provided by a study of the products of partial,
acidic hydrolysis.[275] Thus, cleavage at b gave lactose plus a new disaccharide, "lacto-N-biose I" (see p. 275). Cleavage at a and c gave, in addition
to D-galactose and D-glucose, a second disaccharide ("lacto-N-biose II").
Establishment of the stuctures of the two disaccharide fragments permitted
allocation of a structure to the tetrasaccharide. Two new trisaccharides,
"lacto-N-triose II" and "lacto-N-triose I" were also obtained by cleavage
at a and c, respectively, on graded, acidic hydrolysis.[278]

Lacto-N-triose I is readily cleaved by a β-galactosidase from hog mam-
mary-gland, to give lacto-N-biose II plus galactose, establishing the configuration of the linkage at a. The positive Morgan–Elson test given by this
trisaccharide is of interest in that it results from cleavage of the reducing
unit's $(1 \rightarrow 3)$-link under the alkaline conditions of the test, thereby expos-
ing the amino sugar moiety.

(277) R. Kuhn, H. H. Baer and A. Gauhe, *Chem. Ber.*, **89,** 2513 (1956).
(278) R. Kuhn, A. Gauhe and H. H. Baer, *Chem. Ber.*, **89,** 1027 (1956).

Lacto-N-triose II[278] is split (by the "*β-N*-acetylglucosaminidase" from *Aspergillus oryzae*) into 2-acetamido-2-deoxy-D-glucose plus lactose, which would be expected on the basis of the structure proposed. Lacto-*N*-triose I is unaffected by this enzyme.

Two *pentasaccharides* occur in the mixture of milk oligosaccharides. Lacto-*N*-fucopentaose I readily gives an alkali-stable disaccharide, 2-*O*-(α-L-fucosyl)-D-galactose on alkaline degradation; knowledge of the structure of this disaccharide, together with data from methylation studies, leads to the assignment of the structure of an α-L-fucosyl-(lacto-*N*-tetraose) for the pentasaccharide.[273]

"Lacto-N-fucopentaose I"

Lacto-N-fucopentaose II also contains an α-L-fucosyl residue linked to a lacto-*N*-tetraose molecule, but in this case it is linked to C4 of the 2-acetamido-2-deoxy-D-glucose unit. The sequence and linkages were again established by hydrolysis of the permethylated saccharide alcohol.[279]

The consitution of the hexasaccharide lacto-*N*-difucohexaose has not yet been fully elucidated, but it appears to have the structure of lacto-*N*-fucopentaose I, together with an extra L-fucosyl residue, probably linked as in lacto-*N*-fucopentaose II.[253]

There is ample evidence for the presence, in milk oligosaccharides, of amino sugar-containing oligosaccharides of molecular weight higher than that of lacto-*N*-difucohexaose,[280] probably containing 2-amino-2-deoxy-D-galactose as well as 2-amino-2-deoxy-D-glucose.[281, 282] Several related, non-nitrogenous oligosaccharides have been described.[283] Partial hydrolysis of the capsular polysaccharide from strains of *Pseudomonas fluorescens* yields a crystalline tetrasaccharide containing L-fucose (2 molecular residues per molecule), D-glucose, and 2-acetamido-2-deoxy-D-glucose.[284]

6-O-(2-Acetamido-2-deoxy-β-D-glucopyranosyl)-D-glucose and 6-O-(2-acetamido-2-deoxy-β-D-glucopyranosyl)-D-galactose were synthesized[285] by the

(279) R. Kuhn, H. H. Baer and A. Gauhe, *Chem. Ber.*, **91**, 364 (1958).

(280) P. György, J. R. E. Hoover, R. Kuhn and C. S. Rose, *Arch. Biochem. Biophys.*, **48**, 209 (1954).

(281) H. W. Ruelius and M. M. Girard, *Arch. Biochem. Biophys.*, **50**, 512 (1954).

(282) E. J. Bigwood, C. Czajkowska and A. Drèze, *Biochem. J.*, **66**, 16P (1957).

(283) J. Montreuil, *Compt. rend.*, **242**, 192, 828 (1956); *Bull. soc. chim. biol.*, **39**, 395 (1957); R. Kuhn and A. Gauhe, *Ann.*, **611**, 249 (1958).

(284) R. G. Eagon and R. Dedonder, *Compt. rend.*, **241**, 579 (1955).

(285) R. Kuhn and W. Kirschenlohr, *Chem. Ber.*, **87**, 384 (1954).

reaction of 2-acetamido-3,4,6-tri-O-acetyl-2-deoxy-D-glucosyl bromide (see p. 247) with 1,2,3,4-tetra-O-acetyl-D-glucose or the corresponding D-galactose derivative, in benzene solution in the presence of a mercuric cyanide catalyst (the Koenigs–Knorr synthesis). The crystalline octaacetates resulting were readily de-O-acetylated by means of ammonia, to give the amorphous N-acetyl disaccharides. The N-benzoyl derivative of the former disaccharide and of its methyl α-glycoside have been synthesized by interaction of the oxazoline derivative (LXIII) either with 1,2,3,4-tetra-O-acetyl-β-D-glucose or with methyl 2,3,4-tri-O-acetyl-α-D-glucoside.[151]

By the Koenigs–Knorr procedure, *2-acetamido-2-deoxy-6-O-(β-D-galactopyranosyl)-D-glucose* ("*N*-acetyl-allolactosamine") was synthesized from 2,3,4,6-tetra-O-acetyl-α-D-galactosyl bromide plus 2-acetamido-1,3,4-tri-O-acetyl-2-deoxy-D-glucose.[178] The amorphous, N-acetylated disaccharide was characterized as the N^1-(p-aminobiphenylyl)glycosylamine heptaacetate. An identical derivative was prepared from the disaccharide synthesized enzymically (by *Escherichia coli*) by the transfer of the sugar moiety of phenyl β-D-galactoside to 2-acetamido-2-deoxy-D-glucose.[178]

2-Acetamido-2-deoxy-4-O-(β-D-galactopyranosyl)-D-glucose (*N*-acetyl-lactosamine) was isolated in a crude state from hydrolyzed mucin[286] (hog gastric), and was synthesized[286] in very low yield, and in an impure state, using an adaptation of Fischer's cyanohydrin synthesis (see p. 214). An improved synthesis[15] (compare Ref. 287) involved treatment of the "anilide" of 3-O-(β-D-galactopyranosyl)-D-arabinose (obtained from lactose, either by the Wohl–Zemplén degradation of the oxime or by the Ruff method from calcium lactobionate) with hydrogen cyanide, to yield the 1-phenylamino nitrile. The latter compound was hydrogenolyzed (see p. 215 and 216), to give lactosamine. N-Acetyl-lactosamine has also been isolated after graded hydrolysis of blood-group substances[288, 289] and of certain of the oligosaccharides present in human milk.[249] Enzymic synthesis of the disaccharide takes place in a medium containing lactose, 2-acetamido-2-deoxy-D-glucose, and intact cells of *Lactobacillus bifidus* var. *Penn.*[290]; cell-free extracts of *L. bifidus* produce a mixture of the β-D-(1 → 4)- and β-D-(1 → 6)-linked isomers.[291] The structure of N-acetyl-lactosamine was indicated, prior to its synthesis, by the periodate-oxidation pattern[286] and by its reaction with phenylhydrazine to yield "lactose" phenylosazone[287, 289] (with elimination

(286) Z. Yosizawa, *Tôhoku J. Exptl. Med.*, **52,** 145 (1950).

(287) R. Kuhn and W. Kirschenlohr, *Chem. Ber.*, **87,** 1547 (1954).

(288) R. H. Côté and W. T. J. Morgan, *Nature*, **178,** 1171 (1956).

(289) R. Kuhn and W. Kirschenlohr, *Chem. Ber.*, **87,** 560 (1954).

(290) F. Zilliken, P. N. Smith, C. S. Rose and P. György, *J. Biol. Chem.*, **217,** 79 (1955).

(291) F. Zilliken, P. N. Smith, C. S. Rose and P. György, *J. Biol. Chem.*, **208,** 299 (1954).

of the acetamido group). Reduction of "lactose" phenylosazone with hydrogen in the presence of palladium regenerated lactosamine,[287] but this reaction is of little value for synthetic work since the corresponding 1-amino-1-deoxy-ketose ("isolactosamine") is the major reaction-product. Degradation of N-acetyl-lactosamine to 3-O-(β-D-galactopyranosyl)-D-arabinose may also be accomplished by means of ninhydrin.[292]

Although N-acetyl-lactosamine contains a free, reducing N-acetylhexosamine residue, it does not give the Morgan–Elson reaction, since the C4-hydroxyl group is blocked with a group stable to alkali (see p. 267). Glycosidation of the disaccharide takes place readily with diazomethane, with the formation of a methyl β-glycoside.[15] Free N-acetyl-lactosamine is a powerful growth-factor for *Lactobacillus bifidus* var. *Penn.*[293]

*2-Acetamido-2-deoxy-3-*O*-(β-*D*-galactopyranosyl)-*D*-glucose* ("*Lacto-*N-*biose I*") was first isolated after partial, acidic hydrolysis of "lacto-N-tetraose" (see p. 272),[275] and it was obtained, together with four other amino sugar-containing disaccharides, after graded, acidic hydrolysis of a blood-group A substance isolated from ovarian cyst.[288] It has not yet been synthesized chemically, but an enzymic synthesis involving D-galactosyl transfer to 2-acetamido-2-deoxy-D-glucose has been achieved.[294] The disaccharide shows the extreme alkali-lability characteristic of many (1 → 3)-linked disaccharides (see p. 267), and its constitution was proved by conversion (with elimination of the acetamido group) into a phenylosazone identical with that obtained from both 3-O-(β-D-galactopyranosyl)-D-glucose and 3-O-(β-D-galactopyranosyl)-D-fructose.[249, 295]

*2-Acetamido-2-deoxy-6-*O*-(α-*D*-galactopyranosyl)-*D*-glucose* has been synthesized enzymically,[296] by using the α-galactosidase in autolyzed *Trichomonas foetus* cells to transfer the D-galactose moiety of melibiose or of phenyl α-D-galactoside to 2-acetamido-2-deoxy-D-glucose. The response of the disaccharide in the Morgan–Elson test indicates that the glycosidic linkage is neither (1 → 3) nor (1 → 4), and evidence from reactions with spray reagents indicates a (1 → 6)-linkage, an observation substantiated by the periodate-oxidation pattern. The high specific rotation (+118°) and the mode of formation indicate that the residues are α-D linked.

*2-Acetamido-2-deoxy-6-*O*-(*L*-fucopyranosyl)-*D*-glucose.* An unequivocal proof of the structure of this disaccharide (isolated from a hydrolyzate of

(292) F. Zilliken, P. N. Smith, R. M. Tomarelli and P. György, *Arch. Biochem. Biophys*, **54**, 398 (1955).

(293) R. M. Tomarelli, J. B. Hassinen, E. R. Eckhardt, R. H. Clark and F. W. Bernhardt, *Arch. Biochem. Biophys.*, **48**, 225 (1954).

(294) A. Alessandrini, E. Schmidt, F. Zilliken and P. György, *J. Biol. Chem.*, **220**, 71 (1956).

(295) R. Kuhn and H. H. Baer, *Chem. Ber.*, **87**, 1560 (1954).

(296) W. M. Watkins, *Nature*, **181**, 117 (1958).

blood-group A substance[288]) has not been reported, but the response in the Morgan–Elson reaction indicates that the linkage is neither $(1 \rightarrow 4)$ nor $(1 \rightarrow 3)$. The presence of a $(1 \rightarrow 6)$-link is supported by the color reaction with benzidine–trichloroacetic acid reagent.

2-Amino-2-deoxy-1-O-*(α-D-glucopyranosyl)-α-D-glucopyranose* (*2-Amino-α,α-trehalose, Trehalosamine*) constitutes the first example of a nonreducing, amino sugar oligosaccharide, and is also noteworthy in that it occurs as the free amino derivative and not as the *N*-acetyl amide. It is produced by a *Streptomycetes* culture and shows some antibiotic activity.[297] It exhibits the stability toward acidic hydrolysis characteristic of glycosides of amino sugars, and gives a crystalline octaacetate hydrochloride and a *N*-salicylidene azomethine; on acidic hydrolysis, it gives only D-glucose and 2-amino-2-deoxy-D-glucose. The absence of mutarotation, and the nonreducing nature of the disaccharide, indicate a $(1 \rightarrow 1)$-linkage, and a positive ninhydrin-test shows a free amino group to be present. An uptake of 4 moles

TABLE IV

Molecular Rotations of Trehaloses and Trehalosamine

Compound	$[M]_D$	$[\alpha]_D$ of octaacetate
α,α-Trehalose	$+67433$	$+162$
α,β-Trehalose	$+31518$	$+82$
β,β-Trehalose	-15575	-19
Trehalosamine	$+66490$	$+163.5$

of periodate per mole, without formaldehyde production, indicates that both units have a pyranoid ring. Comparison of the molecular rotation of trehalosamine with those of the isomers of trehalose suggests that the linkage is α,α (see Table IV).

3-O-*(2-Acetamido-2-deoxy-α-D-galactopyranosyl)-D-galactose* is one of several disaccharides obtained on hydrolysis of blood-group A substance.[288] Its reaction with alkaline 2,3,5-triphenyl-2-*H*-tetrazolium chloride indicates that the C2-hydroxyl group of the reducing-sugar moiety is not substituted. The facile formation of a monosaccharide chromogen in the Morgan–Elson test indicates a $(1 \rightarrow 3)$-linkage, and the high specific rotation $(+150°)$ suggests that the linkage is α. It is believed that the structure of the disaccharide is closely associated with the group A specificity of the parent, blood-group substance.

2-Acetamido-2-deoxy-6-O-*(α-D-galactopyranosyl)-D-galactose* has been synthesized enzymically by transfer of the sugar moiety of phenyl α-D-galactoside to 2-acetamido-2-deoxy-D-galactose.[296] The evidence for the constitu-

(297) F. Arcamone and F. Bizioli, *Gazz. chim. ital.*, **87**, 896 (1957). See Ref. 147.

tion rests on data similar to those already cited for the D-glucose analog (see p. 275).

Other Disaccharides. Amino sugar-containing di- and oligo-saccharides of undetermined structure have been demonstrated in certain enzymic, synthetic reactions.[298]

3. Saccharides Containing Residues of Amino Sugars and of Hexuronic Acids

"Disaccharides" of the hexuronic acid–hexosamine type constitute the fundamental repeating unit of many mucopolysaccharides, from which they are derived by hydrolytic degradation. Further hydrolytic treatment results generally in destruction of the uronic acid moiety of the disaccharide. Structural studies have been made on the "disaccharides" from hyaluronic acid (hyalobiouronic acid), chondroitinsulfate (chondrosine), and heparin (heparosine).

2-Amino-2-deoxy-3-O-(β-D-glucopyranosyluronic acid)-D-glucose Hydrochloride (Hyalobiouronic Acid) can be prepared from the hyaluronic acid of umbilical cord by acidic hydrolysis or by a combination of enzymic and acidic hydrolysis.[299, 300] The stability of the "disaccharide" toward acidic hydrolysis enables a good yield to be obtained from the polysaccharide, and the sparingly-soluble, dipolar ion affords ready crystallization. The structure of hyalobiouronic acid was proved[301] by oxidation of the methyl ester hydrochloride with mercuric oxide to the related 2-amino-2-deoxy-D-gluconic acid derivative, the uronic ester group of which was then reduced with sodium borohydride to give a 2-amino-2-deoxy-(D-glucosyl)-D-gluconic acid. Ninhydrin degradation of this product gave 2-O-(β-D-glucopyranosyl)-D-arabinose, identical with the product obtained by Zemplén degradation 3-O-(β-D-glucopyranosyl)-D-glucose (laminaribiose). In the Elson–Morgan test, hyalobiouronic acid gives 60 % of the color produced by 2-amino-2-deoxy-D-glucose.

Degradation of hyaluronic acid by means of the "acetylglucosaminidase" isolated from purified, testicular hyaluronidase causes scission at the amino sugar (glycosyl) residue, leaving the glucosiduronic linkages intact, to give a series of saccharides containing an even number of units, the first seven of which saccharides have been isolated by column chromatography with ion-exchange resins.[230] Hyalobiouronic acid, the first member, has already

(298) S. Srinivasan and J. H. Quastel, *Science*, **127**, 143 (1958).

(299) M. M. Rapport, B. Weissmann, A. Linker and K. Meyer, *Nature*, **168**, 996 (1951).

(300) B. Weissmann, M. M. Rapport, A. Linker and K. Meyer, *J. Biol. Chem.*, **205**, 205 (1953).

(301) B. Weissmann and K. Meyer, *J. Am. Chem. Soc.*, **74**, 4729 (1952); **76**, 1753 (1954).

been described, but the structures of the "tetrasaccharides" and higher saccharides in the series have not yet been elucidated, and the nature of the hexosamine → uronic acid linkage is still not known.

The crude, testicular-hyaluronidase preparation also contains a β-glucuronidase, and hence it degrades the mucopolysaccharide from the non-reducing end; the two enzymes, acting together, thus give total hydrolysis, to hexosamine plus uronic acid.[302] The *last* glucosiduronic linkage in the chain appears to be stable, however. A pure preparation of β-glucuronidase can be used for removing one uronic acid residue from a molecule of each member of the series of saccharides described above, to give a series containing an odd number of units—the lowest member being a "trisaccharide" with the following sequence of units.

Hexosamine → uronic acid-β-D-(1 → 3)-hexosamine

Other workers give different constants for oligosaccharides prepared similarly.[303] Care should, however, be exercised in the interpretation of results from experiments which are carried out with crude-enzyme preparations, or on systems which have not been investigated with simple, known derivatives, since these enzymes not only can effect hydrolysis, but also can cause transglycosylation.[304]

2-Amino-2-deoxy-3-O-(*β*-D-*glucopyranosyluronic acid*)-D-*galactose* (chondrosine) can be isolated from chondroitinsulfate by hydrolysis[8] or (similarly) from the non-sulfated mucopolysaccharide chondroitin[305]; and its structure was assigned initially by Masamune and coworkers[306] from the results of periodate oxidation and from the Morgan–Elson test on the *N*-acetyl amide. Unequivocal evidence for the structure was provided by Davidson and Meyer,[307] who reduced the methyl ester hydrochloride of the "disaccharide" with sodium borohydride and *N*-acetylated, to give 2-acetamido-2-deoxy-3-O-(β-D-glucopyranosyl)-D-galactitol. Hydrolysis of this product gives D-glucose, derived from the original D-glucuronic acid moiety of chondrosin, as the only reducing sugar, thereby establishing the sequence of units in the "disaccharide." 2-Amino-2-deoxy-D-galactose had been identified in chondrosine by earlier workers.[8] Oxidative deamination (with ninhydrin) of chondrosine methyl ester gives a (glucopyranosyluronic acid)-pentose, the methyl ester of which was reduced to a 2-O-glucopyranosylpentitol, as in-

(302) A. Linker, K. Meyer and B. Weissmann, *J. Biol. Chem.*, **213**, 237 (1955).

(303) E. Schutte and H. Greiling, *Z. physiol. Chem., Hoppe-Seyler's*, **302**, 55 (1955).

(304) B. Weissmann, *J. Biol. Chem.*, **216**, 783 (1955).

(305) E. A. Davidson and K. Meyer, *J. Biol. Chem.*, **211**, 605 (1954).

(306) H. Masamune, Z. Yosizawa and M. Maki, *Tôhoku J. Exptl. Med.*, **55**, 29 (1951).

(307) E. A. Davidson and K. Meyer, *J. Am. Chem. Soc.*, **76**, 5686 (1954); **77**, 4796 (1955).

dicated by the periodate-oxidation pattern. The presence of a $(1 \rightarrow 3)$-link in chondrosine was thus confirmed. The β-D configuration of the linkage was established by its susceptibility to a β-glycosidase (namely, emulsin).

Heparosine. A sulfated "disaccharide" has been isolated[308] by partial, acidic hydrolysis of heparin, and it has been formulated as *4*-O-(*2-amino-2-deoxy*-α-D-*glucopyranosyl 6-sulfate*)-D-*glucuronic acid*. Heparosine and its *N*-acetyl amide are amorphous. An amorphous "disaccharide" prepared by a similar procedure, was, however, believed[309] to be a 2-amino-2-deoxy-(D-glucosyluronic acid)-D-glucose.

The disaccharides discussed in this Section are listed in Table V.

Further Tables relevant to this Chapter will be published in Volume 15 of this Series.

(308) M. L. Wolfrom, R. Montgomery, J. V. Karabinos and P. Rathgeb, *J. Am. Chem. Soc.*, **72**, 5796 (1950).

(309) H. Masamune, T. Ishikawa and Y. Katabira, *Tôhoku J. Exptl. Med.*, **55**, 29 (1951).

TABLE V

Disaccharides Containing 2-Amino Sugars

Glycosyl residue	Linkage: Positions of	Linkage: Configuration of	Glycose residue	M.p., °C.	$[\alpha]_D$, degrees	Rotation solvent	Per-acetate: M.p., °C.	Per-acetate: $[\alpha]_D$, degrees	Per-acetate: Rotation solvent	Trivial name	Mode of isolation	References
2-Acetamido-2-deoxy-D-glucopyranosyl	(1 → 4)	β	2-acetamido-2-deoxy-D-glucose	262	+17.2	H_2O	309	+50.5	CH_3CO_2H	di-*N*-acetylchitobiose	D	261, 265
	(1 → 6)	α		215	+125	H_2O	—	—	—	—	A	177
	(1 → 6)	β		200	+6.4	H_2O	—	—	—	—	A	177
	(1 → 1)	α,α	D-glucopyranosyl	—	+176	H_2O	102	+163.5	$CHCl_3$	trehalosamine	E	297
	(1 → 3)	β	D-galactose	—	—	—	—	—	—	lacto-*N*-biose II	B, C	176, 266, 278, 288
	(1 → 6)	β	D-glucose	—	+3.7	H_2O	219	−9.5	$CHCl_3$	—	A	285
	(1 → 6)	β	D-galactose	—	+9.2	H_2O	198	+6.3	$CHCl_3$	—	A	285
2-Acetamido-2-deoxy-D-galactopyranosyl	(1 → 3)	α		—	+150	—	—	—	—	—	D	288

D-Galactopyrano-syl	(1 → 3)	β	2-acetamido-2-deoxy-D-glu-cose	169	+14.3	H₂O	—	—	—	lacto-N-biose I	B, C, D	249, 275, 287, 288, 294
	(1 → 4)	β		172	+27.5	H₂O	220	+61.5	CHCl₃	N-acetyl-lactosamine	A, B, C, D	15, 249, 286, 288–290, 292–294
	(1 → 6)	β		—	+31	H₂O	—	—	—	N-acetyl-allo-lactosamine	A, B	178, 294
	(1 → 6)	α	2-acetamido-2-deoxy-D-galac-tose	—	+118	H₂O	—	—	—	—	B	296
	(1 → 6)	α		—	+142	H₂O	—	—	—	—	B	296
L-Fucopyranosyl	(1 → 6)	?	2-acetamido-2-deoxy-D-glu-cose	—	—	—	—	—	—	—	D	288
2-Amino-2-deoxy-D-glucopyrano-syl	(1 → 4)	α	D-glucuronic acid	—	+79	H₂O	—	—	—	heparosine (containing one sulfate ester group)	D	308, 309
D-Glucopyrano-syluronic acid	(1 → 3)	β	2-acetamido-2-deoxy-D-glu-cose	—	−32	H₂O	120	+25	CHCl₃	hyalobio-uronic acid	D	299–301
D-Glucopyrano-syluronic acid	(1 → 3)	β	2-amino-2-de-oxy-D-galac-tose	—	+40	0.05 N HCl	—	—	—	chondrosine	D	306, 307

a *Mode of isolation:* A. chemical synthesis; B. enzymic synthesis; C. degradation of oligosaccharide; D. degradation of polysaccharide; E. naturally occurring.

PYRIMIDINE NUCLEOSIDES*

By J. J. Fox and I. Wempen

Sloan-Kettering Institute for Cancer Research, New York, New York

* The authors dedicate this treatise to the memory of the late Cornelius P. Rhoads, M.D., in appreciation of his interest, encouragement and support in this field of endeavor.

I. Introduction

The term "nucleoside" was originally proposed by Levene and Jacobs[1] in 1909 for the carbohydrate derivatives of purines (and, later, of pyrimidines) isolated from the alkaline hydrolyzates of yeast nucleic acid. The phosphate esters of nucleosides are the *nucleotides*, which, in polymerized forms, constitute the nucleic acids of all cells.[2] The sugar moieties of nucleosides derived from the nucleic acids have been shown, thus far, to be either D-ribose or 2-deoxy-D-*erythro*-pentose ("2-deoxy-D-ribose"). The ribonucleosides are constituents of ribonucleic acids, which occur mainly in the cell cytoplasm; whereas "2-deoxyribo"-nucleosides are components of deoxypentonucleic acids, which are localized in the cell nucleus.[3] The nucleic acids are not limited (in occurrence) to cellular components. They have also been found to be important constituents of plant and animal viruses.

Information gathered from metabolic studies[4] places increased importance on compounds *related* to nucleic acid constituents (a) as substances through which the pathways of nucleic acid biosynthesis may be elaborated, and (b) as compounds which may have utility as chemotherapeutic agents against neoplastic diseases. Nucleosides (in the form of nucleotides) are also components of various coenzymes and, as such, relate to many phases of metabolism.[5] Interest in nucleosides is further enhanced by the recent discoveries of other "nucleosides"—seemingly *unrelated* to the nucleic acids —which possess antibiotic properties; for example, cordycepin,[6] nebularine,[7] puromycin,[8] and amicetin.[9] Also to be noted is the need for improved methods, for the synthesis of nucleosides, demanded by the increased use of radioisotope labeling techniques in biochemical studies. With this background, it is indeed not surprising that increasing numbers of organic

(1) P. A. Levene and W. A. Jacobs, *Ber.*, **42**, 2475 (1909).

(2) For a general review of the nucleic acids, see "The Nucleic Acids," E. Chargaff and J. N. Davidson, eds., Academic Press Inc., New York, N. Y., 1955.

(3) Evidence presented by W. C. Schneider [*J. Biol. Chem.*, **216**, 287 (1955)] indicates that pyrimidine deoxyribonucleosides themselves are normally present within certain mammalian tissues. He suggests that these pyrimidine deoxyribonucleosides in tissues function principally in the synthesis of deoxyribonucleic acid.

(4) G. B. Brown and P. M. Roll, Ref. 2, Vol. 2, p. 350.

(5) J. F. Henderson and G. A. LePage, *Chem. Revs.*, **58**, 645 (1958).

(6) K. G. Cunningham, S. A. Hutchison, W. Manson and F. S. Spring, *J. Chem. Soc.*, 2299 (1951); H. R. Bentley, K. G. Cunningham and F. S. Spring, *ibid.*, 2301 (1951).

(7) L. Ehrenberg, H. Hedstrom, N. Löfgren and B. Takman, *Svensk Kem. Tidskr.*, **58**, 269 (1946); N. Löfgren and B. Luning, *Acta Chem. Scand.*, **7**, 225 (1953); N. Löfgren, B. Luning and H. Hedstrom, *ibid.*, **8**, 670 (1954).

(8) C. W. Waller, P. W. Fryth, B. L. Hutchings and J. H. Williams, *J. Am. Chem. Soc.*, **75**, 2025 (1953).

(9) C. DeBoer, E. L. Caron and J. W. Hinman, *J. Am. Chem. Soc.*, **75**, 499 (1953); J. W. Hinman, E. L. Caron and C. DeBoer, *ibid.*, **75**, 5964 (1953); M. H. McCormick and M. M. Hoehn, *Antibiotics & Chemotherapy*, **3**, 718 (1953).

chemists have concerned themselves with the synthesis and properties of nucleic acid components in recent years.

II. Scope and Nomenclature

Although this review deals with the *pyrimidine* nucleosides, it will be necessary to refer occasionally to their purine counterparts. The authors take into account the previous reviews in this series by Tipson,[10] Jeanloz and Fletcher,[11] and Barker,[12] which have dealt in greater or lesser degree with this subject. Some recounting of earlier work in the field of nucleoside chemistry will be necessary, in order to place newer developments in proper historical context.

In this Chapter, nucleosides are defined as *glycosyl*[13] derivatives of purines or pyrimidines, in which the anomeric carbon atom of the sugar is linked to a ring-nitrogen atom of the aglycon residue. The structures of some nucleosides of ribonucleic acid and deoxyribonucleic acid are shown in Figures 1 and 2.[14,15] In keeping with former reviews in this series,[10-12] the numerals refer to carbon atoms in the sugar moiety and the primed numerals to positions on the nitrogenous heterocycle when the *trivial* names of the nucleosides are used. No such distinction is needed in *systematic* names. The numbering system for purines and pyrimidines is in accord with the usage of *Chemical Abstracts*.[16]

III. The Structure of Pyrimidine Nucleosides Derived from Nucleic Acids

Early chemical studies with naturally occurring nucleosides were related primarily to the elucidation of their structures. As a result mainly of the efforts of the Levene group,[17] much of the basic information on the structure and chemical properties of nucleosides was already available by 1930.

(10) R. S. Tipson, *Advances in Carbohydrate Chem.*, **1**, 193 (1945).

(11) R. W. Jeanloz and H. G. Fletcher, Jr., *Advances in Carbohydrate Chem.*, **6**, 135 (1951).

(12) G. R. Barker, *Advances in Carbohydrate Chem.*, **11**, 285 (1956).

(13) The reader is referred to the chapter by Tipson[10] (p. 202), which distinguishes between the terms "glycoside" and "glycosyl." Nucleosides are glycosyl derivatives; that is, the union of the sugar residue to the aglycon involves a C—N bond.

(14) Not included in Figs. 1 and 2 are the several methylated-purine nucleosides found in certain nucleic acids. The deoxynucleoside of 6-methylaminopurine has been found[15] in the deoxyribonucleic acid of *Escherichia coli* 15T⁻ as well as in other microbial sources. Nucleosides of 6-methylaminopurine, 6-dimethylaminopurine, and 6-amino-2-methylpurine have also been isolated from the ribonucleic acid of *Escherichia coli*, as well as from other sources [J. W. Littlefield and D. B. Dunn, *Nature*, **181**, 254 (1958)].

(15) D. B. Dunn and J. D. Smith, *Biochem. J.*, **68**, 627 (1958).

(16) *Chem. Abstracts*, **39**, 5867 (1945).

(17) P. A. Levene and L. W. Bass, "Nucleic Acids," Chemical Catalog Company, New York, N. Y., 1931.

1. *The Aglycons (Pyrimidine Residues)*

Identification of the nitrogenous bases (aglycons) of pyrimidine nucleosides began at the turn of the century, when Kossel and Neumann[18] isolated thymine (5-methyluracil) from nucleic acid and showed this pyrimidine to be identical with the "nucleosin" previously described by Miescher.[19] The isolation of cytosine[20] [4-amino-2(*1H*)-pyrimidinone] and uracil[21] [2,4(*1H*,*3H*)-pyrimidinedione] from the nucleic acids came shortly thereafter and, in fact, by 1903, thymine,[22-24] cytosine,[25] and uracil[23,24] had been *synthesized*.

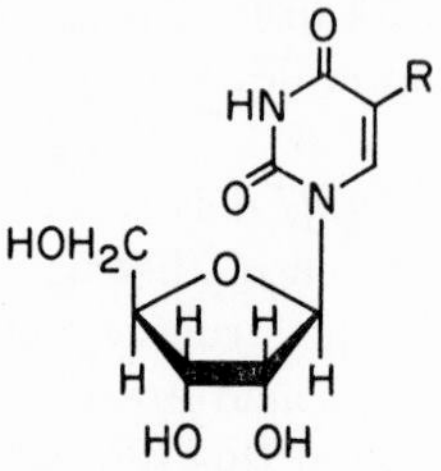

I

URIDINE (R = H)

1-β-D-Ribofuranosyluracil

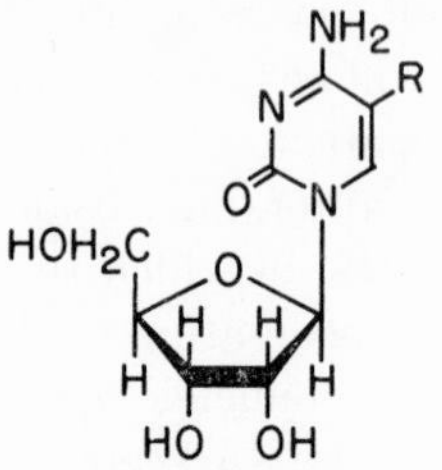

II

CYTIDINE (R = H)

1-β-D-Ribofuranosylcytosine

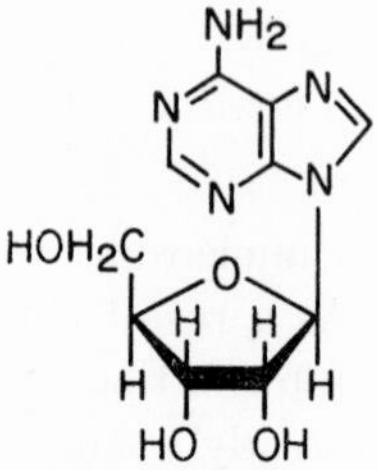

III

ADENOSINE

9-β-D-Ribofuranosyladenine

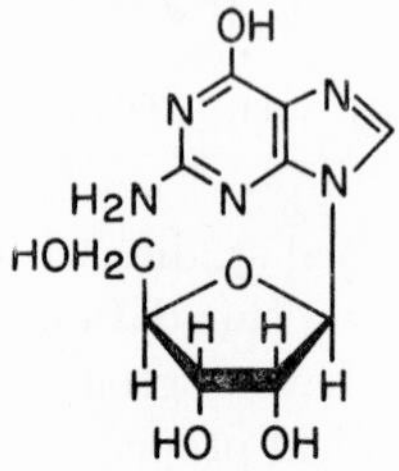

IV

GUANOSINE

9-β-D-Ribofuranosylguanine

FIG. 1.—Nucleosides in Ribonucleic Acid (RNA).

(18) A. Kossel and A. Neumann, *Ber.*, **26**, 2753 (1893).

(19) F. Miescher and O. Schmiedeberg, *Arch. Exptl. Pathol. Pharmakol., Naunyn-Schmiedeberg's*, **37**, 100 (1896).

(20) A. Kossel and A. Neumann, *Ber.*, **27**, 2215 (1894).

(21) A. Ascoli, *Z. physiol. Chem., Hoppe-Seyler's*, **31**, 161 (1900–01).

(22) H. Steudel, *Z. physiol. Chem., Hoppe-Seyler's*, **32**, 241 (1901).

(23) H. L. Wheeler and H. F. Merriam, *Am. Chem. J.*, **29**, 478 (1903).

(24) E. Fischer and G. Roeder, *Ber.*, **34**, 3751 (1901).

(25) H. L. Wheeler and T. B. Johnson, *Am. Chem. J.*, **29**, 492 (1903).

Of these pyrimidines, uracil and cytosine are constituents of ribonucleic acid, whereas thymine and cytosine are components of deoxyribonucleic acid. It was generally accepted that these nitrogenous heterocycles were the only pyrimidine components of the nucleic acids. The possibility that the nucleic acids might contain moieties other than those described had been voiced by Gulland,[26] Chargaff and Vischer,[27] and Davidson.[28] The

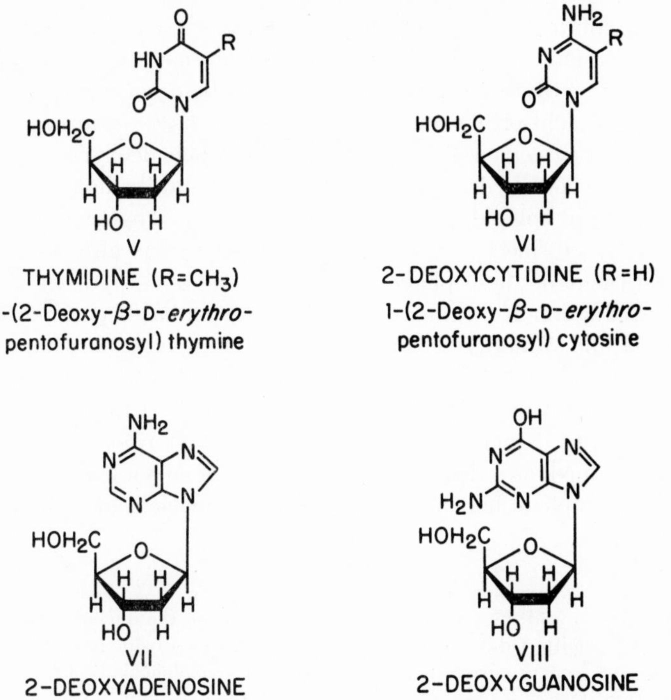

V
THYMIDINE (R=CH₃)
1-(2-Deoxy-β-D-*erythro-*
pentofuranosyl) thymine

VI
2-DEOXYCYTIDINE (R=H)
1-(2-Deoxy-β-D-*erythro-*
pentofuranosyl) cytosine

VII
2-DEOXYADENOSINE
9-(2-Deoxy-β-D-*erythro-*
pentofuranosyl) adenine

VIII
2-DEOXYGUANOSINE
9-(2-Deoxy-β-D-*erythro-*
pentofuranosyl) guanine

FIG. 2.—Nucleosides in Deoxyribonucleic Acid (DNA).

past decade has witnessed the discovery of several new pyrimidine and purine components of the nucleic acids. The presence of 5-methylcytosine as a minor constituent of calf-thymus deoxyribonucleic acid was indicated by Hotchkiss,[29] using paper chromatography,[30] and by Cohn[31] employing

(26) J. M. Gulland, *Cold Spring Harbor Symposia Quant. Biol.*, **12**, 20 (1947).

(27) E. Chargaff and E. Vischer, *Ann. Rev. Biochem.*, **17**, 201 (1948).

(28) J. N. Davidson, *Ann. Rev. Biochem.*, **18**, 155 (1949).

(29) R. D. Hotchkiss, *J. Biol. Chem.*, **175**, 315 (1948).

(30) 5-Methylcytosine was first reported as a constituent of nucleic acid of tubercle bacilli by T. B. Johnson and R. D. Coghill [*J. Am. Chem. Soc.*, **47**, 2838 (1925)]. Later

ion-exchange and spectral techniques. This aminopyrimidine was obtained later from several sources of deoxyribonucleic acid, especially from wheat germ, by Wyatt,[32] who showed it to be identical with synthetic[33] 5-methylcytosine in chromatographic behavior and in ultraviolet absorption properties. The naturally occurring 5-methylcytosine was also deaminated to thymine (with nitrous acid).[32] Soon thereafter, a nucleoside[34] and nucleotide[31] of 5-methylcytosine were also isolated from animal and plant sources, respectively, of deoxyribonucleic acid. 5-Methylcytosine has been reported to be a constituent of the nucleic acids of certain insects.[34a]

5-(Hydroxymethyl)cytosine[35] was shown to be a constituent of the deoxyribonucleic acid of T-even bacteriophage of *Escherichia coli*, following the report that cytosine was absent[36] from this phage deoxyribonucleic acid. The nucleoside of 5-(hydroxymethyl)cytosine[37-39] and its diphosphate ester[40] have since been isolated from the same sources. A glucoside of 5-(hydroxymethyl)cytosine[39] (and of its nucleotide[38,39]) has also been reported as a constituent of these phages. The synthesis of 5-(hydroxymethyl)cytosine by reduction of 5-(ethoxycarbonyl)cytosine has been reported.[41]

Thymine and 5-methylcytosine, at first found only as components of deoxyribonucleic acid, have since been discovered in the ribonucleic acid fraction derived from certain microorganisms.[42,43] [Uracil, on the other hand, previously demonstrated as a constituent of ribonucleic acid only, has been obtained, as a deoxynucleoside, from an enzymic hydrolyzate of a commercial sample of herring-sperm deoxyribonucleic acid.[44] However, this

---

re-investigation [E. Vischer, S. Zamenhof and E. Chargaff, *J. Biol. Chem.*, **177**, 429 (1949)] failed to reveal the presence of this pyrimidine in the nucleic acids of several avian tubercle bacilli. Oddly enough, although 5-methylcytosine is present in deoxyribonucleic acid from diverse sources (see Ref. 32), the nucleic acids of tubercle bacilli do not contain it.

(31) W. E. Cohn, *J. Am. Chem. Soc.*, **72**, 2811 (1950); **73**, 1539 (1951).
(32) G. R. Wyatt, *Nature*, **166**, 237 (1950); *Biochem. J.*, **48**, 581, 584 (1951).
(33) H. L. Wheeler and T. B. Johnson, *Am. Chem. J.*, **31**, 591 (1904).
(34) C. A. Dekker and D. T. Elmore, *J. Chem. Soc.*, 2864 (1951).
(34a) J. L. Rosedale, *J. Entomol. Soc. S. Africa*, **11**, 34 (1948).
(35) G. R. Wyatt and S. S. Cohen, *Nature*, **170**, 1072 (1952).
(36) A. Marshak, *Proc. Natl. Acad. Sci. U. S.*, **37**, 299 (1951).
(37) S. S. Cohen, *Cold Spring Harbor Symposia Quant. Biol.*, **18**, 221 (1953).
(38) E. Volkin, *J. Am. Chem. Soc.*, **76**, 5893 (1954).
(39) R. L. Sinsheimer, *Science*, **120**, 551 (1954).
(40) L. L. Weed and T. A. Courtenay, *J. Biol. Chem.*, **206**, 319 (1954).
(41) C. S. Miller, *J. Am. Chem. Soc.*, **77**, 752 (1955).
(42) J. W. Littlefield and D. B. Dunn, *Biochem. J.*, **68**, 8P (1958); *Nature*, **181**, 254 (1958).
(43) H. Amos and M. Korn, *Biochim. et Biophys. Acta*, **29**, 444 (1958).
(44) C. A. Dekker and A. R. Todd, *Nature*, **166**, 557 (1950).

deoxyuridine is believed to have arisen as the result of enzymic deamination of deoxycytidine (due to bacterial contamination of the preparation of deoxyribonucleic acid).][44]

With further refinement of techniques, it is likely that future years will witness the discovery of new pyrimidines (and purines) as integral components of the nucleic acids. A comprehensive review of the naturally occuring purines and pyrimidines of the nucleic acids has appeared.[45]

2. Identification of the Sugar Moiety

After identification of the pyrimidine base has been accomplished, the determination of the structure of any nucleoside may be divided into four distinct categories: the identification of the sugar, determination of the position of attachment of the sugar moiety to the aglycon, determination of the nature of the lactol ring structure of the sugar (pyranosyl or furanosyl) and, lastly, determination of the configuration of the sugar residue at the anomeric center (C1; α or β). When the paucity of physicochemical techniques available three to four decades ago is considered, it is indeed a tribute to the perspicacity and perseverance of Levene and his colleagues that they contributed so very much to our present knowledge of the structure of nucleosides. Although many of these aspects have been reviewed amply by Tipson,[10] it may be of value to recount briefly some of the salient features from the vantage point of the present day, since some of the reactions involved will be discussed later in this Chapter.

a. In Nucleosides Derived from Ribonucleic Acids.—Pyrimidine nucleosides, unlike glycosides, are resistant to mild acid hydrolysis, a characteristic which also differentiates these nucleosides from their purine counterparts. (It was, therefore, from the acid hydrolysis of the *purine* nucleosides of ribonucleic acid that D-ribose was first isolated in crystalline form[46-48]; it was shown to be identical with synthetic D-ribose.[49])

The pyrimidine nucleosides from ribonucleic acid (uridine and cytidine) present a more formidable problem, since they cannot be hydrolyzed by dilute mineral acid, and the use of concentrated acid usually destroys the sugar moiety. It was observed, however, that simultaneous bromination, hydrolysis, and oxidation of cytidine (with bromine–hydrobromic acid) yields 5-bromouracil plus D-ribonic acid.[50] Since cytidine can be deaminated to uridine with nitrous acid,[51] *both* of these pyrimidine nucleosides must

(45) A. Bendich, Ref. 2, Vol. 1, p. 81.

(46) P. A. Levene and W. A. Jacobs, *Ber.*, **41**, 2703 (1908).

(47) P. A. Levene and W. A. Jacobs, *Ber.*, **42**, 1198 (1909).

(48) P. A. Levene and W. A. Jacobs, *Ber.*, **44**, 746 (1911).

(49) W. Alberda van Ekenstein and J. J. Blanksma, *Chem. Weekblad*, **10**, 664 (1913).

(50) P. A. Levene and F. B. LaForge, *Ber.*, **45**, 608 (1912).

(51) P. A. Levene and W. A. Jacobs, *Ber.*, **43**, 3150 (1910).

contain a D-ribose residue in their structures. The actual isolation of the unaltered sugar component was expedited by the observation of Levene and LaForge[50] that catalytic hydrogenation of the pyrimidine ring renders the linkage between the sugar residue and the aglycon residue susceptible to subsequent (mild) acid hydrolysis. Thus, hydrogenation of uridine, with hydrogen in the presence of colloidal palladium, yielded dihydrouridine, which was readily hydrolyzed to D-ribose plus 5,6-dihydrouracil.

The discovery of a small proportion of a nucleoside containing thymine[42] in the ribonucleic acid of two strains of *Escherichia coli*, in *Aerobacter aerogenes*, and in commercial, yeast-ribonucleic acid emphasizes the point made previously,[26-28] namely, that the nucleic acids may contain constituents other than those heretofore identified. Alkaline hydrolysis of the ribonucleic acid from *E. coli* gave nucleotides[42] (probably the 2- and 3-phosphate esters) which were converted to the nucleoside with prostatic phosphomonoesterase.[52] Enzymic hydrolysis of the nucleic acid preparation *also* led to the nucleoside, which was degraded further to thymine by hydrolysis with perchloric acid.[42] There can be little doubt that this carbohydrate derivative of thymine is intimately bound as part of the polynucleotide chain of this particular ribonucleic acid.

Treatment of this nucleoside with metaperiodate (see page 311 for a discussion of the periodate oxidation of nucleosides), followed by alkaline hydrolysis of the oxidation product, also afforded thymine, thus indicating the presence of an α-glycol system in the sugar component. This nucleoside also complexed with borate[53] (a characteristic of compounds containing a *cis*-diol structure[54]) and migrated differently from thymidine in several chromatographic systems. This thymine nucleoside was also prepared[42] enzymically by incubation of thymine with inosine in the presence of a nucleoside phosphorylase from *E. coli*.[55,56] The enzymically prepared material was similar to the nucleoside derived from ribonucleic acid with respect to paper electrophoresis[57] in borate buffer, ultraviolet absorption spectra, and paper chromatography in several solvent systems. On the basis of these data, the D-ribosyl structure was assigned[42] to this nucleoside.

Conclusive proof of the structure of this naturally occurring nucleoside was established by a comparison with synthetic 1-β-D-ribofuranosylthy-

(52) R. Markham and J. D. Smith, *Biochem. J.*, **52**, 558 (1952).

(53) I. A. Rose and B. S. Schweigert, *J. Am. Chem. Soc.*, **73**, 5903 (1951).

(54) J. Böeseken, *Advances in Carbohydrate Chem.*, **4**, 189 (1949); J. M. Sugihara, *ibid.*, **8**, 14 (1953).

(55) Lampen (see Ref. 56) had prepared a 1-D-ribosylthymine from thymine plus D-ribosyl phosphate in the presence of nucleosidases from *Escherichia coli* B.

(56) J. O. Lampen, in *Phosphorus Metabolism Symposium*, Baltimore, 1952, Vol. 2, p. 368.

(57) R. Markham and J. D. Smith, *Biochem. J.*, **52**, 552 (1952).

mine[58,59] (5'-methyluridine). The substances were identical[60] by paper chromatography in four solvent systems, as well as by paper electrophoresis in borate buffer. The ultraviolet absorption spectrum of the natural material[61] was also similar to that for 1-β-D-ribofuranosylthymine.[58] The biological significance—if any—of 1-β-D-ribofuranosylthymine (I, R = CH$_3$) and of the newly-discovered methylated-purine ribonucleosides[42] in these ribonucleic acids has not yet been demonstrated.

The nucleotide of 5'-methylcytidine has been discovered[43] in the ribonucleic acid of a strain of E. coli. The absorption spectrum of this nucleotide resembled that for 2-deoxy-5'-methylcytidylic acid. Hydrolysis of this nucleotide with formic acid yielded thymine instead of 5-methylcytosine. This fact is explained by the authors as being due to deamination of 5-methylcytosine under the conditions of the degradation. Although they[43] have not yet isolated the nucleoside from this ribonucleic acid (nor converted the corresponding nucleotide to 5'-methylcytidine), Dunn[60] has detected 5'-methylcytidine in the ribonucleic acid of wheat germ, and in other natural sources. Synthetic 5-methyl-1-(β-D-ribofuranosyl)cytosine (5'-methylcytidine) is fortunately available for comparative studies.[62]

b. In Nucleosides Derived from Deoxyribonucleic Acids.—(i) *Thymidine and 2-Deoxycytidine.*—The problem of identification of the sugar components of pyrimidine nucleosides derived from deoxyribonucleic acid was beset with greater difficulties because of the instability of the "2-deoxy-D-ribosyl" moiety. (As the culmination of years of effort by Levene, he and London[63(a)] succeeded in hydrolyzing this acid, to afford 2-deoxyguanosine, by passing an aqueous solution of the acid through a segment of the gastrointestinal tract of a dog and collecting the hydrolyzate from an intestinal fistula.) Again, the first evidence on the nature of the sugar came from the purine nucleosides. Short treatment of deoxyguanosine (VIII) with very dilute mineral acid enabled Levene and his collaborators[63-65] to isolate a sugar as a crystalline material, the formula of which was in accord with

(58) J. J. Fox, N. Yung, J. Davoll and G. B. Brown, *J. Am. Chem. Soc.*, **78**, 2117 (1956).

(59) Interestingly enough, 1-β-D-ribofuranosylthymine represents, thus far, the only pyrimidine nucleoside whose chemical synthesis had been achieved, and whose detailed structure was known, *prior* to its isolation from natural sources.

(60) Private communication from Dr. D. B. Dunn.

(61) J. W. Littlefield and D. B. Dunn, *Biochem. J.*, **70**, 642 (1958).

(62) J. J. Fox, D. Van Praag, I. Wempen, I. L. Doerr, L. Cheong, J. E. Knoll, M. L. Eidinoff, A. Bendich and G. B. Brown, *J. Am. Chem. Soc.*, **81**, 178 (1959).

(63) (a) P. A. Levene and E. S. London, *J. Biol. Chem.*, **81**, 711 (1929); **83**, 793 (1929); (b) F. Bielschowsky and W. Klein, *Z. physiol. Chem., Hoppe-Seyler's*, **207**, 202 (1932).

(64) P. A. Levene and T. Mori, *J. Biol. Chem.*, **83**, 803 (1929).

(65) P. A. Levene, L. A. Mikeska and T. Mori, *J. Biol. Chem.*, **85**, 785 (1930).

that for a deoxypentose. They synthesized 2-deoxy-D-*threo*-pentose ("2-deoxy-D-xylose")[64] and 2-deoxy-L-*erythro*-pentose ("2-deoxy-L-arabinose"; "2-deoxy-L-ribose")[65] and found that the carbohydrate derived from deoxyguanosine possessed optical rotational properties of similar magnitude (but opposite sign) to those of synthetic 2-deoxy-L-*erythro*-pentose. They concluded that the carbohydrate residue of deoxyguanosine is that of 2-deoxy-D-*erythro*-pentose. Later, Klein[66] isolated crystalline 2-deoxy-D-*erythro*-pentose ("2-deoxy-D-ribose") from deoxyinosine (IX) using similar procedures.

Elementary analyses indicated that the sugar moieties of pyrimidine nucleosides derived from deoxyribonucleic acid are also of the deoxypentosyl type. Early attempts to apply the hydrogenation procedure of Levene and LaForge[50] were unsuccessful. It was generally assumed, however, that the sugar portion of the pyrimidine nucleosides of deoxyribonucleic acid is probably also of the "2-deoxy-D-ribosyl" type.

At a much later date, evidence supporting this assumption came from enzymic studies, which indicated that the deoxypentosyl residues of *all* nucleosides of deoxyribonucleic acids are similar. Manson and Lampen[67] demonstrated that deoxyinosine (IX)[68,69] can be synthesized from thy-

IX

midine (V, R = CH$_3$) plus hypoxanthine (6-hydroxypurine) in the presence of a cell-free extract from *Escherichia coli*. Similarly, in incubation mixtures containing deoxyinosine plus thymine or uracil, the pyrimidine nucleosides that formed showed the same R_f as those of nucleosides isolated from deoxyribonucleic acid.

MacNutt[70] achieved an enzymic synthesis of thymidine and deoxyuri-

(66) W. Klein, in "Methoden der Fermentforschung," E. Baumann and K. Myrbäck, eds., Georg Thieme, Leipzig, 1941, Vol. 1, p. 316.

(67) L. A. Manson and J. O. Lampen, *J. Biol. Chem.*, **193**, 539 (1951).

(68) Deoxyinosine is not considered to be a normal constituent of deoxyribonucleic acid. Deaminases are present in deoxyribonucleic acid which convert (see Ref. 69) deoxyadenosine to IX. Earlier methods for isolation of the nucleosides of deoxyribonucleic acid usually yielded the hypoxanthine (6-hydroxypurine) nucleoside instead of deoxyadenosine.

(69) W. Klein, *Z. physiol. Chem., Hoppe-Seyler's*, **224**, 244 (1934); **255**, 82 (1938).

(70) W. S. MacNutt, *Biochem. J.*, **50**, 384 (1952); *Nature*, **166**, 444 (1950).

dine (V, R = H) by incubation of deoxyguanosine (VIII) with thymine or uracil in the presence of an extract from *Lactobacillus helveticus*. Again, paper chromatography was used for establishing the identity of the natural with the enzymically prepared material. Friedkin and Roberts[71] effected an enzymic synthesis of thymidine (isolated in crystalline form) from 2-de-oxy-D-*erythro*-pentosyl phosphate plus thymine, using a purified, horse-liver phosphorylase. (The "deoxyribosyl" phosphate used in their study was obtained by enzymic cleavage of deoxyguanosine and deoxyinosine.) These enzymic studies provided strong evidence that the sugar moiety of the nucleosides of deoxyribonucleic acid is similar to that already characterized by Levene for 2-deoxyguanosine, that is, of the 2-deoxy-D-*erythro*-pentosyl type.

The first chemical demonstration of the presence of "2-deoxy-D-ribose" as the carbohydrate component of the pyrimidine nucleosides of deoxyribonucleic acid was accomplished by Burke,[72] who successfully modified the reduction procedure of Levene and LaForge.[50] Reduction of thymidine or deoxycytidine (VI, R = H), with sodium plus ethanol in liquid ammonia, followed by treatment of the reduction mixture with Dowex-50 ion-exchange resin, yielded 2-deoxy-D-*erythro*-pentose, which was identified by paper chromatography and by paper ionophoresis in a borate buffer. (Burke also applied this procedure to the pyrimidine ribonucleosides, uridine and cytidine, as well as to several synthetic glycosylpyrimidines.) Other catalysts for the reduction of the 5′,6′-ethylenic bond of nucleosides have since been reported. Rhodium on alumina has been employed[73] in the reduction of pyrimidine deoxynucleotides, from which "2-deoxy-D-ribose" phosphates were obtained. This catalyst has also been used in reducing thymidine and deoxyuridine (V, R = H).[74] The deoxypentose liberated was determined quantitatively by the Dische diphenylamine[75-77] color reaction. By use of sodium amalgam in water for the reduction of thymidine, Laland and Roth[78] obtained (in quantitative yield) crystalline 2-deoxy-D-*erythro*-pentose which was liberated from the reduced deoxynucleoside by mild, acid hydrolysis. This method has been extended to the degradation of 2-deoxycytidine and of several pyrimidine nucleotides.[79]

(71) M. Friedkin and D. Roberts, *J. Biol. Chem.*, **207**, 257 (1954).

(72) D. C. Burke, *Chem. & Ind.* (London), 1393 (1954); *J. Org. Chem.*, **20**, 643 (1955).

(73) W. E. Cohn and D. G. Doherty, *J. Am. Chem. Soc.*, **78**, 2863 (1956).

(74) M. Green and S. S. Cohen, *J. Biol. Chem.*, **225**, 397 (1957).

(75) Z. Dische, *Mikrochemie*, **8**, 4 (1930).

(76) Z. Dische, Ref. 2, Vol. 1, p. 285.

(77) W. G. Overend and M. Stacey, *Advances in Carbohydrate Chem.*, **8**, 45 (1953)

(78) S. Laland and E. Roth, *Acta Chem. Scand.*, **10**, 1058 (1956).

(79) S. Laland, J. M. McKee and E. Roth, *Acta Chem. Scand.*, **11**, 1081 (1957).

(ii) *2-Deoxyuridine.*—2-Deoxyuridine (V, R = H) was first prepared by enzymic deamination of 2-deoxycytidine with extracts of *Escherichia coli*.[80] At that time, the isolation of deoxyuridine in crystalline form by enzymic hydrolysis of herring-sperm deoxyribonucleic acid was reported.[44] The occurrence of deoxyuridine in this preparation from deoxyribonucleic acid coincided with a marked decrease in the recovery of deoxycytidine. When the deoxyribonucleic acid was hydrolyzed *directly* with formic acid (a procedure[81] which destroys the sugar moiety of nucleosides and liberates the pyrimidine bases), uracil was *not* detected in the hydrolyzate; whereas treatment of deoxyuridine with formic acid did afford uracil. The authors[80] justifiably concluded, therefore, that the deoxyuridine formerly isolated had been an artifact arising from contamination, with a deoxycytidine deaminase, of one of the enzyme preparations used for the degradation of the deoxyribonucleic acid.

Again, the more convincing pieces of evidence which established the identity of the carbohydrate moiety of deoxyuridine came originally from enzymic studies. MacNutt[70] showed that deoxyuridine can be synthesized from uracil plus 2-deoxyguanosine in the presence of an enzyme preparation from *Lactobacillus helveticus*. Friedkin and Roberts[82] synthesized radioactive deoxyuridine-$2'$-C^{14} by an enzymic reaction of uracil-2-C^{14} with "2-deoxy-D-ribosyl" phosphate. These studies[70,80,82] serve to establish a "2-deoxy-D-ribosyl" moiety as the sugar component of deoxyuridine. *2-Deoxyuridine has not as yet been demonstrated to be an integral component of deoxyribonucleic acid.* Interestingly enough, studies *in vitro*[82] and *in vivo*[83] indicate that this nucleoside, when administered to the rat, is converted uniquely to thymidine of deoxyribonucleic acid.

(iii) *2-Deoxy-5'-methylcytidine.*—Although MacNutt[70] demonstrated that 2-deoxy-5'-methylcytidine could be synthesized enzymically in the exchange reaction of 5-methylcytosine with 2-deoxyguanosine (VIII), evidence for the existence of this pyrimidine as an integral component of certain nucleic acids mainly came from the ion-exchange chromatographic studies of Cohn.[31] A fraction was isolated from enzymic digests of thymus deoxyribonucleic acid which had the properties of a deoxy*nucleotide* containing 5-methylcytosine as the pyrimidine component.

Dekker and Elmore[34] isolated 2-deoxy-5'-methylcytidine (VI, R = CH₃) from enzymic hydrolyzates of wheat-germ deoxyribonucleic acid. (It had been shown previously[32] that wheat germ is relatively rich in 5-methylcytosine.) By use of ion-exchange and partition chromatography, a small

(80) T. P. Wang, H. Z. Sable and J. O. Lampen, *J. Biol. Chem.*, **184**, 17 (1950).
(81) E. Vischer and E. Chargaff, *J. Biol. Chem.*, **176**, 715 (1948).
(82) M. Friedkin and D. Roberts, *J. Biol. Chem.*, **220**, 653 (1956).
(83) P. Reichard, *Acta Chem. Scand.*, **9**, 1275 (1955).

amount of nucleoside was obtained *in crystalline form*. Elemental analyses, ultraviolet absorption data, and a positive Dische reaction[75] showed this nucleoside to be a deoxypentose derivative of 5-methylcytosine. Treatment of this nucleoside with nitrous acid yielded a mixture which, when chromatographed on paper, gave a major spot corresponding to thymidine. The ultraviolet absorption spectrum (in water) of the eluted spot was also similar to that for thymidine. It should be noted that MacNutt[70] also converted 2-deoxy-5'-methylcytidine (prepared enzymically) to thymidine. Most recently, the reverse of this reaction, that is, the chemical conversion of thymidine to 2-deoxy-5'-methylcytidine has also been achieved[62] (see page 355). By virtue of all these interconversions, the sugar moiety of this nucleoside is proved to be identical with that of thymidine.

(iv) *2-Deoxy-5'-(hydroxymethyl)cytidine and its Glucoside.*—A fascinating situation, which relates some properties of a viral deoxyribonucleic acid to its particular components, has developed from studies with T-even viruses.[37-39,84-86] These bacteriophages are believed to be chemically unique, and the extreme pathology which they produce in infected bacteria seems to be related to their specific chemical properties.[86] Soon after the discovery of 5-(hydroxymethyl)cytosine[35] in these phages [5-(hydroxymethyl)cytosine completely replaces cytosine in the deoxyribonucleic acid of the phage], the nucleoside containing this pyrimidine was isolated (by paper chromatography) following acid hydrolysis of deoxyribonucleic acid and subsequent treatment of the nucleotide fraction with phosphatase.[37] The ultraviolet absorption spectrum of this nucleoside greatly resembled[37] that reported for deoxycytidine.[87] It had been shown also that successive treatment of this viral deoxyribonucleic acid with deoxyribonuclease and phosphatase did *not* release significant proportions of 5-(hydroxymethyl)cytosine nucleoside. It was suggested at that time[37] that the relative resistance of the internucleotide (phosphodiester) linkages of the phage deoxyribonucleic acid to phosphodiesterase, as compared to those of bacterial deoxyribonucleic acid, was structurally related in some manner to the presence of the 5-(hydroxymethyl)cytosine residue.

Deoxyribonucleic acid is the only nucleic acid found in T-even phage,[88] and earlier reports[89] of the presence of ribonucleic acid in bacterial virus T2 and T6 in small, variable proportions are now attributed[88] to a contamina-

(84) S. S. Cohen, *Science*, **123**, 653 (1956).

(85) R. L. Sinsheimer, *Science*, **125**, 1123 (1957).

(86) S. S. Cohen, *Symposium on Chem. Basis Heredity, Johns Hopkins Univ., McCollum–Pratt Inst. Contrib. No.* **153**, 651 (1957).

(87) J. J. Fox and D. Shugar, *Biochim. et Biophys. Acta*, **9**, 369 (1952).

(88) S. S. Cohen and R. Arbogast, *J. Exptl. Med.*, **91**, 607 (1950).

(89) A. R. Taylor, *J. Biol. Chem.*, **165**, 271 (1946); F. W. Putnam and L. M. Kozloff, *Science*, **108**, 386 (1948).

tion of the virus by substances derived from host cells. Earlier, Cohen and Anderson[90] had reported the absence of D-ribose from purified bacteriophage, and had noted that "T2 bacteriophage gave a color in the orcinol–sulfuric acid reaction which was not unlike that given by glucose." The significance of this finding was not particularly apparent at that time. However, Jesaitis and Goebel[91] showed that, when phage T4 is treated *in vitro* with a lipocarbohydrate derived from the dysentery bacillus Phase II *Shigella sonnei*, the viral contents of the phage are released into the surrounding medium. This intraviral material has properties similar to those of polymerized nucleic acid and, in preliminary analyses, the presence of a hexose was reported. Later, Jesaitis[92] prepared nucleic acid from phage T4 and showed that it, too, contains a hexose. Deoxypentose was determined by the Dische test[75] and hexose with cysteine–sulfuric acid.[93] Acid hydrolyzates of the phage nucleic acid produced, on paper chromatograms stained with aniline hydrogen phthalate,[94] a spot which migrated at the same rate as did D-glucose. The hexose in the phage was therefore tentatively identified as glucose. Since enzymic hydrolysis of this phage deoxyribonucleic acid liberated glucose-containing moieties to the same extent as other components, it was concluded that this hexose is a constituent of the nucleic acid of T4 phage.[92]

The structural basis for the relative resistance of viral deoxyribonucleic acid of T2- and T4-bacteriophage to deoxyribonuclease was elucidated to a considerable extent by the discovery[38,39] of a glycoside of 5-(hydroxymethyl)cytosine and its nucleotide in enzymic hydrolyzates of this phage deoxyribonucleic acid. Sinsheimer[39] obtained two nucleotides from T2 phage (in addition to the nucleotides of thymidine, deoxyadenosine, and deoxyguanosine) which, upon hydrolysis in 6 N hydrochloric acid yielded 5-(hydroxymethyl)cytosine. Both of these 5-(hydroxymethyl)cytosine nucleotides gave a Stumpf test[95] for deoxyribose which paralleled that given by deoxycytidylic acid. One of these nucleotides gave a positive Dische test,[96] producing *in 24 hours* an absorption peak at 380 mμ, characteristic for deoxypentose. The other nucleotide produced an *immediate* positive Dische test,[96] characteristic of hexoses, with an absorption maximum at

(90) S. S. Cohen and T. F. Anderson, *J. Exptl. Med.*, **84**, 511 (1946).

(91) M. A. Jesaitis and W. F. Goebel, *Cold Spring Harbor Symposia Quant. Biol.*, **18**, 205 (1953).

(92) (a) M. A. Jesaitis, *Microbiol. Genetics Bull.*, **10**, 16 (1954). (b) *Nature*, **178**, 637 (1956).

(93) Z. Dische, L. B. Shettles and M. Osnos, *Arch. Biochem.*, **22**, 169 (1949).

(94) L. Hough, J. K. N. Jones and W. H. Wadman, *J. Chem. Soc.*, 1702 (1950).

(95) P. K. Stumpf, *J. Biol. Chem.*, **169**, 367 (1947). The Stumpf test is a quantitative application of the Dische cysteine–sulfuric acid test for estimation of deoxyribonucleic acid.

(96) Z. Dische, *J. Biol. Chem.*, **181**, 379 (1949).

410 mμ. After 24 hours, the spectrum of the latter shifted to one resembling that for a mixture of hexose and deoxypentose. Hydrolysis of that hexose-containing nucleotide with N hydrochloric acid (1 hour), followed by chromatography of the hydrolyzate and staining with aniline hydrogen phthalate,[94] showed the presence of a hexose which migrated like glucose. Ion-exchange chromatography of this N acid hydrolyzate gave (in addition to starting nucleotide) a glucose-free, 5-(hydroxymethyl)cytosine nucleotide and a deoxypentose-free, 5-(hydroxymethyl)cytosine–glucose derivative. The latter substance gave a positive Dische test[96] for glucose.

It was concluded[39] from these studies that the two nucleotides obtained by enzymic hydrolysis of the deoxyribonucleic acid of T2 bacteriophage are 2-deoxy-5'-(hydroxymethyl)cytidylic acid and a glucose derivative thereof. It was also concluded that the glucose residue is affixed to the pyrimidine portion of the nucleotide and nucleoside of 5-(hydroxymethyl)-cytosine and, on the basis of the near identity of the spectra of the two nucleotides of 5-(hydroxymethyl)cytosine, it was suggested that the hexose is attached to the hydroxymethyl group of the pyrimidine.

Independently and almost simultaneously, Volkin,[38] working with T4-phage deoxyribonucleic acid, also arrived at similar conclusions regarding the linkage of glucose. Enzymic hydrolysis of a highly purified T4 deoxyribonucleic acid yielded a mixture which was fractionated by ion-exchange techniques.[97] In each fraction, 5-(hydroxymethyl)cytosine was determined by spectrophotometric methods, and hexose by the anthrone test.[98] 5-(Hydroxymethyl)cytosine and hexose were present in equimolar proportions in this phage. By boiling this deoxyribonucleic acid for 7 hours with Dowex-50 cation exchanger, glucose was liberated. This sugar was characterized by anion-exchange chromatography in a borate system[99] and by means of the hexokinase, firefly-luminescence system.[100] Milder acid hydrolysis (N hydrochloric acid, 1 hr., 100°) liberated 88 % of the glucose as the free sugar, whereas most of the 5-(hydroxymethyl)cytosine remained in the nucleotide or polynucleotide form. Therefore, most of the glucose *cannot* be involved in the 5-(hydroxymethyl)cytosine internucleotide linkage. Since glucose is relatively easily liberated by mild, acid hydrolysis, Volkin further concluded that the glucose is bound in glycosidic linkage; and, on this basis, he tentatively assigned the position of attachment of the hexose as being at the hydroxymethyl group of 5-(hydroxymethyl)cytosine. The glucoside of 5-(hydroxymethyl)cytosine nucleoside may therefore be portrayed as X. Although more precise structures have been listed[84-86] for the glucoside moiety, conclusive chemical evidence is lacking. It must be noted

(97) E. Volkin and W. E. Cohn, *J. Biol. Chem.*, **205**, 767 (1953).
(98) D. L. Morris, *Science*, **107**, 254 (1948).
(99) J. X. Khym and L. P. Zill, *J. Am. Chem. Soc.*, **74**, 2090 (1952).
(100) B. L. Strehler and J. R. Totter, *Arch. Biochem. Biophys.*, **40**, 28 (1952).

here that, as of this writing, the nucleoside (or nucleotide) containing 5-(hydroxymethyl)cytosine has *not* been isolated in crystalline form. Such ques-

tions as the lactol ring structure of the hexose and the configuration at the anomeric center (C1 of glucose) have not been studied. Moreover, although it is almost a certainty that the hexose is D-glucose (since L-glucose is a rarity in Nature), a *chemical* demonstration regarding this point is to be desired.

Both Volkin[38] and Sinsheimer[39,101] have indicated that the presence of combined glucose in the 5-(hydroxymethyl)cytosine nucleotide in phage deoxyribonucleic acid confers a resistance to deoxyribonuclease attack on the polynucleotide chain. The proportion of glucose in the deoxyribonucleic acid of T-even phages varies. Whereas 100% of the 5-(hydroxymethyl)-cytosine of T4-phage is glucose-substituted,[38,101,102] only 77% is glucose-bound in T2-phage. Further studies have been made by Cohen[84] and by Jesaitis[103] which have not only confirmed the results with T2- and T4-phage but have also shown that T6-phage contains almost double the proportion of glucose residue per 5-(hydroxymethyl)cytosine residue. Cohen[84] found that the T2-phage deoxyribonucleic acid is more readily degraded by pancreatic deoxyribonuclease than is that from T6-phage, which supports the contention[38,39,101] that resistance to enzymic cleavage is related to the 5-(hydroxymethyl)cytosine-bound glucose. Jesaitis suggests that, in T6-phage, the sugar moiety might be linked to 5-(hydroxymethyl)cytosine as a disaccharide. T16-Phage deoxyribonucleic acid *also* contains more than one molar equivalent of glucose residue per molar equivalent of 5-(hydroxymethyl)cytosine residue.[92(b),103]

The discovery of the presence of glucose in the nucleoside of 5-(hydroxymethyl)cytosine was as unexpected as the original finding of the presence[35] of 5-(hydroxymethyl)cytosine and the absence of cytosine.[36] As Cohen suggests,[84] other viruses contain cytosine; they therefore lack the hydroxy-

(101) R. L. Sinsheimer, *Proc. Natl. Acad. Sci. U. S.*, **42**, 502 (1956).

(102) G. Streisinger and J. Weigle, *Proc. Natl. Acad. Sci. U. S.*, **42**, 504 (1956).

(103) M. A. Jesaitis, *J. Exptl. Med.*, **106**, 233 (1957); *Intern. Congr. Microbiol.*, *7th Congr. Stockholm*, **1958**, p. 269.

methyl group (on position 5′) as a site of attachment for the hexose. The glucose seems to stabilize the T-even, viral deoxyribonucleic acid. Even at the nucleotide level, the 5-(hydroxymethyl)cytosine nucleotide having a free hydroxymethyl group is readily dephosphorylated by phosphatase, whereas the *glucoside* of this nucleotide is relatively resistant to this enzyme.[85]

It is to be noted that nucleoside 5-pyrophosphates containing glucose[104] [for example, uridine 5-(D-glucosyl dihydrogen pyrophosphate)] and other hexoses have been isolated as part of a series of coenzymes. Since the hexose is linked to the nucleotide by way of the pyrophosphate group, these coenzymes are more properly to be considered as derivatives of *nucleotides* and thus fall outside the scope of this Chapter.

The assignment of the 2-deoxy-D-*erythro*-pentose type of structure to the 5-(hydroxymethyl)cytosine deoxynucleoside rested, at first, on the fact that purine nucleosides of T6 nucleic acid liberated, on weak acid hydrolysis, a deoxypentose having the same R_f value as the deoxypentose of thymus deoxyribonucleic acid.[37] In addition, the glucose-free nucleotide of 5-(hydroxymethyl)cytosine[39] gave a positive Dische test[75] for deoxypentose.

Previous work[105] had shown that the pyrimidine ring of viral 5-(hydroxymethyl)cytosine can be derived from the cytosine in the deoxyribonucleic acid of *Escherichia coli*. 2-Deoxy-5′-(hydroxymethyl)cytidine phosphate has been isolated as a product of the reaction of 2-deoxycytidine 5-phosphate with formaldehyde and tetrahydrofolic acid (in the presence of an enzyme preparation derived from T6 phage-infected cells).[106] Treatment of this enzymically produced 5-(hydroxymethyl)cytosine nucleotide with a phosphorylase yielded 2-deoxy-5′-(hydroxymethyl)cytidine having chromatographic behavior identical with that of the nucleoside[37] isolated directly from T6-phage deoxyribonucleic acid. Acid hydrolysis of the 5-(hydroxymethyl)cytosine nucleotide yielded 5-(hydroxymethyl)cytosine. It may be concluded from these studies that the deoxypentose component in the nucleoside containing 5-(hydroxymethyl)cytosine is identical with that in 2-deoxycytidine.

3. The Position of the Glycosyl Linkage

From indirect chemical evidence, Levene and his collaborators assigned the N1 position as the point of attachment of the D-*ribosyl* moiety to the pyrimidine ring. Those reactions have been described by Tipson[10] and are presented in summary form in Table I.

(104) R. Caputto, L. F. Leloir, C. E. Cardini and A. C. Paladini, *J. Biol. Chem.*, **184**, 333 (1950).

(105) S. S. Cohen and L. L. Weed, *J. Biol. Chem.*, **209**, 789 (1954).

(106) J. G. Flaks and S. S. Cohen, *Biochim. et Biophys. Acta*, **25**, 667 (1957).

TABLE I

Chemical Evidence which Established N1 as the Position of Attachment of the Ribosyl Moiety to the Pyrimidine Ring

Reaction	Reaction Product	Conclusion (Positions excluded)	References
General stability of uridine and cytidine to cleavage by dilute acids	starting material	2	50
Cytidine + nitrous acid	uridine	4	50
Uridine + bromine water	5'-bromouridine	5	50
Uridine + nitric acid	a 5'-nitro-nucleoside	5	50
Uridine + bromine water; digestion with phenylhydrazine	5',6'-bis(phenylhydrazino)uridine	5 and 6	50, 107(a)
Uridine + hydrazine hydrate	a pentose-free pyrazolone	4, 5, and 6	107(b)
Mono-N-methyluridine + 10% sulfuric acid (125°; 4 hr.)	3-methyluracil	3	108

A highly interesting and often overlooked aspect of this structure proof was brought out by the titrimetric measurements on nucleosides and their free bases by Levene, Bass, and Simms.[109] They reasoned, quite justifiably, that uracil should possess two acidic dissociation constants, because of the presence of two potentially dissociable protons in the molecule. (At that time, the problem as to the position of attachment of the carbohydrate to the nitrogenous base had essentially been diminished to a choice between positions 1 and 6.) They demonstrated in an early paper[109(a)] that *uracil possesses two acidic dissociation constants (9.28 and 13.56)*. If the sugar radical were substituted on position 6 of uridine, both of the dissociation constants of uracil should be demonstrable in uridine; whereas, if substitution by the sugar were on position 1, only one of these pK_a values should be observable.

They showed that, in fact, *uridine possesses two acidic dissociations*, and on this basis would have had to conclude that the sugar moiety was affixed to position 6! (At this time, the 5',6'-bis(phenylhydrazino)uridine[107] had already been prepared, which excluded position 6'.) A re-examination[109(b)] of the titrimetric measurements revealed that (a) uracil possesses *only one* acidic dissociation (pK_a 9.42), (b) the higher acidic pK_a value for uridine (12.52) is due to dissociation of the sugar moiety rather than being that of the pyrimidine, and (c) 1- and 3-methyluracil possess only one dissociation constant each. Therefore, they concluded that the dissociation constants of uridine and uracil "did not contradict the theory of the union at position

(107)(a) P. A. Levene, *J. Biol. Chem.*, **63**, 653 (1925); (b) P. A. Levene and L. W. Bass, *ibid.*, **71**, 167 (1926–27).

(108) P. A. Levene and R. S. Tipson, *J. Biol. Chem.*, **104**, 385 (1934).

(109) (a) P. A. Levene and H. S. Simms, *J. Biol. Chem.*, **65**, 519 (1925); (b) P. A. Levene, L. W. Bass and H. S. Simms, *ibid.*, **70**, 229 (1926).

1 of the pyrimidine" in the nucleoside. (Ironically enough, it was demonstrated years later by Shugar and Fox,[110] by spectral techniques, that *uracil does*, indeed, *possess two acidic* pK_as of 9.5 and 13!)

A less ambiguous situation prevailed when cytosine and cytidine were compared. The former possesses a pK_a for the ammonium function (4.60) and an acidic pK_a (12.16) for the 2-hydroxyl group. The nucleoside *also* shows two dissociations (4.22 and 12.3). Since the higher dissociation constant was stated[109] to be due to the sugar moiety, it followed that the pyrimidine portion, itself, shows no acidic dissociations in this nucleoside. The authors[109] concluded, therefore, that cytidine (and uridine) bear the sugar radical on position 1 rather than 6 of the base.

Some of the reasoning employed by Levene and his collaborators[109] was used decades later in interpreting the detailed ultraviolet absorption spectra of pyrimidines and their nucleosides[87,110] in terms of their degrees of dissociation and their ionization constants, including a spectral demonstration of the dissociation of the sugar moiety. Indeed, as will be described later (see page 302), the entire problem of the position of attachment of the sugar moiety in pyrimidine nucleosides *could* have been solved readily by spectrophotometric methods. Unfortunately, these techniques were not then available to the Levene group.

More difficulty was encountered with the *pyrimidine deoxynucleosides*. It was tacitly assumed that the sugar radical in thymidine and deoxycytidine, by analogy with the ribonucleosides, is attached to position N1. The first significant experiment[111] to shed some light upon the validity of this assumption was *based* upon the methylation studies of Levene and Tipson.[108] Deoxyribonucleic acid from thymus was methylated with dimethyl sulfate plus alkali, and the product was degraded by strong-acid hydrolysis. One of the products obtained was 3-methylthymine (XI).[111] A

dimethylated cytosine was also obtained, to which the authors[111] assigned the pyrimidinone structure (XII); this pyrimidine derivative was also isolated by acid degradation of methylated cytidine. Bredereck and coworkers concluded that thymidine and deoxycytidine, like cytidine, bear the sugar substituent on position N1.

It should be stated, however, that these experiments *do not*, of themselves, *justify* the authors' conclusions. The isolation of 3-methylthymine surely excludes position 3′ in thymidine as a point of union between the aglycon residue and the sugar residue. The isolation of a *di*-methylated cytosine does not even exclude position 3′, since no experimental evidence what-

(110) D. Shugar and J. J. Fox, *Biochim. et Biophys. Acta*, **9**, 199 (1952).
(111) H. Bredereck, G. Müller and E. Berger, *Ber.*, **73**, 1058 (1940).

soever was provided to justify the assignment of structure XII to this pyrimidine. The structure could possibly have been 4-(dimethylamino)-2(*1H*)-pyrimidinone which, in theory at least, could have arisen from a 1-ribosylcytosine (cytidine) and, for example, a "3-(2-deoxy-D-*erythro*-pentosyl)cytosine." Admittedly, both 1-methyl-4-methylamino-2(*1H*)-pyrimidinone and 1,3-dimethylcytosine could be excluded as alternate structures for XII, since they could not have arisen from cytidine.

The problem of the location of the deoxypentosyl moiety on the pyrimidine ring was solved by the application of ultraviolet absorption spectrophotometry. Gulland and coworkers[112] had demonstrated that purine ribo- and deoxypentonucleosides resemble their parent 9-methylated purines rather than the 7-methylated purine isomer. On this basis, they concluded that the sugar–purine linkage is at position 9 of the base. Ploeser and Loring[113] applied this method to the pyrimidine nucleosides and showed that the spectrum of thymidine (at *p*H 1, 7, and 12) is similar to that for uridine. Since the D-ribosyl moiety in uridine was known to be at position N1 of the base, they concluded that the sugar residue in this deoxynucleoside is also on N1. The spectra of cytidine and 2-deoxycytidine (at *p*H 7) were also similar, hence the same conclusion was reached for deoxycytidine.[114]

As mentioned by Tipson,[10] the question arises as to whether ultraviolet absorption spectra of the type described[112-114] can serve as *proof* for the positional assignment of the carbohydrate moiety on the pyrimidine ring of nucleosides. The increasing usage of spectrophotometry in the isolation, and in structural and enzymic studies, of nucleosides and nucleotides warrants a detailed consideration of this technique. The studies described above,[112-114] for example, may be open to question (despite the fact that the *conclusions* were correct), since the *p*H of the curves selected was *not* predicated upon the ionization constants of the compounds under investigation. A series of comprehensive spectral studies of nucleosides of nucleic acids, their parent pyrimidines, and related compounds have been reported,[87,110] and much of the following discussion is derived from them.

It was demonstrated by Stenstrom and Goldsmith[115] that, when the absorption spectrum of a compound is dependent upon the *p*H of the medium, a study of these spectral changes may be used for determining the limiting neutral or ionic forms of the substance, as well as the dissociation constant(s). The application of this method to pyrimidines has been illustrated[110] by the spectrum of 1-methyluracil (see Fig. 3).

(112) J. M. Gulland, E. R. Holiday and T. F. Macrae, *J. Chem. Soc.*, 1639 (1934); J. M. Gulland and E. R. Holiday, *ibid.*, 765 (1936); J. M. Gulland and L. F. Story, *ibid.*, **259**, 692 (1938).

(113) J. M. Ploeser and H. S. Loring, *J. Biol. Chem.*, **178**, 431 (1949).

(114) L. A. Manson and J. O. Lampen, *J. Biol. Chem.*, **191**, 87 (1951).

(115) W. Stenstrom and N. Goldsmith, *J. Phys. Chem.*, **30**, 1683 (1926).

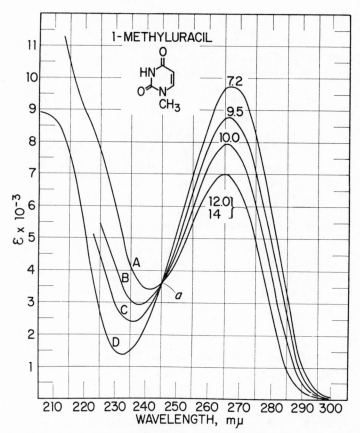

Fig. 3.—Ultraviolet Absorption Spectrum of 1-Methyluracil at pH Values Indicated. (Adapted from Shugar and Fox.[110])

This compound (XIIIa) possesses only one potentially dissociable proton in the molecule. The spectrum of XIIIa is unaltered between pH 0–7 (see curve D). As the pH

of the medium is increased to 12.0, the spectrum shifts to curve A. Further increase in alkalinity of the medium does not alter curve A. Curve D resembles the spectrum of 1,3-dimethyluracil (XIV); the latter shows no spectral shifts at different pH values (1–14), in accord with the absence of dissociable hydrogen atoms in the molecule.[110]

It must be concluded that XIIIa (see curve D) represents the neutral species of 1-methyluracil and, since curve D resembles the spectrum of 1,3-dimethyluracil, XIIIa exists in solution in the *di*-carbonyl form (pH 0–7). Curve A (for XIIIb) represents the mono-anionic species of 1-methyluracil in aqueous solution, in which one oxygen atom is in the carbonyl form and the other in the enolic form. Evidence for this structure was derived from a comparison of curve A (pH 12–14) with that of the 4-alkoxy derivative (XV), the structure and spectrum of which are fixed. The spectrum of XIIIb (curve A) and that of XV are similar.

$$
\begin{array}{cccc}
\text{XIV} & \text{XV} & \text{XVI} & \text{XVII}
\end{array}
$$

Curves A and D (Fig. 3) cross at 245.5 mμ, which means that, at this particular wavelength, the neutral and anionic forms of 1-methyluracil have the same extinction (optical density). All curves at intermediate pH values (7–12)—such as B and C, which represent mixtures of the two species of XIII—should also pass through this point of equal extinction (*isosbestic point*) at 245.5 mμ—as, indeed, they do. That curve which lies exactly midway between curves A and D represents a 50/50 mixture of the two species. The pH of the solution which gives this midway curve would represent the pK of the compound. If a sufficient number of curves are determined, a plot of the extinction *versus* pH at a given wavelength would result in a "titration" curve. In essence, this procedure was employed by Cohn[31] to determine the pK$_a$ of 2-deoxy-5'-methylcytidylic acid. The pK$_a$ value(s) may be calculated from the following equation.[116,117]

$$ pK_a = pH - \log \frac{E_{HA} - E}{E - E_A} $$

where E_{HA} and E_A are the extinctions of the neutral and ionic species, respectively, and E is the extinction determined at a given pH. In actual practice,[87,110,118,119] however, it is usually adequate to run several curves in the vicinity of the pK$_a$, and to determine the pK$_a$ by simple extrapolation. The spectrally determined "apparent"[120] pK$_a$ value for 1-methyluracil (see Fig. 3) is 9.75, as compared to 9.71 obtained by Levene and coworkers[109] by electrometric titration.

It is apparent that a knowledge of the pK is essential for the interpretation of spectra of compounds which ionize so that curves representing *pure* species can be

(116) L. A. Flexser, L. P. Hammett and A. Dingwall, *J. Am. Chem. Soc.*, **57**, 2103 (1935); L. J. Edwards, *Trans. Faraday Soc.*, **46**, 723 (1950).

(117) See Chapter by G. H. Beaven, E. R. Holiday, and E. A. Johnson on the optical properties of nucleic acids and their components in Ref. 2, Vol. 1, p. 493.

(118) J. J. Fox, L. F. Cavalieri and N. Chang, *J. Am. Chem. Soc.*, **75**, 4315 (1953).

(119) J. J. Fox, N. Yung and I. Wempen, *Biochim. et Biophys. Acta*, **23**, 295 (1957).

(120) The term "apparent" is used, since activity coefficients have not been determined. As pointed out by Sager and coworkers, the correction would probably be negligible, as the dilution of compound used in spectrophotometry is very high [see E. E. Sager, M. R. Schooley, A. S. Carr and S. F. Acree, *J. Research Natl. Bur. Standards*, **35**, 521 (1945)].

compared. An appreciation of this point was shown by Marshall and Walker,[121] who first measured the pK values of pyrimidines electrometrically, after which they determined the spectra at *selected* pH values (sufficiently removed from the pK values, in order to eliminate the presence of more than one species in solution). The procedure of Shugar and Fox[87,110,122,123] uses spectral measurements for the determination both of pK values and the curves for the pure species.

Although it has been established that carbohydrates do not exhibit selective absorption in the ultraviolet region,[124] they *do* influence the spectra of the pyrimidines to which their residues are attached in nucleosides. Clearly, if the sugar moiety is on

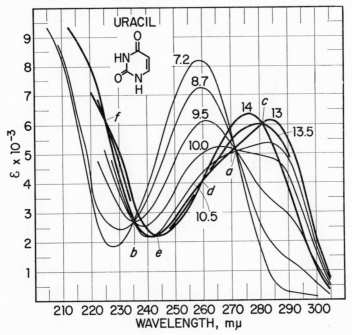

Fig. 4.—Ultraviolet Absorption Spectrum of Uracil at pH Values Indicated (Adapted from Shugar and Fox.[110])

position 1, 2, 3, or 4 of uracil, it should have replaced one of the dissociable protons. The spectrum of uracil (see Fig. 4) exhibits two dissociation patterns,[110] in accord with the presence of two dissociable hydrogen atoms. The first dissociation between pH 0 and pH 13 (all curves passing through *isosbestic* points a and b) gives an "apparent" pK_a value of 9.5 for the *mono*-anion. The second dissociation is shown by curves between pH 13 and pH 14 (isosbestic points c, d, e, and f) with a pK_a of >13

(121) J. R. Marshall and J. Walker, *J. Chem. Soc.*, 1004 (1951).

(122) J. J. Fox and D. Shugar, *Bull. soc. chim. Belges*, **61**, 44 (1952).

(123) D. Shugar and J. J. Fox, *Bull. soc. chim. Belges*, **61**, 293 (1952).

(124) F. Goos, H. H. Schlubach and G. Schroeter, *Z. physiol. Chem., Hoppe-Seyler's*, **186**, 148 (1930).

for the di-anionic form. When an alkyl group is substituted on position 3 (3-methyl-uracil, see Fig. 5), the spectrum is akin to that for uracil, except that the second dissociation pattern of uracil (pH 12–14) has been eliminated.

Substitution of an alkyl group on position 1 (see Fig. 3) *also* eliminates one ionization pattern. The ionization pattern (pH 1–14) of 1-methyluracil differs markedly from that for 3-methyluracil, although the spectra of the neutral species of both

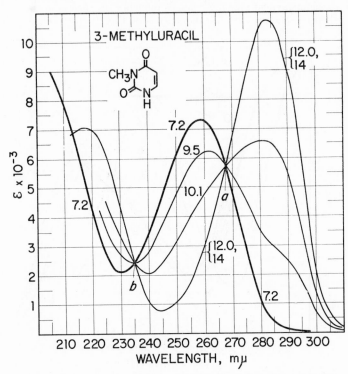

Fig. 5.—Ultraviolet Absorption Spectrum of 3-Methyluracil at pH Values Indicated. (Adapted from Shugar and Fox.[110])

compounds (pH 1–7) are similar. This difference arises from the fact that, in 1-methyl-uracil, proton removal (ionization) occurs at the 3,4 position to give structure XIIIb, whereas, with 3-methyluracil, the pattern is due to ionization at[110] positions 1,2. The different electronic arrangements of the resulting mono-anions of these mono-methylated uracils are reflected in their spectra. It was also demonstrated[110] that the spectra of the 4-alkoxy (XVI) and 2-alkoxy (XVII) derivatives (to pH 14) are very different from those of 1- and 3-methyluracil.

The spectra of the neutral species (pH 1–7) of uridine[87] (see Fig. 6), 2-deoxy-uridine,[44,87] thymidine (see Fig. 7),[87] and 1-β-D-ribofuranosylthymine[53] (see Fig. 8) resemble those for the neutral species of uracil, 1-methyluracil, and 3-methyluracil, and, on *this* basis, it would be impossible to assign the position of the carbohydrate on the pyrimidine ring of those nucleosides. However, as the *p*H is increased to 12 (to the mono-anionic species), an ionization pattern is produced which is *similar to* that for 1-methyluracil and *differs from* that of 3-methyluracil, uracil, XVI, and XVII. On the basis of these spectra and the foregoing discussion, it is obvious that the sugar moiety may be allocated unmistakably to position 1 of the bases in the

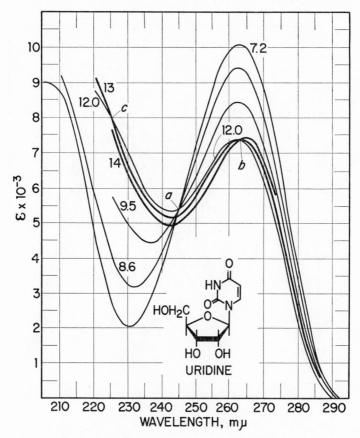

Fig. 6.—Ultraviolet Absorption Spectrum of Uridine at *p*H Values Indicated. (Adapted from Fox and Shugar.[87])

nucleosides.[58,87] Above *p*H 12 (see Figs. 6–8), spectral shifts were observed (denoting a second dissociation) which are not present in the spectrum of 1-methyluracil. Since glycosides are known to ionize in this *p*H region,[125] this second dissociation in the high alkaline region (*p*H 12–14) was ascribed to the effect of ionization, of the sugar moiety, upon the aglycon.[87]

By similar reasoning, the position of the sugar in cytosine nucleosides and deoxy-

(125) R. Kuhn and H. Sobotka, *Z. physik. Chem.* (Leipzig), **109**, 65 (1924).

nucleosides may also be assigned[87] to N1 of cytosine. Cytosine (see Fig. 9) exhibits two pK_a values spectrally,[110] namely, 4.45 and 12.2. 1-Methylcytosine (see Fig. 10) shows only one ionization pattern, that for the amino group on position 4. This pattern (cationic and neutral species) differs from that of 4-amino-2-methoxypyrimidine (pK 5.3). The spectra of cytidine (pK_a 4.11), 2-deoxycytidine[87] (pK_a 4.3), and 5'-methyl-2-deoxycytidine[62] (see Fig. 11; pK_a 4.55) are similar to that for 1-methyl-

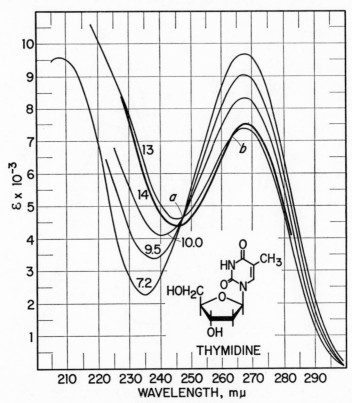

FIG. 7.—Ultraviolet Absorption Spectrum of Thymidine at pH Values Indicated. (Adapted from Fox and Shugar.[87])

cytosine, with the exception that, above pH 12, there is manifested a *new* dissociation (which is absent for 1-methylcytosine) which again must be ascribed to the effect of dissociation of the sugar moiety upon the chromophore in the pyrimidine. Similarly, the spectrum of 2-deoxy-5'-(hydroxymethyl)cytidine, reported by Cohen[37] for the neutral and cationic species, leaves no doubt that the deoxyribosyl moiety is on N1 of the base. *In general, therefore, ultraviolet absorption spectroscopy not only confirmed N1 as the position of attachment of the ribosyl moiety to the base in pyrimidine nucleosides of ribonucleic acid, but offered a similar proof to substantiate the view that the deoxyribosyl components of the pyrimidine nucleosides of deoxyribonucleic acid are also affixed at the same position.*

Most significant has been the chemical conversion[126] of 1-β-D-ribofuranosylthymine and uridine to thymidine and 1-(2-deoxy-β-D-*erythro*-pentofuranosyl)uracil (V, R = H), respectively; these conversions provide

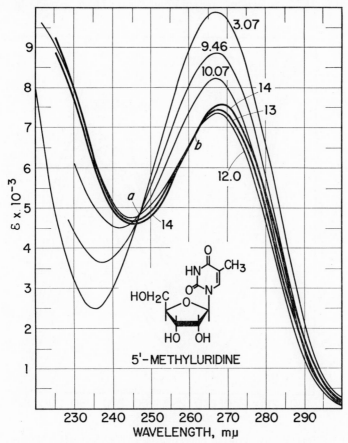

Fig. 8.—Ultraviolet Absorption Spectrum of 1-β-D-Ribofuranosylthymine (5'-Methyluridine) at pH Values Indicated. (Adapted from Fox, Yung, Davoll and Brown.[58])

direct chemical evidence that the two deoxynucleosides mentioned are N1-substituted pyrimidines. This aspect of the subject will be discussed later.

4. *The Lactol Ring Structure*

Determination of the ring structure of the pyrimidine ribonucleosides, uridine and cytidine, as being furanoid was accomplished by Levene and

(126) D. M. Brown, D. P. Parihar, C. B. Reese and A. R. Todd, *J. Chem. Soc.*, 3035 (1958); *Proc. Chem. Soc.*, 321 (1957).

Tipson[108,127-129] by the effective use of degradative procedures, tritylation and tosylation methods, and acetonation reactions.

Their tritylation and tosylation studies[130] also indicated that the ring structure in thymidine is of the furanoid form. These aspects have been

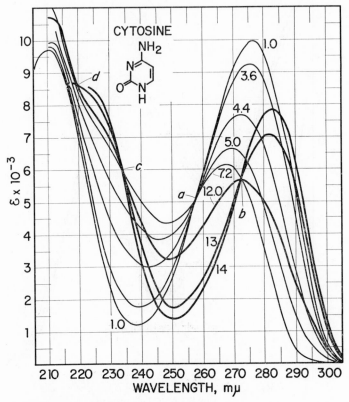

FIG. 9.—Ultraviolet Absorption Spectrum of Cytosine at pH Values Indicated. (Adapted from Shugar and Fox.[110])

reviewed in detail by Tipson[10] and will not be elaborated here. It was also demonstrated[131] that thymidine, unlike ribonucleosides (which possess ad-

(127) P. A. Levene and R. S. Tipson, *J. Biol. Chem.*, **101**, 529 (1933).

(128) P. A. Levene and R. S. Tipson, *J. Biol. Chem.*, **105**, 419 (1934).

(129) P. A. Levene and R. S. Tipson, *J. Biol. Chem.*, **106**, 113 (1934).

(130) P. A. Levene and R. S. Tipson, *J. Biol. Chem.*, **109**, 623 (1935); *Science*, **81**, 98 (1935).

(131) P. A. Levene and R. S. Tipson, *Z. physiol. Chem., Hoppe-Seyler's*, **234**, v (1935); K. Makino, *Biochem. Z.*, **282**, 263 (1935).

jacent *cis* hydroxyl groups), does not increase the acidity of boric acid (does not complex with borate) in the Böeseken test.[54,132]

An important technique which arose from the periodate oxidation studies

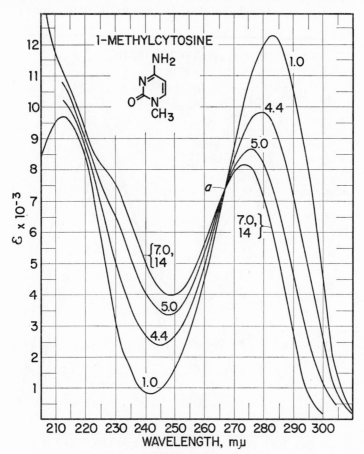

FIG. 10.—Ultraviolet Absorption Spectrum of 1-Methylcytosine at *p*H Values Indicated. (Adapted from Fox and Shugar.[87])

of Hudson and coworkers[133] with glycosides was applied[134] to the determination of the unknown lactol ring structure of nucleosides ("*N*-glycosides").

(132) J. Böeseken, *Ber.*, **46**, 2612 (1913).

(133) E. L. Jackson and C. S. Hudson, *J. Am. Chem. Soc.*, **59**, 994 (1937); **61**, 1530 (1939); W. D. Maclay and C. S. Hudson, *ibid.*, **60**, 2059 (1938); W. D. Maclay, R. M. Hahn and C. S. Hudson, *ibid.*, **61**, 1660 (1939); N. K. Richtmyer and C. S. Hudson, *ibid.*, **65**, 64 (1943).

(134) B. Lythgoe and A. R. Todd, *J. Chem. Soc.*, 592 (1944).

The method is based on the fact that periodic acid or the reagent more commonly used, sodium metaperiodate, will oxidize α-glycols and cleave the carbon–carbon bond, with the formation of dialdehydes.[135,136] A pentofuranosylpyrimidine (XVIII, R = a pyrimidyl group) would be expected to consume one mole of metaperiodate per mole of nucleoside. The dialdehyde (XIX) resulting from this oxidation would

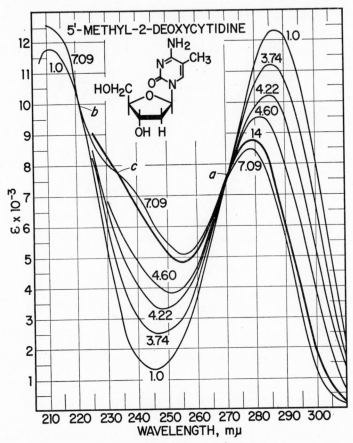

FIG. 11.—Ultraviolet Absorption Spectrum of 5′-Methyl-2-deoxycytidine at pH Values Indicated. (Adapted from Fox and coworkers.[62])

contain only two centers of asymmetry, carried over from C1 and C4 of the nucleoside's sugar moiety. A hexopyranosyl nucleoside (XX) would consume two moles of oxidant per mole and liberate one mole of formic acid (from C3 of the hexose residue). The same dialdehyde (XIX) would be produced from XX. A pentopyranosylpyrimidine (XXI) should consume two moles of oxidant per mole, liberate one mole of acid,

(135) E. L. Jackson, *Org. Reactions*, **2**, 341 (1944); see also p. 9 this vol.

(136) J. M. Bobbitt, *Advances in Carbohydrate Chem.*, **11**, 1 (1956).

and produce the dialdehyde XXII. Thus, a quantitative measurement of the uptake of oxidant and of the acid liberated (if any) can identify the lactol ring-structure of

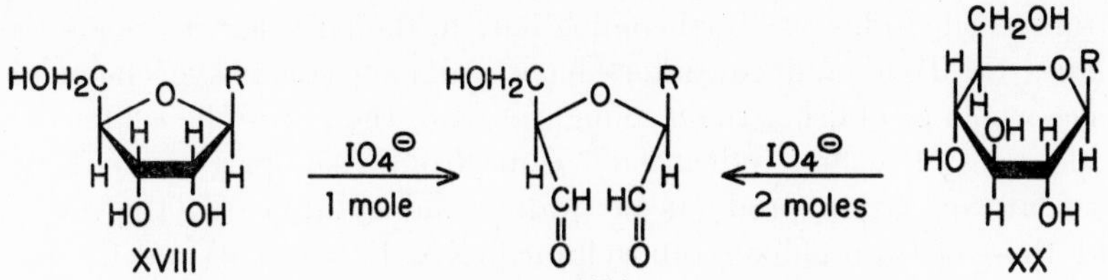

1-aldosylpyrimidines. Furthermore, since the asymmetric center of the anomeric carbon atom of the sugar is maintained in the dialdehyde, information relative to the α or β configuration may be obtained by the use of optical rotational measurements on the products of metaperiodate oxidation. A 1-β-D-hexopyranosylthymine (XX, R = thyminyl), would give the same dialdehyde as 1-β-D-ribofuranosylthymine (XVIII), although the consumption of oxidant and amount of acid liberated would not be the same in the two cases.

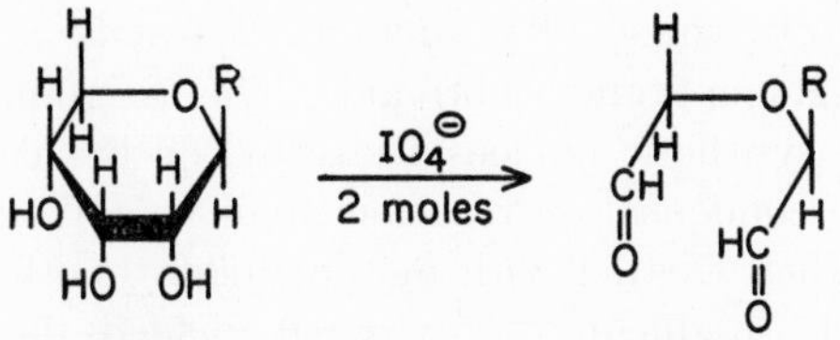

Oxidation of the naturally occurring nucleosides, uridine and cytidine,[137] with metaperiodate showed an uptake of one mole of oxidant per mole of nucleoside *without* the liberation of formic acid, in agreement with and in confirmation of the furanoid ring structure which had been established long previously by Levene and Tipson.[108,127-129]

Thymidine and 2-deoxycytidine proved to be resistant to oxidation by this reagent, an observation which can best be explained[138] by the fact that a furanoid ring (see XXIII), in which the α-glycol system is absent, was known to be present in the former and was suspected in the latter. Independently, Manson and Lampen[114] arrived at the same conclusions from similar metaperiodate studies.

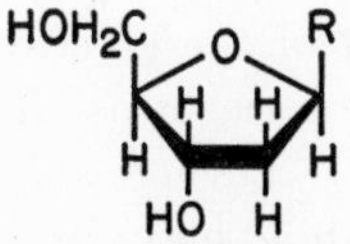

(137) J. Davoll, B. Lythgoe and A. R. Todd, *J. Chem. Soc.*, 833 (1946).
(138) D. M. Brown and B. Lythgoe, *J. Chem. Soc.*, 1990 (1950).

5. *The Configuration at the Glycosyl Center*

Information as to the configuration of the anomeric center (C1) of the natural nucleosides was forthcoming only in the past decade. Some elegant studies by Todd and coworkers have provided conclusive chemical evidence which establishes the β configuration of the glycosylic center of these nucleosides. The first indication[137] came from a comparison of the metaperiodate oxidation products of uridine and cytidine, on the one hand, with those of 1-β-D-glucopyranosyluracil (XX, R = uracil) and 1-β-D-glucopyranosylcytosine (XX, R = cytosine) on the other. The latter two compounds were synthetic nucleosides prepared by the method of Hilbert[139,140] (see page 329) by the condensation of a 2,4-dialkoxypyrimidine with tetra-O-acetyl-α-D-glucopyranosyl bromide. The assignment of the β configuration to these synthetic nucleosides rested on the very reasonable assumption that the condensation reaction involves a Walden inversion at C1 of the sugar. When treated with metaperiodate, both uridine (XVIII, R = uracil) and 1-β-D-glucopyranosyluracil yielded the same dialdehyde, although the synthetic nucleoside consumed 2 moles of oxidant per mole and liberated one mole of formic acid. Similarly, both cytidine (XVIII, R = cytosine) and 1-β-D-glucopyranosylcytosine afforded an identical crystalline dialdehyde which was isolated as the picrate. It was therefore concluded[137] that uridine and cytidine are nucleosides of the β configuration.

Direct confirmation of this structural assignment was provided by Furberg[141] by physical methods. The crystal structure of cytidine was determined in detail by the use of two-dimensional Fourier synthesis (see Fig. 12). The stereochemical orientation of the bonds C1—N1′ and C2—O2 were shown to be in *trans* position, an observation which proved that the glycosyl linkage in cytidine (and, thereby, in uridine) is of the β type. The planar pyrimidine ring is nearly perpendicular to the carbohydrate ring, and the latter is *not quite* planar. The C1—N1′ bond lies in the plane of the pyrimidine ring. These studies not only confirmed the configuration at the glycosyl center, but also provided independent confirmation of the furanoid ring structure and the attachment of the ribosyl moiety to N1 of the bases. No crystals of deoxyglycosylpyrimidines were examined, although Furberg suggested that the results from the cytidine study could probably be applied to them.

Unequivocal *chemical* proof of the glycosyl configuration of nucleosides in the ribose and deoxyribose series arose from studies of the anhydronucleosides ("cyclonucleosides"). Levene and Tipson[129] had demonstrated that 2,3-O-isopropylideneuridine may be sulfonylated to the 5-O-tosyl

(139) G. E. Hilbert and T. B. Johnson, *J. Am. Chem. Soc.*, **52**, 2001, 4489 (1930).

(140) G. E. Hilbert and E. F. Jansen, *J. Am. Chem. Soc.*, **58**, 60 (1936).

(141) S. Furberg, *Acta Cryst.*, **3**, 325 (1950); *Acta Chem. Scand.*, **4**, 751 (1950).

derivative which, in turn, may be converted to the 5-deoxy-5-iodo nucleoside with sodium iodide in acetone. Todd and coworkers[142] (in attempting to prepare 5-deoxy-5-iodocytidine) similarly tosylated 2,3-O-isopropylidenecytidine (XXIV) and obtained a mixture of products, presumed

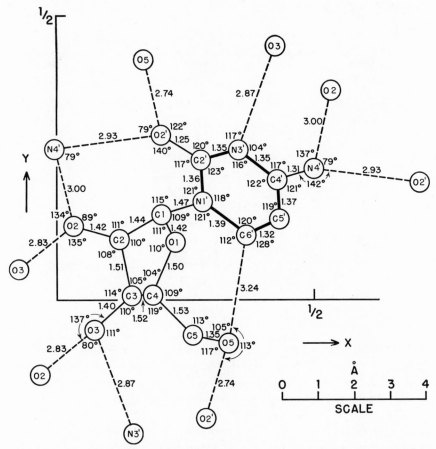

Fig. 12.—The Crystal Structure of Cytidine, with the Pyrimidine Ring Shown in Heavy Lines. (Adapted from Furberg.[141])

to be the 5-tosylate ester (XXV) and the N'-p-toluenesulfonamide (XXVI). Treatment of this crude mixture with acetone (at 100°) yielded an ionic compound (XXVII). Concurrent studies on tosylated 2,3-O-isopropylidene-adenosine indicated (on the basis of x-ray diffraction studies, molecular-weight determination, and spectroscopic data) that intramolecular anhydride formation had occurred. The fact that XXVII could be converted

(142) V. M. Clark, A. R. Todd and J. Zussman, J. Chem. Soc., 2952 (1951).

to cytidine was explained in terms of an oxygen bridge between C5 of the sugar and C2 of the pyrimidine (a 2′,5-anhydrocytidine),[143] which places

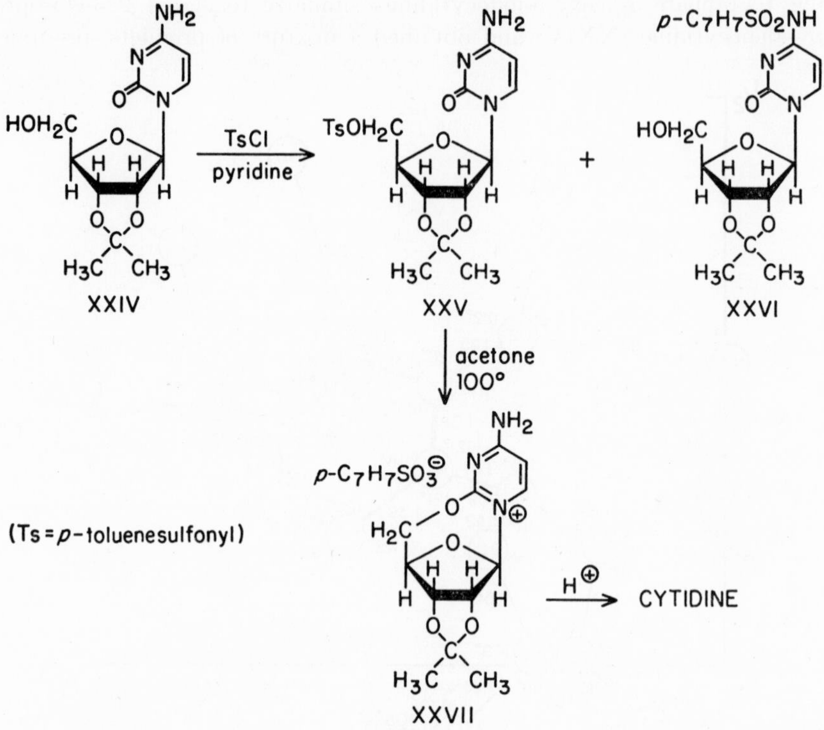

XXVII in the class of 2-alkoxypyrimidines. These pyrimidine "ethers" are known[139,140] to be readily dealkylated by acids, to afford 2-hydroxypyrimidine derivatives. Examination of molecular models revealed that the formation of an anhydronucleoside is possible *only* if the original nucleoside, cytidine, is of the β configuration.[142]

Essentially similar results[144] were obtained from the 3-O-acetyl-5-O-tosyl derivative of deoxycytidine (and deoxyadenosine). Although the expected 2′,5-anhydro-2-deoxycytidine tosylate was unstable and was not isolated, it broke down, upon heating in acetone, to several components, including cytosine and deoxycytidine. The lability of the C1—N1′ and C5—O2′ linkages was explained by the supposed presence of a positive charge on N1′

(143) Although the term "cyclonucleoside" has been employed (see Ref. 144) for naming this class of compounds, the term "anhydronucleoside," which is more in keeping with carbohydrate nomenclature, will be used in this Chapter.

(144) W. Andersen, D. H. Hayes, A. M. Michelson and A. R. Todd, *J. Chem. Soc.*, 1882 (1954).

of the anhydronucleoside. These results were, therefore, considered to be evidence supporting the β configuration at C1 of 2-deoxycytidine.

On extending these studies to thymidine,[145] a new facet of nucleoside chemistry was revealed. Aside from providing chemical evidence for the β configuration of this deoxynucleoside, their study showed that the anhydronucleoside process may be a useful method for isomerization of the carbohydrate portion of certain nucleosides with *retention* of the β configuration at the glycosyl center. Further, their work[145] confirmed the observation made previously by Levene and Tipson[130] that secondary sulfonyloxy groups on the sugar moiety could be replaced under appropriate conditions.[145a] Treatment of 3-O-mesyl-5-O-tritylthymidine[145] with sodium iodide in acetone for 2 hours at 100° yielded the 3-deoxy-3-iodo-5-O-trityl derivative in high yield as compared to a 50 % reaction with 3-O-tosyl-5-O-tritylthymidine[130] under more prolonged treatment. After removal of the trityl group and treatment of the dideoxyiodonucleoside with silver acetate in acetonitrile (containing traces of aliphatic amines) crystalline 2',3-anhydrothymidine (XXVIII) was obtained. Infrared and ultraviolet absorption spectra of this anhydronucleoside were in accord with structure XXVIII

XXVIII   XXIX

which would be formed by a process of intramolecular alkylation involving a rearward attack by O2' on C3 of the sugar. Acid hydrolysis of XXVIII afforded thymine plus a sugar whose R_f was identical with that for 2-deoxyD-*threo*-pentose ("2-deoxy-D-xylose"). Alkaline hydrolysis of XXVIII yielded a nucleoside (not isolated), with chromatographic and infrared properties akin to those of thymidine. This compound is most likely 1-(2-deoxy-β-D-*threo*-pentofuranosyl)thymine (XXIX).[145]

A parallel experiment[145] was performed with 5-deoxy-5-iodothymidine (XXX), a nucleoside derivative which was prepared[145,146] by a series of reactions from thymidine. Treatment of XXX with silver acetate in acetonitrile yielded the 2',5-anhydronucleoside (XXXI) in crystalline form. Alkaline hydrolysis of XXXI regenerated thymidine. An x-ray crystallo-

(145) A. M. Michelson and A. R. Todd, *J. Chem. Soc.*, 816 (1955).
(145a) See Ref. 254, pages 191–211.
(146) A. M. Michelson and A. R. Todd, *J. Chem. Soc.*, 951 (1953).

graphic analysis of the deoxyhalogeno-nucleoside (XXX) showed unequivocally that it possesses the β configuration[145] at C1. Since XXX had been

prepared from thymidine, this study yet again confirms by independent
means the structure of thymidine as 1-(2-deoxy-β-D-*erythro*-pentofurano-
syl)thymine (V, R = CH₃).

From these studies,[137,141,142,144,145] it is concluded that the β-D-glycosyl
formulation applies to all the nucleosides described in this Section. Since
1-(2-deoxy-β-"D-ribo"-furanosyl)cytosine (VI, R = H) may be deaminated
chemically[70] to 2-deoxyuridine, it follows that the latter is 1-(2-deoxy-β-
"D-ribo"-furanosyl)uracil (V, R = H). Similarly, since thymidine and
2-deoxy-5'-methylcytidine are chemically interconvertible,[34,62] the latter
is 1-(2-deoxy-β-D-*erythro*-pentofuranosyl)-5-methylcytosine (VI, R = CH₃).
The deoxynucleoside containing 5-(hydroxymethyl)cytosine is most likely
1-(2-deoxy-β-"D-ribo"-furanosyl)-5-(hydroxymethyl)cytosine, since it has
been obtained (enzymically) from the nucleotide of 2-deoxycytidine.[106] Indeed, it is to be noted that *all* pyrimidine nucleosides which have been
isolated from the nucleic acids (and characterized) have been shown, thus
far, to contain either β-D-ribofuranosyl or 2-deoxy-β-D-*erythro*-pentosyl
moieties in their structure.

IV. OTHER NATURALLY OCCURRING PYRIMIDINE NUCLEOSIDES[146a]

1. *Orotidine*

Orotic acid (uracil-6-carboxylic acid), first isolated[147] from milk, has been
amply demonstrated to be an effective precursor of nucleic acid and nu-

(146a) Vicine, which contains the divicine residue as the aglucon, was discovered
in 1870 by H. Ritthausen and U. Kreusler [*J. prakt. Chem.*, [2] **2**, 333 (1870)] as a con-

(R = D-glucosyl)
LEVENE'S FORMULATION OF VICINE

cleotide pyrimidines[148] in certain microorganisms and animal tissues. Although orotic acid was synthesized by Wheeler in 1907,[149] not until 1930 was the identity of the naturally occurring material with a synthetic sample confirmed by Bachstez,[150] who showed that an erroneous melting point of the natural substance had been reported by the early workers.[147]

Michelson and coworkers[151] isolated a nucleoside containing orotic acid from the mycelia of certain uridine-requiring mutants of *Neurospora*. Unlike uridine or cytidine, this nucleoside is cleaved by acid hydrolysis (0.5 N sulfuric acid, 100°) to orotic acid and ribose, the latter being identified by paper chromatography (in several solvents) and by typical color reactions for pentoses. The relatively facile cleavage of this nucleoside by acid would tend to indicate that orotidine might be a pentoside rather than a pentosyl derivative. The authors[151] suggested, however, that this unexpected lability of orotidine might be ascribable to the presence of a carboxyl function at C6 (of the base) adjacent to N1.

More definitive information on the structure of orotidine came from metabolic studies.[152] These experiments showed that orotic acid and 5-*O*-

---

stituent of vetch seeds. The tautomeric nucleoside structures were proposed by P. A. Levene [*J. Biol. Chem.*, **18**, 305 (1914)] although it was known that the behavior of the "nucleoside" toward acid is similar to that for common glycosides. Recently, this formulation has been conclusively shown to be incorrect by A. Bendich and G. C. Clements [*Biochim. et Biophys. Acta*, **12**, 462 (1953)], who have established the isomeric *glycoside* (rather than the nucleoside) structure for this hexose derivative.

VICINE

(147) G. Biscaro and E. Belloni, *Ann. Soc. Chim. Milano*, **11**, 18, 71 (1905); *Chem. Zentr.*, **76**(II), 63 (1905).

(148) L. D. Wright, C. S. Miller, N. R. Skeggs, L. L. Weed and D. W. Wilson, *J. Am. Chem. Soc.*, **73**, 1898 (1951); H. Arvidson, N. A. Eliasson, E. Hammarsten, P. Reichard, H. von Ubisch and S. Bergström, *J. Biol. Chem.*, **179**, 169 (1949); R. B. Hurlbert and V. R. Potter, *ibid.*, **195**, 257 (1952).

(149) H. L. Wheeler, *Am. Chem. J.*, **38**, 358 (1907).

(150) M. Bachstez, *Ber.*, **63**, 1000 (1930).

(151) A. M. Michelson, W. Drell and H. K. Mitchell, *Proc. Natl. Acad. Sci. U. S.*, **37**, 396 (1951).

(152) I. Lieberman, A. Kornberg and E. S. Simms, *J. Am. Chem. Soc.*, **76**, 2844 (1954); *J. Biol. Chem.*, **215**, 403 (1955).

phospho-D-ribosyl pyrophosphate interact in the presence of a phosphorylase to produce orotidine 5-phosphate ("O5P"). The latter is decarboxylated enzymically to uridine 5-phosphate (uridylic acid). Orotidine 5-phosphate was also synthesized[152] enzymically by phosphorylation of orotidine. These studies strongly indicate that the ribosyl moiety of orotidine is similar to that in uridine.

Application of ultraviolet absorption spectroscopy[119] (see p. 302–308) showed that the detailed spectrum of orotidine at different pH values is very similar to that for 1-methylorotic acid, which confirmed the assignment of the carbohydrate–pyrimidine linkage to N1 of the aglycon.

When treated with sodium metaperiodate, the barium salt of orotidine consumes one mole of oxidant per mole *without* the liberation of formic acid, in accord with a pentofuranosyl structure.[119] The structure of orotidine, therefore, is certainly 1-(D-ribofuranosyl)uracil-6-carboxylic acid (XXXII).

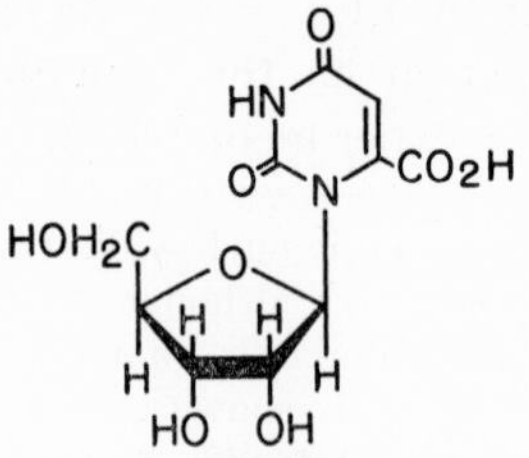

XXXII

Although it is reasonable to assume from the enzymic studies cited[152] that orotidine possesses the β configuration at the anomeric center, unequivocal determination of this feature is to be desired. Of interest is the fact that 1,3-dimethylorotic acid,[119] 3-methylorotic acid,[119,153] and orotic acid itself are decarboxylated to the corresponding uracil derivatives at elevated temperatures. If orotidine could be decarboxylated in some similar fashion to uridine, the complete structure of XXXII would be established.

2. The "Sponge" Nucleosides

W. Bergmann and coworkers[154,155] isolated, from the Caribbean sponge (*Cryptotethia crypta*), a mixture of nucleosides which had not previously been encountered in Nature. These were given the trivial names of spongothymidine,[154] spongouridine,[155] and spongosine.[154] Spongothymidine was degraded by strong acid to thymine. The ultraviolet absorption spectrum of spongothymidine resembled that for thymidine. The presence of a

(153) M. R. Atkinson, M. H. Maguire, R. K. Ralph, G. Shaw and R. N. Warrener, *J. Chem. Soc.*, 2363 (1957).

(154) W. Bergmann and R. J. Feeney, *J. Org. Chem.*, **16,** 981 (1951).

(155) W. Bergmann and D. C. Burke, *J. Org. Chem.*, **20,** 1501 (1955).

pentose fragment in the nucleoside was indicated by the facile formation of a tribenzoate ester, and metaperiodate titration gave evidence that the lactol ring structure is of the furanoid type.[154] Spongothymidine proved to be resistant to catalytic reduction, even under conditions more vigorous than those used by Levene and LaForge[50] for the reduction of uridine. The high positive optical rotation exhibited by spongothymidine led to the suggestion that this nucleoside was possibly a xylosyl rather than a ribosyl derivative of thymine.[154]

Makino and Satoh[156] observed that spongothymidine shows a negative Böeseken boric acid reaction[132] and this result therefore excluded both ribose and lyxose as the sugar component. They also reported the supposed presence of xylose (but not arabinose) on a paper chromatogram of a sulfuric acid hydrolyzate of spongothymidine, and they concluded therefrom that this nucleoside was a xylofuranosylthymine. Attempts to repeat this acid hydrolysis experiment without destruction of the sugar moiety were unsuccessful.[155]

A study of the detailed ultraviolet absorption spectrum of spongothymidine at different pH values, especially in the high alkaline region (pH 12–14) where the influence of the sugar moiety upon the spectrum is markedly manifested, supported the view that the sugar component is not a ribose residue.[87] The rate of consumption of metaperiodate was low,[155] in accord with the presence of a *trans*-glycol system. The ionophoretic migration[157] of spongothymidine was not accelerated by borate ions, which indicated the absence of an α-*cis*-glycol structure.[155] Application of the mild, reductive hydrolysis procedure of Burke[72] (see page 293) yielded D-*arabinose*,[155] which was identified by paper chromatography, paper ionophoresis in borate buffer, and a comparison of the phenylosazone with authentic material. When treated with metaperiodate, spongothymidine yielded a dialdehyde solution of almost the same optical rotation and sign as that obtained from uridine. The conclusion was reached, therefore, that spongothymidine is 1-β-D-arabinofuranosylthymine (XXXIII, R = CH₃).

XXXIII

---

(156) K. Makino and K. Satoh, *Intern. Congr. Pure and Appl. Chem., 12th Congr. Abstracts*, 316 (1951).

(157) A. B. Foster, *Chem. & Ind.* (London), 828 (1952).

An almost analogous series of experiments[155] was carried out with spongo-uridine, which established the structure of this sponge nucleoside as 1-β-D-arabinofuranosyluracil (XXXIII, R = H). Independent proof of the complete structure of these sponge nucleosides has now been unequivocally established[158,159] by synthesis. The third nucleoside, spongosine, has been shown by degradative studies[160] and by synthesis[161] to be 6-amino-2-methoxy-9-(β-D-ribofuranosyl)purine (2'-methoxyadenosine).

The presence of spongothymidine and spongouridine in *Cryptotethia crypta* would, perhaps, suggest that those nucleosides might be intimately associated with the nucleic acids of this particular sponge. However, in a report by Bergmann and co-workers[162] on the degradation of the nucleic acids of this (as well as fifteen other) species of sponge, only the four usual ribonucleosides and 2-deoxyribonucleosides were detected. Because of the exceptionally low content of ribonucleic acid in *Cryptotethia crypta*, they[162] suggest that perhaps there exists in this species a metabolic aberration which diverts most of the intermediates of ribonucleic acid synthesis to (a) the formation of these arabinonucleosides or, possibly, (b) an unstable substance of greater complexity incorporating these nucleosides.[162]

3. *Amicetin and Related Nucleosides*

Amicetin, the first nucleoside in a series of structurally related, antibiotic substances isolated from *Streptomyces* cultures, was shown to possess antituberculous activity.[9] Proof of the main structural features of this rather complex nucleoside (XXXIV) represents an interesting example of the use of degradative procedures coupled with periodate oxidations, spectrophotometric methods, and potentiometric titrations[163-167] (see XXXIV–XL).

Flynn and coworkers[163] showed by titration that amicetin has four ioniz-

(158) D. M. Brown, A. R. Todd and S. Varadarajan, *J. Chem. Soc.*, 2388 (1956).

(159) J. J. Fox, N. Yung and A. Bendich, *J. Am. Chem. Soc.*, **79**, 2775 (1957).

(160) W. Bergmann and D. C. Burke, *J. Org. Chem.*, **21**, 226 (1956).

(161) W. Bergmann and M. F. Stempien, Jr., *J. Org. Chem.*, **22**, 1575 (1957).

(162) W. Bergmann, J. C. Watkins and M. F. Stempien, Jr., *J. Org. Chem.*, **22**, 1308 (1957).

(163) E. H. Flynn, J. W. Hinman, E. L. Caron and D. O. Woolf, Jr., *J. Am. Chem. Soc.*, **65**, 5867 (1953).

(164) G. W. Kenner, C. B. Reese and A. R. Todd., *J. Chem. Soc.*, 855 (1955).

(165) P. Sensi, A. M. Greco, G. G. Gallo and G. Rolland, *Antibiotics & Chemotherapy*, **7**, 645 (1957).

(165a) The spectra of cytosamine and 2-deoxycytidine[87] are practically identical with regard to the wavelength of the maxima, the minima, and the *isosbestic* point. It should be noted, further, that the spectrum of cytosamine differs markedly from that listed for 4-amino-2-methoxypyrimidine,[87] which excludes position 2 of cytosine as a point of linkage.

(166) C. L. Stevens, R. J. Gasser, T. K. Mukherjee and T. H. Haskell, *J. Am. Chem. Soc.*, **78**, 6212 (1956).

(167) T. H. Haskell, *J. Am. Chem. Soc.*, **80**, 747 (1958).

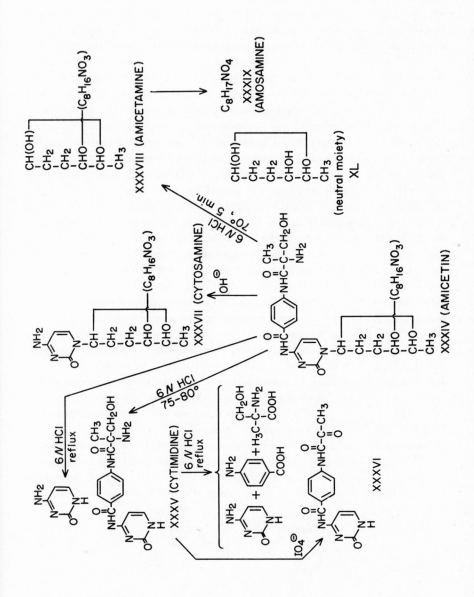

able groups (pK_a values of 10.4, 7.0, 7.0, and 1.1), and analytical determinations revealed the presence of two N-methyl groups, three C-methyl groups, and one primary amino group. Treatment of amicetin with 6 N hydrochloric acid at reflux temperature degraded the antibiotic substance to cytosine, whereas, at lower temperatures, this reagent produced a cytosine derivative, namely, cytimidine (XXXV). Degradation of cytimidine with acid yielded cytosine, p-aminobenzoic acid, and an amino acid which (on the basis of infrared spectral comparisons with related, synthetic amino acids) was assigned the *dextro*-α-methylserine structure. Potentiometric titration of cytimidine indicated the presence of two dissociable groups (with pK_a values of 9.8 and 6.9) and the absence of a carboxyl function, which led to the conclusion that the two amino acids (p-aminobenzoic acid and *dextro*-α-methylserine) are joined in amide linkages. A Bratton–Marshall test[168] on cytimidine was negative, which indicated that the amino group of p-aminobenzoic acid is bound. Cytimidine consumes one mole of metaperiodate per mole, with the liberation of formaldehyde and ammonia. The elemental analyses of the metaperiodate oxidation product agreed with the elemental composition for a pyruvyl derivative of (p-aminobenzoyl)cytosine (XXXVI). From these data, structure XXXV was advanced for cytimidine.[163] Hydrolysis of amicetin with dilute alkali yielded cytosamine (XXXVII), a nucleoside containing two ionizable groups (pK_a values, 3.9 and 7.0) with concomitant loss of the weakly acidic group (pK_a 10.4) present in amicetin. Hydrolysis of cytosamine with strong acid produced cytosine, a constituent which is also common to cytimidine. It was deduced therefrom that alkaline hydrolysis cleaves the amide linkage between cytosine and p-aminobenzoic acid, whereas acid hydrolysis ruptures the bond between cytosine and the portion as yet uncharacterized (the 14-carbon fragment) of the amicetin molecule.[163]

Assignment of the weakly acidic group (pK_a 10.4) of amicetin to the amide linkage between cytosine and p-aminobenzoic acid was confirmed[163] by the synthesis of N-benzoyl-1-methylcytosine (XLIa) by benzoylation of 1-methylcytosine. This cytosine derivative (XLIa), upon titration,

XLIa   XLIb

showed a pK_a of 10.6. However, the alternative structure, XLIb, is also possible. This ambiguity was removed by Kenner, Reese, and Todd,[164] who demonstrated, on the basis of spectral comparisons and dissociation con-

(168) A. C. Bratton and E. K. Marshall, *J. Biol. Chem.*, **128**, 537 (1939).

stants, that acylation of 1-methylcytosine produces compounds of the XLIa (instead of the XLIb) type of structure, and further, that the amide hydrogen atom resides predominantly on the exocyclic nitrogen function.

The acid-labile linkage between the portion as yet uncharacterized of amicetin and the pyrimidine has also to be considered. Although Flynn and coworkers presented evidence which would indicate *position 1* of the cytosine residue as being the point of union of the carbohydrate moiety in the nucleoside cytosamine and the antibiotic amicetin, the best and most direct evidence was provided by Sensi and coworkers.[165] These investigators showed simply that the ultraviolet absorption spectrum of cytosamine (neutral and cationic species) greatly resembles the detailed spectrum of 1-methylcytosine[165a] described (see Fig. 10) by Fox and Shugar.[87] On this basis, the linkage of the carbohydrate moiety (14-carbon fragment) to cytosine may be assigned with certainty to N1, that is, to a position similar to that found in pyrimidine nucleosides derived from the nucleic acids.

Determination of the structure of the carbohydrate moiety (14-carbon fragment) was aided by the observation[166,167] that treatment of amicetin (XXXIV) with 6 N hydrochloric acid at 70° for 5 minutes liberates the glycoside, amicetamine (XXXVIII). This fragment contains two acylable hydroxyl functions, two N-methyl groups, and two C-methyl groups. Amicetamine does not reduce Fehling or Benedict solution, although a hydroxylamine titration[169] has indicated the presence of a potential carbonyl group. Amicetamine gives a positive iodoform test, whereas cytosamine (XXXVII) does not. These data suggest that the cytosine moiety of cytosamine (and amicetin) is attached to the carbohydrate fragment by way of a "potential methyl ketone." Treatment of amicetamine with metaperiodate (over a period of 24 hours) resulted in a consumption of approximately three moles of oxidant per mole of XXXVIII, with the liberation of dimethylamine,[170] formic acid, glyoxal (presumably from C1 and C2 of the deoxydimethylamino sugar), formaldehyde, and a small proportion of acetaldehyde.

On the basis of these and other degradative studies, the following structure was suggested[166] for amicetamine.

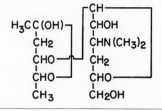

---

(169) A. R. Trimm and R. Hill, *Biochem. J.*, **50**, 310 (1952).

(170) Tertiary amines vicinal to a hydroxyl or an amine function are oxidized slowly by metaperiodate, with the liberation of secondary amines (see Ref. 136).

However, further structural studies by the same authors[171] indicate that this proposed structure for the 14-carbon fragment is not valid. Hydrolysis of amicetamine by the use of Dowex-50(H) resin yields a new dimethylamino hexose, amosamine (XXXIX), whose structure is still in doubt.[171] Cleavage of amicetin with methanolic hydrogen chloride yields the methyl glycoside of amicetamine. Further cleavage of this methyl glycoside with Dowex-50 (sulfonic acid) resin affords a *neutral* moiety (XL methyl glycoside) which does not reduce metaperiodate. However, the free sugar (XL) does consume one mole of metaperiodate per mole, with the formation of acetaldehyde and succindialdehyde. In addition, the neutral moiety contains but *one* C-methyl group as determined by the Kuhn–Roth procedure. These data[171] allow only of structure XL for the neutral moiety, namely, a 2,3,6-trideoxyaldohexose. The previously cited, positive iodoform test given by amicetamine but not by cytosamine indicates that the pyrimidine moiety of cytosamine (XXXVII) is linked to the 14-carbon fragment through the anomeric carbon atom of the trideoxy-aldohexose (XL). Since amicetamine does not reduce Benedict solution, whereas amosamine does, and since amicetamine is cleaved easily with acid, the glycosidic linkage between the two sugars of amicetamine involves (most probably) the anomeric carbon atom (C1) of amosamine and the only remaining hydroxyl group (C4) in the 2,3,6-trideoxyaldohexose (XL).

Antibiotic substances related in structure to amicetin have been isolated from other *Streptomyces* cultures. Sensi and coworkers[165] have isolated amicetin B, which only differs from amicetin by the absence of the *dextro-α*-methylserine moiety in its structure. This antibiotic substance is identical with Plicacetin, an antibiotic substance isolated by Haskell and coworkers[167,172] from *Streptomyces plicatus*. The structural relationship of Plicacetin (amicetin B) to amicetin was also established by partial synthesis.[167] Acylation of cytosamine (XXXVII) with *p*-nitrobenzoyl chloride, followed by reduction of the nitro group of the mono-acylated derivative, yielded Plicacetin.

Streptomyces plicatus yielded another antibiotic substance, Bamicetin, which, upon acid hydrolysis, affords cytimidine (XXXV).[167,172] The difference between amicetin and Bamicetin must therefore reside in the carbohydrate fragment. Periodate oxidation of the glycosidic fragment (bamicetamine) of Bamicetin yielded monomethylamine and formic acid in the oxidation mixture. It appears, therefore, that one major difference between amicetin and Bamicetin is to be found in the amine function of the carbohydrate moiety. Still unknown are (a) the identity of the hexoses and (b) the configuration at the glycosyl center of all three antibiotic substances.

It is noteworthy that deosamines structurally related to amosamine (XXXIX) had previously been found in fermentation liquors of *Streptomyces erythreus*, but not as *constituents* of nucleosides. For example, a 3,4,6-trideoxy-3-dimethylamino-aldo-

---

(171) C. L. Stevens, K. Nagarajan and T. H. Haskell, private communication.

(172) T. H. Haskell, A. Ryder, R. P. Frohardt, S. A. Fusari, Z. L. Jakubowski and Q. R. Bartz, *J. Am. Chem. Soc.*, **80**, 743 (1958).

hexose had been isolated by Clark,[173] by acid degradation of the antibiotic substance erythromycin, and assigned the structure XLII[173,174] and the trivial name "desos-

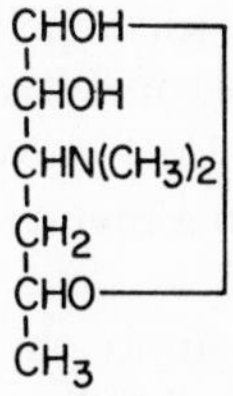

CHOH—⌐   CHOH—⌐
CHOH   CHOH
CHN(CH₃)₂   CHN(CH₃)₂
CH₂   CHOH
CHO—⌐   CHO—⌐
CH₃   CH₃
XLII 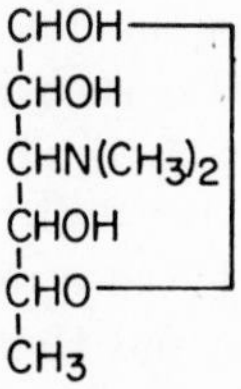   XLIII

amine." A closely related sugar, mycaminose, was isolated by acid degradation of the antibiotic substance carbomycin (elaborated by strains of the microorganism *Streptomyces halstedii*). The structure of this 6-deoxyhexosamine was shown[174a] to be XLIII. Chemical studies[173-174a] dealing with the proof of structure of XLII and XLIII did much to facilitate elucidation of some of the problems involved in the determination of the structure of the 14-carbon fragment (amicetamine) of amicetin.

It is not unlikely that more antibiotic substances having nucleoside structures will be found in Nature. Already, just in the realm of the *purine* nucleosides, three antibiotic substances, nebularine,[7,175] cordycepin,[6] and puromycin[8,176] have been isolated from natural sources.

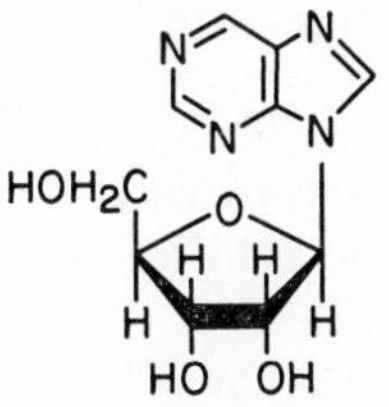

NEBULARINE 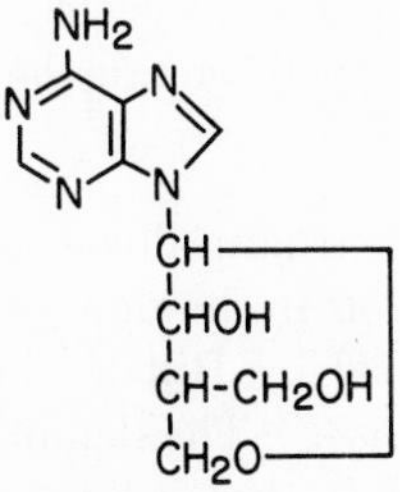   CORDYCEPIN 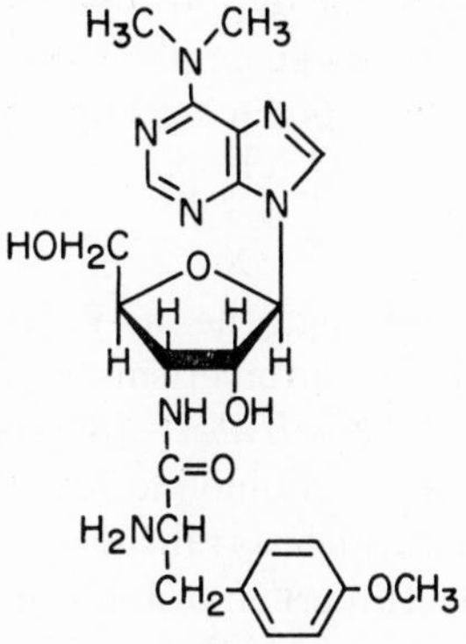   PUROMYCIN

V. SYNTHESES OF PYRIMIDINE NUCLEOSIDES

1. General Methods

a. Historical Background.—Several of the methods actively in use today for the preparation of pyrimidine nucleosides have their origin in the classi-

(173) R. K. Clark, *Antibiotics & Chemotherapy*, **3**, 663 (1953).

(174) E. H. Flynn, M. V. Sigal, P. F. Wiley and K. Gerzon, *J. Am. Chem. Soc.*, **76**, 3121 (1954).

(174a) F. A. Hochstein and P. P. Regna, *J. Am. Chem. Soc.*, **77**, 3353 (1953).

(175) G. B. Brown and V. Weliky, *J. Biol. Chem.*, **204**, 1019 (1953).

(176) B. R. Baker, R. E. Schaub, J. P. Joseph and J. H. Williams, *J. Am. Chem. Soc.*, **77**, 12 (1955).

cal Fischer–Helferich method[177] for the synthesis of glycosylpurines. In this procedure, the silver salt of an appropriate purine (for example, 2,8-dichloroadenine) is condensed in hot xylene with a poly-O-acylglycosyl halide ("acylohalogeno sugar"), such as tetra-O-acetyl-α-D-glucopyranosyl bromide, to yield an O-acylated nucleoside. In this example, deacetylation of this derivative afforded 2,8-dichloro-9-(D-glucopyranosyl)adenine, one of the first synthetic nucleosides reported.[177]

Attempts by Fischer and Helferich to apply their procedure to *pyrimidines* failed. The silver salts of various pyrimidines, when caused to react with tetra-O-acetyl-α-D-glucopyranosyl bromide, yielded substances[177,178] which were readily hydrolyzed to the aglycon plus the sugar, and which reduced Fehling solution (properties not common for pyrimidine nucleosides). In 1925, Levene and Sobotka[179] re-investigated this reaction, using pyrimidines substituted in various positions. The reaction of the silver or alkali salts of 3-methyluracil, 5-nitrouracil, 2-S-ethyl-2-thio-4-hydroxypyrimidine and 3-methyl-5-nitrouracil with tri-O-acetyl-α-D-xylopyranosyl bromide led to the formation of *glycosides*, as was evidenced by the ease with which these products underwent hydrolysis by dilute acid or alkali.[180] Cytosine did not react at all.

It was generally conceded[139,179] that glycosylation at N1 of the pyrimidine ring is not a feasible approach where lactam–lactim tautomerism of the type

$$\begin{array}{ccc} \text{O} & \text{H} & \text{OH} \\ \parallel & \mid & \mid \\ -\text{C}-\text{N}- & \rightleftharpoons & -\text{C}=\text{N}- \end{array}$$

is structurally possible. In accord with this reasoning, the first synthesis (of pyrimidine nucleosides) which *avoids* these tautomerisms was developed by Hilbert and Johnson.[139]

b. The Hilbert–Johnson Procedure.—The demonstration by Knorr[181] that 2-ethoxyquinoline interacts with methyl iodide to yield an addition product which is transformed to 1-methyl-2($1H$)-quinolone by heating suggested to Hilbert and Johnson[139] that similar transformations might be effected with pyrimidines containing the imido-ester grouping. Treatment of 2,4-dimethoxypyrimidine with methyl iodide at room temperature afforded 4-methoxy-1-methyl-2($1H$)-pyrimidinone (XLVI) which, upon treatment with acid, was converted to 1-methyluracil (XLVII).

The authors suggested that the intermediate addition product (XLV; not isolated) might be very unstable. Even when much less than one molar proportion of alkyl halide was used in this reaction, complete transformation of XLIV to XLVI was

(177) E. Fischer and B. Helferich, *Ber.*, **47**, 210 (1914).

(178) E. Fischer, *Ber.*, **47**, 1377 (1914).

(179) P. A. Levene and H. Sobotka, *J. Biol. Chem.*, **65**, 469 (1925).

(180) See C. E. Ballou, *Advances in Carbohydrate Chem.*, **9**, 59 (1954), for a discussion of alkali-sensitive glycosides of enols, including pyrimidine glycosides.

(181) L. Knorr, *Ann.*, **293**, 5 (1896); *Ber.*, **30**, 922, 927, 937 (1897).

noted, an observation which supported the notion that, in the breakdown of XLV to XLVI, alkyl halide is continuously liberated.[182] The fact that only *one* of the two lactim ethers (imido-esters) in the dialkoxypyrimidine structure was converted into the lactam (amide) structure by this reaction indicated that, in the pyrimidine (XLIV), N1 is the more basic nitrogen.[139] It was also shown[183] that ammonia reacts with alkoxypyrimidines to yield the corresponding aminopyrimidines ("amides"); this observation, incidentally, testifies to the ester-like behavior of pyrimidines containing the —N=C—OR grouping.

Extension of these studies to poly-O-acetylglycosyl halides led to the synthesis of 1-D-glycosyluracils and 1-D-glucosylcytosine.[139,140,184] Condensation of 2,4-diethoxypyrimidine with tetra-O-acetyl-α-D-glucopyranosyl bromide afforded the nucleoside intermediate (XLVIII). Treatment of this intermediate with methanolic hydrogen chloride gave 1-β-D-glucopyranosyluracil (XLIX), whereas ammonolysis with alcoholic ammonia yielded 1-β-D-glucopyranosylcytosine (L). The supposition that glycosylation had occurred at position N1 rested, of course, on a presumed analogy with the reaction (XLIV → XLVII) of dialkoxypyrimidines with methyl iodide.[139] Most significant was the fact that these synthetic nucleosides exhibit properties much akin to those of their naturally occurring analogs, uridine and cytidine, especially with regard to the resistance of XLIX and L to scission by acids. As in the case of uridine,[50] catalytic reduction of XLIX gave a

(182) Hilbert also investigated the reaction between 4-amino-2-methoxypyrimidine and methyl iodide, and, in this case, isolated a methoiodide intermediate which, upon treatment with silver sulfate, was converted to 1-methylcytosine. This was the

first case in which a stable methoiodide was isolated from this type of pyrimidine and it was considered to be evidence in favor of a mechanism involving the intermediate formation of a methoiodide in the reaction between alkyl halides and 2,4-dialkoxypyrimidines. See G. E. Hilbert, *J. Am. Chem. Soc.*, **56**, 190 (1934).

(183) G. E. Hilbert and E. F. Jansen, *J. Am. Chem. Soc.*, **56**, 134 (1934); **57**, 552 (1935).

(184) G. E. Hilbert, *J. Am. Chem. Soc.*, **59**, 330 (1937).

5,6-dihydro derivative which was readily cleaved by dilute acid to 5,6-dihydrouracil plus D-glucose.[139] Confirmation of the 1-β-D-pyranosyl structure assigned to XLIX and L has already been discussed (see p. 314).

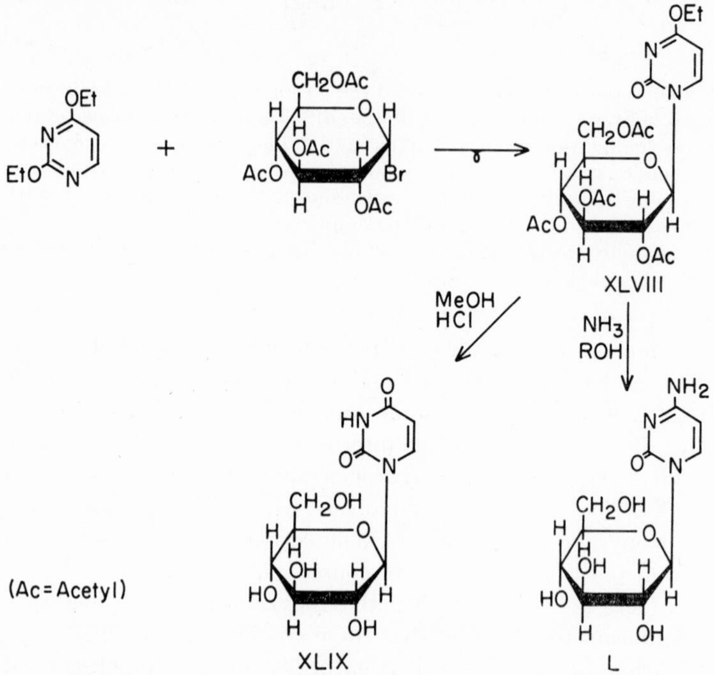

By use of the Hilbert–Johnson procedure,[139,140] a synthesis[185] of cytidine (II) was effected; this involved condensation of crude tri-O-acetyl-D-ribofuranosyl bromide with a 2,4-dialkoxypyrimidine, followed by treatment of the crude reaction mixture with alcoholic ammonia. Although the yields were low, this achievement marked the first synthesis of a naturally occurring nucleoside.

The Hilbert–Johnson procedure has since been applied to the synthesis of 1-glycopyranosylpyrimidines, containing such aglycons as uracil,[184,186] thymine,[187,188] cytosine,[188] 5-methylcytosine,[188] and N,N-dimethylcytosine.[189] 1-(D-Glucosyluronic acid) and 1-(D-galactosyluronic acid) nucleosides,[190] which were prepared by the use of the appropriate "acetohalogeno"

(185) G. A. Howard, B. Lythgoe and A. R. Todd., J. Chem. Soc., 1052 (1947).

(186) G. E. Hilbert and C. E. Rist, J. Biol. Chem., 117, 371 (1937).

(187) D. W. Visser, I. Goodman and K. Dittmer, J. Am. Chem. Soc., 70, 1926 (1948).

(188) J. J. Fox and I. Goodman, J. Am. Chem. Soc., 73, 3256 (1951).

(189) H. T. Miles, J. Am. Chem. Soc., 79, 2565 (1957).

(190) I. Goodman, Federation Proc., 12, 210 (1953).

uronic acid derivatives in the Hilbert–Johnson reaction, have been reported in abstract. This procedure has also led to the synthesis of 1-(2-deoxy-D-*arabino*-hexopyranosyl)uracil,[118,191] when tri-*O*-acetyl-2-deoxy-D-*arabino*-hexopyranosyl bromide[191] or chloride[118] were employed.

Aside from the successful synthesis of cytidine,[185] attempts made thus far to apply the Hilbert reaction to the preparation of 1-glyco*furanosyl*-pyrimidines have yielded anomalous results. Although the syntheses of 5′-methyluridine (I, R = CH₃) and 5′-methylcytidine (II, R = CH₃) by the condensation of sirupy tri-*O*-acetyl-D-ribofuranosyl bromide with 2,4-diethoxypyrimidine have been reported,[192] the properties of these nucleosides *differ* from those of the verified substances synthesized by other routes.[58,62] Other aspects of the Hilbert–Johnson procedure are discussed below.

  c. *The Mercuri Procedure.*—(i) *General Features.*—It was demonstrated by Davoll and Lowy[193] that monochloromercury derivatives of certain purines may be employed to greater advantage than their corresponding silver salts in the Fischer–Helferich[177] procedure for the preparation of *purine* nucleosides. A re-investigation with *pyrimidines*, by Fox, Yung, Davoll, and Brown, showed that this type of reaction could succeed (where silver and alkali metal salts failed[177-179]) and these studies led to a relatively facile synthetic route to pyrimidine nucleosides.[58]

Initial studies[58] had indicated that 1-glyco*pyranosyl* nucleosides prepared by the mercuri procedure are identical with those prepared by the Hilbert–Johnson method, when similar poly-*O*-acylglycosyl halides are employed. The applicability of the mercuri procedure to the synthesis of 1-aldopento*furanosyl* nucleosides was demonstrated by the preparation of 5′-methyluridine (LIV). Condensation of dithyminylmercury (LI) with tri-*O*-benzoyl-

D-ribofuranosyl chloride or bromide[194] (LII) yielded[58] a tri-*O*-benzoylated

  (191) I. Goodman and J. P. Howard, *Abstracts Papers Am. Chem. Soc.*, **115**, 24C (1949).
  (192) M. Roberts and D. W. Visser, *J. Am. Chem. Soc.*, **74**, 668 (1952).
  (193) J. Davoll and B. A. Lowy, *J. Am. Chem. Soc.*, **73**, 1650 (1951).
  (194) R. K. Ness, H. W. Diehl and H. G. Fletcher, Jr., *J. Am. Chem. Soc.*, **76**, 763 (1954); H. M. Kissman, C. Pidacks and B. R. Baker, *ibid.*, **77**, 18 (1955).

nucleoside which, upon deacylation with alcoholic ammonia, gave 1-β-D-ribofuranosylthymine (LIV), identical with the naturally occurring pyrimidine nucleoside[59-61] (see p. 290). 5'-Methyluridine (LIV) was also identical with a ribosylthymine prepared enzymically by Lampen,[56] but it differed in properties (optical rotation, melting point) from a "5'-methyluridine" synthesized[192] by way of the Hilbert–Johnson procedure. Verification of the β configuration of 5'-methyluridine was demonstrated conclusively by epimerization of LIV to 1-β-D-arabinofuranosylthymine (spongothymidine) by way of an anhydronucleoside intermediate.[58,159] The problem of the nature of the "5'-methyluridine" prepared by Roberts and Visser[192] is still not settled.[195]

Similarly, when sirupy tri-O-benzoyl-D-xylofuranosyl bromide[196] or chloride was condensed with dithyminylmercury, followed by debenzoylation with alcoholic ammonia, 1-β-D-xylofuranosylthymine was obtained.[58,197] The β configuration of this nucleoside was established by periodate techniques, as well as by conversion to 1-β-D-lyxofuranosylthymine by way of the anhydronucleoside intermediate.[197]

It has been noted[58] that, although the *precise* structure of dithyminylmercury (as well as that of other mercuri derivatives of pyrimidines, to be described later) is not known, the possibility of lactim–lactam tautomerism exists in this molecule. Aside from considerations of reaction mechanisms, the mercuri condensation is far more rapid (usually requiring 0.5 to one hour duration) than the Hilbert–Johnson reaction, which requires days to run its course. This factor is probably of importance where (a) the purity of "acylohalogeno" sugars is questionable (as is often the case with sirupy poly-O-acylglycofuranosyl halides, in which may be present some traces of mineral acid), and (b) the stability of the halide at elevated temperatures is likely to be of a low order.

Cytidine and related pyrimidine nucleosides have also been synthesized by the mercuri procedure.[198] In the case of the cytosine nucleoside, prior blocking of the amino function is necessary, in order to obtain a mercury derivative [(N-acetylcytosine)mercury] adaptable for nucleoside synthesis. Reaction of one mole of LV with two moles[199] of tri-O-benzoyl-D-ribofuran-

(195) As has been pointed out,[58] the fact that LIV is a nucleoside having the β configuration does not permit the designation of the "5'-methyluridine" prepared by Roberts and Visser[192] as an α-D nucleoside, since the optical rotation of the latter compound is far more negative than that of LIV.

(196) H. G. Fletcher, Jr., *J. Am. Chem. Soc.*, **75**, 2624 (1953).

(197) J. J. Fox, J. F. Codington, N. C. Yung, L. Kaplan and J. O. Lampen, *J. Am. Chem. Soc.*, **80**, 5155 (1958).

(198) J. J. Fox, N. Yung, I. Wempen, and I. L. Doerr, *J. Am. Chem. Soc.*, **79**, 5060 (1957).

(199) Unlike thymine, N-acetylcytosine [4-acetamido-2(1H)-pyrimidinone] forms a mercuri derivative containing mercury and pyrimidine in a 1:1 ratio. With an intermediate of this type (LV, precise structure unknown), two moles of poly-O-acyl-

osyl chloride (LII) yielded the fully acylated nucleoside (LVI), which was deacylated to cytidine. This facile synthesis of a naturally occurring nu-

cleoside has since been adapted to the preparation of cytidine-2-C^{14}-*ribosyl-t* ("doubly-labeled cytidine").[200] Cytidine was also synthesized from the monochloromercuri derivative of 4-ethoxy-2(*1H*)-pyrimidinone (LVII) which, upon reaction with LII, afforded LVIII.[198] This intermediate (LVIII) is analogous to those obtained by the Hilbert–Johnson reaction (see XLVIII). Compound LVIII was converted to cytidine with alcoholic ammonia, and to uridine by acidification with mineral acid.

(ii) *Variations Using Other Acylglycosyl Halides.*—The mercuri-pyrimidines (LI, LV, and LVII) have been individually coupled with a host of other poly-*O*-acylglycosyl halides in the mercuri reaction. Kissman and Weiss[201] have prepared several 1-(3-deoxy-3-amino-β-D-ribofuranosyl)pyrimidines by the use of 2,5-di-*O*-benzoyl-3-deoxy-3-phthalimido-β-D-ribosyl chloride[202] as the "acylohalogeno" sugar (LIX). Condensation with

glycosyl halide are required in order to effect the condensation reaction, a fact which, as the authors pointed out,[198] emphasizes the necessity of knowing precisely the type of mercuri-pyrimidine being employed.

(200) J. F. Codington, R. Fecher, M. H. Maguire, R. Y. Thomson and G. B. Brown, *J. Am. Chem. Soc.*, **80**, 5164 (1958).

(201) H. M. Kissman and M. J. Weiss, *J. Am. Chem. Soc.*, **80**, 2575 (1958).

(202) B. R. Baker, J. P. Joseph and R. E. Schaub, *J. Am. Chem. Soc.*, **77**, 5905 (1955).

dithiminylmercury (LI) gave an acylated-nucleoside intermediate which, after removal of the blocking groups, produced 3-amino-3-deoxy-5'-methyl-

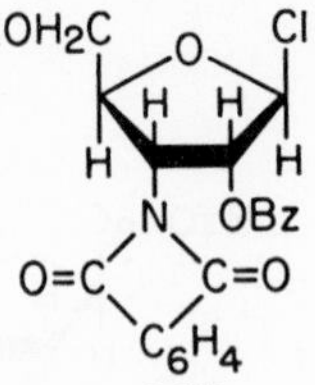

BzOH₂C   Cl

N   OBz

O=C   C=O

C₆H₄

LIX

uridine. Use of (*N*-acetylcytosine)mercury (LV) and LIX, in reactions akin to the previously described synthesis of cytidine,[198] yielded the 3-amino-3-deoxy analog of this naturally occurring nucleoside.[201] Condensation of the mercury derivative of 4-ethoxy-2(*1H*)-pyrimidinone (LVII) with LIX produced the intermediate LX (analogous to LVIII) which, upon treatment with methanolic ammonia, afforded 3-amino-3-deoxycytidine (LXI; R = R' = H). *N*'-Substituted amino derivatives of LXI [R = R' = CH₃ ; R = H, R' = (CH₂)₃CH₃] were obtained from LX when appropriate amines

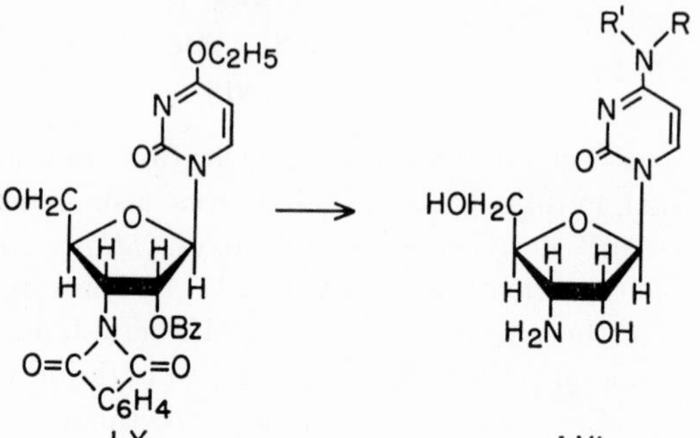

OC₂H₅

BzOH₂C   →   HOH₂C

N   OBz

O=C   C=O

C₆H₄

LX   H₂N   OH

         LXI

were employed in the deacylation reaction. 3-Amino-3-deoxyuridine was obtained by treatment of LX with methanolic hydrogen chloride.[201] In a similar manner, interaction of 2,3-di-*O*-benzoyl-5-deoxy-5-phthalimido-D-ribosyl chloride with mercuri derivatives of thymine and of *N*-acetylcytosine (LI and LV), respectively, led to the synthesis of 5-amino-5-deoxy-5'-methyluridine and 5-amino-5-deoxycytidine, respectively.[201] When 2,3-di-*O*-acetyl-5-deoxy-5-fluoro-D-ribosyl chloride was employed in similar reactions, 5-deoxy-5-fluoro-uridine and -cytidine, respectively, were obtained.[203] The mercuri procedure has also been applied to the synthesis of 6-deoxy-L-mannosyl nucleosides[204] (such as 1-α-L-rhamnopyranosyl-thymine

(203) H. M. Kissman and M. J. Weiss, *J. Am. Chem. Soc.*, **80**, 5559 (1958).
(204) B. R. Baker and K. Hewson, *J. Org. Chem.*, **22**, 959, 966 (1957).

and -cytosine) by condensation of the appropriate mercuri derivatives with tri-O-benzoyl-α-L-rhamnopyranosyl bromide.[205] Attempts to synthesize the corresponding 1-L-rhamnofuranosylpyrimidines have, however, so far been unsuccessful.[204]

(iii) *Variations Using Other Mercury–pyrimidines.*—Some extensions of the mercuri procedure for nucleoside syntheses to pyrimidines *other* than thymine, N-acetylcytosine, or 4-ethoxy-2($1H$)-pyrimidinone have been reported in abstract[206,207] and in a recent review.[208] The reaction between a mercuri derivative of 2-thiouracil and tetra-O-acetyl-α-D-glucopyranosyl bromide gave rise to 1-D-glucopyranosyl-2-thiouracil (in poor yield).[206] The condensation of the monochloromercuri derivative of 5-(ethoxycarbonyl)cytosine with tri-O-benzoyl-D-ribofuranosyl chloride (LII) yielded a tri-O-benzoylated nucleoside intermediate which, upon debenzoylation with alcoholic ammonia, afforded cytidine-5′-carboxamide and 5′-(ethoxycarbonyl)cytidine.[207,208] Monochloromercuri-(5-nitrocytosine), when condensed with tetra-O-acetyl-α-D-glucopyranosyl bromide, afforded 1-D-glucopyranosyl-5-nitrouracil. Duschinsky and coworkers[209] have synthesized 5′-fluorouridine by reaction of bis(5-fluorouracil)mercury with LII, followed by removal of the blocking groups with sodium alkoxide.

Although it may be expected that other mercury derivatives of pyrimidines will be applied in this general reaction, several limitations warrant consideration. Oddly enough, attempts to employ a mercuri derivative of uracil in this condensation reaction have thus far been unsuccessful.[210] As has been pointed out, since many of the mercurypyrimidines are insoluble, it is both desirable and usually possible to prepare them in essentially quantitative yield by the use of stoichiometric proportions of the reactants (pyrimidine, alkali, and mercuric halide), in order to obtain a pure product.[198] With uracil, however, it has not thus far been possible to prepare a pure mercury salt (that is, monochloromercuriuracil, diuracilmercury, or uracilmercury). Instead, mixtures, which probably contained some unreacted uracil, were obtained.[211] Lack of a solution to this problem may account for the consistent failure to adapt uracil to the mercuri synthesis.

Attempts to synthesize 6′-alkylated nucleosides by the mercuri procedure have led to the formation of glycosides instead of N1-glycosyl derivatives.[210(a)] Similar results have been reported when 2,4-diethoxy-6-methylpyrimidine was employed in

(205) R. K. Ness, H. G. Fletcher, Jr., and C. S. Hudson, *J. Am. Chem. Soc.*, **73**, 296 (1951).

(206) J. J. Fox, N. Chang and J. Davoll, *Federation Proc.*, **13**, 211 (1954).

(207) J. J. Fox, N. Yung and D. Van Praag, *Federation Proc.*, **16**, 182 (1957).

(208) J. J. Fox, *Record Chem. Progr.* (*Kresge–Hooker Sci. Lib.*), **19**, 173 (1958).

(209) R. Duschinsky, E. Pleven, J. Malbica and C. Heidelberger, *Abstracts Papers Am. Chem. Soc.*, **132**, 19C (1957).

(210) (a) J. J. Fox and N. C. Yung, unpublished data. (b) B. R. Baker, private communication.

(211) Mercury derivatives of uracil and thymine, stated to be $C_4H_2HgN_2O_2$ and $C_5H_4HgN_2O_2$, respectively, were reported by V. C. Myers [*J. Biol. Chem.*, **7**, 249 (1909–1910)]. Attempts to repeat those preparations have been unsuccessful.[58]

the Hilbert–Johnson procedure.[212] Exploratory studies[119] on the alkylation of orotic acid have afforded 3-methylorotic acid as the preponderant product. An examination of molecular models shows that the 6-carboxyl function exerts considerable steric hindrance at the N1 position. It was suggested, therefore, that N1-D-ribosylation of a mercury derivative of orotic acid ester (or amide) to orotidine (see p. 320) would be difficult, even if it should occur.[119]

As yet, examples of glycosylation at N3 of pyrimidines by use of the mercuri or Hilbert–Johnson reactions have not been observed. With the triazine "azathymine," however, Hall[213] has noted that the condensation of LXII with a mercury salt of

$$\underset{\text{"AZATHYMINE"}}{\text{(structure)}}$$

"AZATHYMINE"

6-methyl-asym-triazine-3,5-(2,4)-dione produces a mixture of three "nucleosides." These have been identified as the 2-, the 2,4-, and the 4-(D-ribofuranosyl) derivatives of "azathymine."

(iv) *Stereospecificity in the Hilbert–Johnson and Mercuri Syntheses.*— Baker and associates[214] have noted that the configuration of C1 of *purine* nucleosides prepared by the Fischer–Helferich procedure[177] appears to depend upon the position of the substituent at C2 of the sugar moiety, that is, a *trans* relationship exists[214a] between the purinyl group at C1 and the substituted hydroxyl function of C2. This observation resembles that previously made by Tipson,[215] who noted that treatment of poly-O-acylglycosyl halides with silver acetate in acetic acid, toluene, or other similar solvent yields sugar acetates bearing a *trans* relationship of substituents at C1–C2, regardless of the configuration of the poly-O-acylglycosyl halide employed in the reaction. Synthetic purine nucleosides containing the D-glucopyranosyl,[137] D-galactopyranosyl,[134] D-xylofuranosyl,[215a] or D-ribofuranosyl[216] moiety are of the β configuration (type LXIIa). In agreement

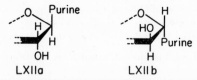

LXIIa   LXIIb

(212) P. Newmark and I. Goodman, *J. Am. Chem. Soc.*, **79**, 6446 (1957).

(213) R. H. Hall, *J. Am. Chem. Soc.*, **80**, 1145 (1958).

(214) B. R. Baker, J. P. Joseph, R. E. Schaub and J. H. Williams, *J. Org. Chem.*, **19**, 1786 (1954).

(214a) For a historical account of the broader aspects of this subject, see Ref. 224, p. 2.

(215) R. S. Tipson, *J. Biol. Chem.*, **130**, 55 (1939).

(215a) P. Chang and B. Lythgoe, *J. Chem. Soc.*, 1992 (1950).

(216) J. Davoll, B. Lythgoe and A. R. Todd., *J. Chem. Soc.*, 967 (1948).

with these observations, in synthetic purine nucleosides containing the
D-arabinofuranosyl[217] or D-arabinopyranosyl[134] moiety, the α configuration
(LXIIb) prevails. In both LXIIa and LXIIb, the C1–C2 substituents are
trans. Bristow and Lythgoe[217] have proposed that the poly-O-acylglycosyl
halides employed in all these cases possess the C1–C2-*cis* relationship and,
further, that the entering purinyl group displaces the halogen atom with
Walden inversion[214a] at C1, thus giving rise to a *trans* nucleoside. The
possibility of a double inversion at C1 in the case of C1–C2-*trans* acylglycosyl halides, by intervention of an orthoester ion[217a] with net retention
of configuration, was raised by Howard.[218]

A unifying hypothesis (the *trans* rule)[215] has been advanced by Baker
and coworkers[214,219] to explain the stereochemical control of the reaction
between poly-O-acylglycosyl halides and heavy metal salts of purines or
pyrimidines. This hypothesis states that the entering nitrogen heterocycle
will affix to the 1-position of the sugar on a side *trans* to the C2 acyloxy
substituent *regardless* of the anomeric configuration of the glycosyl halide.
If the halide possesses a C1–C2-*cis* configuration (as in LXIV), the purinyl
(or pyrimidinyl) group will displace the halogen atom with Walden inversion and produce the *trans* nucleoside (LXVI), as proposed previously by
Bristow and Lythgoe.[217] With C1–C2-*trans* acylglycosyl halides (as in

LXIII), the *trans* nucleoside (LXVI) would arise by way of a double
Walden inversion by either of two mechanisms. Inversion of LXIII to

(217) N. W. Bristow and B. Lythgoe, *J. Chem. Soc.*, 2306 (1949).

(217a) H. S. Isbell, *Ann. Rev. Biochem.*, **9**, 65 (1940).

(218) G. A. Howard, *J. Chem. Soc.*, 1045 (1950).

(219) B. R. Baker, in *Ciba Foundation Symposium, Chem. and Biol. of Purines*,
1957, p. 120.

LXIV could occur possibly by an attack by a halide ion[220] after which the purinyl group would attack C1 to yield LXVI. The more likely mechanism,[214,219] which relates directly to the acyloxy group at C2, is the formation of the orthoester ion (LXV). This transient carbonium ion would be subject to attack by the nitrogen heterocycle from the side opposite to the C1–C2 cyclic ion (with a second inversion) to yield LXVI. It should be noted that the observations and the mechanisms postulated by Baker and associates[214,219] for the Fischer–Helferich type syntheses are much akin to those made and applied previously to reactions of the Koenigs–Knorr type (glycoside synthesis from poly-O-acylglycosyl halides) by Tipson,rs. Frush and Isbell,[221] Pacsu,[222] Ness, Fletcher and Hudson,[223] and othe[215] Reviews dealing with the mechanisms of glycoside synthesis from poly-O-acylglycosyl halides have appeared.[11,217a,222,224-226]

An example which supports the "trans rule" is the condensation of 2,5-di-O-benzoyl-3-deoxy-3-phthalimido-β-D-ribosyl chloride, a glycosyl halide containing the C1–C2-trans structure, with mercuri derivatives of certain purines; only nucleosides of the β-D type are obtained.[202,227]

Wherever comparisons have been possible, the Hilbert–Johnson[139] and the mercuri[58] procedures have been found to yield, except for the "anomaly" noted previously,[192,195] identical products when identical poly-O-acylglycosyl halides are employed[58,197,198]; this finding indicates that a similar stereochemical control of the configuration at the glycosyl center of the resulting nucleosides is operative in these processes. With regard to the Hilbert–Johnson method, it has been shown that both the α and β anomers of tetra-O-acetyl-D-glucopyranosyl chloride (when condensed with 2,4-diethoxypyrimidine) yield the same nucleoside (1-β-D-glucopyranosyluracil, XLIX),[188] a fact which can be interpreted adequately in terms of the extensions of the "trans rule" made by Baker and coworkers.[214,219] It has

(220) Baker[219] has cited the conversion of tetra-O-acetyl-α-D-glucopyranosyl bromide (a cis halogeno sugar) to the less stable beta (trans) isomer with silver chloride [H. H. Schlubach, Ber., **59**, 840 (1926)] as an example of this reaction. Lemieux (see Ref. 224) suggested that, in this anomerization, the mechanism is of the S_N1 rather than the S_N2 type (proceeding by way of an orthoester ion).

(221) H. L. Frush and H. S. Isbell, J. Research Natl. Bur. Standards., **27**, 412 (1941).

(222) E. Pacsu, Advances in Carbohydrate Chem., **1**, 77 (1945).

(223) R. K. Ness, H. G. Fletcher, Jr., and C. S. Hudson, J. Am. Chem. Soc., **73**, 959 (1951).

(224) R. U. Lemieux, Advances in Carbohydrate Chem., **9**, 1 (1954).

(225) W. L. Evans, D. D. Reynolds and E. A. Talley, Advances in Carbohydrate Chem., **6**, 27 (1951).

(226) J. Conchie, G. A. Levvy and C. A. Marsh, Advances in Carbohydrate Chem., **12**, 157 (1957).

(227) B. R. Baker, R. E. Schaub and H. M. Kissman, J. Am. Chem. Soc., **77**, 5911 (1955).

therefore been concluded that the "*trans* rule" is operative in both procedures heretofore described for the synthesis of pyrimidine nucleosides.[197,219]

These two synthetic methods have, therefore, the "built-in" feature
which limits them to the synthesis of aldoglycosyl nucleosides having a
trans relationship between C1 and C2 substituents. From the practical
point of view, however, in any successful synthesis of a D-ribofuranosyl
analog of ribonucleosides, the β configuration of the product is assured.
In contrast, where the 2-acyloxy function is absent (as in poly-O-acyl-
2-deoxyglycosyl halides), stereochemical controls of the condensation reaction, by the mechanisms involved in the "*trans* rule," are lacking, and
both the α and the β nucleoside should be formed.[219]

(v) *Syntheses of 2-Deoxynucleosides.*—The *direct* synthesis of the naturally
occurring deoxynucleosides, thymidine and 2-deoxycytidine, by use of the
mercuri procedure[58] has been reported recently.[228] Attempts to condense
dithyminylmercury (LI) with a crude acylglycosyl halide sugar prepared
from 1-O-acetyl-3,5-di-O-benzoyl-2-deoxy-D-*erythro*-pentose failed to yield
a nucleoside, due, apparently, to the extreme lability of the di-O-benzoyl-2-
deoxy-D-*erythro*-pentofuranosyl chloride.[228a] It was found, however, that
crystalline 3,5-di-O-p-chloro(or p-methyl)benzoyl-2-deoxy-D-*erythro*-pento-
syl chloride (LXVIa, R = p-chlorobenzoyl or p-toluyl) couples readily with
the relatively more reactive monomercuripyrimidines (containing a 1:1
ratio of mercury to pyrimidine[199]) to afford, after deacylation, the α and β
anomers of 2-deoxynucleosides.[228]

LXVIa   LXVIb   LXVIc

Condensation of LXVIa (R = p-toluyl) with monomercurithymine (prepared from 1-acetylthymine) produces a mixture of acylated nucleoside
anomers (LXVIb and LXVIc, R' = thyminyl) which are separated and
de-esterified to thymidine and "α-thymidine." Similarly, reaction of
N-acetylcytosinemercury (LV) with LXVIa (R = p-chlorobenzoyl) yields
the α and β anomers of acylated 2-deoxycytidine which, after separation
and deacylation, are converted smoothly to 2-deoxycytidine (LXVIb,
R = H, R' = cytosinyl) and its α anomer (LXVIc). In like manner,
2-deoxy-5'-fluoro-uridine and -cytidine were synthesized, along with their

(228) M. Hoffer, R. Duschinsky, J. J. Fox and N. C. Yung, *J. Am. Chem. Soc.*, **81**,
4112 (1959).
(228a) J. J. Fox and I. Wempen, unpublished data.

α anomers.[228] Independently, Ness and Fletcher have reported the synthesis of 2-deoxyadenosine and its α isomer by essentially similar procedures. The fact that *both* anomers are obtained in these 2-deoxynucleoside syntheses[228,228b] is consonant with the *"trans* rule" described in the preceding Section.

An interesting aspect of this work[228] has been the finding that β anomers of these pyrimidine 2-deoxynucleosides are more *dextro*-rotatory than the corresponding α anomer of a nucleoside pair. It would be expected, according to Hudson's rule,[228c] that the reverse should hold true. In this regard, the much overlooked study of Davoll and Lythgoe[228d] has direct pertinence. They synthesized (by the Fischer–Helferich procedure[177]) the anomeric forms of 9-(2-deoxy-D-*erythro*-pento*pyranosyl*)theophylline from the corresponding diacetate esters of these purine 2-deoxynucleosides. The more *dextro*-rotatory anomer of the acylated theophylline 2-deoxynucleoside yielded, after saponification, the more *levo*-rotatory anomer of the free purine nucleoside. In light of this "anomaly," they could not assign a definite configuration to either anomer.[228d] However, in the case of the pyrimidine 2-deoxynucleosides previously described,[228] there can be no question of the identity of the anomers, since the β configuration of the naturally occurring 2-deoxyribonucleosides has been established (see p. 317). As suggested by Davoll and Lythgoe (and now substantiated[228]), the isorotation rules of Hudson[228c] have only a limited validity in the case of "N-glycosides" of 2-deoxy-D-*erythro*-pentose; this would indicate strongly that assignment of configuration to derivatives of 2-deoxyribose on the basis of rotational data *only* is certainly unwarranted. It would be of interest to examine the rotations of anomeric pairs of new pyrimidine and purine 2-deoxynucleosides which should now be more readily accessible by use of the mercuri process.

d. *The "Glycosylamine" Procedure.*—A new method for the synthesis of pyrimidine nucleosides has been developed.[229,230] Shaw[229] observed that 2-cyano-3-ethoxy-N-(ethoxycarbonyl)acrylamide[231] (LXVII, R′ = H) reacts with amines to yield 1-substituted 5-cyanouracils (LXIX). The reaction proceeds by way of the acyclic compound LXVIII which, upon acidifi-

(228b) R. K. Ness and H. G. Fletcher, Jr., *J. Am. Chem. Soc.*, **81**, 4752 (1959).

(228c) C. S. Hudson, *J. Am. Chem. Soc.*, **31**, 66 (1909).

(228d) J. Davoll and B. Lythgoe, *J. Chem. Soc.*, 2526 (1949).

(229) G. Shaw, *J. Chem. Soc.*, 1834 (1955).

(230) R. K. Ralph and G. Shaw, *J. Chem. Soc.*, 1877 (1956).

(231) This compound is prepared[229,230] by reaction of cyanoacetic acid with urethan or with N-methylurethan, to yield N-cyanoacetylurethan [M. Conrad and A. Schultze, *Ber.*, **42**, 735 (1909)] or its methyl analog which, upon treatment with ethyl orthoformate in acetic anhydride affords LXVII (R′ = H or CH₃).

cation of the reaction mixture with acetic acid, affords the pyrimidine (LXIX). This reaction was applied[230] to the synthesis, in good yields, of

LXVII   LXVIII   LXIX

the 5-cyano-1-(D-glycopyranosyl)uracil derivatives containing D-glucose, D-galactose, D-xylose, and D-ribose residues, by the use of the appropriate glycosylamines (or tautomers thereof). The β formulation of the nucleosides thus obtained was indicated by their specific rotations; this suggested that stereochemical control of the configuration at the glycosyl center of the nucleosides synthesized is operative in this reaction, too. A series of 3'-methyl derivatives of these nucleosides (LXIX, R' = CH₃) was obtained by the use of LXVII (R' = CH₃) in this synthesis.[230]

Baddiley and associates[232] have prepared tri-O-benzoyl-D-ribofuranosyl-amine (LXX) by treatment of tri-O-benzoyl-D-ribofuranosyl chloride (LII) with sodium azide in acetonitrile to yield the intermediate 2,3,5-tri-O-benzoyl-β-D-ribofuranosyl azide, which was reduced catalytically to LXX. Shaw and his associates[233] have prepared 5'-cyanouridine by reaction of LXVII (R' = H) with LXX in ethyl acetate in the presence of triethyl-

LXX

amine, followed by debenzoylation of the product with sodium methoxide. In analogous fashion, LXX was treated with 3-ethoxy-N-(ethoxycarbonyl)-acrylamide (prepared from ethyl propiolate plus sodium urethan),[153] to afford uridine.[233] It was also demonstrated[234] that acyl isothiocyanates (LXXI, R' = H or CH₃ ; R" = alkyl) will react with amines to give the linear compounds LXXII (acylthioureas) which may be cyclized directly to 2-thiouracils (LXXIII). Condensation of the D-ribosylamine ester (LXX) with 3-methoxy-2-methylacryloyl isothiocyanate in the presence of tri-ethylamine afforded LXXIII (R = 2,3,5-tri-O-benzoyl-D-ribosyl, R' =

(232) J. Baddiley, J. G. Buchanan, R. Hodges and J. F. Prescott, *Proc. Chem. Soc.*, 148 (1957); *J. Chem. Soc.*, 4769 (1958).

(233) G. Shaw, R. N. Warrener, M. H. Maguire and R. K. Ralph, *J. Chem. Soc.*, 2294 (1958).

(234) G. Shaw and R. N. Warrener, *J. Chem. Soc.*, 153 (1958).

CH_3), which was converted with aqueous alkali to 5'-methyl-2'-thiouridine.[233] Similarly, 3-ethoxyacryloyl isothiocyanate (LXXI, R' = H, R" = C_2H_5) plus LXX yielded the tribenzoate ester of LXXIII (R' = H) which was converted with sodium alkoxide or ammonia to 2'-thiouridine. These D-ribo-2'-thionucleosides exhibit ultraviolet spectral properties similar to those shown by 1-methyl-2-thiouracil[123] and an enzymically prepared sample of 2'-thiouridine.[235] Treatment of 2'-thiouridine with monochloroacetic acid afforded uridine; this finding permitted assignment of the 1-(β-D-ribofuranosyl) structure to these 2-thiouracil nucleosides.[233]

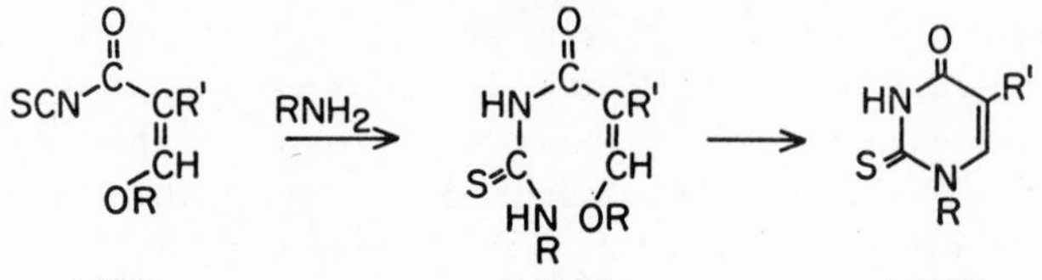

LXXI   LXXII   LXXIII

On the basis of experience derived from previous successful syntheses of 1-substituted 5-cyano-2-thiouracils,[236] Shaw and coworkers[233] synthesized 5'-cyano-2'-thiouridine. This synthesis was accomplished, interestingly enough, from the 1,3-thiazine (LXXIV) which, when reacted with the tribenzoate ester of D-ribofuranosylamine (LXX), proceeded by way of the acyclic compound LXXV (not isolated) to afford the tribenzoate ester of LXXVI (R = D-ribofuranosyl). Removal of the benzoyl groups yielded 5'-cyano-2'-thiouridine.

LXXIV   LXXV   LXXVI

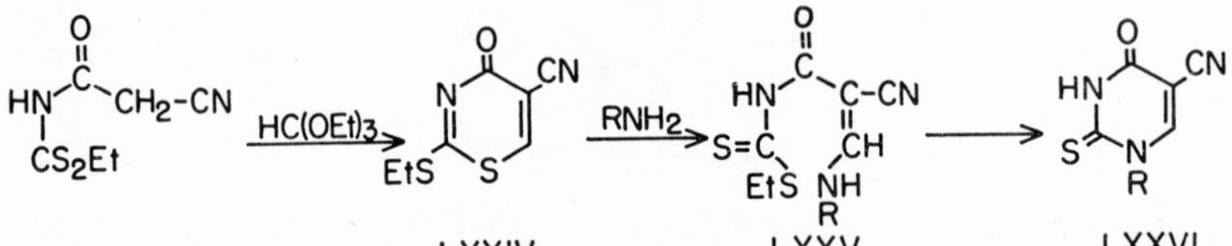

The apparently exclusive formation of pyrimidine nucleosides of the β configuration in these reactions (no α isomers have been detected thus far) would seem more than fortuitous. In experiments with simple primary amines, these investigators[229,234] have isolated acyclic compounds (such as LXVIII and LXXII, R = alkyl); this justifies their view that, in reactions with the D-ribosylamine derivative (LXX), analogous acyclic compounds are intermediates. Shaw[233] has suggested that cyclization of the β anomer of these acyclic compounds would occur more readily than for the corresponding α anomer (which may accompany them). In the case of the α

(235) D. B. Strominger and M. Friedkin, J. Biol. Chem., 208, 663 (1954).

(236) M. R. Atkinson, G. Shaw, K. Schaffner and R. N. Warrener, J. Chem. Soc., 3847 (1956).

anomers (LXXVII, R′ = —CS—NH—CO—CR=CH—OR″ or —CH=
CR—CO—NH—COOEt) cyclization of the chain, to give nucleosides,
would be sterically hindered by the presence of the 2-O-benzoyl function.
This hindrance could be enhanced, furthermore, by a tendency to oxazoline

LXXVII   LXXVIII

formation, as in formation of LXXVIII. This suggested hypothesis[233]
would seem adequate to account for the failure to isolate nucleosides of
the α configuration and may be partially responsible for the relatively low
yields (20–40%) obtained, in these reactions, with LXX. This mechanism
of stereochemical control, if correct, would signify that the "glycosylamine
procedure" as applied to compounds analogous to LXX would lead only
to pyrimidine nucleosides having a *trans* relationship between the aglycon
and the C2-acyloxy substituent. In this regard, the similarity to the *"trans*
rule," as extended by Baker and coworkers,[214,219] is striking.

A test of this hypothesis would lie in studying the products of the reaction of a 2-deoxy analog of LXX with LXVII, LXXI, or LXXIV, in order
to ascertain whether the *α and β* anomers of the nucleoside would be
formed. Such a 2-deoxyglycosylamine derivative has not yet been synthesized; for the present, this effectively precludes the use of the "glycosylamine reaction" for the synthesis of 2-deoxypentonucleosides.

e. Miscellaneous Syntheses.—The procedure of Johnson and Litvak[237] for
the conversion of β-substituted β-alanines to 6-substituted 5,6-dihydro-
uracils has been adapted by Gearien and Binkley[238] to the synthesis of
1-substituted uracil analogs. Treatment of LXXIX (R = CH₃), in aqueous
hydrochloric acid, with potassium cyanate afforded the dihydrouracil derivative (LXXX), which was brominated to the 5-bromo-5,6-dihydrouracil
(LXXXI). The latter compound was dehydrohalogenated to LXXXII in
boiling N,N-dimethylformamide. Gabel and Binkley[239] have prepared
several 3-acyl-1-arylureas (LXXXIII), by the method of Lieser and Kemmner,[240] from acrylyl isocyanate and primary amines. Ring closure of these
acylureas in N,N-dimethylformamide (with a small proportion of glacial
acetic acid) converted them to the 1-substituted 5,6-dihydrouracils

(237) T. B. Johnson and J. Litvak, *J. Am. Chem. Soc.*, **58**, 299 (1936).
(238) J. E. Gearien and S. B. Binkley, *J. Org. Chem.*, **23**, 491 (1958).
(239) W. G. Gabel and S. B. Binkley, *J. Org. Chem.*, **23**, 643 (1958).
(240) T. Lieser and K. Kemmner, *Chem. Ber.*, **84**, 4 (1951).

(LXXX).[239] Whether these reactions could be adapted to the synthesis of 5,6-dihydropyrimidine nucleosides, starting from the appropriate sugar

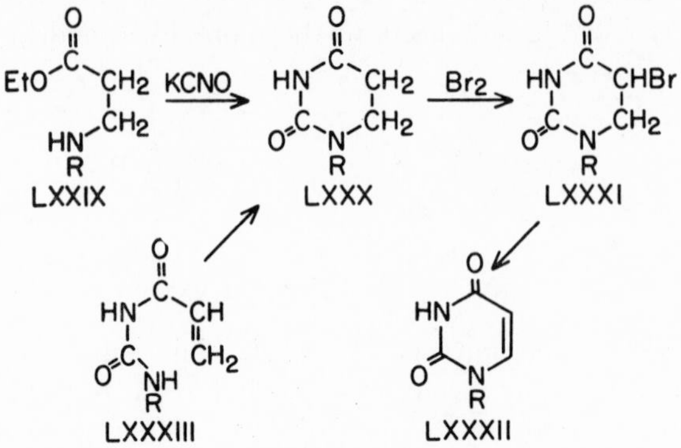

derivatives of LXXIX or LXXXIII (R = glycosyl), warrants investigation. It is noteworthy that these reactions and especially those of the earlier investigators[229,230] (LXVII → LXXVI) give a new role to glycosylamines as starting materials for the synthesis of nucleosides.

It had been demonstrated long ago that 1-(cyanoacetyl)urea (LXXXIV

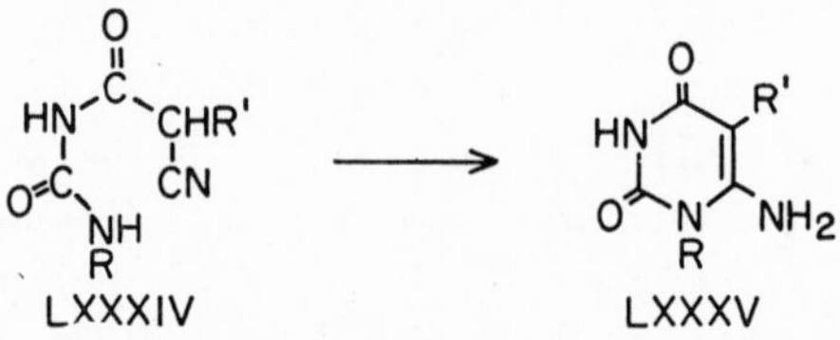

R = R' = H) or 1-(2-cyanopropionyl)urea (R = H, R' = CH₃) cyclize smoothly, in basic media, to 6-aminouracil (R = R' = H)[241] and 6-amino-thymine (R = H, R' = CH₃),[242] respectively. Johnson and Bergmann[243] then synthesized LXXXIV (R = tetra-O-acetyl-D-glucopyranosyl, R' = H) by the condensation of (tetra-O-acetyl-D-glucopyranosyl)urea with cyanacetic acid, but were unsuccessful in their attempts to cyclize this intermediate to the acetylated nucleoside (LXXXV). Goodman, however, reported (in abstract[244]) the successful cyclization of this tetra-O-acetyl-D-glucopyranosyl ureide (LXXXIV, R' = H or CH₃) to the 6'-aminonucleoside derivative (LXXXV, R' = H or CH₃) by a modification of Traube's procedure.[241] Deacetylation of LXXXV afforded 6-amino-1-(D-gluco-

(241) W. Traube, *Ber.*, **41**, 532 (1908).

(242) W. Bergmann and T. B. Johnson, *J. Am. Chem. Soc.*, **55**, 1733 (1933).

(243) T. B. Johnson and W. Bergmann, *J. Am. Chem. Soc.*, **60**, 916 (1938).

(244) I. Goodman, *Federation Proc.*, **15**, 264 (1956). See also, I. Goodman, *Advances in Carbohydrate Chem.*, **13**, 215 (1958).

pyranosyl)uracil and the 5-methyluracil homolog.[244] Application of this Traube reaction to the synthesis of other 6-aminouracil nucleosides, especially glycofuranosyl analogs, merits further study.

2. Nucleoside Interconversions

a. By Way of Anhydronucleosides.—The use of anhydronucleoside derivatives as a method for the preparation of nucleoside analogs has been described previously (see p. 317) for the conversion of 2′,3-anhydrothymidine (XXVIII) to 1-(2-deoxy-β-D-*threo*-pentofuranosyl)thymine (XXIX).[145] This method has been extended[158] to the synthesis of spongouridine (XXXIII, R = H), proceeding from the appropriate sulfonic ester derivatives of uridine. When LXXXVI (R = acetyl or H) was caused to react with methanolic ammonia, the crystalline 2′,2-anhydronucleoside (LXXXVII) was obtained; this, after treatment with dilute mineral acid,

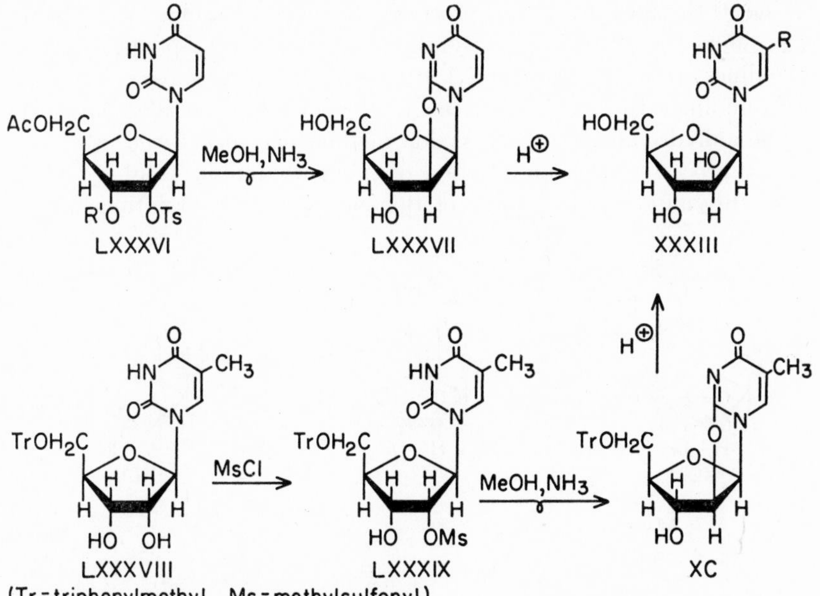

(Tr = triphenylmethyl, Ms = methylsulfonyl)

yielded the epimer of uridine (XXXIII, R = H) identical with spongouridine. The identity of the sugar component was established[158] by reductive cleavage of XXXIII, by the sodium–liquid ammonia procedure,[72] to D-arabinose. The structure of the anhydronucleoside (LXXXVII) has been confirmed by an x-ray crystallographic examination of its 5-deoxy-5-iodo derivative,[245] which was also converted to XXXIII. It was, therefore, con-

(245) D. M. Brown, W. Cochran, E. H. Medlin and S. Varadarajan, *J. Chem. Soc.*, 4873 (1956).

cluded that inversion at C2 occurs in the formation of the anhydronucleoside (LXXXVII), with displacement of the tosylate ion as a result of a
rearward nucleophilic attack by the 2'-carbonyl group upon C2 of the
sugar moiety.[158,245]

Concurrently with this work, Fox, Yung, and Bendich[159,246] synthesized
"spongothymidine" (XXXIII, R = CH₃) by mesylation of the 5-trityl
ether (LXXXVIII) of 1-β-D-ribofuranosylthymine[58] (LIV), followed by
treatment of the sirupy mesylate ester with alcoholic ammonia, and detritylation and anhydride-ring opening with dilute acid. A nucleoside was
obtained which was identical with spongothymidine (1-β-D-arabinofuran-
osylthymine). By virtue of the epimerization sequence (LXXXVIII →
XXXIII; R = CH₃), LXXXIX and XC were probably intermediates in
the synthesis of this sponge nucleoside.[159]

It is evident that the anhydronucleoside route, in contrast to the Hilbert–
Johnson,[139] the mercuri,[58] and, probably, the glycosylamine[229 230,233] procedures, offers the possibility of synthesizing C1–C2-cis-β-D nucleosides of
pyrimidines, from pre-formed C1–C2-trans-β-D-aldofuranosyl derivatives
of pyrimidines. In this regard, the total syntheses described previously
and the anhydronucleoside-conversion method may be viewed as complementary processes. The preparation of spongothymidine from 1-β-D-ribo-
furanosylthymine is an example of this complementary relationship. An-

(Ip=isopropylidene)

(246) J. J. Fox and N. Yung, Federation Proc., 15, 254 (1956).

other example is the synthesis of 1-β-D-lyxofuranosylthymine (XCIV)[197] from 1-β-D-xylofuranosylthymine (XCI, prepared[58] by the mercuri procedure).

Strangely, XCII (unlike LXXXVI or LXXXIX) is resistant to treatment with methanolic ammonia. To effect the formation of anhydronucleoside XCIII, several hours of refluxing with dilute alkali are required.[197] It appears, therefore, that the substituents or the configuration at C3, or both, have some influence on the ease of this displacement reaction (anhydronucleoside formation). Incidentally, the preparation of 1-β-D-lyxofuranosylthymine completes the synthesis of all four possible 1-β-D-aldopentofuranosylthymines.[58,159,197]

The anhydronucleoside process has also been used for replacing the oxygen atom at C2 of the *aglycon* residue with other substituents. It has been observed[247] that 5-deoxy-5-iodo-2,3-O-isopropylideneuridine is converted by silver acetate[247a] to the 2′,5-anhydronucleoside XCVI. Unlike the 2′,2-anhydronucleoside (LXXXVII), XCVI is readily hydrolyzed to 2,3-O-isopropylideneuridine by 25 % acetic acid or 0.3 N alkali at room temperature. Treatment of XCVI with methanolic ammonia (or methanolic triethylamine) at room temperature affords XCVII which, on subsequent acid hydrolysis, yields uridine. The ultraviolet absorption spectrum of XCVII is similar to that for 2′,2-anhydronucleoside LXXXVII[247] [and resembles that for 2-ethoxy-4(3H)-pyrimidinone (XVII)[110]], but differs markedly from that given by the 2′,5-anhydronucleoside (XCVI).[247b] Infrared spectroscopy of these anhydronucleoside derivatives also revealed differences between the 2′,5-anhydronucleoside and the others. The authors[247] tentatively attribute these spectral differences (as well as the relative ease of hydrolysis of XCVI) to greater strain in XCVI. Prolonged treatment of the 2′-O-methyluridine derivative (XCVII) with alcoholic ammonia converts it to 1-(2,3-O-isopropylidene-β-D-ribofuranosyl)isocytosine (XCVIII) which, after treatment with cold formic acid, affords isocytidine (1-β-D-ribofuranosyl-isocytosine). The latter structure was confirmed by deamination of isocytidine with nitrous acid, to give uridine. It was observed later[248] that 1-β-D-arabinofuranosyl-isocytosine may be obtained (along with

---

(247) D. M. Brown, A. R. Todd and S. Varadarajan, *J. Chem. Soc.*, 868 (1957).

(247a) Whereas methanolic ammonia will convert LXXXVI to the 2′,2-anhydronucleoside (LXXXVII), neither 5-deoxy-5-iodo- nor 5-O-tosyl-uridine is cyclized by this reagent (or by other bases). It was suggested[247] that the reaction of XCV with silver ion involves a carbonium-ion intermediate, rather than the displacement by a stereochemically controlled, nucleophilic attack by O2′ on a carbon atom of the sugar moiety (such as in the reaction of LXXXVI → LXXXVII).

(247b) It is of interest that the spectrum of the 2′,5-anhydronucleoside XCVI is quite similar to that exhibited by 2-S-ethyl-2-thio-1-methyl-4(1H)-pyrimidinone.[123]

(248) D. M. Brown, D. B. Parihar, A. R. Todd and S. Varadarajan, *J. Chem. Soc.*, 3028 (1958).

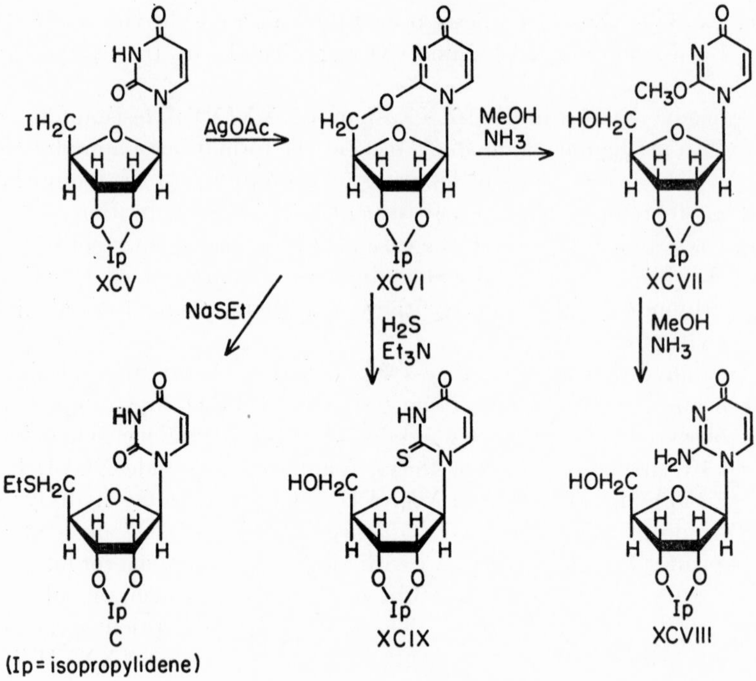

(Ip = isopropylidene)

spongouridine) by prolonged treatment of LXXXVI with alcoholic ammonia.

In all of the aforementioned anhydronucleoside studies, cleavage of the anhydride bridge occurs, apparently, by nucleophilic attack on C2 of the aglycon residue, with rupture of the linkage between the pyrimidine ring and the oxygen atom of the anhydride bridge ("aryl-oxygen" fission; see CI, fission type a). Where an asymmetric carbon atom in the sugar is involved in the anhydride linkage, ring opening leads to isomeric sugar moieties. A second type of cleavage has also been observed, as exemplified by the treatment of an anhydrothymidine (XXVIII) with acid; this resulted in the formation of the free aglycon plus a sugar. It has been suggested[145] that, in this case, acid cleavage (CI, type b) occurs at the glycosyl

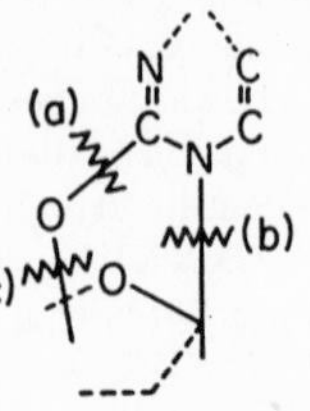

CI

linkage, followed by fission of the resulting 2′-glycoside under the acidic conditions employed. [The instability of XXVIII and 2′,5-anhydro-2-deoxycytidine tosylate salt has been discussed (see p. 316)]. Michelson[249] has proposed that, under acidic conditions, a positive charge on N1 of the base (with a methylene group β to it) labilizes the glycosyl linkage in these anhydro-2-deoxynucleosides. It should be added that, during the synthesis of 1-β-D-arabinofuranosylthymine (LXXXVIII → XXXIII) or 1-β-D-lyxo-furanosylthymine (XCI → XCIV), small proportions of thymine are found in the final reaction mixture.[159,197,249a] It is obvious that some degree of fission of the glycosyl bond (type *b* cleavage) has occurred in these cases as well.

Todd and associates[248] investigated the action of nucleophilic reagents on the anhydrouridine XCVI. When treated with hydrogen sulfide plus triethylamine in *N*,*N*-dimethylformamide, XCVI was converted into a mixture containing XCIX (as the major product) plus higher sulfides thereof (probably the di-, tetra- and hexa-sulfide derivatives). The fact that the sulfur atom is affixed to C2 of the aglycon residue in XCIX was shown[248] by the similarity of its ultraviolet absorption spectrum to that of 1-methyl-2-thiouracil.[123] The action of dilute acetic acid converted XCIX to 2′-thiouridine. When a stronger nucleophile was employed (sodium thioethoxide), XCVI was converted to a sulfur-containing nucleoside (C) whose ultraviolet absorption spectrum was similar to that for uridine. Since the aglycon was sulfur-free and, further, since (C) could be synthesized directly (by the action of the same nucleophile on 2,3-*O*-isopropylidene-5-*O*-tosyluridine[129]), assigning of the 5-*S*-ethyl-5-thio structure to compound C is justified. The synthesis of compound C from XCVI is, therefore, an example of alkyl–oxygen fission[250] (CI, type *c*) which indicates that, depending upon the reagent and the reaction conditions employed, anhydro-bridge opening should be effectible in either direction (type *a* or *c* in CI).[248]

Application of this reaction to 2′,2-anhydrouridine (LXXXVII) led to a 3-substituted nucleoside (CIV) which, upon acylation followed by reduction with Raney nickel, yielded 3-deoxyuridine (CV, R = uracilyl). Reductive cleavage of CV, by the sodium–liquid ammonia procedure,[72] afforded 3-deoxy-D-*erythro*-pentose ("3-deoxy-D-ribose"), a result which establishes position 3 as the site originally containing the ethylthio function. The authors suggest,[248] as a plausible route to CIV, the initial formation of the anion CII, followed by formation of the 2,3-anhydride structure. The anhydride (CIII) is then attacked, at C3, by the ethanethiol ion, to yield

(249) A. M. Michelson, *Tetrahedron*, **2**, 333 (1958).
(249a) See footnote 10 in Ref. 159.
(250) See Ref. 254.

1-(3-S-ethyl-3-thio-β-D-xylofuranosyl)uracil (CIV). Although no *direct* experimental evidence exists for the *xylo* configuration in CIV, previous work

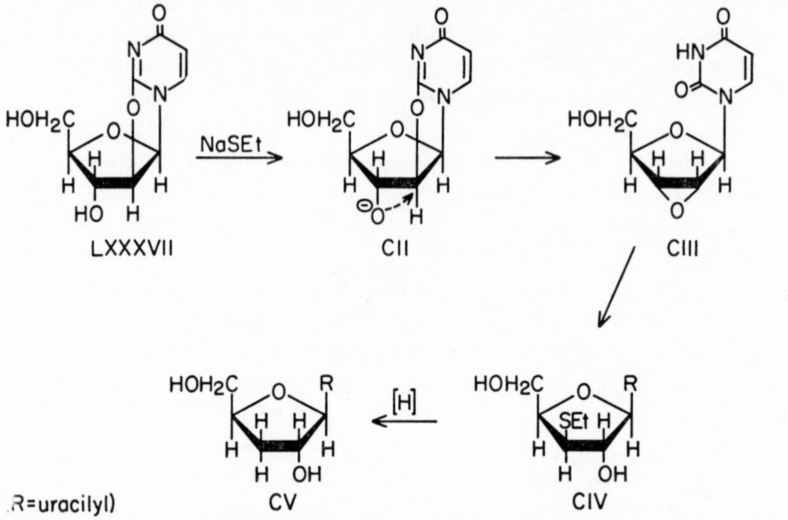

.R=uracilyl)

with 2,3-anhydronucleosides has shown that nucleophilic attack occurs predominantly[250a,251] on C3. The fact that a small proportion of 2-deoxy-D-*erythro*-pentose ("2-deoxy-D-ribose") is obtained, along with 3-deoxy-D-*erythro*-pentose ("3-deoxy-D-ribose"), from the reductive cleavage of crude 3-deoxyuridine (CV, obtained from the mother liquors) supports their suggestion[248] that anhydride CIII is an intermediate in the synthesis of 3-deoxyuridine from LXXXVII. Attempts to convert 3-O-tosyluridine to an anhydronucleoside with a variety of reagents were unsuccessful,[248] despite the fact that both 3,5-di-O-mesylthymidine and 3-deoxy-3-iodothymidine yield 2′,3-anhydronucleosides[145] under these conditions.

As a direct result of these anhydronucleoside studies, methods have been developed[126,252] for the chemical synthesis of 2-deoxynucleosides of pyrimidines. It was noted[126] that the 2-O-tosyluridine derivative LXXXVI, when caused to react with sodium iodide in hot 2,5-hexanedione (acetonylacetone), is converted into a 5-O-acetyl-2-deoxy-2-iodo nucleoside which, upon reduction under alkaline conditions, yields 2-deoxyuridine (V, R = H). In analogous fashion, the 5-O-acetyl derivative of 1-β-D-ribofuranosylthymine[58] is converted by sodium iodide to CVI which, after deacetylation followed by reduction in the presence of palladium catalyst, yields thymidine (V, R = CH₃).[126]

(250a) J. Davoll, B. Lythgoe and S. Trippett, *J. Chem. Soc.*, 2230 (1951).

(251) S. Mukherjee and A. R. Todd, *J. Chem. Soc.*, 969 (1947).

(252) G. Shaw and R. N. Warrener, *Proc. Chem. Soc.*, 81 (1958); *J. Chem. Soc.*, 50 (1959).

The assignment of the configuration of the deoxyiodonucleoside as being *arabino* (CVIa) or *ribo* (CVIb) is surely warranted. The *arabino* configuration could arise by inversion at C2, with displacement of the tosylate ion of LXXXVI. The fact that the deoxyiodonucleoside (CVI), as well as LXXXVI (R = H), is converted to the anhydronucleoside LXXXVII by means of methanolic ammonia[126] would be consonant with either configura-

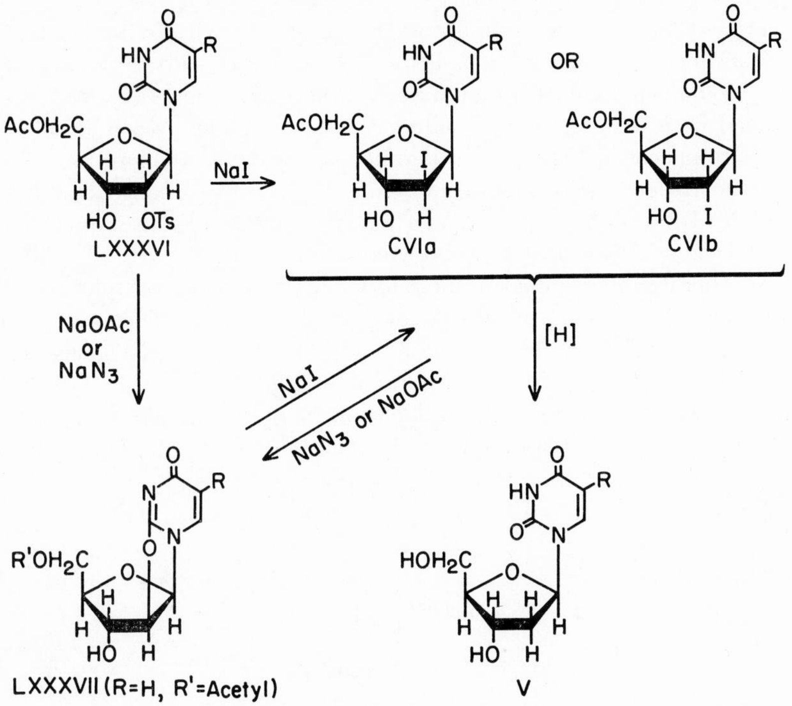

LXXXVII (R=H, R'=Acetyl)   V

tion (CVIa or CVIb). The *ribo* configuration (CVIb) could afford the 2′,2-anhydronucleoside (LXXXVII) by nucleophilic attack on C2 by O2′. The *arabino* configuration (CVIa) could lead to this *same* anhydronucleoside, by preliminary formation of the 2,3-anhydronucleoside (CIII) which could then be attacked at C2 by the 2′ oxygen atom (second inversion) to yield LXXXVII. Past experience[248,250a,251] would suggest, however, that nucleophilic attack on the anhydride[253] derivative (CIII) would occur predominantly at C3. It has been shown[253a] that treatment of LXXXVI (R = H) with sodium azide in acetonitrile or with sodium acetate in 2,5-hexanedione affords the anhydronucleoside LXXXVII (R = H, R' =

(253) See also, the Chapter by S. Peat, *Advances in Carbohydrate Chem.*, **2**, 37 (1946); and R. E. Schaub and M. J. Weiss, *J. Am. Chem. Soc.*, **80**, 4683 (1958), for a discussion of the scission of anhydro sugars.

(253a) D. M. Brown, D. B. Parihar and A. R. Todd, *J. Chem. Soc.*, 4242 (1958).

acetyl). The failure to form an acetoxy or an azido derivative was ascribed to the relatively low solubility of these sodium salts in those solvents, as compared to that of sodium iodide in 2,5-hexanedione. The formation of LXXXVII under these conditions suggested[253a] that an anhydronucleoside intermediate is involved in the formation of CVI from LXXXVI and, further, that cleavage of the oxazolidine ring is caused by an attack by iodide ion (a second inversion) at C2 (type *c* cleavage, see CI). Indeed, treatment of the anhydronucleoside LXXXVII with sodium iodide in 2,5-hexanedione containing a little glacial acetic acid yielded the *same* deoxyiodonucleoside (CVI) obtained originally from LXXXVI. When reacted with sodium azide or sodium acetate, CVI was reconverted to the anhydronucleoside. These data permit only the *ribo* configuration (CVIb) for the 2-deoxy-2-iodonucleoside, and support the conclusion[253a] that LXXXVI → LXXXVII → CVIb represents the reaction sequence leading to the synthesis of the 2-deoxynucleosides (V).

Another example of displacement at C2 with fission of the anhydro bridge has been observed[253a] in the hydrolysis of the 3,5-diacetate ester of LXXXVII with dilute mineral acid. Aside from the expected spongouridine (XXXIII, R = H), uridine was obtained in appreciable yield. The production of uridine finds a ready explanation in the formation, in part, of an intermediate orthoester ion during the reaction, as a result of a nucleophilic

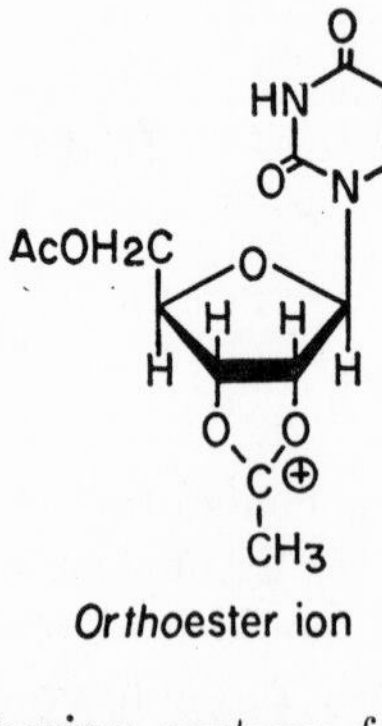

Orthoester ion

attack at C2 by the neighboring acetoxy function. This orthoester ion would then hydrolyze in dilute acid (without inversion) to afford uridine.[253a] It is to be noted that the reaction mechanism proposed[248] for the preparation of 3-*S*-ethyl-3-thio-1-β-D-xylofuranosyluracil (CIV) *also* involves cleavage of the oxazolidine ring (with inversion) by an attack from the neighboring group (at C3) upon C2.

Shaw and Warrener[252] have reported a synthesis of thymidine based on variations of the anhydronucleoside procedures previously described for the synthesis of spongouridine[158] and spongothymidine.[159] 5'-Methyl-2'-

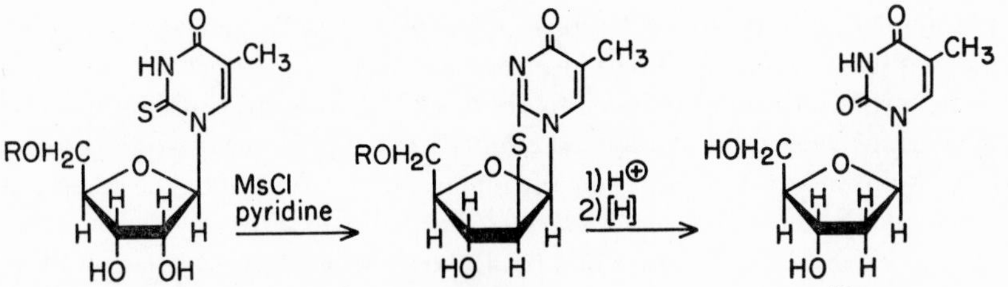

thiouridine (prepared by the "glycosylamine process")[233] was tritylated to CVII (R = triphenylmethyl = trityl). Treatment of CVII with methane-sulfonyl chloride in pyridine produces the S2′,2-anhydronucleoside deriva-tive (CVIII) *directly* (in high yield) instead of the C2- or C3-O-mesylated intermediate (that might have been expected from the behavior of corre-sponding oxygen analogs; see LXXXVI or LXXXIX on p. 345). The trityl group was removed with dilute, aqueous sulfuric acid, and the product (pre-sumably CVIII, R = H) was reduced with Raney nickel in 0.1 N sodium hydroxide. A small yield[253b] was obtained of crystalline material which was indistinguishable from naturally occurring thymidine (V). As in the syn-thesis of 2,3-O-isopropylidene-isocytidine (XCVIII) and the "sponge nu-cleosides" (XXXIII) from XCVI and LXXXVII (or LXXXIX), respec-tively, fission of the anhydro bridge of CVIII probably occurred through a nucleophilic attack on C2 of the aglycon residue (see CI, type *a* cleavage), with the formation of a 2-thio intermediate which, under the reducing conditions employed, was desulfurized to thymidine. In model experi-ments,[252] 1-(2-hydroxypropyl)-2-thiothymine was cyclized, under mesylat-ing conditions, to CIX which, after treatment with alkali, produced 1-(2-mercaptopropyl)thymine (CX).

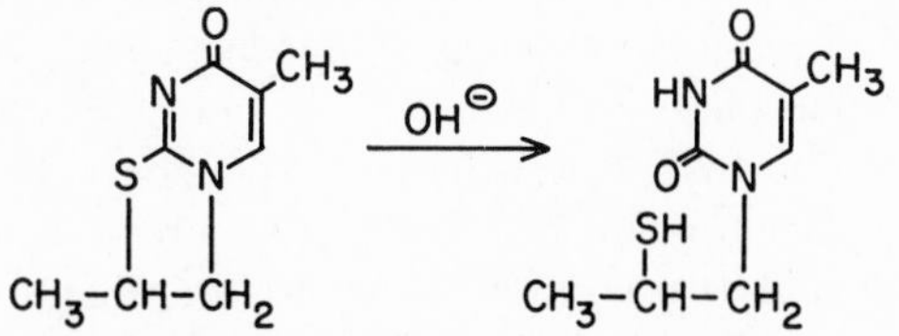

All in all, these anhydronucleoside studies represent an exciting advance in the field of pyrimidine-nucleoside chemistry. Aside from the achievement

(253b) The low yield of thymidine may be due, among other factors, to reduction of the 5′,6′-double bond by the catalyst. Indeed, Todd and coworkers[248] have noted that 1-methyluracil is reduced by Raney nickel to 5,6-dihydro-1-methyluracil in 4 hours. J. J. Fox and D. Van Praag (unpublished data) have observed that the tri-benzoate ester of "4-thiothymidine" (CXIIIa) is converted smoothly by Raney nickel to a 2-oxo-hexahydropyrimidine deoxynucleoside.

of a synthesis of deoxynucleosides, these studies have placed anew a striking emphasis upon the great usefulness of sulfonic ester[254] derivatives of these carbohydrates. Whereas, in the past,[10,128] such pyrimidine nucleoside derivatives were used as blocked agents in structure-proof studies, secondary-tosyloxy derivatives of certain nucleosides may, today, be regarded as *useful intermediates for* the *synthesis* of new nucleosides.

In this regard, pertinent work by Baker and associates[255] has shown unequivocally that the (*secondary*) 5-tosyloxy group of a blocked D-allofuranoside or L-talofuranoside can undergo a direct S_N2 displacement by use of sodium benzoate in boiling N,N-dimethylformamide under conditions which preclude the intervention of neighboring-group effects. It should be of interest to examine the effect of these reagents upon 3-O-tosyluridine, which is inert[248] toward *both* methanolic ammonia and sodium iodide. An abstract[256] reports the application of this reaction (sodium benzoate in boiling N,N-dimethylformamide) to 2,3,5-tri-O-mesyluridine, which led to the synthesis of 1-β-D-arabinofuranosyluracil, 1-β-D-xylofuranosyluracil, and 1-β-D-lyxofuranosyluracil. Although 2′,2-anhydronucleoside intermediates are formed in the process (and other neighboring-group reactions intervene in the formation of the isomers of uridine), the *complete* replacement of the mesyloxy functions was effected by this reagent.

It is known, from metabolic experiments[4,256a,b] in the rat, that exogenously-supplied pyrimidine ribonucleosides or ribonucleotides are extensively incorporated into the polynucleotides of deoxyribonucleic acid *without* cleavage of the glycosyl linkage. Although the mechanism of this *in vivo* conversion is still obscure, it has been suggested[253a] that formation of anhydronucleosides by displacement of a C2 substituent of a pyrimidine nucleoside, followed by reductive fission of the anhydro bridge, might represent a biosynthetic pathway by which ribonucleosides are converted into the 2-deoxyribonucleosides of deoxyribonucleic acid. Some evidence for this hypothesis (phosphate displacement) is indicated in a recent note by Dekker,[256c] who reported the synthesis of spongouridine 3,5-diphosphate by the phosphorylation of uridine with a mixture of phosphoric acid and phosphorus pentoxide. It is conceivable, therefore, that anhydronucleosides may represent a class of nucleoside derivatives of *significant biochemical importance*.

(254) See R. S. Tipson, *Advances in Carbohydrate Chem.*, **8**, 107 (1953).

(255) E. J. Reist, L. Goodman and B. R. Baker, *J. Am. Chem. Soc.*, **80**, 5775 (1958).

(256) J. F. Codington, R. Fecher and J. J. Fox, *Abstracts Papers, Am. Chem. Soc.*, **135**, 80-O (1959).

(256a) I. A. Rose and B. S. Schweigert, *J. Biol. Chem.*, **202**, 635 (1953).

(256b) P. M. Roll, H. Weinfeld and B. Carroll, *J. Biol. Chem.*, **220**, 455 (1956).

(256c) C. A. Dekker, *Abstracts Papers Am. Chem. Soc.*, **133**, 4D (1958).

b. Thiation of Nucleosides.—Following the first reports[257] on the thiation of barbitals and hydantoins, several studies have appeared which deal with the preparation of thio derivatives of pyrimidines.[258] In these studies, uracil and various derivatives of 2-thiouracil were treated with phosphorus penta-sulfide in inert solvents at elevated temperatures. Application of this type of reaction to pyrimidine nucleosides required introduction of suitable blocking groups on the sugar hydroxyl groups and use of milder reaction conditions. The conditions established for the successful thiation of purine nucleosides[259] (that is, benzoyl ester blocking groups, and the use of pyridine as the reaction medium) were also adequate for the thiation of pyrimidine nucleosides.[62] In model experiments with 1-methyluracil, thiation, followed by amination, yielded 1-methylcytosine; this result indicated that thiation of other 1-substituted pyrimidines (including nucleosides) would probably proceed selectively to the 4-thio analogs.

A host of pyrimidine nucleosides have now been synthesized from readily available materials by use of the thiation procedure[62] (see Fig. 13). For example, 3,5-di-O-benzoylthymidine (CXII, *a* series) was thiated in high yield to the 4′-thio intermediate (CXIIIa). This intermediate served as an excellent chemical precursor to many nucleoside analogs. When treated with alcoholic ammonia, CXIIIa was debenzoylated and the 4′-thio function was replaced by an amino group, thus readily yielding 2-deoxy-5′-methylcytidine (CXIVa), the hitherto-rare nucleoside obtained previously[34] from wheat-germ deoxyribonucleic acid. Deamination of CXIVa with nitrous acid afforded the starting material, thymidine (CXIa), which demonstrated that the thiation process had not altered the sugar moiety. By use of appropriate amines (methylamine, 2-phenylethylamine, or hydrazine) the corresponding analogs (CXVa, CXVIa and CXVIIa) of 2-deoxy-5′-methylcytidine were produced. The hydrazino analog (CXVIIa) was converted, by means of nitrous acid, to a nucleoside which, the authors[62] suggested, may possess the tetrazolo, fused-ring structure CXVIIIa. Debenzoylation of intermediate CXIIIa with sodium methoxide yielded 4′-thiothymidine (CXIXa) which was converted to the disulfide (CXXa) by oxidation with iodine. The 4′-thio group of CXIXa or CXXa also undergoes replacement by amine residues, including replacement by a hydroxylamino

(257) H. R. Henze and P. E. Smith, *J. Am. Chem. Soc.*, **65**, 1090 (1943); H. C. Carrington, *J. Chem. Soc.*, 124 (1944); 684 (1947).

(258) G. B. Elion and G. H. Hitchings, *J. Am. Chem. Soc.*, **69**, 2138 (1947); P. B. Russell, G. B. Elion, E. A. Falco and G. H. Hitchings, *ibid.*, **71**, 2279 (1949); E. A. Falco, P. B. Russell and G. H. Hitchings, *ibid.*, **73**, 4466 (1951).

(259) J. J. Fox, I. Wempen, A. Hampton and I. L. Doerr, *J. Am. Chem. Soc.*, **80**, 1669 (1958).

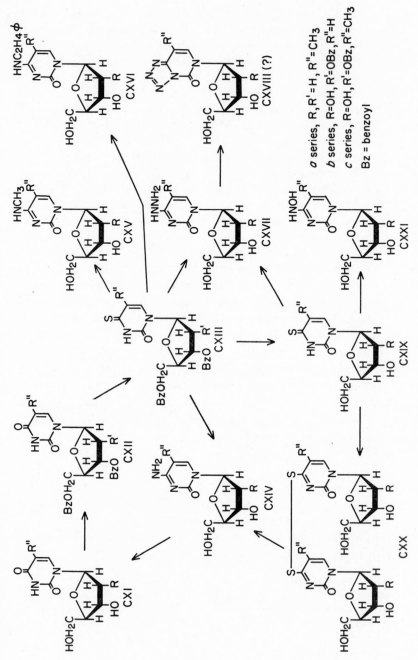

FIG. 13.—Nucleoside Conversions by the Thiation Process.[62]

function to yield CXXIa. Attempts to desulfurize CXIII with Raney nickel resulted in complete reduction of the pyrimidine ring, and yielded a 1'-substituted 2-oxo-hexahydropyrimidine nucleoside.[260]

Analogous reactions have been carried out with uridine (CXI, *b* series) and with 1-β-D-ribofuranosylthymine (CXI, *c* series).[62] The latter series provided an avenue to the synthesis of 5'-methylcytidine, a nucleoside which is probably identical with that detected by Dunn[60] in the ribonucleic acid of wheat germ. The thiation process has also been applied to the synthesis of 5'-fluorocytidine and 2-deoxy-5'-fluorocytidine[261] from 5'-fluorouridine and 2-deoxy-5'-fluorouridine,[209,228] respectively.[261a]

c. Other Conversions.—Conversion of pyrimidine nucleosides to 5'-substituted analogs was reported originally by Levene and LaForge[50] who synthesized 5'-bromouridine by treating uridine with bromine water. 5'-Chlorouridine was obtained[262] by treatment of uridine, in glacial acetic acid, with chlorine in carbon tetrachloride. 5'-Iodouridine was synthesized by Prusoff and associates[263] by modifying procedures used for the iodination of uracil.[264] 5'-Aminouridine was obtained by Roberts and Visser[192] by treating 5'-bromouridine with liquid ammonia. The 5'-hydroxy analog was prepared[192] from uridine by modifications of the procedure of Levene and LaForge[50] (bromine water, followed by lead dioxide). The syntheses of 5'-chloro- and 5'-bromo-cytidine by a photocatalytic process, and the preparation of 5'-aminocytidine from the 5'-bromo analog have been reported.[265] 5'-Halogeno and 5'-hydroxy analogs of 2-deoxyuridine have also been synthesized by methods previously described.[266,267] Diazomethane has been

(260) J. J. Fox and D. Van Praag, *J. Am. Chem. Soc.*, in press.

(261) J. J. Fox, I. Wempen and R. Duschinsky, *Intern. Congr. Biochem.*, *4th Congr. Vienna*, 6 (1958).

(261a) These fluorinated nucleosides (as well as 5-fluorouracil) exhibit anti-cancer activity in experimental tumors [C. Heidelberger, L. Griesbach, O. Cruz, R. J. Schnitzer and E. Grunberg, *Proc. Soc. Exptl. Biol. Med.*, **97**, 470 (1958)]. They also inhibit the growth of several types of transplanted mouse leukemias [J. H. Burchenal, E. A. D. Holmberg and J. J. Fox, *Intern. Congr. Biochem.*, *4th Congr. Vienna*, 185 (1958); J. H. Burchenal, E. A. D. Holmberg, J. J. Fox, S. C. Hemphill and J. A. Reppert, *Cancer Research*, **19**, 494 (1959)].

(262) T. K. Fukuhara and D. W. Visser, *J. Biol. Chem.*, **190**, 95 (1951).

(263) W. H. Prusoff, W. L. Holmes and A. D. Welch, *Cancer Research*, **13**, 221 (1953).

(264) T. B. Johnson and C. O. Johns, *J. Biol. Chem.*, **1**, 305 (1906).

(265) T. K. Fukuhara and D. W. Visser, *J. Am. Chem. Soc.*, **77**, 2393 (1955).

(266) R. Beltz and D. W. Visser, *J. Am. Chem. Soc.*, **77**, 736 (1955).

(267) T. J. Bardos, G. M. Levin, R. R. Herr and H. L. Gordon, *J. Am. Chem. Soc.*, **77**, 4279 (1955).

used for alkylating tri-O-substituted uridine as well as suitably protected
1-D-glucopyranosylpyrimidines[108,189,268] at position 3'.

The studies of Levene and LaForge[50] on the nitration of uridine have
since been re-investigated. It had been reported, several decades ago, that
treatment of uridine with nitric acid produced a *"Nitro-Uridin-Carbon-
säure"* which was stated to be a dimer containing an anhydro type of linkage
(positions unspecified) between two nucleoside residues.[50] According to an
abstract,[269] this compound has now been identified as the *monomeric* 5-ni-
tro-1-(β-D-ribosyluronic acid)uracil (CXXII); this was converted to the
isopropyl ester and the 2,3-O-isopropylidene acetal thereof. Nitration of
the pyrimidine moiety of uridine *without* oxidation of the 4-(hydroxy-

methyl) group of the sugar was accomplished[269] by treating the tri-O-(3,5-
dinitrobenzoyl) ester of uridine with fuming nitric–sulfuric acid reagent.
Deacylation of the product of this reaction afforded 5'-nitrouridine
(CXXIII), the identity of which was established by reduction to 5'-amino-
uridine in the presence of palladium–carbon catalyst.

Reduction of pyrimidine nucleosides to their 5',6'-dihydro derivatives
by various reagents has been discussed (see p. 293). As stated previously
(see p. 290), reduction of the ethylenic linkage at C5'–C6' renders the nucleoside susceptible to cleavage at the glycosyl link by dilute mineral acid.
It is noteworthy that, as of this date, conclusive experimental evidence
which would provide an explanation of the observed stability of pyrimidine
nucleosides toward dilute acids is still lacking.

It might have been expected that "N-glycosides" derived from secondary amines
(pyrimidine nucleosides) would resemble true glycosides ("O-glycosides") in their
behavior toward acids. (Moreover, 1-D-glucosylurea is hydrolyzed to D-glucose plus
urea when refluxed with dilute sulfuric acid.[270]) The resistance of 1-glycosylpyrimi-

(268) D. W. Visser, G. Barron and R. Beltz, *J. Am. Chem. Soc.*, **75**, 2017 (1953).

(269) I. Wempen, I. L. Doerr, L. Kaplan and J. J. Fox, *Federation Proc.*, **18**, 350
(1959).

(270) M. N. Schoorl, *Rec. trav. chim.*, **22**, 1 (1903).

dines to cleavage (in contrast to their 5,6-dihydro derivatives) obviously implicates the ethylenic group as a factor to be considered in any explanation of this apparent anomaly.

On the basis of x-ray diffraction studies (see Fig. 12), Furberg[141] suggests that the resistance of cytidine to glycosyl cleavage is related to the abnormally short distance between C6 of the aglycon residue and the C5 oxygen atom of the sugar moiety, which would permit the formation of a hydrogen bond between these atoms. This hydrogen bond, which might form as a result of polarization of the CH group at position 6 to give $C^{\ominus}----H^{\oplus}$ because of the effect of the electronegative substituents in the pyrimidine ring, may be partly implicated in the stability of cytidine to cleavage at the C1—N1 bond by dilute acids. 5′,6′-Dihydrocytidine, in which polarization of the type described would hardly be possible, behaves like a normal glycoside. Kenner[271] has suggested a mechanism for the glycosyl cleavage of nucleosides which, in some respects, resembles that proposed by Frush and Isbell[272,273] for the acid-catalyzed cleavage of glycosylamines.

As noted previously (see p. 324), the glycosyl bond of the nucleoside, amicetin, is subject to cleavage by acids. This acid-lability may be due, in part, to the presence of the N-acyl function at C4′. Indeed, short treatment of N'-acetyl-3-O-acetyl-2-deoxy-5-O-tritylcytidine with hot 80 % acetic acid *also* produced[274] some cleavage of the C1–N1 bond.

3. Enzymic Syntheses

Many syntheses of pyrimidine nucleosides by enzymic methods have been described.[42,56,67,70,71,80,82,106,152] In general, these syntheses have been effected on a small scale (for biochemical studies). 2-Deoxy-5′-fluorouridine has, however, been prepared[209] on a large scale by enzymic transfer of 2-deoxy-D-*erythro*-pentose from thymidine to 5-fluorouracil[275]; the last two compounds were incubated, together, with resting cells of *Streptococcus fecalis*, according to modifications of the procedure of Prusoff.[276] "Un-natural" pyrimidine nucleosides containing the D-ribosyl or 2-deoxy-D-*erythro*-pentosyl ("2-deoxy-D-ribosyl") moieties have been synthesized by enzymic methods.[71,277] In almost all cases, these syntheses have involved the use of

(271) G. W. Kenner, *Ciba Foundation Symposium, Chem. and Biol. of Purines*, **1957**, p. 313.

(272) H. L. Frush and H. S. Isbell, *J. Research Natl. Bur. Standards*, **46,** 132 (1951).

(273) See G. P. Ellis and J. Honeyman, *Advances in Carbohydrate Chem.*, **10,** 95 (1955).

(274) A. M. Michelson and A. R. Todd, *J. Chem. Soc.*, 34 (1954).

(275) R. Duschinsky, E. Pleven and C. Heidelberger, *J. Am. Chem. Soc.*, **79,** 4559 (1957).

(276) W. H. Prusoff, *J. Biol. Chem.*, **215,** 809 (1955).

(277) W. E. Razzell and H. G. Khorana, *Biochim. et Biophys. Acta*, **28,** 562 (1958).

5-halogeno or 2-thio analogs of the pyrimidines of nucleic acids, which would indicate the relative *low* order of specificity required, in the structure of the *aglycon residue*, by nucleosidases.

By contrast, the *high* degree of specificity of nucleosidases for the *sugar moieties* in the synthesis, *or* glycosyl cleavage, of pyrimidine nucleosides has been demonstrated.[197,277] Razzell and Khorana[277] have shown that a purified preparation of "pyrimidine deoxyribonucleoside phosphorylase" obtained from *Escherichia coli* is specific for 2-deoxy-D-*erythro*-pentosyl phosphate, but will permit the use of a variety of pyrimidines as substrates for the synthesis of 2-deoxynucleosides. On the other hand, no reaction was observed when D-ribosyl phosphate or other D-pentosyl phosphates were provided, along with such pyrimidines as thymine, uracil, or 2-thiouracil as substrates.

The structural specificity which nucleosidases require in the sugar moiety of 1-aldosylpyrimidines was demonstrated[197] in a study of the susceptibility of all four possible 1-β-D-aldopentofuranosylthymine isomers, and related nucleosides, to glycosyl cleavage. By using intact-cell suspensions of *Escherichia coli* B or cell-free extracts of *Escherichia coli* or of *Lactobacillus pentosus*, it was shown[197] that only with the 1-β-D-ribofuranosyl isomer is fission of the glycosyl bond effected. Although uridine was cleaved to uracil under these conditions, 1-β-D-ribo*pyranosyl*uracil and 1-β-D-gluco*pyranosyl*thymine were unaffected by these enzymes. The authors suggest[197] that an essential structural requirement for enzymic action is, possibly, the *trans* relationship between the aglycon residue and the C2–C3-*cis* hydroxyl functions of the glycofuranosyl moiety, a condition which is satisfied in both 1-β-D-ribofuranosylthymine and uridine. That the C4-substituent (containing C5) of the sugar also plays a role is indicated by the observation[267] that 5'-nitrouridine (CXXIII) is cleaved by cell suspensions of *Escherichia coli* B, whereas 5-nitro-1-(β-D-ribosyluronic acid)uracil (CXXII) is not. It should be of interest to test 5-deoxyuridine or 1-(5-deoxy-β-D-ribofuranosyl)thymine, or both, in these enzymic systems.

VI. TABLE OF PROPERTIES OF 1-GLYCOSYLPYRIMIDINES

Table II records the melting points and optical rotations of the 1-glycosylpyrimidines. References are also provided for sources of information on (a) their ultraviolet and infrared absorption spectra, and (b) their paper chromatography.

The compounds in this Table are arranged in order of position of the substituents, with regard to the pyrimidinyl and the sugar moieties, as follows: (a) for *pyrimidinyl substituents* the order is that of increasing positional number, beginning with all 2-substituents, then the 3, and so on, and within each positional group, the arrangement is alphabetical; (b) for the *sugar moieties*, the order is determined first by the number of substituents, then by the position of the substituent (beginning at C2), and, finally, within each positional group, the order is alphabetical.

TABLE II

Physical Properties of 1-Glycosylpyrimidines

Pyrimidinyl moiety	Glycosyl moiety	Melting point, °C.	[α]D, degrees (solvent)[a]	References[b]	References to spectra[c]	References[b] to paper chromatography
Uracil	β-D-ribofuranosyl-	165		50	87, 113, 281, 281a	203, 233, 247
		165	5.15 (w)	51		
			4.0 (w)	108		
		164.5		137		
		165	8 (w)	233		
		164–165	4.8 (w)	278		
		166–167		279		
		163.5–166	9.6 (w)	280		
	3-amino-3-deoxy-	183–184	67 (w)	201	201	201
	3-S-ethyl-3-thio-	glass		248	248	
	3-O-tosyl-	205–206		248	248	248
	5-O-acetyl-	163–164	9.1 (w)	158	158	158
		glass		282, 282a		
	5-O-benzyl-	162		283		
	5-bromo-5-deoxy-	182–184		245		
	5-S-ethyl-5-thio-	177–178		248		248
	5-deoxy-5-fluoro-	141–142	−1.9 (w)	203	203	
	5-deoxy-5-iodo-	182–183		247		247
	5-O-tosyl-	162–163		247		247
	5-O-trityl-	200	9.5 (a)	108		
		200	18.8 (m)	283		

Compound	M.p., °C	$[\alpha]_D$	Ref.	Ref.	Ref.
2,3-di-*O*-acetyl-	142–143		284	247	247
2,3-di-*O*-benzyl-	147		283		
2,3-*O*-benzylidene-	189–190		278, 282a		247
2,3-*O*-isopropylidene-	159–160; 159–160; 162	–15.8 (m)	118, 129, 285	118	
2,3-di-*O*-methyl-	168–169	68.0 (a)	128		
2,3-di-*O*-tosyl-	199	–26.6 (a)	128		
5-*O*-acetyl-2-deoxy-2-iodo-	167		126	126	126
5-*O*-acetyl-2-*O*-tosyl-	173–175		158	158	158
5-bromo-5-deoxy-2-*O*-tosyl-	176–177		248		
5-deoxy-5-iodo-2-*O*-tosyl-	162–163		245		158
3,5-di-*O*-acetyl-	168–169		245	245	
3 (or 2),5-di-*O*-trityl-	138–140		158		158
tri-*O*-acetyl-	223–224; glass	91.4 (a)	128, 127		
tri-*O*-benzoyl-	128–130; none		158, 268		
2,3-di-*O*-acetyl-5-deoxy-5-iodo-	142–143		62		247
2,3-di-*O*-acetyl-5-*O*-trityl-	162–163		247, 108		
2,3-*O*-benzylidene-5-*O*-acetyl-	glass; glass	50.9 (m)	282, 282a		
5-*O*-acetyl-2,3-*O*-isopropylidene-	146–147		158		
5-bromo-5-deoxy-2,3-*O*-isopropylidene-	184–186		254	248, *248*	
5-*S*-ethyl-5-thio-2,3-*O*-isopropylidene-	140–142		248		248
5-deoxy-5-iodo-2,3-*O*-isopropylidene-	164	–16.3 (a)	129		

TABLE II—Continued

Pyrimidinyl moiety	Compound / Glycosyl moiety	Melting point, °C.	$[\alpha]_D$, degrees (solvent)[a]	References[b]	References to spectra[c]	References[b] to paper chromatography
Uracil—continued	β-D-ribofuranosyl—continued					
	5-deoxy-2,3-O-isopropylidene-5-thiol-	200-215		285		
	2,3-O-isopropylidene-5-O-tosyl-	glass 150	17.4 (a)	129 285		
	5-deoxy-5-iodo-2,3-di-O-methyl-	94	49.4 (a)	128		
	2,3-di-O-methyl-5-O-tosyl-	impure	69.2 (a)	128		
	5-chloro-5-deoxy-2,3-di-O-tosyl-	170-171	-9.3 (a)	128		
	5-deoxy-5-iodo-2,3-di-O-tosyl-	160	-25.0 (a)	128		
	2,3-di-O-tosyl-5-O-trityl-	glass	27.7 (a)	128		
	D-ribopyranosyl-	257-258 257	-140.0 (w)	186 286	87	
	tri-O-acetyl-	184-185 (slow)	-25.1 (c)	186		
	D-xylopyranosyl-	245	21.8 (w)	184	87	
	β-D-arabinofuranosyl-	226-228 220-221	97 (n) 126 (w)	155 158	158	155, 158
	tri-O-acetyl-	129-130	131.1 (w)	158		158
	D-arabinopyranosyl-	250-252	-88.4 (w)	286	87, 286	
	L-arabinopyranosyl-	251-252	88.2 (w)	184		
	β-D-glucopyranosyl-	206-208	22.2 (w)	137	87, 281, 281, 286	203
	tetra-O-acetyl-	199-201		198 281		
	D-galactopyranosyl-	204-206 207-209	21.4 (w)	287 287		
	α-L-rhamnopyranosyl-	154-155 250-251	59.9 (w)	184	87	288

	M.p.	[α]D			
2-Amino-4(3H)-pyrimidinone					
β-D-ribofuranosyl-	glass		247	247	247
2,3-O-isopropylidene-	206–207		247	247, *247*	247
β-D-arabinofuranosyl-	235–236		248	248, *248*	126, 248
Uracil					
2-O-ethyl-					
β-D-ribofuranosyl-	183–185		247	247	247
2,3-di-O-acetyl-	171–172		247	247	247
2,3-O-isopropylidene-	173		247	247	247
2-O-methyl-					
β-D-ribofuranosyl-	198–200		247	247	247
2,3-di-O-acetyl-	155–156		247	247	247
2,3-O-isopropylidene-	214–215	39 (w)	233, 289	248	233, 289
2-thio-					
β-D-ribofuranosyl-	205–207		248	248	248
2,3-O-isopropylidene-	192		248		
2,2′-dithiodi-					
bis(2,3-O-isopropylidene-)-	205–206		248	248, *248*	248
tetrathio derivative	232 (dec.)		248		
hexathio derivative	215 (dec.)		248		
5-cyano-2-thio-					
β-D-ribofuranosyl-	185–186	10 (w)	233	233	233
2,3-O-isopropylidene-	189		233		
tri-O-benzoyl-	169		233		
3-methyl-					
β-D-ribofuranosyl-	108–110	16.5 (w)	108	281, *281*	189, 281
5-O-trityl-	122–123	20.1 (w)	268		
2,3-di-O-acetyl-5-O-trityl-	119–120	17.1 (a)	281		
β-D-glucopyranosyl-	173–174	55.3 (m)	108		
tetra-O-acetyl-	glass		108		189
	247–248.5	18.0 (w)	290	290, *290*	
5-amino-3-methyl-					
β-D-ribofuranosyl-	105–108		189		
	166–167		268		
5-bromo-3-methyl-					
β-D-ribofuranosyl-	164–164.5		268		
5-chloro-3-methyl-					
β-D-ribofuranosyl-	158–159		268		
5-cyano-3-methyl-					
β-D-ribopyranosyl-	223	−16.91 (w)	230	230	
β-D-xylopyranosyl-	120 (dec.)	−17.2 (w)	230	230	
β-D-glucopyranosyl-	204	13.4 (w)	230	230, *281*	
β-D-galactopyranosyl-	240 (dec.)	42.2 (w)	230	230	

TABLE II—Continued

Pyrimidinyl moiety	Glycosyl moiety (Compound)	Melting point, °C.	$[\alpha]_D$, degrees (solvent)[a]	References[b]	References to spectra[c]	References[b] to paper chromatography
Uracil—continued						
5,6-dihydro-3-methyl-	β-D-ribofuranosyl-	amorph.		290	290	
	β-D-glucopyranosyl-	183–184	10.2 (w)	290	290	
3(4)-benzoyl-	β-D-ribofuranosyl- tri-O-benzoyl-	96–106		198		
4-O-ethyl-	β-D-ribofuranosyl-	gum		203		
	2,3-di-O-acetyl-5-deoxy-5-fluoro-	138–148	41.5 (c)	201	201, 201	
	2,5-di-O-benzoyl-3-deoxy-3-phthalimido-	60–66		286		
	D-ribopyranosyl- tri-O-acetyl-	208	47.9 (w)	184		
	D-xylopyranosyl- tri-O-acetyl-	218	58.4 (c)	184		
	L-arabinopyranosyl- tri-O-acetyl-	157, 167.5 (di-morph.)	108.8 (c)	184		
	β-D-glucopyranosyl- tetra-O-acetyl-	amorph.	30.2 (w)	281	281, 281	281
		206	36.1 (c)	140	198	
		203–204		198		
		204–205		281		
		205		291		
	D-galactopyranosyl- tetra-O-acetyl-	159	59.2 (c)	184		
4-(Hydroxylamino)-2(1H)-pyrimidinone	β-D-ribofuranosyl-	169–172		62	62	
Uracil						
4-O-methyl-	β-D-ribofuranosyl- 2,3-di-O-methyl-5-O-trityl-	177–178	96.1 (a)	128		

5-Substituent	Glycosyl	M.p., °C	[α]			
4-thio-	β-D-glucopyranosyl-	220–221		287		189
	tetra-O-acetyl-	glass		62	62	
	β-D-ribofuranosyl-	128–130		62	62	
	tri-O-benzoyl-	188–190		62	62	
4,4'-dithiodi-	bis-(β-D-ribofuranosyl)-	183.5–184		292	192	
5-fluoro-4-thio-	β-D-ribofuranosyl-	214–216		192	192	
	tri-O-benzoyl-	181–184		50		
5-amino-	β-D-ribofuranosyl-	260	−15.38 (w)	286	286	
5-bromo-	β-D-ribofuranosyl-	238 (dec.)	61.8 (w)	287	286	
	D-ribopyranosyl-	amorph.	−27.7 (w)	50	286	
	D-arabinopyranosyl-	217–217.5	10.3 (w)	286	286	
	β-D-glucopyranosyl-	245		287	286	
	D-galactopyranosyl-	258		286	286	
5-chloro-	β-D-ribofuranosyl-	263–264	−87.3 (w)	262	286	
	D-ribopyranosyl-	indef.	−50.4 (w)	286	286	
	D-arabinopyranosyl-	185	13.9 (w)	286	286	
	D-glucopyranosyl-	190		286	286	
	D-galactopyranosyl-	231		286	286	
5-cyano-	β-D-ribofuranosyl-	247	−6 (w)	233	233	
	tri-O-benzoyl-	240		233	233	
5-fluoro-	β-D-ribopyranosyl-	254	−22.85 (w)	230	230	
	β-D-xylopyranosyl-	184–185 (178)	−25.1 (w)	230	230	
	β-D-glucopyranosyl-		44.2 (w)	230	230	
	β-D-galactopyranosyl-		50.2 (w)	230	230	
	β-D-ribofuranosyl-	215–217, 206–207 (dimorphous ?)	13.8 (m)	293	293	
	tri-O-benzoyl-	222–223	17 (w)	293	293	
5-hydroxy-	β-D-ribofuranosyl-	242–245		50 / 192	192	
5-iodo-I¹³¹-	β-D-ribofuranosyl-	205–208 (dec.)		263	263	263

TABLE II—*Continued*

Pyrimidinyl moiety	Compound — Glycosyl moiety	Melting point, °C	[α]D, degrees (solvent)a	Referencesb	References to spectrac	Referencesb to paper chromatography
Uracil—*continued*						
5-nitro-	β-D-ribofuranosyl-	189–191 (dec.)	−45.4 (d)	267		
	2,3-O-isopropylidene-(β-D-ribosyluronic acid)-	206–207	−63.8 (d)	267		
		>200 (dec.)		50		
	butyl ester	221–227 (dec.)	−28.3 (d)	267		
	ethyl ester	190–192		50		
	isopropyl ester	>200 (dec.)		50		
	2,3-O-isopropylidene-β-D-ribofuranosyl-	236–239 (dec.)	−31.7 (d)	267		
		188–190		267		
5,6-dihydro-	β-D-ribofuranosyl-	sirup	39.1 (w)	74		
		hygroscopic		290	*290*	
		amorph.		127		
	tri-O-acetyl-β-D-glucopyranosyl-	238 (dec.)	9.3 (w)	287		
		243–244	9.7 (w)	290	*290*	
5,6-bis(phenyl-hydrazino)-	β-D-ribofuranosyl-	209		50		
6-amino-	β-D-glucopyranosyl-	212		107a		
	tetra-O-acetyl-			244		
	β-D-ribofuranosyl-			244	119, 294	
6-carboxylic acid cyclohexylamine salt	β-D-ribofuranosyl-	183–184		151		
"diazo"-	β-D-ribofuranosyl-	178–182 (dec.)		192	192	
Thymine	β-D-ribofuranosyl-	183–185	−10 (w)	58	58, 61	61
	3-amino-3-deoxy-	223–225	41.0 (w)	201	201	201
	5-O-acetyl-	95		126	126	126

	M.p.	[α]D	Ref.	Ref.	
5-amino-5-deoxy- hydrochloride salt	155–165	−4.0 (w)	201	201	
5-O-trityl-	223–225		159		
2,3-O-isopropylidene- tri-O-benzoyl-	167–168	−83 (c)	129	58	
2,3-di-O-benzoyl-5-deoxy-5- phthalimido-	120–124	−32.6 (e)	58 201	201	
2,5-di-O-benzoyl-3-deoxy-3- phthalimido-	222–223	−37.8 (c)	201	201	
D-ribopyranosyl-	252	−110 (w)	187	187	
β-D-xylofuranosyl-	156–157.5	−2 (w) −1 (w)	58 197	58, 197	
3,5-O-isopropylidene-	186.5–187.5	−8 (w)	197	197	
tri-O-benzoyl-	197.5–198.5	58 (c)	58	58	
3,5-O-isopropylidene-2-O- mesyl-	163–165.5	−12 (p)	197	197	
D-xylopyranosyl-	285–286 284–285 (dec.)	3 (w)	58 188	87	
β-D-arabinofuranosyl-	246–247	80.0 (n) 92.0 (p)	154	87, 197	
	238–242	93 (w)	159, 197		155
tri-O-benzoyl-	190–191		154		
tri-O-(p-bromobenzoyl)-	251–252		154		
D-arabinopyranosyl-	250–251	−69 (w)	187	87, 187	
L-arabinopyranosyl-	248–250 250–251		58 187		
tri-O-acetyl-	137–141	69 (w)	58	58	
	238–239	28 (c)	187		
DL-arabinopyranosyl-	186–187.5				
β-D-lyxofuranosyl-	269–270	60 (w)	197	197	
β-D-glucopyranosyl-	271	16 (w)	58	87, 187, 290	189
	272–274.5	14.6 (w)	187		
tetra-O-acetyl-	156–158	−10 (c)	189 58	58	

TABLE II—Continued

Compound		Melting point, °C.	$[\alpha]_D$, degrees (solvent)[a]	References[b]	References to spectra[c]	References[b] to paper chromatography
Pyrimidinyl moiety	Glycosyl moiety					
Thymine—continued	D-galactopyranosyl-	indef.		187		
	α-L-rhamnopyranosyl- tri-O-benzoyl-	glass	−40 (w)	288	288, 288	288
2-thio-	β-D-ribofuranosyl- tri-O-benzoyl-	amorph. 217; 156–157	31 (w)	233, 233	288, 233	233
3-methyl-	β-D-glucopyranosyl-	196–202	16.9 (w)	189	290, 290	189
	tetra-O-acetyl-	120–122		290		
4-O-ethyl-	β-D-xylopyranosyl- tri-O-acetyl-	189–190		189, 188		
	D-arabinopyranosyl- tri-O-acetyl-	181	−93.6 (de)	187		
	L-arabinopyranosyl- tri-O-acetyl-	181	93.5 (de)	187		
	β-D-glucopyranosyl- tetra-O-acetyl-	glass; 131.5–133		189, 189	290	189
4-thio-	β-D-ribofuranosyl- tri-O-benzoyl-	190–191		62		
	β-D-xylofuranosyl- tri-O-benzoyl-	166–168		62		
5,6-dihydro-	β-D-glucopyranosyl-	138.5–141	29.63 (w)	290, 50	290	
Cytosine	β-D-ribofuranosyl-	230 (dec.); amorph.; 215–216; 211–214	19.14 (w); 31 (w); 29.7 (w)	51; 185; 198; 295	87, 113, 118, 198, 281, 290	70, 142, 189, 296, 297

Salt	Sugar	m.p.	[α]	Ref.	Ref.	Ref.
nitrate		197 (dec.)		50, 185		
hydrochloride		218		51		
picrate		185–187		51		
		183		137		
sulfate		183–186		295		
		233	29.7 (s)	51		
		222–223	12 (Nn)	62		
		218–219		142		
		224 (dec.)	35 (s)	185		
		224–225 (dec.)	33 (w)	198		
		224–225 (dec.)	37.5 (s)	280		
		230–233		295		
	3-amino-3-deoxy-	221–223 (sl. dec.)	91.7 (w)	201	201	201
monopicrate	5-amino-5-deoxy-	about 145	93.8 (w)	201		
		218–220 (dec.)		201		
	5-deoxy-5-fluoro-	205–207	21.5 (mC)	203	203	203
	2,3-O-benzylidene-	193–195	51.8 (m)	282a, 295		
	2,3-O-isopropylidene-tri-O-benzoyl-	glass		282		
		205		51		
hydrochloride	β-D-xylofuranosyl-	237–238	48 (w)	198	198	
nitrate	D-xylopyranosyl-	251–252 (dec.)	24 (w)	188	87	
		225–230 (dec.)	21 (w)	188		
		223–227 (dec.)		188		
nitrate	D-arabinopyranosyl-	265–267 (dec.)	−101 (w)	188	87	
		223–225 (dec.)	100 (w)	188		
nitrate	L-arabinopyranosyl-	265–267 (dec.)		188	87	
nitrate	β-D-glucopyranosyl-	197–199 (dec.)	25.6 (w)	140		
		143 (dec.)		140		
picrate		214 (dec.)	21.3 (w)	137		
		216–218 (dec.)		140		

TABLE II—Continued

Compound Pyrimidinyl moiety	Glycosyl moiety	Melting point, °C.	$[\alpha]_D$, degrees (solvent)[a]	References[b]	References to spectra[c]	References[b] to paper chromatography
Cytosine—continued hydrochloride	β-D-glucopyranosyl-—continued	200-201 (dec.) 199	20 (w)	188 291		
	tetra-O-acetyl-	201-202		291, 298	291	
hydrochloride	D-galactopyranosyl-	140-141 (dec.)	49 (w)	188	87	
nitrate hydrochloride		115-120 (dec.)	48 (w)	188		
N-acetyl-	α-L-rhamnopyranosyl-	glass		288	288, 288	
	β-D-ribofuranosyl- tri-O-benzoyl-	191-192	−58 (c)	198	198	
	2,3-di-O-benzoyl-5-deoxy-5-phthalimido-	146-148	37.5 (c)	201	201	
	2,5-di-O-benzoyl-3-deoxy-3-phthalimido-	245-246	−20.3 (c)	201	201, 201	
	β-D-xylofuranosyl- tri-O-benzoyl-	172-173	70 (c)	198	198	
	D-xylopyranosyl- tri-O-acetyl-	277-278 (dec.)		188		
	D-glucopyranosyl- tetra-O-acetyl-	225 217-218 225	38.1 (c)	140 198 291	198, 291, 299	
N-butyl-	β-D-ribofuranosyl- 3-amino-3-deoxy-	95-98	65 (w)	201	201	201

Cytosine		M.p. (°C)	[α]			
(N-benzyloxycarbonyl-alanyl)-	tetra-O-acetyl-β-D-glucopyranosyl-	143–145 (dec.)		291	291	
(N-benzyloxycarbonyl-glycyl)-		119–121 (dec.)		291	291, 299	
(N-benzyloxycarbonyl-phenylalanylglycylglycyl)-		139–140 (dec.)		291	291, 299	
(N-benzyloxycarbonyl-valyl)-		92 (dec.)		291	291, 299	
(N-benzyloxycarbonyl-valylglycyl)-		120–123 (dec.)		291	291	
(N-benzyloxycarbonyl-valylleucyl)-					299	
(N-benzyloxycarbonyl-valylphenylalanyl)-(phenylalanyl)-		128–130 (dec.)		291	291, 299	
(phenylalanylglycylglycyl)-		143–145 (dec.)		298	298	
		139–140		298	298	
(N,N-phthaloylglycyl)-		152–154		291	291	
		152–153		298		
N-(N,N-phthaloylglycyl)-	tetra-O-(N,N-phthaloylglycyl)-β-D-glucopyranosyl-	239–240		298	298	
N-methyl-	β-D-ribofuranosyl-	202–203		62	62	
N-(2-phenylethyl)-hydrochloride	β-D-ribofuranosyl-	205–206		62	62	
N,N-dimethyl-	β-D-ribofuranosyl-	223–225	13.2 (e)	201	201	201
	3-amino-3-deoxy-β-D-glucopyranosyl-	271–273	12.5 (w)	189		189
	β-D-glucopyranosyl-	281–282		290	290, 290	
N,5-dimethyl-	tetra-O-acetyl-β-D-ribofuranosyl-	190–191		189		
	β-D-ribofuranosyl-			62	62	

TABLE II—Continued

| Compound | | Melting point, °C. | $[\alpha]_D$, degrees (solvent)[a] | References[b] | References to spectra[c] | References[b] to paper chromatography |
Pyrimidinyl moiety	Glycosyl moiety					
Cytosine—continued						
5-amino-	β-D-ribofuranosyl-	180–182.5		265	265	
picrate		211–212 (dec.)		265		
sulfate		182–183		265		
5-bromo-	β-D-ribofuranosyl-	190.5–191.5		265	265	
	tri-O-acetyl-	162–163		265		
5-chloro-	β-D-ribofuranosyl-	202–202.5		265	265	
picrate		173–174		265		
	tri-O-acetyl-	157.2–158		265		
5-fluoro-	β-D-ribofuranosyl-	199–200		293	293	
5-methyl-	β-D-ribofuranosyl-	177–179		293	293	
	β-D-xylofuranosyl-	210–211 (dec.)	−3 (Nn)	62	62	
hydrochloride		207–208 (dec.)	−2.5 (Nn)	62	62	
	D-xylopyranosyl-	254–256 (dec.)	14 (w)	188	87	
hydrochloride		246–247 (dec.)		188		
	D-arabinopyranosyl-	231–232 (dec.)		188		
nitrate		290–291 (dec.)	−79 (w)	188	87	
	L-arabinopyranosyl-	206–210 (dec.)		188		
nitrate		290–291 (dec.)	78 (w)	62		
	β-D-glucopyranosyl-	279–280 (dec.)	−4 (Nn)	300		
5,6-dihydro-	β-D-ribofuranosyl-	163	50 (Nn)	44	87, 290, 302	67, 70, 301
Uracil	"2-deoxy-β-D-ribo''-furanosyl-	163–163.5	30 (w)	70		
		167		126		

Compound	Derivative	M.p., °C	[α]_D	Ref.	Ref.	Ref.
	5-O-acetyl-	161–162		302		
	"2-deoxy-D-gluco"-pyranosyl-	96		126	126	126
2-thio-		168–169		118	118	
		169–170		303		
4-O-ethyl-	"2-deoxy-β-D-ribo"-furanosyl-	136–138		235	235	
	"2-deoxy-β-D-gluco"-pyranosyl- tetra-O-acetyl-			118		
5-fluoro-4-thio-	"2-deoxy-β-D-ribo"-furanosyl- di-O-benzoyl-	210–211		293		
5-bromo-	"2-deoxy-β-D-ribo"-furanosyl-	187–189		266	266	
		181–183		267		
5-fluoro-	"2-deoxy-β-D-ribo"-furanosyl-	152–153		293		
		150–151	37.5 (w)	228		
	di-O-benzoyl-	236.5–237.5		293		
	3,5-di-O-(p-toluyl)-	229	–17 (p)	228		
	"2-deoxy-α-D-ribo"-furanosyl-	150–151	–21 (w)	228		
	3,5-di-O-(p-toluyl)-	214–215	–72.5 (p)	228		
		209–211				
5-hydroxy-	"2-deoxy-β-D-ribo"-furanosyl-	136–138	18.5 (w)	266	266	37
5-(hydroxymethyl)-	"2-deoxy-β-D-ribo"-furanosyl-	178		37	37	
5,6-dihydro-	"2-deoxy-β-D-ribo"-furanosyl-	184–186		74		
Uracil	"3-deoxy-β-D-ribo"-furanosyl-	186–187		248	248	248
Thymine	"2-deoxy-β-D-ribo"-furanosyl-	180		34	34, 87, 70, 114, 145, 281, 281a, 302	34, 67, 70, 126, 145, 146, 189, 302, 306, 307
		184.5–185.5		70		
		183–184		252		
		182–185		114		
		184	30.6 (w)	62		
		186		126		
		185	32.5 (Nn)	130		
		182–183		137		
3-O-acetyl-		187–188		304, 305		
3-deoxy-3-iodo-		176	0.7 (de)	302, 307		
		166–167 (dec.)		308		146
				146		
				145		

TABLE II—Continued

Pyrimidinyl moiety	Glycosyl moiety	Melting point, °C.	$[\alpha]_D$, degrees (solvent)[a]	References[b]	References to spectra[c]	References[b] to paper chromatography
Thymine—continued	"2-deoxy-β-D-ribo"-furanosyl- —continued					
	3-O-mesyl-	116		145		
	5-O-acetyl-	146		145, 306		145
	5-bromo-5-deoxy-	129 (dec.)		145		145
	5-deoxy-5-iodo-	168 (dec.)		145		145
	5-O-tosyl-	172 (dec.)		145		145
	5-O-trityl-	125	11.4 (a)	130		
		128	19.2 (de)	146		
	3,5-di-O-acetyl-	123–125		266		145
		125		145, 306		
	3,5-di-O-benzoyl-	192.5–193.5		62		
		196	−53.4 (p)	308		
	3,5-dibromo-3,5-dideoxy-	159 (dec.)		145		145
	3,5-di-O-mesyl-	168–169 (dec.)		145		
	3,5-di-O-(p-toluyl)-	197	−50 (p)	228		
	3-O-acetyl-5-deoxy-5-iodo-	131	−5.6 (de)	146		146
	3-O-acetyl-5-O-trityl-	105 (subl.)	18.6 (de)	146		
	3-bromo-3-deoxy-5-O-trityl-	144		145		
	3-deoxy-3-iodo-5-O-trityl-	147		145		
	5-deoxy-5-iodo-3-O-mesyl-	161–162 (dec.)		145		
	3-O-mesyl-5-O-trityl-			145		
	3-O-tosyl-5-O-trityl-	187	29.7 (a)	130		
	"2-deoxy-α-D-ribo"-furanosyl-		7.2 (w)	228		
	3,5-di-O-(p-toluyl)-	138	−14.5 (p)	228		
3-methyl-	"2-deoxy-β-D-xylo"-furanosyl-	132.5–134		189	266, 290	145
	"2-deoxy-β-D-ribo"-furanosyl-	129–131		266		189

	M.p., °C	Rotation			
4-"Azido"-5-methyl-2(1H)-pyrimidinone					
"2-deoxy-β-D-ribo"-furanosyl-	148–149		62	62	
Thymine, 4(or 3)-benzoyl-					
"2-deoxy-β-D-ribo"-furanosyl-	125–126		62		
tri-O-benzoyl-	114		62		
4-Hydrazino-5-methyl-2(1H)-pyrimidinone					
"2-deoxy-β-D-ribo"-furanosyl-	169–170		62		
Thymine, 4-thio-					
3,5-di-O-benzoyl-	glass		62		
"2-deoxy-β-D-ribo"-furanosyl-	159–160	−52 (c)	62	62	
3,5-di-O-benzoyl-	200–203		62	62	
4,4'-dithiodi-					
bis-("2-deoxy-β-D-ribo"-furanosyl)-	152–153 (dec.)		74		
5,6-dihydro-					
"2-deoxy-β-D-ribo"-furanosyl-	206–209	−25.6 (w)	290	290	
Thymine					
"2,3-dideoxy-β-D-ribo"-furanosyl-5-bromo-5-deoxy-	145		145		145
"2,5-dideoxy-β-D-ribo"-furanosyl-	155–156		145		145
"2-deoxy-β-D-ribo"-furanosyl-	188		145		145
Cytosine	207–209	57.6 (w)	70	87, 114, 118, 281a, 290, 302	34, 70, 144, 274, 290, 296, 302
	206–208		114		
	213–215	82.4 (Nn)	305		
	210		138		
	200–201	78 (Nn)	228		
hydrochloride	188–192 (dec.)		70	290	
picrate	191 (dec.)		114		
	190 (shrinks)	40 (w)	304		
3-O-acetyl-	173 (dec.)		274		274
picrate	120		144		144
5-O-tosyl-	239		274		274
5-O-trityl-	166–167 (dec.)		274		
3(or 2),5-di-O-trityl-	172–173 (dec.)		274		
picrate					

TABLE II—Continued

	Compound	Melting point, °C	$[\alpha]_D$, degrees (solvent)[a]	References[b]	References to spectra[c]	References[b] to paper chromatography
Pyrimidinyl moiety	Glycosyl moiety					
Cytosine—continued						
N-acetyl-	"2-deoxy-α-D-ribo"-furanosyl-	192–193	−44 (Nn)	228		
	"2-deoxy-β-D-ribo"-furanosyl-3-O-acetyl-	171	−19 (c)	274	274	144, 274
	3,5-di-O-(p-chlorobenzoyl)-	128–130	(c)	228		144
	3-O-acetyl-5-O-tosyl-	crude		144		
	3-O-acetyl-5-O-trityl-	196		274		274
	"2-deoxy-α-D-ribo"-furanosyl-3,5-di-O-(p-chlorobenzoyl)-	204.5–205	−66 (c)	228	62	
N,5-dimethyl-N-(2-phenyl-ethyl)-	"2-deoxy-β-D-ribo"-furanosyl-	225–227	28 (w)	62	62	
5-methyl-N-(2-phenyl-ethyl)-	"2-deoxy-β-D-ribo"-furanosyl-	183–185	(w)	62		
5-fluoro-	"2-deoxy-β-D-ribo"-furanosyl-	196.5–197.5	65.6 (w)	293	293	37
				228		
5-(hydroxymethyl)-	"2-deoxy-β-D-ribo"-furanosyl-	hygroscopic		34	37	34, 70, 302, 306
5-methyl-	"2-deoxy-β-D-ribo"-furanosyl-			34	34, 62, 306	
hydrochloride		156	65 (Nn)	34		
		154–155 (dec.)	54 (Nn)	62	62	
picrate		175–178 (dec.)		34		
5,6-dihydro-	"2-deoxy-β-D-ribo"-furanosyl-	>230		62		
				300		
2,2'-Anhydrides of						
Uracil	β-D-arabinofuranosyl-	234–235		126		126, 158, 248
		234–236 (dec.)		158, 248		

Thymine					
5-O-acetyl-	168–169		253a	253a	253a
5-bromo-5-deoxy-	185–186		245	245, *245*	
5-deoxy-5-iodo-	194–195 (dec.)		245	245, *245*	
3,5-di-O-acetyl-β-D-lyxofuranosyl-	186–187	−41 (w)	253a	253a	253a
2-thio-					
3,5-O-isopropylidene-β-D-arabinofuranosyl-	259–262		197	197	
5-O-trityl-			252		
3,2'-Anhydride of					
Thymine					
"2-deoxy-β-D-xylo"-furanosyl-	230		145	145	145
5-O-mesyl-	176 (dec.)		145	145	
5,2'-Anhydrides of					
Thymine					
"2-deoxy-β-D-ribo"-furanosyl-	230		145	145	145
3-O-acetyl-β-D-ribofuranosyl-	252		145	145	145
Cytosine					
p-toluenesulfonate					
2,3-O-isopropylidene-	242 (dec.)		142		

[a] The solvent used in the determination of rotations appears in parentheses. Key to solvents: (a) acetone; (c) chloroform; (d) dioxane; (de) 95% ethanol; (e) ethanol; (m) methanol; (mC) methyl Cellosolve; (n) 8% sodium hydroxide; (Nn) N sodium hydroxide; (p) pyridine; (s) 1% sulfuric acid; (w) water. The temperature range is from 13 to 31°. [b] References 278 to 308 appear in a separate list starting on page 380. [c] Italicized references are for infrared absorption spectra; all others refer to ultraviolet absorption spectra.

(278) J. M. Gulland and H. Smith, *J. Chem. Soc.*, 338 (1947).

(279) H. S. Loring and J. M. Ploeser, *J. Biol. Chem.*, **178**, 439 (1949).

(280) D. T. Elmore, *J. Chem. Soc.*, 2084 (1950).

(281) H. T. Miles, *Biochim. et Biophys. Acta*, **22**, 247 (1956); **30**, 324 (1958).

(281a) R. L. Sinsheimer, R. L. Nutter and G. R. Hopkins, *Biochim. et Biophys. Acta*, **18**, 13 (1955).

(282) A. M. Michelson and A. R. Todd, *J. Chem. Soc.*, 2476 (1949).

(282a) D. M. Brown, L. J. Haynes and A. R. Todd, *J. Chem. Soc.*, 408, 3299 (1950).

(283) A. M. Michelson and A. R. Todd, *J. Chem. Soc.*, 3459 (1956).

(284) G. W. Kenner, A. R. Todd, R. F. Webb and F. J. Weymouth, *J. Chem. Soc.*, 2288 (1954).

(285) J. Baddiley and G. A. Jamieson, *J. Chem. Soc.*, 1085 (1955).

(286) D. W. Visser, K. Dittmer and I. Goodman, *J. Biol. Chem.*, **171**, 377 (1947).

(287) G. E. Hilbert and T. B. Johnson, *J. Am. Chem. Soc.*, **52**, 4489 (1930).

(288) B. R. Baker and K. Hewson, *J. Org. Chem.*, **22**, 959 (1957).

(289) G. Shaw and R. N. Warrener, *Proc. Chem. Soc.*, 351 (1957).

(290) H. T. Miles, *Biochim. et Biophys. Acta*, **27**, 46 (1958).

(291) Z. A. Shabarova, N. I. Sokolova and M. A. Prokof'ev, *Zhur. Obshchei Khim.*, **27**, 2891 (1957); *Chem. Abstracts*, **52**, 8058 (1958).

(292) J. J. Fox, I. Wempen and R. Duschinsky, unpublished data.

(293) R. Duschinsky, private communication.

(294) I. Lieberman, A. Kornberg and E. S. Simms, *J. Am. Chem. Soc.*, **76**, 2844 (1954).

(295) J. M. Gulland and H. Smith, *J. Chem. Soc.*, 1527 (1948).

(296) G. R. Wyatt, *Biochem. J.*, **48**, 584 (1951).

(297) D. M. Brown, C. A. Dekker and A. R. Todd, *J. Chem. Soc.*, 2715 (1952).

(298) Z. A. Shabarova and M. A. Prokof'ev, *Doklady Akad. Nauk S. S. S. R.*, **109**, 340 (1956).

(299) Z. A. Shabarova, N. I. Sokolova and M. A. Prokof'ev, *Zhur. Obshchei Khim.*, **27**, 3028 (1957); *Chem. Abstracts*, **52**, 8059 (1958).

(300) M. Green and S. S. Cohen, *J. Biol. Chem.*, **228**, 601 (1957).

(301) J. G. Buchanan, *Nature*, **168**, 1091 (1951).

(302) W. Anderson, C. A. Dekker and A. R. Todd, *J. Chem. Soc.*, 2721 (1952).

(303) I. Goodman, private communication.

(304) P. A. Levene and E. S. London, *J. Biol. Chem.*, **83**, 793 (1929).

(305) O. Schindler, *Helv. Chim. Acta*, **32**, 979 (1949).

(306) S. S. Cohen and H. D. Barner, *J. Biol. Chem.*, **226**, 631 (1957).

(307) A. M. Michelson and A. R. Todd, *J. Chem. Soc.*, 2632 (1955).

(308) F. Weygand and W. Sigmund, *Z. Naturforsch.*, **9b**, 800 (1954).

PREPARATION AND PROPERTIES OF β-GLUCURONIDASE

By G. A. Levvy and C. A. Marsh

Rowett Research Institute, Bucksburn, Aberdeenshire, Scotland

I. Introduction

In the mammal, many alcohols and phenols, as well as certain carboxylic acids, are combined with D-glucuronic acid to form β-D-glucopyranosiduronic acids. Several hormones, including many of the steroids, and a large number of synthetic drugs undergo this biosynthetic reaction. It is generally regarded as a mechanism for the circulation of physiologically active compounds in the blood, and for their rapid excretion in the urine or bile.

Compounds known to behave in this way *in vivo* are listed in recent reviews in this Series.[1,2] The structures of some of the β-D-glucopyranosiduronic acids isolated from urine have been proved by chemical synthesis.[3] A few similar derivatives of flavones and triterpenes have been isolated from plants. D-Glucuronic acid also occurs in mammalian tissues as a constituent of acid mucopolysaccharides (aminodeoxypolysaccharides, containing uronic acid), such as hyaluronic acid, chondroitinsulfate, and heparin,[4] and it is a direct precursor of L-ascorbic acid in plants and mammals.[5] It is present in many of the plant polysaccharides classified as hemicelluloses[6] and gums,[7] and it has also been found in certain bacterial polysaccharides.[4]

All mammalian tissues contain a group-specific enzyme that catalyzes the hydrolysis of the biosynthetic β-D-glucopyranosiduronic acids (I) of[7a] all types to the aglycons and D-glucuronic acid. This enzyme is commonly known as *β-glucuronidase*, a term that will be employed in the following pages. In the same way, for the sake of brevity, β-D-glucopyranosiduronic acids will often be referred to as β-glucuronides. Enzymes that decompose β-glucuronides have been obtained from diverse sources other than the mammalian cell. Whilst formal proof of their specificity and mode of action is sometimes incomplete or entirely lacking, they are all probably similar to the mammalian enzyme in these respects, and can safely be regarded as β-glucuronidases.

A great deal of work has been done on the changes that can be induced in the β-glucuronidase activity of certain mammalian tissues *in vivo* in a number of different ways. This work has already been reviewed,[2,8,9] and it may be accepted that the enzyme is under endocrine control. Still a matter for speculation is the function of the enzyme in the animal body. Whilst the enzyme is almost certainly essential for the release of the active hormones from steroid hormone β-glucuronides in target organs, the alterations in activity displayed by the enzyme in certain organs in response to the treatment of animals with the free hormones, in common with certain other mammalian glycosidases,[10] suggest that β-glucuronidase has some

(1) H. G. Bray, *Advances in Carbohydrate Chem.*, **8**, 251 (1953).

(2) R. S. Teague, *Advances in Carbohydrate Chem.*, **9**, 185 (1954).

(3) J. Conchie, G. A. Levvy and C. A. Marsh, *Advances in Carbohydrate Chem.*, **12**, 158 (1957).

(4) M. Stacey, *Advances in Carbohydrate Chem.*, **2**, 161 (1946).

(5) M. ul Hassan and A. L. Lehninger, *J. Biol. Chem.*, **223**, 123 (1956).

(6) W. J. Polglase, *Advances in Carbohydrate Chem.*, **10**, 283 (1955); G. O. Aspinall, *ibid.*, **14**, 429 (1959).

(7) J. K. N. Jones and F. Smith, *Advances in Carbohydrate Chem.*, **4**, 243 (1949).

(7a) See page 412 for all formulas.

(8) G. A. Levvy, *Brit. Med. Bull.*, **9**, 126 (1953).

(9) G. A. Levvy, *Vitamins and Hormones*, **14**, 267 (1956).

(10) J. Conchie and J. Findlay, *J. Endocrinol.*, **18**, 132 (1959).

additional action. One possible function that would apply equally to the enzyme from the mammalian cell and from other sources is participation in the catabolism of polysaccharides containing glucuronic acid. β-Glucuronidase has been shown to be present in crude preparations of testicular hyaluronidase, and to act on oligosaccharides formed after partial degradation of hyaluronic acid and chondroitinsulfate.[11] The recent suggestion[12,13,13a] that cats are exceptional in that they are unable to form β-glucuronides of alcohols and phenols, although their tissues display the usual mammalian levels of β-glucuronidase activity, favors the possibility that the primary function of the enzyme lies in mucopolysaccharide catabolism.

β-Glucuronidase finds its major application at the present time as a reagent for the hydrolysis of urinary steroid D-glucuronides,[9] for which purpose it has certain advantages over mineral acids, and the rapid changes in tissue β-glucuronidase activity induced *in vivo* by certain steroid and pituitary hormones offer possibilities for the rapid measurement of the hormones. The enzyme might perhaps be employed with advantage as a hydrolytic agent in carbohydrate chemistry. The purpose of the present article is to review the literature dealing with the preparation and assay of the enzyme, and with its properties *in vitro*. Because of the very intensity with which it has been studied, many complexities have been encountered with β-glucuronidase, some of which may equally apply to other enzymes.

II. Occurrence

The earliest reports of the decomposition of β-glucuronides by plant[14] and mammalian[15] preparations appeared in 1904 and 1908, respectively. It was not until 1934, however, that the systematic study of β-glucuronidase commenced, with the characterization of the enzyme in ox kidney by Masamune.[16]

Table I gives approximate figures for the β-glucuronidase activity of nearly all known sources of the enzyme. It can be seen that the enzyme is universally distributed in mammalian tissues and body fluids. This generalization probably extends to other vertebrates, and to insects and molluscs. The occurrence of the enzyme in micro-organisms is random, and bears no relation to their pathogenicity for man. The microbial enzyme may be adaptive or constitutive, and extracellular or intracellular: the enzyme in *Escherichia coli* is adaptive and extracellular, whilst that in

(11) A. Linker, K. Meyer and B. Weissmann, *J. Biol. Chem.*, **213**, 237 (1955).
(12) G. J. Dutton and C. G. Greig, *Biochem. J.*, **66**, 52P (1957).
(13) D. Robinson and R. T. Williams, *Biochem. J.*, **68**, 23P (1958).
(13a) S. Borrell, *Biochem. J.*, **70**, 727 (1958).
(14) C. Neuberg, *Ergeb. Physiol.*, **3**, 373 (1904).
(15) F. Röhmann, "Biochemie," Julius Springer, Berlin, 1908.
(16) H. Masamune, *J. Biochem.* (Tokyo), **19**, 353 (1934).

Streptococci is essentially constitutive and intracellular. β-Glucuronidase occurs only sporadically in the plant kingdom, and the activity is not high.

TABLE I

β-Glucuronidase Activity[a] of Mammalian and Non-mammalian Tissues

a. Phenolphthalein Liberated from Phenolphthalein β-D-Glucosiduronic Acid

MOUSE (*"high" strains*): blood serum[17] 11; brain[18,19] 150; breast,[17] *about* 1000; cancer tissue[17,20] 2000; epididymis[19] 4000; epididymis (castrate)[19] 900; epididymis (infant)[19] 1500; kidney[21-27] 1500–4500; kidney (infant)[23] 4000; liver[20,21,23-33] 2000–4000; liver (infant)[23,32,33] 4000–5500; ovary[19] 1500; preputial gland (male)[19] 800; preputial gland (female)[19] 800; prostate[19] 0; seminal vesicle[19] 1000,[26] 4000; seminal vesicle (castrate)[26] 15,000; spleen[18,21,25-27] 4500–11,000; testis[19] 500; urine[27] 5; uterus[21,26] 3000; uterus (castrate)[21,23,26] 1500; uterus (infant)[19] 1200; vagina[19,21] 800–1600.

MOUSE (*"low" strains*): blood serum[17] 7; brain[19] 10; breast,[17] *about* 50; cancer tissue[17,20] 650; epididymis[19] 1000; kidney[19,22,26] 300–700; liver[19,20,26,28-31] 200–400; liver (infant)[19] 2500; seminal vesicle[26] 100; seminal vesicle (castrate)[26] 3000; spleen[26] 1300; urine[27] 0; uterus[19,26] 1000; uterus (castrate)[26] 1000.

RAT: adrenal[34-37] 5000–10,000; amniotic fluid[34] 20–100; blood serum[34] 2–10; brain[18,34] 150; breast[34,38] 2000–5000,[39] 350; choroid plexus[37] 2500; epididymis[19] 10,000; epididymis (castrate)[19] 2500; epididymis (infant)[19] 3000; eye[19] 500; heart[34] 350; intestinal contents (small intestine)[40] 100; intestinal contents (large intestine)[40] 3000; jejunum[34] 5000; kidney[18,24,34,36,37,41,42] 4000–6000; liver[24,34,36-38,41-45] 20,000–30,000; liver (infant)[24,43] 10,000–20,000; lung[34,36,37] 5000; lymph node[46] 14,000; muscle (voluntary)[34,36] 110; ovary[19,34,36,37] 9000; placenta[34] 4000; preputial gland (male)[19] 100,000; preputial gland (female)[38,47-49] 2,000,000; preputial gland (infant female)[19] 500,000; prostate[19,36,39] 2000–6000; prostate (castrate),[39] *about* 6000; prostate (infant)[19] 3000; salivary gland[37] 700; seminal vesicle[19,36] 300,[37,39] 1300; seminal vesicle (castrate),[39] *about* 2500; seminal vesicle (infant)[19] 2500; spleen[18,24,34,36,37,41,42,46] 15,000–30,000; testis[19,36,50] 150–400; testis (infant)[19] 1200; thymus[34,46] 6000; thyroid[34] 2500,[36] 6000; uterus[34,36,38,39,51] 7000–9000; uterus (castrate)[39,51] 2000; uterus (infant)[19,39] 5000; vagina[34] 4000,[19] 9000.

MAN: amniotic fluid[52] 3; blood plasma or serum[53-59] 1–10; breast[60-63] 100–1000; cancer tissue[20,60,63-67] 500–20,000; cerebrospinal fluid[53,68] 0.3; colon[60-62] 2000; erythrocytes[53] 0; kidney[20] 2000,[55] 7000; leucocytes,[53,59,69] *present*; liver[62] 3000,[55] 11,000; lung[60] 500; lymph node[60,70] 500–800; mesentery[62,63] 550; esophagus[61,64] 400–700; ovary[60,66] 300–600,[55] 4000; pancreas[60,62,63] 600; parotid[60] 1500; penis[63] 300; placenta[55,60,71] 500–2000; rectum[62] 2000; saliva,[53] *trace*; semen[72] 350; skin[63] 200; spleen[55] 6500; stomach[60-64] 200–1000; tears,[53] *trace*; urine[53,73] 0.6; urine (infant)[52] 1–10; uterus[20,60,62,63,65-67,74] 200–1000; uterine endometrium[55,60,67,74,75] 1000–10,000; vagina[60,66] 100–800; vaginal fluid (premenopausal)[65,74,76-79] 0–300; vaginal fluid (postmenopausal)[77,78] 0–800.

OX: intestinal contents (small intestine)[40] 60; intestinal contents (large intestine)[40] 1000; kidney,[42] *about* 2000; liver[42,80,81] 6000; semen[72] 1000; spleen,[42] *about* 1500.

RABBIT: blood plasma[82] 1; brain[18] 150; intestinal contents (small intestine)[40] 10; intestinal contents (large intestine)[40] 2500; leucocytes,[69,82] *present*; liver[18] 4000; liver (infant)[18] 3000; seminal plasma[72] 70.

SHEEP: intestinal wall,[83] *about* 300; intestinal contents (small intestine)[40] 150; intestinal contents (large intestine)[40] 3000; liver[18,19] 5000–10,000; semen[72] 400.

DOG: brain[84] 150; semen[72] 12.

HORSE: intestinal contents (small intestine)[40] 2; intestinal contents (large intestine)[40] 300; semen[72] 31; seminal plasma (epididymal)[72] 840.

TABLE 1—*Continued*

CAT: intestinal contents (small intestine)[40] 120; intestinal contents (large intestine)[40] 350; nerve (sciatic)[85] 350.

PIG: epididymis[19] 20; epididymis (infant)[19] 45; intestinal contents (small intestine)[40] 30; intestinal contents (large intestine)[40] 1000; kidney[19,42] 20; liver[19,42] 150; semen[72] 0; spleen[19,42] 60; testis[19] 40; testis (infant)[19] 150.

GUINEA PIG: *about* 500 in kidney, and *about* 3000 in liver and spleen.[42]

MONKEY: vesicular secretion[72] 186.

HEDGEHOG: prostatic secretion[72] 122.

FOWL: cecal contents[40] 8000; intestinal contents (small intestine)[40] 300; *about* 4000 in kidney and liver, and *about* 1500 in spleen.[42]

TURKEY: *about* 5000 in kidney, liver, and spleen.[42]

TROUT: *about* 8000 in kidney and liver, and *about* 3000 in spleen.[42]

MOLLUSCS: visceral hump of limpet (*Patella vulgata*)[86] 100,000; digestive juice of snail (*Helix pomatia*)[87] 150,000.

PLANTS: *Scutellaria baicalensis* root[88] 200; *S. albida* root[88] 25; *none* in *S. tournefortii, S. columnae, S. galericulata, Centaurea scabiosa*,[88] and a number of other plants.[83]

PROTOZOA: *none* in *Trichomonas vaginalis*,[78] and in *oligotrich* and *holotrich* ciliates from sheep-rumen liquor.[89]

FUNGI: *present* in *Coniophora cerebella* and *Lenzites trabea*;[90] *none* in *Aspergillus fumigatus, A. niger, A. oryzae, A. terreus*,[90] and *Myrothecium verrucaria*.[83]

BACTERIA: *present* in certain strains of *Escherichia coli, Streptococcus* and *Staphylococcus*,[91-99] but *none* in others; also *present* in certain *Corynebacteria*[91,92,97] and in sheep-rumen micro-organisms.[100,101]

b. 8-Quinolinol Liberated from 8-Quinolinyl β-D-Glucosiduronic Acid

INSECTS: *Locusta migratoria*[102]—brown crop fluid 64,000; green crop fluid 4000–14,000; hemolymph 300; ecdysial fluid, *trace. Drosophila melanogaster* embryo[b103] 6000.

AMPHIBIA: embryo of clawed toad (*Xenopus laevis*)[b][104] 400; liver of newt (*Triturus vulgaris* and *T. cristatus*)[c][105] *about* 30,000.

MOLLUSCS:[106] *Helix pomatia*[c]—digestive gland 30,000; crop fluid 12,000; kidney 400; albumin gland 1600; salivary gland 700; mantle ridge 50; foot 400; ovotestis 2500. Digestive gland of[c]—*H. aspersa* 13,500, *Limnea stagnalis* 500, *Anodonta cygnea* 5000, *Planorbis corneus* 4000.

c. p-Chlorophenol Liberated from p-Chlorophenyl β-D-Glucosiduronic Acid

INSECTS:[102] brown crop fluid of—*Locusta migratoria* 12,000, *Schistocerca gregaria* 20,000.

MOLLUSCS (*marine*):[107] *Buccinum undatum*—posterior digestive gland 9000; anterior digestive gland 1500; ovary 3000. *Gibbula cineraria* (entire) 5000. Digestive gland of—*Mytilus edulis* 14,000, *Osterea edulis* 10,000. Visceral hump of—*Calliostoma zizyphinum* 8000, *Nucella lapillus* 9000, *Osilinus lineatus* 53,000, *Littorina littorea* 20,000, *Patella vulgata* 45,000, *G. umbilicalis* 44,000, *Scaphander lignarius* 2300.

d. 4-Methylumbelliferone Liberated from 4-Methylumbelliferone
β-D-Glucosiduronic Acid[d]

MOUSE ("*high*" strain): liver[83] *about* 2500.

RAT:[108] blood plasma 7; liver 23,000; liver (infant) 15,000; muscle (voluntary) 200; nerve (phrenic) 500; spleen 15,000; testis 100.

MAN:[108] blood plasma 10; saliva 0.6; urine 1.

CAT:[109] heart 600; heart (infant) 4000; intestine (small) 3000; intestine (small—in-

TABLE 1—*Continued*

fant) 9000; liver 6000; liver (infant) 30,000; kidney 7000; kidney (infant) 10,000; spleen 8000; spleen (infant) 25,000.

RABBIT:[108] blood plasma 100.

GUINEA PIG:[108] adrenal 300; blood plasma 10; liver 9000; muscle (voluntary) 60; spleen 7000

INSECTS:[109,110] entire insect—*Acyrthosiphum pisum* 163, *Megoura vicia* 118, *Pieris brassicae* 60, *Diataraxia oleracea* 524, *Tribolium castaneum* 3560, *Phaedon cochleariae* 2820, *Dysdercus fasciatus* 3920, *Blatta orientalis* 280, *B. germanica* 1180, *Musca domestica* 1100. Crop fluid of *Locusta migratoria* 112,500.

MOLLUSCS: visceral hump of *Patella vulgata*[83] about 50,000.

e. Phenol Liberated from Phenyl β-D-Glucosiduronic Acid

MOUSE (*"high"* strains): breast[111] 100; cancer tissue[111,112] 400–700; kidney[111,113,114] 300; kidney (infant)[114] 550; liver[111-115] 300; liver (infant)[112,114] 1000; lung[112] 200; spleen[113,115] 700; uterus[111,114] 300; uterus (castrate)[114,111] 150; uterus (infant)[114] 600.

RAT: liver[111] 1500; preputial gland (female)[116] 500,000.

FOWL:[117] cancer tissue 800; liver 230.

PLANTS: *present* in almond emulsin.[14]

f. Liberation of D-Glucuronic Acid from levo-Menthyl β-D-Glucosiduronic Acid

MOUSE (*"high"* strains): blood plasma[118] 80–160; kidney[118,119] 1000; liver[118-120] 2000; ovary[119] 1000; spleen[119] 1600,[118] 6000; testis[119] 140; uterus[119,120] 1300; uterus (castrate)[118,120] 700; vagina[118,119] 800.

RAT:[121] kidney 470; liver 314; spleen 1600.

MAN: blood plasma[61] 0.5–5.

OX: spleen[122] 2200; *present* in many other organs.[123]

RABBIT:[121] kidney 100; liver 600; spleen 760.

DOG:[119,123] kidney 200; liver 150; spleen 600; uterus 160; *present* in many other organs.

HORSE: *present* in kidney.[124]

FISH:[125] *present* in livers of dog-fish (*Mustulis laevis*) and conger eel (*Conger conger*).

MOLLUSCS: *present* in snails.[126,127]

PLANTS: *present* in almond emulsin.[128]

---

a Expressed as μg. of aglycon or D-glucuronic acid liberated per g. of moist tissue in 1hr. at 38°. *b* Activity per g. of *dry* material at *25°*. *c* Activity per g. of moist material at *25°*. *d* $10^{-4} M$.

(17) S. L. Cohen and J. J. Bittner, *Cancer Research*, **11**, 723 (1951).

(18) P. G. Walker, Ph.D. Thesis, University of Aberdeen, Scotland (1952).

(19) J. Conchie, private communication.

(20) J. Conchie and G. A. Levvy, *Brit. J. Cancer*, **11**, 487 (1957).

(21) R. S. Harris and S. L. Cohen, *Endocrinology*, **48**, 264 (1951).

(22) A. G. Morrow, D. M. Carroll and E. M. Greenspan, *J. Natl. Cancer Inst.*, **11**, 663 (1951).

(23) L. M. H. Kerr and G. A. Levvy, *Biochem. J.*, **48**, 209 (1951).

(24) P. G. Walker and G. A. Levvy, *Biochem. J.*, **54**, 56 (1953).

(25) W. H. Fishman, M. Artenstein and S. Green, *Endocrinology*, **57**, 646 (1955).

(26) W. H. Fishman and M. H. Farmelant, *Endocrinology*, **52**, 536 (1953).

(27) G. Riotton and W. H. Fishman, *Endocrinology*, **52**, 692 (1953).

(28) A. G. Morrow, E. M. Greenspan and D. M. Carroll, *J. Natl. Cancer Inst.*, **10**, 657 (1949).

TABLE 1—*Continued*

(29) L. W. Law, A. G. Morrow and E. M. Greenspan, *J. Natl. Cancer Inst.*, **12**, 909 (1952).

(30) A. G. Morrow, E. M. Greenspan and D. M. Carroll, *J. Natl. Cancer Inst.*, **10**, 1199 (1950).

(31) H.-G. Sie and W. H. Fishman, *Cancer Research*, **13**, 590 (1953).

(32) P. G. Walker and G. A. Levvy, *Biochem. J.*, **49**, 620 (1951).

(33) P. G. Walker, *Biochem. J.*, **51**, 223 (1952).

(34) R. M. Bernard and L. D. Odell, *J. Lab. Clin. Med.*, **35**, 940 (1950).

(35) E. Knobil, *Proc. Soc. Exptl. Biol. Med.*, **83**, 769 (1953).

(36) P. Talalay, W. H. Fishman and C. Huggins, *J. Biol. Chem.*, **166**, 757 (1946).

(37) B. Becker and J. S. Friedenwald, *Arch. Biochem.*, **22**, 101 (1949).

(38) A. L. Beyler and C. M. Szego, *Endocrinology*, **54**, 323 (1954).

(39) E. Knobil, *Endocrinology*, **50**, 16 (1952).

(40) C. A. Marsh, F. Alexander and G. A. Levvy, *Nature*, **170**, 163 (1952).

(41) W. H. Fishman and P. Talalay, *Science*, **105**, 131 (1947).

(42) N. K. Sarkar and J. B. Sumner, *Arch. Biochem.*, **27**, 453 (1950).

(43) G. T. Mills, J. Paul and E. E. B. Smith, *Biochem. J.*, **53**, 245 (1953).

(44) G. T. Mills and E. E. B. Smith, *Science*, **114**, 690 (1951).

(45) J. Tuba, *Can. J. Med. Sci.*, **31**, 18 (1953).

(46) C. Pellegrino and G. Villani, *Biochem. J.*, **62**, 235 (1956).

(47) A. L. Beyler and Clara M. Szego, *Endocrinology*, **54**, 334 (1954).

(48) G. A. Levvy and C. A. Marsh, *Nature*, **180**, 919 (1957).

(49) G. A. Levvy, A. McAllan and C. A. Marsh, *Biochem. J.*, **69**, 22 (1958).

(50) M. Hayashi, K. Ogata, T. Shiraogawa and O. Kawase, *Nature*, **181**, 186 (1958).

(51) S. L. Leonard and E. Knobil, *Endocrinology*, **47**, 331 (1950).

(52) L. D. Odell, W. H. Fishman and W. R. Hepner, *Science*, **108**, 355 (1948).

(53) W. H. Fishman, B. Springer and R. Brunetti, *J. Biol. Chem.*, **173**, 449 (1948).

(54) W. H. Fishman, M. Smith, D. B. Thompson, C. D. Bonner, S. C. Kasdon and F. Homburger, *J. Clin. Invest.*, **30**, 685 (1951).

(55) D. F. McDonald and L. D. Odell, *J. Clin. Endocrinol.*, **7**, 535 (1947).

(56) W. H. Fishman, L. D. Odell, J. E. Gill and R. A. Christensen, *Am. J. Obstet. Gynecol.*, **59**, 414 (1950).

(57) S. L. Cohen and R. A. Huseby, *Cancer Research*, **11**, 52 (1951).

(58) S. L. Cohen and R. A. Huseby, *Proc. Soc. Exptl. Biol. Med.*, **76**, 304 (1951).

(59) A. J. Anlyan, J. Gamble and H. A. Hoster, *Cancer*, **3**, 116 (1950).

(60) W. H. Fishman and A. J. Anlyan, *Cancer Research*, **7**, 808 (1947).

(61) W. H. Fishman, *Science*, **105**, 646 (1947).

(62) W. H. Fishman and A. J. Anlyan, *Science*, **106**, 66 (1947).

(63) W. H. Fishman and A. J. Anlyan, *Intern. Cancer Congr.*, 4th, St. Louis, 1947; *Acta Union Intern. Contre Cancer*, **6**, 1034 (1950).

(64) W. H. Fishman and R. Bigelow, *J. Natl. Cancer Inst.*, **10**, 1115 (1950).

(65) S. C. Kasdon, W. H. Fishman and F. Homburger, *J. Am. Med. Assoc.*, **144**, 892 (1950).

(66) L. D. Odell and J. C. Burt, *Cancer Research*, **9**, 362 (1949).

(67) L. D. Odell, J. C. Burt and R. Bethea, *Science*, **109**, 564 (1949).

(68) A. J. Anlyan and A. Starr, *Cancer*, **5**, 578 (1952).

(69) R. J. Rossiter and E. Wong, *Blood*, **5**, 864 (1950).

(70) W. H. Fishman and A. J. Anlyan, *J. Biol. Chem.*, **169**, 449 (1947).

(71) E. S. Cohen, W. R. Moore and B. P. Smith, *Harper Hosp. Bull.*, **8**, 152 (1950).

(72) J. Conchie and T. Mann, *Nature*, **179**, 1190 (1957).

TABLE 1—*Continued*

(73) E. Boyland and D. C. Williams, *Biochem. J.*, **64**, 578 (1956).

(74) L. D. Odell and J. C. Burt, *J. Am. Med. Assoc.*, **142**, 226 (1950).

(75) L. D. Odell and W. H. Fishman, *Am. J. Obstet. Gynecol.*, **59**, 200 (1950).

(76) S. C. Kasdon, J. McGowan, W. H. Fishman and F. Homburger, *Am. J. Obstet. Gynecol.*, **61**, 647 (1951).

(77) S. C. Kasdon, E. Romsey, F. Homburger and W. H. Fishman, *Am. J. Obstet. Gynecol.*, **61**, 1142 (1951).

(78) W. H. Fishman, S. C. Kasdon and F. Homburger, *J. Am. Med. Assoc.*, **143**, 350 (1950).

(79) W. H. Fishman, S. C. Kasdon, C. D. Bonner, L. W. Fishman and F. Homburger, *J. Clin. Endocrinol.*, **11**, 1425 (1951).

(80) E. E. B. Smith and G. T. Mills, *Biochem. J.*, **54**, 164 (1953).

(81) P. Bernfeld, J. S. Nisselbaum and W. H. Fishman, *J. Biol. Chem.*, **202**, 763 (1953).

(82) R. J. Rossiter and E. Wong. *Can. J. Research*, **E28**, 69 (1950).

(83) G. A. Levvy and C. A. Marsh, unpublished results.

(84) A. R. McNabb, *Can. J. Med. Sci.*, **29**, 208 (1951).

(85) D. M. Hollinger, J. E. Logan, W. A. Mannell and R. J. Rossiter, *Nature*, **169**, 670 (1952).

(86) G. A. Levvy, A. J. Hay and C. A. Marsh, *Biochem. J.*, **65**, 203 (1957).

(87) P. Jarrige and R. Henry, *Bull. soc. chim. biol.*, **34**, 872 (1952).

(88) G. A. Levvy, *Biochem. J.*, **58**, 462 (1954).

(89) M. C. Karunairatnam, Ph. D. Thesis, University of Edinburgh, Scotland (1950).

(90) C. A. Marsh, Ph. D. Thesis, Aberdeen University, Scotland (1953).

(91) H. J. Buehler, P. A. Katzman and E. A. Doisy, *Federation Proc.*, **8**, 189 (1949).

(92) H. J. Buehler, P. A. Katzman and E. A. Doisy, *Proc. Soc. Exptl. Biol. Med.*, **76**, 672 (1951).

(93) E. E. B. Smith and G. T. Mills, *Biochem. J.*, **47**, xlix (1950).

(94) R. F. Jacox, *J. Bacteriol.*, **65**, 700 (1953).

(95) J. J. Robinson, C. W. Blinn and P. F. Frank, *J. Bacteriol.*, **64**, 719 (1952).

(96) M. Barber, B. W. L. Brooksbank and S. W. A. Kuper, *J. Pathol. Bacteriol.*, **63**, 57 (1951).

(97) L. D. Odell, H. D. Priddle and J. C. Burt, *Am. J. Clin. Pathol.*, **20**, 133 (1950).

(98) D. Beall and G. A. Grant, *Rev. can. biol.*, **11**, 51 (1952).

(99) P. L. Lorina, V. F. Lisanti and H. H. Chauncey, *Oral Surg., Oral Med. Oral Pathol.*, **7**, 998 (1954).

(100) M. C. Karunairatnam and G. A. Levvy, *Biochem. J.*, **49**, 210 (1951).

(101) C. A. Marsh, *Biochem. J.*, **58**, 609 (1954).

(102) D. Robinson, J. N. Smith and R. T. Williams, *Biochem. J.*, **53**, 125 (1953).

(103) F. Billett and S. J. Counce, *Exptl. Cell. Research*, **13**, 427 (1957).

(104) F. Billett, *Biochem. J.*, **67**, 463 (1957).

(105) F. Billett and S. M. McGee-Russell, *Quart. J. Microscop. Sci.*, **97**, 155 (1956).

(106) F. Billett, *Biochem. J.*, **57**, 159 (1954).

(107) K. S. Dodgson, J. I. M. Lewis and B. Spencer, *Biochem. J.*, **55**, 253 (1953).

(108) J. A. R. Mead, J. N. Smith and R. T. Williams, *Biochem. J.*, **61**, 569 (1955).

(109) D. Robinson and R. T. Williams, private communication.

(110) D. Robinson, *Biochem. J.*, **67**, 6P (1957).

(111) L. M. H. Kerr, J. G. Campbell and G. A. Levvy, *Biochem. J.*, **46**, 278 (1950).

TABLE 1—*Concluded*

(112) M. C. Karunairatnam, L. M. H. Kerr and G. A. Levvy, *Biochem. J.*, **45**, 496 (1949).

(113) G. A. Levvy, L. M. H. Kerr and J. G. Campbell, *Biochem. J.*, **42**, 462 (1948).

(114) L. M. H. Kerr, J. G. Campbell and G. A. Levvy, *Biochem. J.*, **44**, 487 (1949).

(115) L. M. H. Kerr, A. F. Graham and G. A. Levvy, *Biochem. J.*, **42**, 191 (1948).

(116) C. A. Marsh and G. A. Levvy, *Biochem. J.*, **68**, 610 (1958).

(117) L. M. H. Kerr, Ph. D. Thesis, University of Edinburgh, Scotland (1949).

(118) W. H. Fishman, *J. Biol. Chem.*, **169**, 7 (1947).

(119) W. H. Fishman, *J. Biol. Chem.*, **136**, 229 (1940).

(120) W. H. Fishman and L. W. Fishman, *J. Biol. Chem.*, **152**, 487 (1944).

(121) G. T. Mills, *Biochem. J.*, **40**, 283 (1946).

(122) W. H. Fishman, *J. Biol. Chem.*, **127**, 367 (1939).

(123) G. Oshima, *J. Biochem.* (Tokyo), **20**, 361 (1934).

(124) E. Hofmann, *Biochem. Z.*, **285**, 429 (1936).

(125) C. Neuberg and A. Grauer, *Enzymologia*, **15**, 115 (1951).

(126) M. Utusi, K. Huzi, S. Matumoto and T. Nagaoka, *Tôhoku J. Exptl. Med.*, **50**, 175 (1949).

(127) T. Nagaoka, *Tôhoku J. Exptl. Med.*, **53**, 29 (1950).

(128) B. Helferich and G. Sparmberg, *Z. physiol. Chem., Hoppe-Seyler's*, **221**, 92 (1933).

Although figures obtained for different tissues by any single method of assay are usually comparable, great care is necessary in attempting to compare figures obtained with different substrates, even if the relative rates of hydrolysis of the latter are known. This is particularly true of the older figures in the literature; the precautions that must be observed in extracting the enzyme quantitatively in a state sufficiently pure for assay have only recently been investigated (see Section V). Where, however, the preparation of the enzyme for assay has been done systematically, losses in activity from this source tend to be constant and probably rarely exceed 50 %. Most of the older figures obtained with phenolphthalein β-glucuronide are fairly accurate, since this substrate calls for little, if any, purification of the tissue homogenate or body fluid.

Even if the method of assay is beyond criticism, the figures given in Table I may differ very much in reliability. Some are mean values for large groups of animals and have been confirmed by several groups of workers. At the other extreme are figures based on single samples. Where the value is given as a range, we are convinced that different mean values display a genuine biological spread, due to uncontrolled factors, between the limits shown. In yet other cases, we have had no choice but to quote two widely divergent figures. Where a figure is prefixed by *"about,"* appropriate data are lacking, but we have arrived at an estimate from semi-quantitative measurements.

Morrow and his coworkers[28-30] discovered that certain strains of mice (notably the C_3H strain), bred for susceptibility to cancer, have remarkably low β-glucuronidase activities throughout the body, as compared with most other strains of mice; this effect of the mouse strain is also seen in the figures for cancer tissue.[17,20] It was shown that a "high" β-glucuronidase activity is dependent upon the presence of a single dominant gene. The overwhelming majority of laboratory mice throughout the world belong to "high" strains. Hereditary factors have not as yet been observed in other mammalian species. Different species do, however, show different orders of β-glucuronidase activity in most organs.

Rat tissues display the highest level of mammalian β-glucuronidase activity, and the preputial gland in the female rat is the richest known source of the enzyme. The disproportionately enormous activity of this gland in the rat is not seen in the mouse. Blood β-glucuronidase activity is very largely confined to the leucocytes.[53] Figures for vaginal fluid from women with cancer of the uterine cervix fall within the usual range for human cancer tissue.[65] Pig organs have remarkably low β-glucuronidase activities.[19,42,128a]

The known sources which most closely approach the female-rat preputial gland in activity are the digestive juices of molluscs and of locusts. As shown for the rumen of the sheep,[100] the contents of the mammalian large intestine probably owe most of their β-glucuronidase activity to microbes, whilst in the small intestine the enzyme is probably mammalian in origin.[40]

III. ASSAY

There is a wide variety of sensitive and specific methods for the measurement of β-glucuronidase activity, employing different substrates, after homogenizing a tissue in water. Apart from the sensitivity of the final estimation, a good substrate should be easy to make. Ideally, it should have a high affinity for the enzyme (for economy at enzyme saturation) and be rapidly hydrolyzed when enzyme and substrate are incubated together. The choice of method is influenced by the activity of the enzyme preparation, as well as by the presence of impurities that interfere in the final measurements of extent of hydrolysis. Most of the methods depend upon colorimetric determination of the amount of aglycon liberated from a specified concentration of substrate at a fixed pH, the results being read from a standard curve. Unit β-glucuronidase activity is then almost universally expressed as that which liberates 1 μg. of aglycon in 1 hr. at 38°; a similar type of unit is employed when the liberation of D-glucuronic acid is followed. The substrate concentration should be high enough to ensure saturation, and therefore maximal activity of the enzyme, throughout the incubation period. In selecting the experimental procedures (given below in detail for the mammalian enzyme) from a number of equally suitable alternatives in the literature, our sole criterion has been first-hand knowledge; provision

(128a) The ability of the pig to synthesize β-glucuronides might repay investigation; see F. A. Csonka, *J. Biol. Chem.*, **60**, 545 (1924).

has been made for replacement of water by inhibitor solutions, etc. Interfering substances are removed by procedures essentially similar to that described in Section IV. In all the methods, controls must be done in which the enzyme and the substrate are incubated separately with the buffer.

1. *Reducing-sugar Method*

This, the first method introduced for the assay of β-glucuronidase,[16,122,129] depends upon the reducing power of the D-glucuronic acid released from a β-glucuronide, and is still useful in certain connections. *levo*-Menthyl β-glucuronide has been almost exclusively employed as a substrate for routine purposes. It is easy to prepare biosynthetically[130] and it can also be obtained by an unrewarding chemical synthesis.[131] Neither the aglycon nor the unhydrolyzed substrate interferes in the reducing-sugar determination. The enzyme preparation must be freed from reducing material, including that formed by autolysis on incubation at the pH of assay, by some such procedure as that outlined in Section IV. The content of reducing sugar can be determined by any convenient micro-procedure, for example that described by Levvy.[129] Provided that it contains no interfering material, trichloroacetic acid can be used to precipitate enzyme protein.[88,122,129] In applying the reducing-sugar method to other β-glucuronides, it may be necessary to remove the aglycon and unchanged substrate[88,132,133] by extraction with a suitable solvent.

The incubation mixture consisted of 0.2 ml. of 0.5 M acetic acid–sodium hydroxide buffer (pH 4.5 or 5.2), 0.2 ml. of enzyme preparation, 0.2 ml. of water, and 0.2 ml. of 0.04 M *levo*-menthyl β-glucuronide solution adjusted to the appropriate pH. After 2 hr. of incubation at 38°, the reaction was terminated by adding 0.8 ml. of 10% (w/v) trichloroacetic acid, and the mixture was allowed to stand in the cold for 10 min. and then centrifuged at 1500 g for 15 min. To 0.8 ml. of the supernatant liquor, 0.2 ml. of 11% (w/v) sodium carbonate solution was added (to neutralize the trichloroacetic acid) before the addition of 0.25 ml. of alkaline ferricyanide solution for the estimation of reducing sugar by Levvy's titrimetric procedure.

2. *Phenolphthalein Method*

In the most generally useful method of assay, employing phenolphthalein (mono-)β-glucuronide[134] as substrate, the free aglycon is determined colorimetrically after addition of alkali.[36,53] (The method is barely sensitive enough for some body fluids, for example, blood plasma.) Phenolphthalein β-glucuronide has a high affinity for the enzyme and is rapidly hydrolyzed by it, but unfortunately can only be prepared by a tedious biosynthetic

(129) G. A. Levvy, *Biochem. J.*, **40**, 396 (1946).

(130) A. J. Quick, *J. Biol. Chem.*, **61**, 667 (1924).

(131) C. A. Marsh, *Nature*, **168**, 602 (1951).

(132) C. A. Marsh, *Biochem. J.*, **59**, 375 (1955).

(133) G. A. Levvy and J. T. Worgan, *Biochem. J.*, **59**, 451 (1955).

(134) A. A. di Somma, *J. Biol. Chem.*, **133**, 277 (1940).

procedure.[53] Water homogenates of most tissues can be used for assay without any preliminary treatment, and the reaction is terminated by adding the alkali. The use of a protein precipitant can lead to serious errors due to adsorption of phenolphthalein by the precipitate. One disadvantage of this method, arising from the sensitivity of the alkaline-phenolphthalein color to small changes in pH, is the need for new standard curves whenever the medium is altered in composition. A modification of the method of Fishman, Springer and Brunetti[53] for the preparation of this substrate, developed in our own laboratory, is given in square brackets below; good yields can be obtained after a little practice.

[A solution of 50 g. of disodium phenolphthalein diphosphate (commercial) in 300 ml. of water was adjusted to pH 7 and the volume was made up to 375 ml.; the turbid solution, which contained a little free phenolphthalein, was stored at 0°, and the pH was checked regularly. Six rabbits were each injected subcutaneously with 10 ml., daily for six days; the animals were fed unrestricted amounts of green vegetables and water, and their urine was collected daily and stored at 0°. At convenient intervals, the urine was filtered through gauze, made acid to Congo Red with hydrochloric acid, and extracted with a half-volume of ethyl acetate (pure). Separation of the phases was aided by centrifuging (10 min. at 1500 g); there was still a considerable amount of gel at the interface, which was retained separately. The aqueous layer, re-acidified if necessary, was twice re-extracted with a quarter-volume of ethyl acetate. The combined gels were shaken with one volume of ethyl acetate and solid sodium chloride (about 60 g. per liter of gel), centrifuged (30 min. at 1500 g), and the gel layer re-extracted as before. The combined aqueous layers from the last two extractions were finally re-extracted with one volume of ethyl acetate.

The combined ethyl acetate extracts were filtered to remove water droplets and stored at 0° until all urine extractions were completed, and then refiltered and concentrated to about one-tenth the volume under diminished pressure. The hot solution was treated with decolorizing carbon, dried with anhydrous sodium sulfate, filtered, and the crude product precipitated by means of a slight excess of a hot, saturated solution of cinchonidine in ethyl acetate (analytical grade); completeness of precipitation was tested at intervals by centrifuging a test portion and adding a cold, saturated solution of cinchonidine in ethyl acetate to the supernatant liquor.

The filtered precipitate was partially dried for several hours under vacuum, and reprecipitated twice from boiling methanolic solution by means of four volumes of ethyl acetate (analytical grade), to yield overnight a pure, white product (about 12 g., together with 2–3 g. of an impure second crop). A weighed sample (20–25 mg.) was boiled with 100 ml. of 2 N hydrochloric acid for 2.5 hr. (to complete hydrolysis), neutralized with alkali, made up to standard volume, and the phenolphthalein estimated colorimetrically (theoretical content, 38.8% for the cinchonidine salt of the monoglucuronide).

The cinchonidine salt (1.58 g.) of the glucuronide was suspended in 64 ml. of water and 40 ml. of ethyl acetate (analytical grade), and 2.4 ml. of concentrated hydrochloric acid (or 11 N sulfuric acid) was stirred in until dissolution was complete. After quantitative transfer to a separating funnel and shaking, the aqueous layer was re-extracted four times (with 20 ml. of ethyl acetate each time). The combined ethyl acetate solutions were filtered, evaporated rapidly under diminished pressure, and dried thoroughly under diminished pressure. The residue was redissolved in 70 ml.

of water and 10 ml. of 0.1 N sodium hydroxide, and the solution was adjusted to the required pH and made up to 200 ml. (concentration, 0.01 M). It is stored at 0° after filtering, and is quite stable.]

To 1 ml. of 0.5 or 0.2 M acetic acid–sodium hydroxide buffer (pH 4.5 or 5.2) and 0.5 ml. of 0.005 M phenolphthalein β-glucuronide solution were added 2 ml. of water and 0.5 ml. of enzyme preparation. After 1 hr. of incubation at 38°, the reaction was terminated by adding 4 ml. of 0.4 M glycine solution (adjusted to pH 10.7 with sodium hydroxide). (The use[36] of glycine buffers in which the sodium ion concentration is kept constant by the use of sodium chloride, whilst, according to the pH, the glycine content is varied, is not to be recommended, even when the buffering power is increased by the addition of sodium carbonate.[100]) The mixture was centrifuged at 1500 g for 15 min., and the intensity of the red color in the supernatant liquor was read by means of a Spekker photo-electric absorptiometer (Hilger & Watts Ltd., London), using Ilford No. 605 yellow-green filters (maximum transmission at 545 mμ). (In doing pH–activity experiments, sufficient sodium hydroxide was added, after the glycine-sodium hydroxide buffer, to bring the pH to a final constant value, and the volume was made up to 10 ml. with water before centrifuging.)

When only limited quantities of biological material of weak enzyme-activity were available, the following adaptation for use with the Spekker micro-cells could be employed. A mixture of 0.1 ml. of acetate buffer, 0.1 ml. of 0.0025 M substrate, 0.1 ml. of water, and 0.1 ml. of enzyme preparation was incubated for 2 hr. at 38°, and 0.4 ml. of glycine buffer was added.

Standard solutions are prepared by dissolving dry phenolphthalein in ethanol and diluting with about two volumes of water. Ethanol does not interfere in the color reaction, provided that its final concentration does not exceed 5%.

3. Phenol Method

Although the sensitivity of the color reaction and the rate of liberation of the aglycon together make the phenol method comparable in range with the phenolphthalein method, the former calls for a more elaborate procedure and a rather high substrate-concentration.[115] Because of the greater dilution during the color development, as compared with the phenolphthalein method, more concentrated enzyme must be employed during the incubation with substrate. The enzyme must be freed from phenolic substances by precipitation with ammonium sulfate, but dialysis can usually be omitted. When high concentrations of reducing sugars are added, controls must be done for interference in the color reaction with phenol.[135] Preparation of the substrate by biosynthesis[136] is tedious and unrewarding, but it can now be obtained by chemical synthesis,[137] and the use of biosynthetic 4-biphenylyl β-D-glucosiduronic acid has been suggested as an alternative.[138] Changes in the pH and concentration of the buffer employed in the enzymic hydrolysis do not affect the color reaction.

(135) M. C. Karunairatnam and G. A. Levvy, *Biochem. J.*, **44**, 599 (1949).

(136) G. A. Garton, D. Robinson and R. T. Williams, *Biochem. J.*, **45**, 65 (1949).

(137) K.-C. Tsou and A. M. Seligman, *J. Am. Chem. Soc.*, **75**, 1042 (1953).

(138) P. Bernfeld, H. C. Bernfeld, J. S. Nisselbaum and W. H. Fishman, *J. Am. Chem. Soc.*, **76**, 4872 (1954).

The incubation mixture consisted of 0.25 ml. of 0.5 M or 0.2 M acetic acid–sodium hydroxide buffer (pH 4.5 or 5.2), 0.25 ml. of 0.6 M phenyl β-glucuronide solution at the appropriate pH, 0.25 ml. of water, and 0.25 ml. of enzyme. After 1 hr. at 38°, the reaction was terminated by adding 2.5 ml. of freshly diluted Folin–Ciocalteu phenol reagent[139] (1:5, by volume). Protein was removed by centrifuging at 1500 g for 3 min., and 2.5 ml. of supernatant liquor was measured into 5 ml. of N sodium carbonate solution. After development for 20 min. at 38°, the color intensity was read with the Spekker absorptiometer, using Ilford No. 608 red filters (maximum transmission at 680 mμ), and the degree of hydrolysis was calculated from a curve constructed with a standard phenol solution.[140] A control must be done for the color given by the reagents in the absence of enzyme and substrate.

This method was adapted as follows for use with the Spekker micro-cells. The volume of each component of the incubation mixture was reduced to 0.1 ml.; after incubation for 1 hr., 0.5 ml. of Folin–Ciocalteu reagent, diluted as above, was added. Protein was sedimented, and 0.5 ml. of the supernatant liquor was mixed with 0.5 ml. of 1.33 N sodium carbonate solution. The color was developed as before.

4. *Fluorimetric Method*

4-Methylumbelliferone β-glucuronide, which can readily be prepared biosynthetically[108] or chemically,[141] has been introduced as a substrate for the fluorimetric assay of β-glucuronidase.[86,108] The units of activity are roughly equivalent to phenolphthalein units, but this method can be made 1000 times more sensitive than the phenolphthalein method (macro-scale), and may be very useful when extreme sensitivity is required, as, for example, in measuring the β-glucuronidase activity of some body fluids. The fluorimetric method is, however, too exacting for general application. Two major disadvantages are the instability of 4-methylumbelliferone solutions to light, particularly at the alkaline pH required for fluorescence, and the relatively high reading given by 4-methylumbelliferone β-glucuronide at concentrations that saturate the enzyme. Thus, in the procedure given below, the substrate concentration is only one-tenth of that needed for mammalian β-glucuronidase to display its maximum activity.

The incubation mixture contained 1 ml. of 0.2 M acetic acid–sodium hydroxide buffer at the required pH, 0.5 ml. of 8×10^{-5} M 4-methylumbelliferone β-glucuronide solution, 2 ml. of water, and 0.5 ml. of enzyme. (Before use, the synthetic substrate was freed from last traces of the free aglycon by precipitation with ether from a solution in ethanol.) After incubating for 1 hr. at 38° in the dark, the reaction was terminated by adding 4 ml. of 0.2 M glycine–sodium hydroxide buffer of pH 10.3. (It was important to use glycine of analytical grade.) Light was excluded as much as possible until the fluorescence could be read. The mixture was centrifuged if necessary, and 6.5 ml. was measured into an 8-ml. fluorimeter cell, which was used uncovered. The fluorescence was read against a quinine bisulfate solution (0.2 μg. of quinine bisul-

(139) O. Folin and V. Ciocalteu, *J. Biol. Chem.*, **73**, 627 (1927).

(140) P. B. Hawk and O. Bergeim, "Practical Physiological Chemistry," Churchill, London, 10th Edition, 1931, p. 866.

(141) C. A. Marsh and G. A. Levvy, *Nature*, **178**, 589 (1956).

fate/ml. in 0.1 N sulfuric acid), standardized with purified 4-methylumbelliferone. The instrument was an H-764 Spekker fluorimeter (with photomultiplier), and Wood's glass was employed for the primary filters with a Wratten 47 secondary filter. It was necessary to do a control for transmission by the reagents in the absence of enzyme and substrate.

5. Nitrophenol Method for β-Galacturonidase

The β-galacturonidase activity[49,116] of β-glucuronidase preparations (see Section X, 2) has been measured with synthetic phenyl and o-nitrophenyl β-galacturonides (β-D-galactopyranosiduronic acids).[142] The technique with the former substrate is very similar to that given above for phenyl β-glucuronide. In general, glycosidase assay methods based upon the use of o- and p-nitrophenyl glycosides resemble the phenolphthalein method, but the color reaction with alkali, although not so sensitive as that for phenolphthalein, is less dependent upon small changes in the final pH. Sometimes, the unhydrolyzed substrate is unstable at alkaline pH, particularly in the presence of protein and other tissue constituents, but this does not apply to o-nitrophenyl β-galacturonide.

To 1 ml. of 0.2 M acetic acid–sodium hydroxide buffer at the appropriate pH was added 0.5 ml. of 0.04 M o-nitrophenyl β-galacturonide solution adjusted to the same pH, followed by 2 ml. of water and 0.5 ml. of enzyme. After 1 hr. at 38°, the reaction was terminated by adding 4 ml. of 0.4 M glycine–sodium hydroxide buffer of pH 10.0, and the mixture was centrifuged at 1500 g for 15 min. The intensity of the yellow color was read with the Spekker absorptiometer, using Ilford No. 601 violet filters (maximum transmission at 435 mμ).

6. Other Biochemical Methods

Other substrates that have been employed for the assay of β-glucuronidase are (a) p-chlorophenyl β-glucuronide,[143] with which the aglycon is determined with an ultraviolet spectrophotometer at alkaline pH, and (b) 8-quinolinyl β-glucuronide,[102] with which the liberated 8-quinolinol is estimated by coupling with diazotized 3,3'-dimethoxybenzidine[102] or sulfanilic acid,[106] as well as (c) 8-benzamido-2-naphthyl β-glucuronide.[144] Mention must also be made of the method of Fishman and Green[145] for the determination of free D-glucuronic acid in the presence of excess β-glucuronide, employed in studying the transferase activity of the enzyme (see Section XI). This is a difference measurement, based upon application of the Tollens naphthoresorcinol color reaction for uronic acids, in which total and combined D-glucuronic acid are estimated before and after oxidation of the free sugar with hypoiodite.

(142) C. A. Marsh and G. A. Levvy, *Biochem. J.*, **68**, 617 (1958).
(143) B. Spencer and R. T. Williams, *Biochem. J.*, **48**, 537 (1951).
(144) S. H. Rutenburg and A. M. Seligman, *J. Biol. Chem.*, **203**, 731 (1953).
(145) W. H. Fishman and S. Green, *J. Biol. Chem.*, **215**, 527 (1955).

7. *Histochemical Methods*

Methods for the histochemical localization of β-glucuronidase, employing the β-glucuronides of 1-naphthol, 6-bromo-2-naphthol, 1-(2-hydroxy-phenylazo)-2-naphthol, and 8-quinolinol as substrates, have been critically examined by Burton and Pearse.[146] The last-named substrate gave the least unsatisfactory results, and the technique compares not unfavorably with histochemical methods for other enzymes.

IV. PURIFICATION

Early attempts to purify mammalian β-glucuronidase, employing ox spleen as starting material,[122,147,148] now have only historical interest, because the reducing-sugar method of assay did not give adequate control during the fractionation. Subsequent methods of purification have been facilitated by the use of phenolphthalein β-glucuronide as substrate (see, also, Section V). In comparing the different products below, the specific activities have been converted where necessary into phenolphthalein units per mg. of protein. Before proceeding to fractionation, it has been common practice to precipitate all the enzyme from the aqueous, cell-free, tissue extract by means of ammonium sulfate.

Smith and Mills[80] applied metallo-protein reactions to the enzyme from ox liver and, after 800-fold purification, obtained a product with a specific activity of 32,000 (recovery, 5 %). Starting with calf liver, Fishman and coworkers[81] reached specific activities of the order of 60,000 (1500-fold purification and 10 % recovery) after alkaline ammonium sulfate fractionation, followed by anion exchange (see Section IX, 2) and methanol fractionation. A specific activity of 107,000 was observed with the best individual preparation from calf liver, a preparation which was regarded as 85 % pure on the basis of physical tests of homogeneity; this suggested a limiting value of 120,000 for the specific activity of calf-liver β-glucuronidase. The same procedure was less successful when applied to a commercial calf-spleen powder,[149] the final product having a specific activity of only 7900 (1400-fold purification and 1 % recovery), perhaps due to the presence of inactivated enzyme. Sarkar and Sumner[42] achieved approximately 1000-fold purification of ox-liver β-glucuronidase by dioxane fractionation, but employed a type of enzyme unit that has not been used by other workers in this field. However, from comparative data given by Fishman and coworkers,[81] the specific activity would appear to have reached 31,000. (The figures quoted by Sarkar and Sumner[42] and by Fishman and coworkers[81]

(146) J. F. Burton and A. G. E. Pearse, *Brit. J. Exptl. Pathol.*, **33**, 87 (1952).
(147) G. Oshima, *J. Biochem.* (Tokyo), **23**, 305 (1936).
(148) A. F. Graham, *Biochem. J.*, **40**, 603 (1946).
(149) P. Bernfeld and W. H. Fishman, *J. Biol. Chem.*, **202**, 757 (1953).

for the degree of purification attained were calculated by comparing the initial activity per mg. of moist tissue with the final activity per mg. of protein. These figures have been recalculated above, throughout, on the more usual basis of protein.)

A somewhat different approach was adopted in the most recently published method for the purification of mammalian β-glucuronidase.[49] Instead of a tissue readily available in bulk, but with a relatively low enzyme activity, the tissue with the highest known activity,[38] namely, female-rat preputial gland, was chosen as starting material. Although the total weight of glandular tissue from one rat weighed only 100 mg., it had an initial specific activity of about 18,000, and a figure of 455,000 was attained after a simple fractionation procedure employing ammonium sulfate and ethanol alternately (25-fold purification and 26% recovery). The activity of 0.02 μg. of protein could be readily measured by the usual phenolphthalein method. At the final stage, the limits for precipitation of the enzyme were 40% and 45% of ethanol (v/v). Specific activities as high as 800,000 have subsequently been observed.[83] The product obtained at stage 3, as described below, has a specific activity of 45,000 and is pure enough for most purposes. This procedure removes all impurities likely to interfere in any of the methods of assay given in Section II.

The glandular tissue was suspended in water by means of a glass homogenizer, and the homogenate was adjusted to a final volume of 10 ml./g. of tissue, containing acetic acid–sodium hydroxide buffer (pH 5.2), in a final concentration of 0.1 M. After incubation for 4 hr. at 38°, the extract was freed from insoluble material by centrifuging at 1500 g for 15 min. A saturated solution of ammonium sulfate (preferably analytical grade) was added to the extract to give a final saturation of 20%, and the precipitate was allowed to settle for 30 min. This step was done at 0°. The precipitate was removed by centrifuging as above and discarded, and the supernatant was brought to 80% saturation with ammonium sulfate at 0° to precipitate the enzyme. After sedimentation at 10,000 g for 15 min., the enzyme was dissolved in the minimal volume of 0.01 M acetate buffer (pH 5.2), and dialyzed against the same buffer for 2 days. For some purposes, the 0.01 M buffer can be replaced by water.

Some preparations of mammalian β-glucuronidase of high specific activity display a fall in net activity on dilution, an effect that can be prevented by adding a variety of substances (see Section IX, 2), of which albumin is, perhaps, the most satisfactory.[49,138] When this phenomenon is encountered, the enzyme is assayed in the presence of an "activator" (see Fig. 4), and some of the figures quoted above were obtained in this way, as well as the kinetic constants quoted in subsequent Sections. (Failure to observe the dilution phenomenon with one highly-active preparation,[80] although the customary activation was seen with substances like albumin, may be explained by the fact that the enzyme had undergone partial inactivation.)

The purified enzyme gives colorless aqueous solutions, and is stable for at least 18 months[49,81,83] if buffered to pH 5; it is said[80] to be a globulin of isoelectric point 4.85. It has not been obtained crystalline.

The only non-mammalian β-glucuronidase that has been subjected to systematic purification is the enzyme from sheep-rumen microorganisms. After repeated ammonium sulfate fractionation, Marsh[101] obtained a colorless preparation with a specific activity of 1,900 (400-fold purification and 2 % recovery). The final product gave a linear, specific-property, solubility test from which a figure of 2,200 was derived for the ultimate specific activity of the enzyme, but it was considered that the enzyme may have formed a solid solution with inactive protein.

For purification in bulk, the visceral hump of the limpet (*Patella vulgata*) or the digestive gland of the snail would appear to be the most promising sources of the enzyme, since these are the richest alternatives to the female-rat preputial gland in activity (see Section II). The presence of sulfatases, in particular steroid sulfatase,[150] in limpet extracts can be a disadvantage in employing them as a source of β-glucuronidase: the preputial-gland extracts lack steroid sulfatase.[151]

V. Location of the Enzyme in the Mammalian Cell, with Particular Reference to Activity Measurements

The intracellular distribution of β-glucuronidase activity has been studied in homogenates of mouse and rat tissues made in different ways.[23,24,32,33,152] Sub-cellular particles were separated by centrifuging at high speeds, or at low speeds after agglutination with slightly acidic buffers, to yield optically clear supernatant liquors. Measurements of the insoluble and soluble enzyme fractions thus obtained were paralleled by microscopic observations. Apart from its physiological interest, this work has put the purification and assay of the enzyme on a more rational basis than previously existed. In brief, it was concluded that, whatever the level of β-glucuronidase activity, nearly all the enzyme in the mammalian cell was present in the cytoplasmic granules (mitochondria and microsomes), and was apparently spread over granules of all sizes; little, if any, was present in the nuclei or free in the cytoplasm.

On suspending a tissue in water by means of a glass homogenizer, there were visible osmotic changes (in the granules) whereby more than half of the enzyme passed into the surrounding medium.[23,32] Meanwhile the fraction retained within the granules became completely accessible to substrate and fully active, except in abnormally concentrated preparations. All the enzyme in a water homogenate thus displayed its full potential activity

(150) A. B. Roy, *Biochem. J.*, **62**, 41 (1956).
(151) M. I. Stern, private communication.
(152) P. G. Walker and G. A. Levvy, *Biochem. J.*, **49**, lxxvi (1951).

(ignoring possible complications due to the action of endogenous inhibitor in the case of rat preparations—see Section IX, 3); and changes in tissue activity measured in such preparations, in accordance with the usual practice, did not represent mere changes in intracellular permeability but real changes in the amount of active-enzyme protein.

When the integrity of the cytoplasmic granules was maintained by homogenizing the tissue in isotonic media, the enzyme within them was not freely accessible to substrate and hence not completely active.[33,152] It is therefore quite possible that permeability changes within the cell play a part in the action of the enzyme *in vivo*. Dilution of isotonic preparations with water caused a progressive release of enzyme to the medium until the partition (and the total activity) observed in water homogenates was reached. Release of the enzyme from the granules in either type of preparation could be effected in a number of ways, notably by addition of the nonionic, surface-active agent Triton X-100 (Rohm and Haas Co., Philadelphia, Pa.), mechanical disruption in the Waring Blendor, or incubation in acetate buffer of *p*H 5.2.

The practical application of this work in measuring the β-glucuronidase activity of a mammalian tissue is illustrated in Fig. 1, which is of assistance in assessing some of the earlier published figures for tissue β-glucuronidase activity. Normal mouse liver is contrasted with regenerating liver; there is a rise in β-glucuronidase activity after partial hepatectomy in this species.[23] The unfractionated, water homogenate gives the total activity. So, essentially, does the supernatant liquor obtained after centrifuging the unbuffered preparation at low speed, since only a little of the particulate fraction is sedimented under these conditions. If, however, the granules are first agglutinated by the addition of acetate or citrate buffer (*p*H 5.2), the supernatant liquor contains only a fraction of the total enzyme in the tissue. (Small inhibitory effects due to citrate are discussed in Section IX, 1.) Prior incubation in acetate buffer, but not citrate buffer, for short periods will then lead to variable results (depending upon the amount of enzyme released from the agglutinated granules) when only the supernatant liquor is taken for assay. At the end of four hours of incubation in acetate buffer, release of granular enzyme reaches completion and all the enzyme is in the supernatant liquor. One or more of these variables (buffering, incubation, centrifuging) will be found to have been introduced into nearly all the earlier measurements of tissue β-glucuronidase activity. Whilst errors arising from loss of enzyme in the granules are usually of minor importance, they can be very important in comparative measurements.

Particular attention must be paid to the position that arises when the agglutinated granules in a water homogenate are discarded without *any* release of the enzyme retained by the granules; that is, after centrifuging in acetate buffer before incubation, or in citrate buffer before or after brief periods of incubation. This gives perfectly reproducible results for the β-glucuronidase activity of a tissue, but rises in activity *in vivo* are exaggerated, since they are always accompanied by a greater proportional release of enzyme when the tissue is first homogenized in water (see Fig. 1): the amount of activity retained by the granules tends to remain constant. The physiological significance of this apparent increase in the release of the enzyme from the granules during osmotic changes is unknown.

Two more complications should be mentioned. (To guard against them, Triton X-100 may be added during the assay of new tissues.) When part of the enzyme is still retained by the granules, the use of the whole homogenate in too high a concentration during the incubation with substrate leads to false, low results for the total β-glucuronidase activity.[23] No tissue assays have actually been carried out under these conditions, but the phenomenon is of interest since it simulates the effect of an enzyme-precursor in the preparation. Because the high tissue-concentration has no effect on the net activity of the preparation when all of the enzyme is made soluble, there is an apparent rise in its total β-glucuronidase activity when it is incubated in acetate buffer beforehand (see Table II).

The effect of high tissue-concentrations must be distinguished from the action of the insoluble, endogenous inhibitor in rat-tissue homogenates, which cannot be abol-

TABLE II

Effect of Varying the Concentration of a Water Homogenate of Normal Adult Mouse Liver, Buffered with Acetate, During the Incubation with Substrate (0.00125 M Phenolphthalein β-D-Glucosiduronic Acid).[23] Homogenate Fractionated Before and After Incubation at 38°, and then Assayed

Final Concentration of Moist Liver in Assay (%)	Net Activity (units/g. liver)			
	Immediate Fractionation		Fractionation after 4 hr. at 38°	
	Whole Homogenate	Soluble Fraction	Whole Homogenate	Soluble Fraction
5	1100	815	1920	1930
1	2080	1100	2110	2060
0.31[a]	2040	1080	2020	1940

[a] Usual level for assay of mouse liver.

ished either by diluting the preparation or by simply converting all the enzyme to the soluble state.[24] Figures for the β-glucuronidase activity of rat organs may be subject to variable errors from this source unless the homogenate has been freed from insoluble material, or the incubation with substrate has been carried out in the presence of Triton X-100 (see Section IX, 3). Mouse β-glucuronidase is not affected by the endogenous inhibitor.

Observations made in studying the behavior of β-glucuronidase in homogenates in isotonic media[33,152] closely resembled the results obtained in contemporary work on acid phosphatase by de Duve and his colleagues,[153-155] who later confirmed the work on β-glucuronidase in many of its essential

(153) C. de Duve, J. Berthet, L. Berthet and F. Appelmans, *Nature*, **167**, 389 (1951).

(154) J. Berthet and C. de Duve, *Biochem. J.*, **50**, 174 (1951).

(155) J. Berthet, L. Berthet, F. Appelmans and C. de Duve, *Biochem. J.*, **50**, 182 (1951).

features.[156-158] The close parallelism between the behavior of acid phosphatase, β-glucuronidase, and certain other hydrolytic enzymes in this type of preparation has led de Duve to postulate the existence of a special type of cytoplasmic granule, the "lysosome," within which these enzymes are

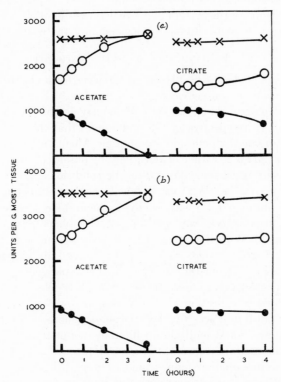

Fig. 1.—Fractionation[23] of Water Homogenates of Mouse Liver at 1500 *g* after Varying Periods of Incubation at 38° in Acetate or Citrate Buffer, pH 5.2. (Homogenate and fractions assayed in the usual way with 0.00125 *M* phenolphthalein β-D-glucosiduronic acid in the same buffer: (*a*), normal adult liver; (*b*), liver regenerating 4 days after partial hepatectomy; X——X, total homogenate; ●——●, agglutinated granules; O——O, soluble enzyme in supernatant.)

confined together in the mammalian cell.[157] It is not possible at present to pass an opinion on the lysosome theory, but it should be pointed out that different enzymes, all requiring the same degree of organization, and associated with *different* cytoplasmic granules of the same mean size, will sedi-

(156) R. Gianetto and C. de Duve, *Biochem. J.*, **59**, 433 (1955).

(157) C. de Duve, B. C. Pressman, R. Gianetto, R. Wattiaux and F. Appelmans, *Biochem. J.*, **60**, 604 (1955).

(158) R. Wattiaux and C. de Duve, *Biochem. J.*, **63**, 606 (1956).

ment together. Thus, whilst a simple hydrolytic enzyme like β-glucuronidase may be retained by granules of all sizes, only comparatively large granules will retain all the components of a more complex enzyme system like succinic oxidase.[159] This difference is demonstrated by the action of nonionic, surface-active agents which inhibit succinic oxidase,[160] presumably by dispersing components of the system, but which do not inhibit β-glucuronidase, and can increase the net activity by dispersion of the particulate fraction.

VI. VARIATION IN ACTIVITY WITH pH

Table III lists peaks in the pH–activity curves for β-glucuronidase from different mammalian sources acting on a number of β-glucuronides. It is probably true to state that the mammalian enzyme has the same pH optimum (or optima) irrespective of the source, and that there is little change on passing from one β-glucuronide to another. Mean values for the optima are pH 4.5 and pH 5.2. Either or both may be observed, depending on the source and purity of the enzyme and on the conditions of assay. Thus, the purified enzyme (see Section IV) from female-rat preputial gland[49] displayed a single optimum at pH 4.5 with phenyl β-glucuronide as substrate, and a double optimum at pH 4.5 and pH 5.0–5.2 with phenolphthalein β-glucuronide (see Fig. 4). With the latter substrate, certain purified ox-spleen[149,161] and ox-liver[81,162] preparations were stated to have only single optima: so far as one can judge from the rather confusing reports, these were at pH 4.5 and 5.0, respectively, but it is not made clear whether deoxyribonucleate was added (see Section IX, 2). From our own experience in trying to measure small differences by the fluorimetric method, we feel that the individual figures for 4-methylumbelliferone β-glucuronide are not significantly different from a mean at about pH 4.3.

The fact that mammalian β-glucuronidase preparations show little change in the pH optimum (or optima) with different substrates is explained by the finding[168] that the nature of the aglycon has little effect on the ionization of a β-glucuronide. As one might anticipate, however, the pH optimum for the hydrolysis of phenyl β-galacturonide (3.9) by a female-rat, preputial-gland preparation differed appreciably from the figure for phenyl β-glucuronide (4.5) when both were determined under exactly comparable conditions.[116]

Mills,[164] using an ox-spleen preparation, was the first to observe that the pH–activity curve has two peaks, and that they show little shift in pH

(159) W. C. Schneider and G. H. Hogeboom, *J. Biol. Chem.*, **183**, 123 (1950).

(160) D. Hockenhull, *Nature*, **162**, 850 (1948).

(161) P. Bernfeld and W. H. Fishman, *Arch. Biochem.*, **27**, 475 (1950).

(162) W. H. Fishman and P. Bernfeld, "Methods in Enzymology," Academic Press Inc., New York, N. Y., 1955, Vol. 1, p. 262.

TABLE III

pH Optima for the Hydrolysis of β-D-Glucosiduronic Acids by Mammalian
β-Glucuronidase Preparations in Acetate or Citrate Buffer

Source	Aglycon	pH Optimum	References
Ox			
liver	phenolphthalein	4.4–4.5 & 5.0–5.2	42, 80, 81, 162
kidney	*levo*-menthol	5.3	16
	phenol	5.3–5.6	16
spleen	*levo*-menthol	4.5 & 5.0–5.2	147, 163–165
	phenolphthalein	4.5 & 5.2	149, 161, 164, 165
	phenol	4.5 & 5.2	164, 165
	p-chlorophenol	4.1 & 5.2	143
	estriol	4.3–4.9	163, 166
	pregnanediol	4.5	166
	borneol	4.4	163
adrenal gland	phenolphthalein	4.5–5.6	167
Rat			
liver	phenolphthalein	4.6 & 5.3	157
	8-benzoylamido-2-naph-thol[a]	5.0	144
spleen	8-benzoylamido-2-naph-thol[a]	5.0	144
female preputial gland	phenolphthalein	4.5 & 5.0–5.2	49
	phenol	4.5	49, 116
lymph node	phenolphthalein	4.2 & 5.2	46
plasma	4-methylumbelliferone	4.4	108
Horse			
kidney	*levo*-menthol[b]	5.3	124
	2-naphthol[b]	5.3	124
Mouse			
liver	phenolphthalein[c]	4.5 & 5.2	23, 30, 31
	phenol	4.5 & 5.2	113
	2-ethylhexanoic acid	4.4 & 5.1–5.2	133
kidney	phenolphthalein[d]	4.4–4.6	22
	phenol	4.5 & 5.2	114
spleen	phenol	4.5 & 5.2	115
uterus	phenol	4.5	114
Rabbit			
plasma	4-methylumbelliferone	4.0	108
leucocytes	phenolphthalein	4.5	82
Guinea pig			
plasma	4-methylumbelliferone	4.0	108
Man			
plasma	4-methylumbelliferone[e]	3.3–3.4	108
male urine	4-methylumbelliferone	4.6	108

[a] Phosphate–citrate buffer. [b] Phosphate–acetate buffer. [c] "High" or "low" mouse strains (see Section II). [d] Phthalate buffer. [e] Veronal–acetate buffer.

(163) W. H. Fishman, *J. Biol. Chem.*, **131,** 225 (1939).
(164) G. T. Mills, *Biochem. J.*, **43,** 125 (1948).
(165) G. T. Mills, J. Paul and E. E. B. Smith, *Biochem. J.*, **53,** 232 (1953).
(166) S. L. Cohen, *J. Biol. Chem.*, **192,** 147 (1951).
(167) S. N. Nayyar and D. Glick, *J. Biol. Chem.*, **222,** 73 (1956).

with different substrates. He was able to separate the enzyme into two fractions of identical specificity corresponding to the individual pH optima, and his work was subsequently confirmed with mouse-liver and kidney preparations.[114] In later work,[80,165] Mills and his colleagues, on varying the substrate concentration, noted additional peaks, at pH 3.4 and pH 6.3, in the pH–activity curves for ox-spleen and ox-liver preparations, and they separated an enzyme fraction corresponding to the first of these. No other

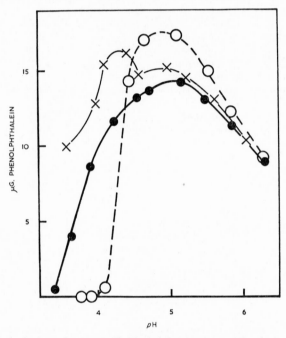

FIG. 2.—Hydrolysis[83] of 0.00125 M Phenolphthalein β-D-Glucosiduronic acid by Partially Purified Mouse-liver β-Glucuronidase at Various pHs (in 0.125 N acetate ($\times$), 0.125 N citrate ($\bullet$), and 0.125 N phthalate ($\bigcirc$) buffer).

worker has, however, observed either of these two additional peaks, and the enzyme is usually very unstable below pH 4 (see Fig. 3).

Mammalian β-glucuronidase shows a shift in optimum toward a more alkaline pH in the presence of certain anions, such as deoxyribonucleate (see Fig. 4) and phthalate,[8,49,80,157,169] and the optimum at about pH 5.2 becomes predominant over whatever peak or peaks the pH–activity curve may previously have displayed (see Section IX, 2). Certain heavy-metal ions in trace amounts cause a shift in the optimum toward a more acid pH

(168) D. Robinson, J. N. Smith and R. T. Williams, *Biochem. J.*, **55**, 151 (1953).
(169) P. Bernfeld and W. H. Fishman, *Federation Proc.*, **9**, 150 (1950).

(see Section IX, 4), and these two opposing effects may not be entirely un-related. Whilst Mills and his colleagues[165] consider that each of their en-zyme fractions, with optima at pH 3.4, 4.5, and 5.2, respectively, contains a distinct enzyme protein, other workers[8,49,157,169] believe that, in every case, they merely represent a single protein in combination with different ions derived from the tissue, or introduced during the purification and assay of the enzyme. Although the crucial experiment, an attempted inter-conversion of Mills' separated fractions, has not been done, the behavior of the purified enzyme from female-rat preputial gland[49] provides convincing evidence for the single-enzyme theory. Fig. 2 shows[83] (a) the effect of phthal-ate[80] on the pH–activity curve for a partially purified, mouse-liver, β-glu-curonidase preparation, and (b) the slight alteration in shape which occurs on changing from acetate to citrate buffer.

Non-mammalian β-glucuronidase preparations (see Table IV) display only single pH optima, on which the nature of the aglycon has little effect: the position of the optimum may, however, alter slightly with the purity of the enzyme preparation[101] and with the concentration of buffer intro-duced during the assay.[86,88] There was little difference between the optima for phenyl β-glucuronide (at pH 3.6) and phenyl β-galacturonide (at pH 3.4) with the preparation from the limpet (*Patella vulgata*)[116]; phthalate caused a shift in the optimum toward a more alkaline pH with this prep-aration.[86,171a] The most striking feature revealed in Table IV is the way in which the different enzyme preparations tend to fall into two groups—the first, with an optimum near neutrality, containing the two bacterial prep-arations and the rumen microbial (probably bacterial) enzyme, and the other, with an optimum well below pH 6, comprising all the remaining preparations, from sources as diverse as molluscs, amphibia, insects, and plants. Due to inadequacies in the original experiments,[170,171] the figures quoted for the hydrolysis of baicalin (5,6,7-trihydroxyflavone β-D-glu-cosiduronic acid) and scutellarin (5,6,7,4'-tetrahydroxyflavone β-glu-curonide) by the *S. baicalensis* preparation may well be inaccurate.[88]

VII. VARIATION IN STABILITY WITH pH AND THE EFFECT OF TEMPERATURE

Figure 3 shows the effect[86] of pH adjustment (with sodium hydroxide or hydrochloric acid) on the stability of mouse-liver β-glucuronidase at 0°. Inactivation was presumably instantaneous, since the preparation was brought back to pH 6–7 after only 1 minute (followed by assay in the usual way). The range of stability of limpet β-glucuronidase was greater by one pH unit on both the alkaline and the acid side of neutrality.[86,172] With this preparation it was demonstrated[86] that there was no further inactiva-tion when the period of contact with acid or alkali was increased from 1 minute to 1 hour: raising the temperature to 37° did, however, narrow the range of pH stability slightly. Limpet β-glucuronidase and β-galacturonidase activity gave identical pH–stability curves.[116] Rumen β-glucu-

TABLE IV

pH Optima for the Hydrolysis of β-D-Glucosiduronic Acids by Non-mammalian β-Glucuronidase Preparations in Acetate, Citrate, Phosphate, or Phosphate–citrate Buffers

Source	Aglycon	pH Optimum	References
Escherichia coli	phenolphthalein	6.2	92, 93
	estriol	4.5–7.0	92
Streptococcus	phenolphthalein	5.5–7.0	94, 99
Sheep-rumen micro-organisms	phenolphthalein	6.5–6.6[a]	101
	phenol	6.6	101
Helix pomatia digestive gland	phenolphthalein	4.4–4.8	87
	8-quinolinol	4.2	106
Mixed Helix species, digestive glands	levo-menthol	4.5	127
	phenol	4.1–4.5	127
Patella vulgata visceral hump	phenolphthalein	3.8	86
	phenol	3.6	116
	pregnanediol	3.5	169a
	p-chlorophenol	4.0	107
	4-methylumbelliferone	3.8	86
Littorina littorea visceral hump	p-chlorophenol	4.0	107
Locusta migratoria crop fluid	8-quinolinol	4.5	102
	4-methylumbelliferone	4.5–5.5	108
	umbelliferone	4.5–5.3	108
Schistocerca gregaria crop fluid	4-methylumbelliferone	5.3	109
Housefly (Musca domestica)	4-methylumbelliferone	5.5	109
Xenopus laevis embryo	8-quinolinol	4.5	104
Scutellaria baicalensis root	phenolphthalein	3.8–4.6	88
	baicalein (5,6,7-trihydroxyflavone)[b]	5.9–6.0	170
	scutellarein (5,6,7,4'-tetrahydroxyflavone)[b]	5.7	171
Almond emulsin	levo-menthol	4–5	16, 128
	phenol	about 4	16

[a] 6.1 in impure preparations of enzyme.[100,101] [b] The buffer composition varied over the pH range.

ronidase was stable only at pH 6–7 on incubating for 15 minutes or 1 hour at 37° prior to assay, and the pH–stability curve was very similar to the pH–activity curve.[100]

(169a) S. R. Stitch, I. D. K. Halkerston and J. Hillman, *Biochem. J.*, **63,** 705 (1956).
(170) T. Miwa, *Acta Phytochim.* (Japan), **6,** 154 (1932).
(171) T. Miwa, *Acta Phytochim.* (Japan), **8,** 231 (1935).

Ox-liver β-glucuronidase was found to be stable to 30 minutes of heating at 50°, but there was considerable inactivation[42] at 55°. Heating a limpet preparation (of pH 5) for 5 minutes caused a 15 % inactivation[86] of β-glucuronidase at 60° and 35 % at 70°. Within the range of temperature-stability of the enzyme, mammalian β-glucuronidase activity was approximately doubled for every 10° rise in temperature.[31,42,147,165] This would also appear to be true of mollusc preparations.[107,171a]

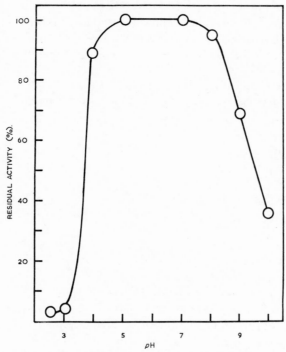

Fig. 3.—Effect[86] of Varying the pH, on the Stability of Mouse-liver β-Glucuronidase at 0°.

VIII. Dissociation Constants for Different Substrates

Values for K_m, the dissociation constant of the active, enzyme–substrate complex, for mammalian β-glucuronidase and various substrates are shown in Table V. Table VI gives the values of K_m that have been recorded for non-mammalian β-glucuronidase preparations. Most of the figures have

(171a) R. I. Cox [*Biochem. J.*, **71**, 763 (1959)] found the Australian limpet, *Cellana tramoserica*, to resemble *P. vulgata* in β-glucuronidase activity: the pH optimum fell with decreasing substrate concentration, and he concluded that only un-ionized substrate was attacked by the enzyme.

(172) K. S. Dodgson and B. Spencer, *Biochem. J.*, **55**, 315 (1953).

been calculated by the method of Lineweaver and Burk,[173] but, in some cases, this method was inapplicable and K_m was then derived by finding the substrate concentration that gave half the observed maximum rate of hydrolysis. This procedure is open to the objection that the observed maximum velocity of hydrolysis may be less than the theoretical maximum, particularly when there is inhibition by excess substrate. On the other hand, the fitting of a straight line to the continuous curve that is sometimes obtained in the analysis by the method of Lineweaver and Burk cannot be too strongly deprecated.[101,174]

For any one substrate, there appears to be no significant change in K_m on passing from one mammalian species to another or from organ to organ (see Table V); there was no difference in liver figures for "high" and "low" strains of mice (see Section II).[31] The purity of the enzyme preparation would appear to have a marked effect on K_m (see, also, Section IX, 3). This is illustrated by the figures for female-rat preputial gland, which also illustrate the general tendency for K_m to increase with the pH of assay. These two factors, but particularly the latter, may well explain the different values obtained by Mills and his colleagues[165] for the enzyme fractions corresponding to the individual pH optima in mammalian preparations (see Section VI).

β-Glucuronidase from mammalian and non-mammalian sources, including the purified enzyme from female-rat preputial gland, often displays marked inhibition in the presence of excess substrate. The number of substrate molecules per active-enzyme center in the inactive enzyme–substrate complex is[24,100,165,167] usually 2, but values of[165] 3 and[143] 4 have also been reported.

When, for any reason, there is difficulty in determining K_m for a new substrate directly, this constant is sometimes derived indirectly by treating the new substrate as a competitive inhibitor for the hydrolysis of a standard substrate with a known K_m value; K_i, the dissociation constant of the enzyme–inhibitor complex, should then be equal to K_m for the new substrate.[176] Figures obtained in this way for a number of β-glucuronides acting as competing substrates in the hydrolysis of phenolphthalein β-glucuronide by β-glucuronidase preparations of varied origin are shown in Table VII.

When this treatment was applied to "β-glucosidase" (β-D-glucopyranosidase),[179] discrepancies were noted between K_i and K_m when the latter was determined directly for the same compound. Such discrepancies can be explained in two ways. If the en-

(173) H. Lineweaver and D. Burk, J. Am. Chem. Soc., 56, 658 (1934).
(174) B. H. J. Hofstee, Science, 116, 329 (1952).
(176) G. A. Levvy and C. A. Marsh, Science, 119, 337 (1954).
(179) M. A. Jermyn, Australian J. Biol. Sci., 8, 577 (1955).

TABLE V

Dissociation Constants (K_m) of the Active Enzyme–substrate Complex for Mammalian
β-Glucuronidase and Various Substrates

Aglycon	Source and Purity of Enzyme	pH of Test	K_m (M)	References
β-D-*Glucosiduronic Acids*				
levo-Menthol	ox spleen (partially purified)	5.3	4×10^{-3}	163
" " (purified)	5.0	1.9×10^{-2a}	165
		4.5	4.7×10^{-3a}	165
Phenol	mouse liver (partially purified)	5.2	3.5×10^{-3}	115
	mouse spleen (" ")	5.2	3.5×10^{-3}	115
	mouse uterus (" ")	4.5	3.5×10^{-3}	114
	female rat preputial gland (partially purified)	4.5	1.4×10^{-3}	116
	female rat preputial gland (partially purified)	3.9	5.9×10^{-4}	116
	female rat preputial gland (purified)	4.5	5.1×10^{-4}	49
	ox spleen (purified)	5.2	5.1×10^{-3a}	165
		4.5	2×10^{-3a}	165
		3.4	1.2×10^{-3a}	165
Phenolphthalein	mouse liver (partially purified)	5.2	1.3×10^{-4}	175
		4.5	4.7×10^{-5}	31
	rat liver (partially purified)	5.2	2.9×10^{-4}	24
	female rat preputial gland (purified)	4.5	5.7×10^{-5}	49
	ox liver (purified)	5.0	1.4×10^{-4}	162
	ox spleen (purified)	5.2	2.3×10^{-3a}	165
		4.5	8×10^{-4a}	165
		3.4	1×10^{-3a}	165
	ox adrenals (partially purified)	5.2	8.8×10^{-5}	167
	rabbit leucocytes (crude)	4.5	1.1×10^{-4}	82
Estriol	ox spleen (partially purified)	4.3	5×10^{-4}	163
Borneol	ox spleen (partially purified)	4.4	1×10^{-2}	163
p-Chlorophenol	ox spleen (partially purified)	5.2	3×10^{-2}	143
β-D-*Galactosiduronic Acids*				
Phenol	female rat preputial gland (partially purified)	4.5	1.1×10^{-2}	116
		3.9	5.2×10^{-3}	116
	female rat preputial gland (purified)	4.5	6.5×10^{-3}	49
o-Nitrophenol	female rat preputial gland (purified)	4.5	8.4×10^{-4}	49

[a] Fractions separated according to individual pH optima.
(175) G. A. Levvy, *Biochem. J.*, **52**, 464 (1952).

zyme is subject to inhibition by excess substrate, K_i may, under certain circumstances, approximate to the dissociation constant of the *inactive* enzyme–substrate complex, rather than to K_m. Even in the absence of inhibition by excess substrate, K_i need not equal K_m for the same compound. In the reactions,

$$E + S \rightarrow ES \rightarrow E + A + B,$$

where E is the enzyme, S the substrate, and $A + B$ the products of hydrolysis, K_m is based on measurements of the over-all process, whereas competitive inhibition

TABLE VI

Dissociation Constants (K_m) of the Active Enzyme–substrate Complex for Non-mammalian β-Glucuronidase and Various Substrates

Aglycon	Source of enzyme	pH of Test	K_m (M)	References
β-D-*Glucosiduronic Acids*				
Phenol	*Patella vulgata* visceral hump	3.6	4×10^{-4}	116
Phenolphthalein	Sheep-rumen micro-organisms	6.5	7.5×10^{-5}	101
		6.1	6×10^{-5a}	101
	Patella vulgata visceral hump	4.1	2.4×10^{-5}	86
	Scutellaria baicalensis root	4.5	5.6×10^{-4}	88
8-Quinolinol	*Helix pomatia* digestive gland	4.2	3.5×10^{-4}	106
β-D-*Galactosiduronic Acids*				
Phenol	*Patella vulgata* visceral hump	3.6	2.3×10^{-3}	116
o-Nitrophenol	*Patella vulgata* visceral hump	3.6	1.2×10^{-3}	49

[a] 3.1×10^{-5} in impure preparations of enzyme.[100]

is exerted at the first step only. If the second step is a rate-determining one, K_i may differ from K_m for the same compound.

No discussion of this subject would be complete without emphasizing the point that the relative rates of hydrolysis of two substrates, which may be quite different from their relative affinities for an enzyme, may be at least as important as regards the physiological action of the enzyme. Dissociation constants measure affinity only (affinity = 1/dissociation constant). Thus, despite its 10-fold smaller affinity, phenyl β-glucuronide is hydrolyzed nearly as rapidly as phenolphthalein β-glucuronide by the purified enzyme from female-rat preputial gland at saturation with both substrates, in terms of moles of aglycon liberated.[49] In the presence of a "combined" inhibitor (see Section IX, 3), there is a fall in the rate of hydrolysis, despite the increased affinity of the enzyme for the substrate.

IX. INHIBITORS AND ACTIVATORS

1. D-*Glucaro-1,4-lactone and Related Compounds*

Hydrolysis of β-glucuronides (I; R = alkyl, aryl, or acyl) by the enzyme from mammalian or non-mammalian sources is powerfully and competi-

TABLE VII

Dissociation Constants (K_i) for Various β-D-Glucosiduronic Acids Treated as Competing Substrates in the Hydrolysis of Phenolphthalein β-D-Glucosiduronic Acid by Mammalian and Non-mammalian β-Glucuronidase

Aglycon	Source of enzyme	pH of Test	K_i (M)	References
levo-Menthol	Sheep-rumen micro-organisms	6.1	2.9×10^{-3}	101
	Scutellaria baicalensis root	4.5	1.4×10^{-2}	88
Phenol	Sheep-rumen micro-organisms	6.1	2.7×10^{-3}	101
Chrysin	Mouse liver	5.2	1×10^{-5}	88
(5,7-dihydroxyflavone)	" "	4.5	6.2×10^{-6}	88
Baicalein				
(5,6,7-trihydroxyflavone)	" "	5.2	1.2×10^{-5}	88
	" "	4.5	8.8×10^{-6}	88
Quercetin	" "	5.2	9.8×10^{-6}	177
(3,5,7,3',4'-pentahydroxy-	" "	4.5	6.9×10^{-6}	177
flavone)				
4-Methylumbelliferone	*Patella vulgata* visceral hump	4.1	1.8×10^{-5}	86
Glycyrrhetic acid	Mouse liver	5.2	1.9×10^{-4a}	178
	" "	4.5	3.7×10^{-4a}	178
2-Ethylbutyric acid	" "	5.2	7.9×10^{-5}	133
2-Ethylhexanoic acid	" "	5.2	2.2×10^{-4}	133
Veratric acid	" "	5.2	3.5×10^{-5}	133

[a] Composite figure for the two β-D-glucosiduronic acid groups in the glycyrrhizinic acid molecule: there is, in addition, an element of non-competitive inhibition with this di-D-glucosiduronic acid.

tively inhibited[175] by D-glucaro-1,4-lactone[180] ("saccharo-1,4-lactone"; II); at the usual substrate-concentrations employed for assay, 2.5×10^{-6} M lactone causes nearly 50% inhibition of the mammalian enzyme. Inhibition

(177) C. A. Marsh, *Nature*, **176**, 176 (1955).
(178) C. A. Marsh and G. A. Levvy, *Biochem. J.*, **63**, 9 (1956).
(180) F. Smith, *J. Chem. Soc.*, 633 (1944).

is highly specific[181]; the lactone has been shown to have no action on a number of other glycosidases, whilst several, closely related aldonolactones were without effect on β-glucuronidase. For example, β-glucuronidase is unaffected by the D-gluconolactones which are powerful inhibitors of β-glucosidase.

```
1   ROCH┐           CO┐            CO₂H
2   HCOH│           HCOH│          HCOH
3   HOCH│           HOCH│          HOCH
4   HCOH│           HCO─┘          HCOH
5   HCO─┘           HCOH           HCOH
6   CO₂H            CO₂H           CO₂H

      I               II              III


1   CO₂H          CO₂H         ROCH┐          CHOH┐
2   HCOH          HCOH         HCOH│          HCOH│
3 ┌─OCH           HOCH         HOCH│        ┌─OCH │
4   HCOH          HOCH         HOCH│          HCO─┘
5   HCOH          HCOH         HCO─┘          HCOH
6   CO┘           CO₂H         CO₂H           CO┘

      IV              V              VI             VII
```

Following the discovery[135] that β-glucuronidase is strongly inhibited by solutions of D-glucaric acid ("saccharic acid"; III), it was proved[175] that the inhibitory action is due to D-glucaro-1,4-lactone present in the solutions. D-Glucarate ion itself is not an inhibitor for the enzyme, but occurrence of lactonization can only be abolished at an alkaline pH. It can be seen that 0.025 % (w/w) of D-glucaro-1,4-lactone, present as an impurity in any other compound, will lead to nearly 50 % inhibition of β-glucuronidase if the latter compound is tested in 0.01 M concentration. Traces of the 1,4-lactone are rapidly and spontaneously formed when potassium hydrogen D-glucarate is dissolved in water, and the lactone content of the solution increases at a rate dependent upon the pH and temperature. Appreciable lactonization occurs at the slightly acid pH and elevated temperature usually employed for β-glucuronidase assay. Once formed, the lactone is stable at acid pH, over relatively long time-periods at least.

(181) J. Conchie and G. A. Levvy, *Biochem. J.*, **65**, 389 (1957).

When solutions of potassium hydrogen D-glucarate are boiled at their own slightly acid pH for 30 minutes, an equilibrium value for the inhibitory power is reached, corresponding to the conversion of one third of the anion into the 1,4-lactone. Such "boiled saccharate" solutions provide a convenient alternative to the use of the pure lactone. D-Glucaro-6,3-lactone[180] (IV) is also formed in D-glucarate solutions, but this compound as such does not appear to inhibit β-glucuronidase.

This work has recently been extended[181,182] to a study of the inhibition of other glycopyranosidases by the aldonolactones corresponding in structure and configuration to the sugar residues in the substrates. All the β- and certain of the α-glycosidases studied were powerfully and selectively inhibited by the appropriate aldonolactones. In general, the requirements for efficient inhibition were found to be identity of the grouping at C6, and of the substituents and configuration at C2 to C5, whereas the lactone ring could be either 5- or 6-membered. In the light of this specificity of action, the marked inhibition of mammalian and limpet β-glucuronidase known to be caused[135,143,165,175,181,183] by solutions of galactaric acid (mucic acid; V) appeared to be anomalous, until it was realized[116] (see Section X) that the enzyme from these sources can hydrolyze β-D-galactopyranosiduronic acids (VI). Although inhibition is at a lower level, galactarate solutions behave like D-glucarate solutions in experiments with β-glucuronidase, and inhibition is presumably due to the formation of an unidentified lactone. Lactonization appears to be slightly slower than in D-glucarate solutions, requiring 1 hour at 100° for the maximum inhibitory power to be reached. (The possible value, in carbohydrate chemistry, of enzyme experiments of this type in following intramolecular changes in solutions of sugar acids is exemplified by the preparation of 2-acetamido-2-deoxy-D-gluconolactone[182]; the behavior of this lactone and its D-galactose analog toward β-N-acetylglucosaminidase follows the same pattern as that described for the inhibition of β-glucuronidase.)

Inhibition of β-glucuronidase by D-glucaro-1,4-lactone or D-glucarate solutions has been repeatedly confirmed by a great many different workers, using all types of mammalian and non-mammalian enzyme preparations. The inhibitor has been employed in various kinds of controls in studies of the enzyme, and to prevent hydrolysis of estriol β-glucuronide in labor urine[184]; it is administered by mouth to patients having bladder tumors, with a view to arresting the liberation of the active agent from carcinogen glucuronides.[73]

Unfortunately, ignorance of the significance of lactonization robs earlier

(182) J. Findlay, G. A. Levvy and C. A. Marsh, *Biochem. J.*, **69**, 467 (1958).
(183) E. Wong and R. J. Rossiter, *Can. J. Med. Sci.*, **29**, 195 (1951).
(184) B. E. Clayton and G. F. Marrian, *J. Endocrinol.*, **6**, 332 (1950).

quantitative data on the action of D-glucarate and galactarate solutions of much of their value. Thus, since the increase in the inhibitory power of freshly prepared solutions of both compounds is greater at lower pH, differing degrees of lactonization may well explain the different effects observed by Mills and his colleagues[165] with separated mammalian β-glucuronidase fractions assayed at their different pH optima (see Section VI, and Wong and Rossiter[183]). This factor may also influence the shift in pH optimum to a higher value that is said to occur on adding D-glucarate to the purified enzyme from ox spleen.[169] It almost certainly explains the relatively low

TABLE VIII

Competitive Inhibitors[a] of Mammalian β-Glucuronidase[175]

	Dissociation Constant $(10^{-6}\,M)$	Relative Affinity
Phenolphthalein β-D-glucosiduronic acid	130	1
D-Glucaro-1,4-lactone	0.54	240
Boiled D-glucarate solution[b]	1.6	81
3-O-Methyl-D-glucaro-1,4-lactone	130	1
Boiled galactarate solution[b]	89	1.5
D-Glucuronate	1600	0.08
3-O-Methyl-D-glucuronate	no inhibition	—
D-Galacturonate	6000	0.02

[a] The experiments were carried out with partially-purified mouse-liver enzyme and phenolphthalein β-D-glucosiduronic acid, in acetate buffer, pH 5.2, and dissociation constants were calculated by the method of Lineweaver and Burk.[173]

[b] Figures for the dissociation constant and relative affinity have no theoretical significance, but they provide a useful measure of the inhibitory power (of the solution) resulting from lactonization.

efficiency of D-glucarate as an enzyme inhibitor in unbuffered, human urine.[184]

Figures for K_i, the dissociation constant of the enzyme–inhibitor complex, obtained under strictly comparable conditions with mouse-liver preparations, are shown in Table VIII for D-glucaro-1,4-lactone and some closely-related compounds, all of which act competitively. Table IX gives figures obtained with the enzyme from female-rat preputial gland and various substrates; within the limits of these experiments, K_i for boiled D-glucarate or boiled galactarate solutions was little affected by changes in the purity of the enzyme or the pH of test. In accordance with theory, similar values of K_i for any one inhibitor were obtained with different substrates, with the notable exception of o-nitrophenyl β-galacturonide.

This exception is discussed in Section X. Table X shows the wide differences in K_i that have been recorded for different non-mammalian enzyme preparations; in the case of the enzyme from *Patella vulgata*, K_i was again

TABLE IX

Values of K_i for Various Competitive Inhibitors Obtained with the Enzyme from Female Rat Preputial Gland after "Partial" (P)[116] or "Complete" (C)[49] Purification[a]

Inhibitor	Substrate	En-zyme	pH of Test	K_i $(10^{-6}\,M)$
D-Glucaro-1,4-lactone	phenolphthalein β-D-glucosiduronic acid	C	4.5	0.11
Boiled D-glucarate	phenyl β-D-glucosiduronic acid	C	4.5	0.31
		P	4.5	0.31
		P	3.9	0.36
	phenyl β-D-galactosiduronic acid	C	4.5	0.32
		P	4.5	0.47
		P	3.9	0.36
	o-nitrophenyl β-D-galactosiduronic acid	C	4.5	1.1
Boiled galactarate	phenolphthalein β-D-glucosiduronic acid	C	4.5	14
	phenyl β-D-glucosiduronic acid	C	4.5	14
		P	4.5	22
		P	3.9	16
	phenyl β-D-galactosiduronic acid	C	4.5	15
		P	4.5	27
		P	3.9	18
	o-nitrophenyl β-D-galactosiduronic acid	C	4.5	70
D-Glucuronate	phenyl β-D-glucosiduronic acid	P	4.5	1500
	phenyl β-D-galactosiduronic acid	P	4.5	1000
D-Galacturonate	phenyl β-D-glucosiduronic acid	P	4.5	4300
	phenyl β-D-galactosiduronic acid	P	4.5	4000

[a] See Section IV. Results calculated by method of Lineweaver and Burk.[173]

independent of the substrate employed, with the exception of the results for o-nitrophenyl β-galacturonide. In Tables VIII–X, K_i figures for D-glucaro-1,4-lactone and for boiled D-glucarate can be directly compared by dividing the latter by 3 (see above).

Turning to the two remaining compounds listed in Tables VIII–X, it may be seen that the hydrolysis product, D-glucuronic acid (D-glucopyranuronic acid) is a moderately powerful inhibitor. D-Glucuronolactone (D-glucofuranurono-6,3-lactone; VII) is not an inhibitor.[143] There is no

TABLE X

Values of K_i for Competitive Inhibitors Acting on β-Glucuronidase from Non-mammalian Sources[a]

Inhibitor	Substrate	pH of Test	K_i $(10^{-6} M)$	References
Patella vulgata visceral hump				
D-Glucaro-1,4-lactone	phenolphthalein β-D-glucosiduronic acid	4.1	0.11	86
Boiled D-glucarate	phenyl β-D-glucosiduronic acid	4.1	0.32	116
	phenyl β-D-galactosiduronic acid	4.1	0.26	116
	o-nitrophenyl β-D-galactosiduronic acid	4.1	2.9	49
Boiled galactarate	phenolphthalein β-D-glucosiduronic acid	4.1	6.7	86
	phenyl β-D-glucosiduronic acid	4.1	6.9	116
	phenyl β-D-galactosiduronic acid	4.1	5.4	116
	o-nitrophenyl β-D-galactosiduronic acid	4.1	61	49
Sheep-rumen microorganisms				
D-Glucaro-1,4-lactone	phenolphthalein β-D-glucosiduronic acid	6.1	19	132
Boiled galactarate	phenolphthalein β-D-glucosiduronic acid	6.1	no inhibition	132
D-Glucuronate	phenolphthalein β-D-glucosiduronic acid	6.1	3600	132
D-Galacturonate	phenolphthalein β-D-glucosiduronic acid	6.1	no inhibition	132
Scutellaria baicalensis root				
D-Glucaro-1,4-lactone	phenolphthalein β-D-glucosiduronic acid	4.5	200	88

[a] Some figures calculated by method of Lineweaver and Burk,[173] and others derived graphically.

record of any appreciable inhibition by typical aglycons, although this could scarcely have escaped observation if it occurred. The feeble inhibition (of the mammalian enzyme) seen with D-galacturonic acid (D-galactopyranuronic acid)[165,175] appeared to be an anomaly until it was realized that β-glucuronidase is also a β-galacturonidase. It is notable that the rumen bacterial-enzyme is unaffected by D-galacturonate and galactarate.

Some interest also attaches, on stereochemical grounds, to the effects of the isomers of tartaric acid and malic acid. At 0.01 M, erythraric acid (*meso*-tartaric acid) caused slight competitive inhibition,[181,183,185] whilst D- or L-threaric acid (*levo*- or *dextro*-tartaric acid) had no effect[135,181]; commercial DL-threaric acid ("racemic acid") had a small effect that disappeared on purification.[181] Some authors have noted slight inhibition with L-tartaric acid.[147,165,183] L-Malic acid resembled erythraric acid in its action,[135,147,165, 183,185] but D-malic acid appeared to be non-inhibitory.[135,183] Unsubstituted ω-dicarboxylic acids cause little, if any, inhibition.[135,147,165,183]

Three compounds, whose status has been in doubt, can now be stated to be non-inhibitory. Mammalian β-glucuronidase has slightly different pH–activity curves in citrate and acetate buffer (see Fig. 2), and citric acid may[165] or may not[183] appear to cause a small degree of inhibition, depending upon the exact conditions employed. Ascorbic acid reduces cupric ion to the inhibitory cuprous ion (see Section IX, 4), and will thus cause inhibition[37,87,132,165] if traces of the former ion are present,[186] but not otherwise.[135,175,183] Inhibition by D-gluconic acid or one of its lactones[135,165] disappears on purification,[132,175,181,183] and is almost certainly due to traces of D-glucaric acid.

2. Other Organic Compounds

The phenomena described in this Subsection are essentially unspecific. The acid mucopolysaccharides, heparin, chondroitinsulfate, and hyaluronic acid, are all weak, non-competitive inhibitors of mammalian (mouse, rat, and ox) β-glucuronidase[24,37,165]; inhibition is very variable,[135,183,187] and usually stops short of 100 % (partially non-competitive inhibition[187a]). It is increased by decreasing the pH of assay,[24,165] and the effects of heparin and hyaluronic acid[37] or of heparin and chondroitinsulfate[24] are not additive. Inhibition by the last two compounds is not reversed by the nonionic, surface-active agent, Triton X-100. In these respects the mucopolysaccharides can be distinguished from the rat, endogenous-tissue inhibitor (see Section IX, 3). Synthetic, macromolecular polyanions inhibit the enzyme non-competitively, particularly at low protein concentrations[187]; the use of acidic ion-exchange resins in the purification of the enzyme[81,149]

(185) M. A. M. Abul-Fadl, *Biochem. J.*, **65**, 16P (1957).

(186) G. A. Levvy and C. A. Marsh, *Nature*, **180**, 197 (1957).

(187) P. Bernfeld, S. Jacobson and H. C. Bernfeld, *Arch. Biochem. Biophys.*, **69**, 198 (1957).

(187a) M. Dixon and E. C. Webb, "Enzymes," Longmans, Green & Co., London, 1958.

should therefore be avoided.[187] The surface-active agent, Teepol XL (a mixture of secondary alkyl sulfates), unlike the nonionic Triton X-100, also inhibits, and acts non-competitively[32]; the inhibition, at first reversible, rapidly becomes irreversible, with complete inactivation of the enzyme. Very feeble inhibitory effects have been reported with certain flavones and flavone derivatives.[188]

At low protein concentrations, mammalian β-glucuronidase is activated by a variety of compounds of high molecular weight, such as albumin, deoxyribonucleic acid, chitosan (the D-glucosamine polymer), and starch, as well as by heat-inactivated enzyme, suramin (Bayer 205), and certain diamines.[80,138] Crude enzyme preparations from the female-rat preputial gland[49] display this phenomenon, whereas it is only seen with the enzyme from ox spleen[149] or ox liver[81] after purification. Activation is different in character with different compounds (see Fig. 4). Thus, albumin does not alter the position of the pH optimum (or optima) appreciably,[49,189] whereas deoxyribonucleic acid (see Sections IV, VI, and X) inhibits below and activates above pH 4.3, to produce a single optimum at about[49,80] pH 5; with phenyl β-galacturonide as substrate, however, deoxyribonucleic acid inhibits at all pH values.[49] Phthalic acid and certain other aromatic acids in relatively high concentration (0.01 M) produce the same type of effect as deoxyribonucleic acid[80] (see Fig. 2). It seems not impossible that, in certain cases at least,[138,187] large molecules activate β-glucuronidase by combining with inhibitory ions (see, also, Section IX, 4).

In general, it may be said, if β-glucuronidase undergoes loose combination with other molecules, then variable inhibition and activation must be expected, with or without changes in the shape of the pH–activity curve.

3. Endogenous Tissue Inhibitor

Untreated water-homogenates of rat tissues show a steady *rise* in their net β-glucuronidase activity on dilution, without ever reaching a limiting value, from a constant low level at high tissue concentrations.[24] This is due to the presence of excess of an unidentified, thermostable, nondialyzable inhibitor, which can be removed by centrifuging after buffering to pH 5.2. Preparations which have been put through the usual first steps of purification (see Section IV) and in which all the enzyme is in a soluble state are therefore free from the inhibitor, and can be employed for studying the inhibitor in boiled-tissue homogenates. Inhibition is overcome by adding the nonionic, surface-active agent Triton X-100 and the total activity of crude homogenates can be measured in the presence of this reagent. Treat-

(188) G. Rodney, A. L. Swanson, L. M. Wheeler, G. N. Smith and C. S. Worrel, *J. Biol. Chem.*, **183**, 739 (1950).

(189) A. L. Beyler and C. M. Szego, *Federation Proc.*, **11**, 13 (1952).

ment of rat tissues in a Waring Blendor or tissue disintegrator leads to variable destruction of both enzyme and inhibitor,[24] and these two opposing effects may sometimes leave the apparent net activity of the rat preparation unchanged.[43] Although the enzyme from mouse tissues is relatively unaffected by this inhibitor, its presence in them can readily be demonstrated by testing boiled, mouse homogenates with rat enzyme.[24] The inhibitor is apparently akin to the "antiglucuronidase" in blood plasma.[190]

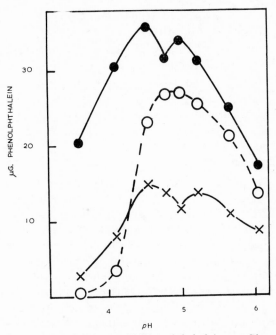

Fig. 4.—Hydrolysis[49] of 6.3×10^{-4} M Phenolphthalein β-D-Glucosiduronic acid at Various pH Values, in 0.05 N Acetate Buffer, by a Highly Purified β-Glucuronidase Preparation from Female-rat Preputial Gland (Section IV), Alone ($\times$), and in Presence of 0.03 % of Deoxyribonucleic Acid (○), or of 0.01% of Albumin (●).

β-Glucuronidase in dog tissues[191] and in *Helix pomatia* preparations[87] may also be subject to its action.

The endogenous inhibitor in rat tissues *resembles* the acid mucopolysaccharides (see Section IX, 2) in that the inhibition never rises beyond a variable maximum, which is always well below 100%. It is *unlike* them in that the effect is *not* pH-dependent, and is additive to that of heparin or chondroitinsulfate at the maximum.[24] A further distinction was seen in the

(190) W. H. Fishman, K. I. Altman and B. Springer, *Federation Proc.*, **7**, 154 (1948).

(191) W. H. Fishman in *CIBA Foundation Colloq. on Endocrinol.*, **1**, 229 (1952).

type of inhibition. The action of the endogenous inhibitor (on the rat enzyme) provided the first well-authenticated example of "combined" inhibition (also known as "uncompetitive" inhibition), other instances of which have since been reported.[192,193] Inhibition increased with increasing substrate concentration, suggesting that the inhibitor combined with the enzyme–substrate complex, rather than with the enzyme alone; there was an increase in the affinity of the substrate for the enzyme, but a fall in its rate of hydrolysis.

One might be more inclined to attach significance to this inhibitor as a means of physiological control if there were tissues that lacked it but contained susceptible enzyme. In any case, the action of this inhibitor does not explain the changes in β-glucuronidase activity that are seen *in vivo*.[9]

4. Heavy-metal Ions

Mammalian β-glucuronidase activity *in vitro* is unaffected by many of the common enzyme poisons, such as fluoride, iodoacetate, cyanide, azide, and dinitrophenol,[42,89,135,165,183] and it was at one time generally believed that the effects, if any, of cations were of little interest.[165,191] This impression may in part have been derived from early experiments with crude, concentrated, tissue extracts. However, marked inhibition of a purified, ox-liver preparation[42] and of the highly active enzyme in the digestive juice of *Helix pomatia*[87] was seen with 10^{-4} M of silver nitrate, 10^{-3} M of cupric sulfate, and 10^{-3} M of uranium nitrate. β-Glucuronidase from *Patella vulgata*[86] displayed similar inhibition with $Ag^{\oplus}$, but practically no effect with $Cu^{\oplus\oplus}$, whilst mercuric chloride was more powerful than $Ag^{\oplus}$. Preparations from *Escherichia coli*[194] were strongly inhibited by 10^{-5} M of $Cu^{\oplus\oplus}$, 10^{-6} M of $Ag^{\oplus}$, and 10^{-7} M of $Hg^{\oplus\oplus}$; it is evident that these particular preparations were already heavily contaminated with inhibitory cations, since chelating agents alone caused very strong activation.

In the belief that the action of the enzyme might be modified by the presence of some of the more prevalent metals in trace amounts, the effects of cations on mammalian β-glucuronidase were re-investigated[186,195]; of a large number studied, only $Cu^{\oplus\oplus}$, $Ag^{\oplus}$, and $Hg^{\oplus\oplus}$ were pronounced in their effects. (Inhibition was also seen with uranium acetate, ammonium chloroplatinate, osmium tetroxide, and sodium tungstate.[83]) Marked inhibition was seen with 2.5×10^{-5} M of $Ag^{\oplus}$ and 1.5×10^{-5} M of $Hg^{\oplus\oplus}$, and inhibition by these two ions was reversed by tissue constituents.

The action[186] of $Cu^{\oplus\oplus}$ was feeble and variable, unless a reducing agent

(192) K. S. Dodgson, B. Spencer and K. Williams, *Nature*, **177**, 432 (1956).
(193) M. A. Jermyn, *Science*, **125**, 12 (1957).
(194) M. L. Doyle, P. A. Katzman and E. A. Doisy, *J. Biol. Chem.*, **217**, 921 (1955).
(195) G. A. Levvy and C. A. Marsh, *Biochem. J.*, **66**, 21P (1957).

such as L-ascorbic acid or sodium bisulfite was also added; in which case, marked inhibition was immediately seen, reaching 50% at 5×10^{-5} M of $Cu^{\oplus\oplus}$ (3 p.p.m.). Versene had no effect on copper inhibition. It was concluded that inhibition by copper depends upon the formation of $Cu^{\oplus}$, since the reducing agents (themselves inactive) did not potentiate the actions of $Ag^{\oplus}$ and $Hg^{\oplus\oplus}$. This action of copper may have physiological significance. All three cations[195] displaced the pH–activity curve of the enzyme toward the acid side, and approximated to non-competitive inhibition in their actions; in the case of copper, at least, however, the effect seemed to be somewhat more complex than straightforward, non-competitive inhibition.

These experiments yielded information on the structure of the enzyme molecule. The inhibitory actions of the cations suggest that a thiol or similar group is required in order to bind the substrate to the enzyme in the active complex. It was also observed that, in the absence of substrate, all three cations catalyzed the progressive decomposition of the enzyme by bisulfite.[186] Much lower metal-concentrations were required than for enzyme inhibition, and L-ascorbic acid could not replace bisulfite in this reaction. Addition of substrate, at any stage, arrested the destruction of the enzyme, from which it may be deduced that a disulfide group[196] *also* is essential for the binding of enzyme and substrate. Whether these two groups in the enzyme bind the glycosyl and carboxyl groups in the substrate is an interesting question.

It seems feasible that traces of heavy-metal ions may have some bearing upon certain features of the action of mammalian β-glucuronidase, such as the fall in net activity seen on dilution of highly purified preparations (see Section IV), the inhibitory action of the unknown constituents of urine,[185,190] and the pH optimum at pH 3.4 observed by Mills, Paul, and Smith[165] but by no other workers (see Section VI). The presence of traces of $Cu^{\oplus\oplus}$ in the assay mixture would provide a completely satisfactory explanation of the variable effects reported with L-ascorbic acid (see Section IX, 2).[196a]

X. Mode of Action and Specificity

1. *Nature of the Reaction*

Strictly speaking, an enzyme can only provisionally be classified as a β-glucuronidase before its action has been shown to be purely hydrolytic— by the isolation of D-glucuronic acid as well as the aglycon. This consideration is of particular importance when whole, bacterial suspensions are employed as a source of the enzyme.

(196) R. Cecil and U. E. Loening, *Biochem. J.*, **66**, 18P (1957).

(196a) A. W. Rowe and C. E. Weill [*J. Am. Chem. Soc.*, **81**, 921 (1959)] explain in the same way the inhibition of β-amylase by L-ascorbic acid.

D-Glucuronic acid, liberated after exhaustive hydrolysis of the flavone D-glucuronides, baicalin and scutellarin, by baicalinase, the β-glucuronidase in the root of *S. baicalensis*, was identified as the potassium and cinchonine salts.[170,171] A better method for the characterization of D-glucuronic acid is to convert it into the bis(benzimidazole) derivative of D-glucaric acid,[197] and this has been isolated after the hydrolysis of the β-glucuronides of *levo*-menthol,[198] estriol,[199] and chrysin[200] by mammalian β-glucuronidase, and of that of phenolphthalein by the bacterial enzyme from the sheep rumen.[132] This method of identification is not unequivocal, since oxidation of L-guluronic acid also yields D-glucaric acid.

Paper chromatography has been employed for identifying the D-glucuronic acid liberated by the action of the enzyme from the sheep rumen,[132] the locust,[102] and the limpet,[86] respectively. D-Glucuronic acid and D-galacturonic acid have similar R_F values, but only the former can be made to give a second spot corresponding to the lactone. The equilibrium point in the reaction catalyzed by β-glucuronidase lies far over in favor of hydrolysis; this is illustrated, for example, by the hydrolysis of the β-D-glucosyluronic acid-$(1 \rightarrow 2)$-β-D-glucosiduronic acid derivative of glycyrrhetic acid ("$\beta\beta'$-diglucuronide"), glycyrrhizinic acid,[178] by mammalian preparations, in which there was almost quantitative liberation of two moles of D-glucuronic acid per mole.

2. Substrate Specificity

a. β-D-Glucopyranosiduronic Acids.—Final proof of the generally accepted β-D-glucopyranosidic structure of the urinary glucuronides (I) has been afforded by the oxidation of the β-D-glucopyranosides of *levo*-menthol,[131] phenol,[137] 2-naphthol,[201] and 4-methylumbelliferone[141] to the corresponding β-D-glucopyranosiduronic acids, identical with the natural products. With regard to the specificity of β-glucuronidase, it can be firmly stated that the mammalian enzyme hydrolyzes alkyl, aryl, alicyclic, and acyl[133,202,203] β-glucuronides (I), but has no action either on α-D-glucopyranosiduronic acids,[16,116,204] or on β-D-glucopyranosides.[16,89] β-D-Glucopyranosyluronic acid phosphate (I; R $=$ PO$_3$H$_2$) is also hydrolyzed by β-glucuronidase, and hydrolysis is inhibited by D-glucaro-1,4-lactone[204] (see

(197) R. Lohmar, R. J. Dimler, S. Moore and K. P. Link, *J. Biol. Chem.*, **143**, 551 (1942).

(198) G. A. Levvy, *Biochem. J.*, **42**, 2 (1948).

(199) J. K. Grant and G. F. Marrian, *Biochem. J.*, **47**, 1 (1950).

(200) C. A. Marsh, *Biochem. J.*, **59**, 58 (1955).

(201) K.-C. Tsou and A. M. Seligman, *J. Am. Chem. Soc.*, **74**, 5605 (1952).

(202) B. H. Billing, P. G. Cole and G. H. Lathe, *Biochem. J.*, **65**, 774 (1957).

(203) G. J. Dutton, *Biochem. J.*, **64**, 693 (1956).

(204) G. A. Levvy and C. A. Marsh, *Biochem. J.*, **52**, 690 (1952).

Section IX, 1). Although they have not been systematically studied, non-mammalian β-glucuronidase preparations appear to resemble the mammalian enzyme in these respects.

b. *β-D-Glucofuranosiduronic Acids.*—In an attempt to overcome some of the difficulties that arise with impure, enzyme preparations, recourse was had to the use of competing substrates in specificity studies with the mammalian enzyme.[176,204] In principle, liberation of the aglycon from a standard substrate should be depressed by presence of a second substrate for the same enzyme. In practice, results obtained in this way were subsequently found to be misleading (see below, and Section VIII). The experiments dealing with the action of β-glucuronidase on β-D-glucofuranosiduronic acids are, however, open to criticism on additional grounds. The competing substrate in this instance was methyl β-D-glucofuranosidurono-6,3-lactone[205,206] which had been treated with alkali in an attempt to open the lactone ring; it was concluded that the D-glucofuranosiduronic acid was not a substrate for the enzyme. In later experiments,[83] it has been observed that this glycoside, unlike its α anomer, is decomposed by alkali, with little evidence of the opening of the lactone ring (see Osman, Hobbs, and Walston[205]). Tsou and Seligman[201] observed that alkali decomposed 2-naphthyl β-D-glucofuranosidurono-6,3-lactone with liberation of 2-naphthol, and therefore employed the untreated lactone in direct hydrolysis experiments with mammalian β-glucuronidase. Since the enzyme did not liberate 2-naphthol, it was concluded that β-D-glucofuranosiduronic acids are not substrates. It is unlikely, however, that any lactone would be a substrate for the enzyme (see Section IX, 1), and whether β-glucuronidase would hydrolyze a β-D-glucofuranosiduronic acid must await the synthesis of a suitable test compound. The suggestion that β-D-glucosyluronic acid p-aminobenzoate ("p-aminobenzoyl β-glucuronide") from dog urine has a furanose structure[207] is of great interest, since this compound from other sources is known to be hydrolyzed by β-glucuronidase.[203]

c. *β-D-Galactopyranosiduronic Acids.*—As pointed out in Section IX, 1, the inhibition of β-glucuronidase by D-glucaro-1,4-lactone provides strong evidence for the distinguishing of this enzyme from other types of glycopyranosidase. Inhibition by solutions of galactarate or galactarolactone, however, raised the suspicion that β-glucuronidase in mammalian and limpet preparations will hydrolyze β-galacturonides (β-D-galactopyranosiduronic acids; VI), and this has been found to be true.[49,116] Purification

(205) E. M. Osman, K. C. Hobbs and W. E. Walston, *J. Am. Chem. Soc.*, **73**, 2726 (1951).

(206) J. E. Cadotte, F. Smith and D. Spriesterbach, *J. Am. Chem. Soc.*, **74**, 1501 (1952).

(207) T. Nakao, M. Nakao and T. Nakajima, *J. Biochem.* (Tokyo), **45**, 207 (1958).

increased the β-galacturonidase activity of β-glucuronidase preparations. Competing-substrate experiments had failed to reveal this action,[204] but, on repeating the experiments at a different pH, addition of a β-galacturonide was seen to depress the hydrolysis of a β-glucuronide.[116]

That β-glucuronidase is *identical* with β-galacturonidase was shown by the fact that the K_i values for different competitive inhibitors did not alter on passing from the one type of substrate to the other (see Section IX, 1), with the exception of the figures obtained when the β-galacturonide of o-nitrophenol was employed as substrate. The possibility that the enzyme preparations contained two different β-galacturonidases was discounted in view of the very high specific-activities observed with all the substrates, and it was considered[49] that the nitro group must modify the combination of the substrate with the enzyme. Whilst the hydrolytic action of β-glucuronidase on β-D-mannopyranosiduronic acids has not been examined, it is, perhaps, significant that D-mannopyranuronic acid, unlike the hydrolysis products, D-gluco- and D-galacto-pyranuronic acids (see Section IX, 1), does not inhibit the mammalian enzyme.[175] The fact that the bacterial β-glucuronidase from the sheep rumen is not inhibited by D-galacturonate or by boiled galactarate solution (see Table X) may, perhaps, indicate that this enzyme has no action on β-galacturonides.

The ratio of β-glucuronidase to β-galacturonidase activity at[49,116] pH 4.5 was 3.1 for partially purified preparations from the female-rat preputial gland, and 1.4 for the highly purified enzyme from the same source, using 0.01 M phenyl β-glucuronide and phenyl β-galacturonide as substrates; in the presence of 0.03 % of deoxyribonucleic acid (see Section IX, 2), however, the latter ratio rose to about 5, there being activation with the former substrate and inhibition with the latter. This differential action of tissue constituents casts doubt on the interpretation of experiments in which the non-identity of two enzymes is deduced from changes in the relative rates of hydrolysis of the two substrates during purification. Such experiments have been claimed to distinguish β-glucuronidase from β-glucosidase in emulsin.[128]

The action of β-glucuronidase on β-galacturonides raises a problem in nomenclature. For the present, at least, it is proposed that the name β-glucuronidase should be retained, since all known natural substrates are in fact β-glucuronides, and since, with a common aglycon, the substrate affinity and the rate of hydrolysis are greater with a β-glucuronide than with a β-galacturonide.

d. α-D-Glucopyranosiduronic Acids.—Limpet preparations have recently been shown to hydrolyze synthetic α-D-glucopyranosiduronic acids[116]; to what extent the same enzyme is responsible for the hydrolytic action of the limpet preparations on α-D-galactopyranosiduronic acids is uncertain. This enzyme can be distinguished at once from β-glucuronidase, however, since it is not present in mammalian tissues, and is not inhibited by D-glucaro-1,4-lactone or by boiled galactarate solutions.[116] The α- and β-glucuronidases in the limpet can also be distinguished by their different stabilities at various pHs or temperatures. Snail extracts, which are as rich as limpet extracts in β-glucuronidase activity (Table I), are said to lack α-glucuronidase activity,[126] and thus might be preferable when β-glucuronidase is employed as a selective hydrolytic agent. The same, of course, is true of mammalian preparations.

   e. *Oligosaccharides.*—The action of β-glucuronidase on oligosaccharides containing the β-D-glucuronic acid residue is of great interest in view of the possible physiological contribution of this enzyme toward mobilizing the end products of hyaluronidase action. Crude, testicular, hyaluronidase preparations contain β-glucuronidase.[208] It is believed that hyaluronic acid is composed predominantly of alternate, β-linked, D-glucuronic acid and N-acetyl-D-glucosamine (2-acetamido-2-deoxy-D-glucose) residues, and that chondroitinsulfate contains the D-glucuronic acid residue in a similar type of molecule in which the amino sugar is N-acetyl-D-galactosamine.[209] Purified, testicular hyaluronidase hydrolyzes *both* polysaccharides as far as oligosaccharides, after which β-glucuronidase and β-N-acetylhexosaminidase act alternately to split off D-glucuronic acid and hexosamine from the nonreducing end of the molecule[11,208,210]; this process also results in the formation, from hyaluronic acid, of the disaccharide, N-acetylhyalobiouronic acid, which is said to be a N-acetyl-D-glucosamine β-D-glucopyranosiduronic acid, but which is resistant to hydrolysis by β-glucuronidase. From the study of its action in these experiments, it was concluded that β-glucuronidase cannot split off O-substituted β-D-glucuronic acid residues, such as occur in polymers like hyaluronic acid itself.[11,208]

   This same consideration arose in studying the action of mammalian β-glucuronidase on plant triterpene glucuronides.[178] Both D-glucuronic acid residues were split off from glycyrrhetic acid 2-O-(β-D-glucopyranosyluronic acid)-β-D-glucopyranosiduronic acid (glycyrrhizinic acid), but the glycoside of oleanolic acid, until then believed to be a mono-D-glucosiduronic acid, was not attacked. This glycoside may of course be an α-D-glucosiduronic acid, but the discovery that it contains one molar equivalent of a second sugar, D-glucose, per mole raised the *possibility* that the glycoside is a D-glucosyl-D-glucosiduronic acid (oleanolic acid contains only one hydroxyl group). It is evident that a further study should be made of O-substituted β-D-glucopyranosiduronic acids as substrates for β-glucuronidase.

   (208) K. Meyer, A. Linker and M. M. Rapport, *J. Biol. Chem.*, **192**, 275 (1951).
   (209) K. Meyer, *Harvey Lectures, Ser.* **51**, 88 (1957).
   (210) L. Hahn, *Arkiv. Kemi, Mineral. Geol.*, **21**, 1 (1946).

The actions of 3-O-methyl-D-glucuronate and 3-O-methyl-D-glucaro-1,4-lactone as inhibitors are of interest in this connection (see Table VIII).

Two further points of interest with regard to the specificity of β-glucuronidase are raised by recent reports that leech hyaluronidase is a poly-β-glucuronidase,[211] and that hydrolysis of certain mucopolysaccharides yielded some L-iduronic acid[212]; oligosaccharides containing this uronic acid resisted hydrolysis by β-glucuronidase.[209]

XI. BIOSYNTHESIS OF β-D-GLUCOSIDURONIC ACIDS AND RELATED POLYSACCHARIDES

The contention that β-glucuronidase is responsible for the synthesis of the hetero-β-glucuronides *in vivo*[213] has been tacitly abandoned.[214] Storey and Dutton[215] found that the immediate precursor in the synthesis of β-glucuronides is "uridine diphosphate D-glucuronic acid" [UDPGA; uridine 5-(D-glucosyluronic acid dihydrogen pyrophosphate)]; under the influence of the newly discovered enzyme, glucuronyl-transferase,[216] the D-glucuronic acid residue is donated directly and almost quantitatively to a suitable aglycon. The latter is usually employed in concentrations of the order of 2–3 × 10⁻⁴ M. This enzyme system has been shown to accomplish the synthesis of all the known types of hetero-β-glucuronides,[203,217] and the successive steps in the formation of "UDPGA" from liver glycogen have been established.[217] Neither β-glucuronidase nor free D-glucuronic acid participates in this process at any stage. Earlier reviews have dealt with this subject.[9,218]

It has still to be demonstrated that the same synthetic enzyme system can introduce the D-glucuronic acid residue into acid mucopolysaccharides. Recent work suggests that this is not the case. The early observation,[112] made with mouse-liver and -kidney slices, that infants, unlike adults, lack the ability to synthesize β-glucuronides, has been confirmed with cell-free, mammalian preparations,[12,219] and is due to lack of both "UDPGA" and glucuronyl-transferase. D-Glucaro-1,4-lactone (see Section IX, 1) might help to overcome those metabolic disorders[219] which are due to a deficiency in D-glucuronide synthesis.

Adult cats have been found, in experiments with tissue slices and cell-

(211) A. Linker, P. Hoffman and K. Meyer, *Nature*, **180**, 810 (1957).

(212) P. Hoffman, A. Linker and K. Meyer, *Science*, **124**, 1252 (1956).

(213) W. H. Fishman, *Ann. N. Y. Acad. Sci.*, **54**, 548 (1951).

(214) W. H. Fishman and S. Green, *J. Biol. Chem.*, **225**, 435 (1957).

(215) I. D. E. Storey and G. J. Dutton, *Biochem. J.*, **59**, 279 (1955).

(216) G. J. Dutton and I. D. E. Storey, *Biochem. J.*, **57**, 275 (1954).

(217) J. L. Strominger, E. S. Maxwell, J. Axelrod and H. M. Kalckar, *J. Biol. Chem.*, **224**, 79 (1957).

(218) R. L. Whistler and E. J. Olson, *Advances in Carbohydrate Chem.*, **12**, 299 (1957).

(219) A. K. Brown and W. W. Zuelzer, *J. Clin. Invest.*, **37**, 332 (1958).

free preparations, to be deficient in glucuronyl-transferase,[12] and cats treated with a number of typical aglycons did not excrete the corresponding β-glucuronides in the urine.[13] (Dogs, on the other hand, have long been known to accomplish this process very efficiently.) It would thus appear that, in cats at least, the synthesis of acid mucopolysaccharides requires an enzyme system different from that described for hetero-β-glucuronides. These experiments also provide further evidence for the non-participation of β-glucuronidase in the synthesis of hetero-β-glucuronides, since cats have their full complement of this enzyme.[13,109]

Fishman and Green[214] have produced convincing evidence that, under certain conditions, β-glucuronidase can transfer the β-D-glucuronic acid residue *in vitro* from aryl and alicyclic β-glucuronides to simple alcohols and glycols, notably ethylene glycol and propylene glycol. This reaction was essentially inefficient as a method of synthesis, requiring acceptor concentrations of the order of 2–3 M (15–20 % of either glycol, w/v) for the transfer of about 10 % of the D-glucuronic acid in the donor, and no success attended attempts to employ phenols or alicyclic alcohols as acceptors. The latter observation is in accord with our own experience in a number of unpublished experiments along similar lines. It should also be mentioned that there was no transfer of C^{14}-labeled D-glucuronic acid from injected 1-naphthyl β-D-glucosiduronic acid to orally-administered o-aminophenol in the rat.[220] Ethylene glycol and propylene glycol do not form β-glucuronides in the rabbit.[221]

It remains to be seen whether the alcoholysis catalyzed by β-glucuronidase has any physiological significance, but it is not impossible that the enzyme catalyzes the transfer of the β-D-glucuronic acid residue between oligosaccharide constituents of the acid mucopolysaccharides. This would leave still unanswered the problem of the ultimate origin of the D-glucuronic acid moiety in this form of combination. The cat experiments described above would appear to exclude a mechanism involving a hetero-β-glucuronide donor and a carbohydrate acceptor.

Whether β-glucuronidase in the organs of the cat would respond to treatment with steroid hormones and other agents in the same fashion as in other species[9] is another interesting problem that arises from these experiments; the enzyme in cat tissues shows the variation in activity with age (see Table I, d) first observed in mice,[112] and a striking elevation in enzyme activity in cat sciatic nerve is seen after injury to the nerve.[85]

XII. SUMMARY

β-Glucuronidase is universally distributed in the mammalian body, and is present in many other organisms. It hydrolyzes β-D-glucopyranosiduronic

(220) M. A. Packham and G. C. Butler, private communication (1955).
(221) R. T. Williams, private communication.

acids and β-D-galactopyranosiduronic acids. The richest source is the preputial gland of the female rat; alternative sources are snail digestive juice and extracts from the limpet *Patella vulgata*. Optimal hydrolysis of β-D-glucopyranosiduronic acids by the mammalian enzyme is displayed at pH 4.5 or 5.2, or both, and by bacterial preparations between pH 6 and 7. The most generally useful method of assay employs biosynthetic phenolphthalein mono-β-D-glucopyranosiduronic acid as substrate, and the liberated aglycon is measured colorimetrically; satisfactory synthetic substrates are also available. D-Glucaro-1,4-lactone inhibits the enzyme (from all sources) powerfully and specifically, and the mammalian enzyme has also been shown to be inhibited by galactarolactone. In very dilute tissue preparations, the enzyme is activated non-specifically by various substances, of which albumin is the most reliable.

STRUCTURAL CHEMISTRY OF THE HEMICELLULOSES

By G. O. Aspinall

Department of Chemistry, The University of Edinburgh, Scotland

I. Introduction

Previous Chapters in this Series[1] have outlined much of the background chemistry of the polysaccharides of the hemicellulose group.[2] In the present article, the advances made during the last ten years or so in our understanding of the structural chemistry of the hemicelluloses are reviewed. The very considerable progress during this period has largely been made possible through the widespread use of chromatographic methods for the separation of the sugars and their derivatives.[3] It is appropriate that we should now take stock of the present position, assess the results so far obtained, and indicate the nature of some of the problems to which no answer has yet been given.

The term hemicellulose is applied to those plant cell-wall polysaccharides which occur in close association with cellulose, especially in lignified tis-

(1) E. Anderson and L. Sands, *Advances in Carbohydrate Chem.*, **1**, 329 (1946); J. K. N. Jones and F. Smith, *ibid.*, **4**, 243 (1949); R. L. Whistler, *ibid.*, **5**, 269 (1950); W. J. Polglase, *ibid.*, **10**, 283 (1955).

(2) For a review of much of the early work, see R. L. Whistler and C. L. Smart, "Polysaccharide Chemistry," Academic Press Inc., New York, N. Y., 1953.

(3) (a) G. N. Kowkabany, *Advances in Carbohydrate Chem.*, **9**, 303 (1954); (b) W. W. Binkley, *ibid.*, **10**, 55 (1955); (c) A. B. Foster, *ibid.*, **12**, 81 (1957).

sues, the term often being restricted to substances extracted with alkaline reagents but not with water. Such a definition lacks precision in respect of both chemical structure and biological function, and in the following account these polysaccharides are classified according to their main chemical features. In the initial broad classification, three main groups of polysaccharides will be recognized, namely, those based on chains of D-xylose, D-mannose (either alone or in association with D-glucose), and D-galactose residues. In such a classification, for example, the term xylan will be used to denote polysaccharides containing a backbone of D-xylose residues, although the several polysaccharides of this group differ considerably in their more detailed structure, notably in the nature and number of other sugar residues which are present and in the mode of attachment of these residues to the basal chains of the molecular structure. The review will include discussion of xylans sometimes referred to as cereal gums, which differ from the xylans of lignified tissues in solubility characteristics and probably also in biological function, but have common features in chemical structure.

II. Xylans

It has been known for nearly thirty years that the xylan from esparto grass[4] is composed of chains of $(1 \rightarrow 4)$-linked β-D-xylopyranose residues. During the past ten years, many xylans from land plants have been examined and all have been shown to contain the same basal structure but to differ in the structural arrangement of other sugar residues, especially L-arabinose, D-glucuronic acid, and its 4-methyl ether, which are attached as side-chains. The evidence for the common backbone in each of the polysaccharides is based either on the isolation of 2,3-di-O-methyl-D-xylose as a major product of hydrolysis of the methylated polysaccharide or on the isolation of 4-O-β-D-xylopyranosyl-D-xylopyranose (xylobiose) and its polymer homologs as products of partial acid hydrolysis. Although 2,3-di-O-methyl-D-xylose could arise from methylated polysaccharides containing either $(1 \rightarrow 4)$-linked D-xylopyranose or $(1 \rightarrow 5)$-linked D-xylofuranose residues, in view of the similarities in optical rotation and rates of hydrolysis it is reasonable to assume that the same essential structures are present as in esparto xylan.[4] The use of carbon, either alone or mixed with Celite, as an adsorbent for the chromatographic separation of oligosaccharides[5] has greatly facilitated the separation of products of partial acid hydrolysis of polysaccharides, and the isolation and characterization

(4) W. N. Haworth, H. A. Hampton and E. L. Hirst, *J. Chem. Soc.*, 1739 (1929); W. N. Haworth and E. G. V. Percival, *ibid.*, 2850 (1931).

(5) See Ref. 3(b), p. 56, for references to original papers by A. Tiselius and collaborators. For modification and extension of this procedure, see R. L. Whistler and D. F. Durso, *J. Am. Chem. Soc.*, **72**, 677 (1950).

of the polymer-homologous series, xylobiose, xylotriose, up to xyloheptaose [containing $(1 \rightarrow 4)$-linked β-D-xylopyranose units] was first achieved by Whistler and Tu[6] from corn (maize) cob xylan. The lower members, especially xylobiose and xylotriose, have since been isolated from the partial acid hydrolysis of several polysaccharides of this type.

Since further elaboration of the evidence for the common structural features of xylans is unnecessary, our attention may be turned to differences in fine structure arising from the proportions and modes of linkage of other sugar residues, the presence or absence of branching in the backbone of xylose residues, and variations in molecular size.

L-Arabinose has long been known as a component sugar of hemicelluloses, but not until 1951 was it first conclusively shown to be a constituent of a polysaccharide based on D-xylose residues. Perlin[7] showed that all the L-arabinose units in a wheat-flour polysaccharide were present as nonreducing end-groups in the furanose form and must be attached to D-xylose units. In many subsequent studies, L-arabinose has only been encountered in the furanose form when linked to D-xylose, and there is no evidence yet for the presence in the hemicellulose group of polysaccharides containing *only* L-arabinose residues (compare with the araban of pectic substances[8]). L-Arabinose residues in arabinoxylans are most commonly found as nonreducing end-groups, and their presence is shown by the isolation of $2,3,5$-tri-O-methyl-L-arabinose on hydrolysis of the methylated polysaccharide. Since $2,3$-di-O-methyl-D-xylose and 2-O-methyl-D-xylose are also found in the hydrolyzate, the partial structures I and II may be put forward for such polysaccharides.

$$-(1 \rightarrow 4)\text{-}\beta\text{-}\text{D-Xyl}p\text{-}(1 \rightarrow 4)\text{-}\beta\text{-}\text{D-Xyl}p\text{-}(1 \rightarrow 4)\text{-}(\beta\text{-}\text{D-Xyl}p)_n\text{-}(1 \rightarrow 4)\text{-}$$
$$\uparrow$$
$$\text{L-Ara}f\text{-}1$$

I

$$-(1 \rightarrow 4)\text{-}\beta\text{-}\text{D-Xyl}p\text{-}(1 \rightarrow 4)\text{-}\beta\text{-}\text{D-Xyl}p\text{-}(1 \rightarrow 4)\text{-}$$
$$3$$
$$\uparrow$$
$$\text{L-Ara}f\text{-}(1 \rightarrow 4)\text{-}(\beta\text{-}\text{D-Xyl}p)_n\text{-}1$$

II

All the arabinoxylans, so far examined, are of this general type, and, where these structures have been distinguished, the evidence points to direct attachment of the L-arabinofuranose units to the backbone as in I. In one case, direct proof of this mode of linkage has been obtained by the isolation

(6) R. L. Whistler and C.-C. Tu, *J. Am. Chem. Soc.*, **74**, 3609 (1952); **75**, 645 (1953).

(7) A. S. Perlin, *Cereal Chem.*, **28**, 370, 382 (1951).

(8) E. L. Hirst and J. K. N. Jones, *Advances in Carbohydrate Chem.*, **2**, 235 (1947).

of an oligosaccharide containing the terminal L-arabinofuranose residue. Wheat-straw xylan was degraded by a cellulolytic enzyme from the mold *Myrothecium verrucaria* to give a series of oligosaccharides containing both D-xylose and L-arabinose units.[9] One of these substances was shown to be the trisaccharide O-L-arabinofuranosyl-(1 → 3)-O-β-D-xylopyranosyl-(1 → 4)-D-xylopyranose (III),[10] which could only have arisen from a polysaccharide with structure I. In another instance, direct proof for this type of linkage follows from the characterization of a partial hydrolysis product from a modified polysaccharide.[10a] Selective oxidation of the primary alcoholic groups in the terminal L-arabinofuranosyl residues to carboxylic acid groups, followed by graded acid hydrolysis of the acidic polysaccharide, gave an aldobiouronic acid, (L-arabinofuranosyluronic acid)-(1 → 3)-D-xylose.

In other cases, the evidence in favor of structure I is based upon the examination of a degraded polysaccharide isolated after controlled acid hydrolysis has resulted in removal of some or all of the acid-labile L-arabinofuranose residues without significant cleavage of D-xylopyranosyl linkages. Thus, arabinoxylans I and II would give rise to the corresponding degraded polysaccharides IV and V. Structures IV and V may be differentiated by

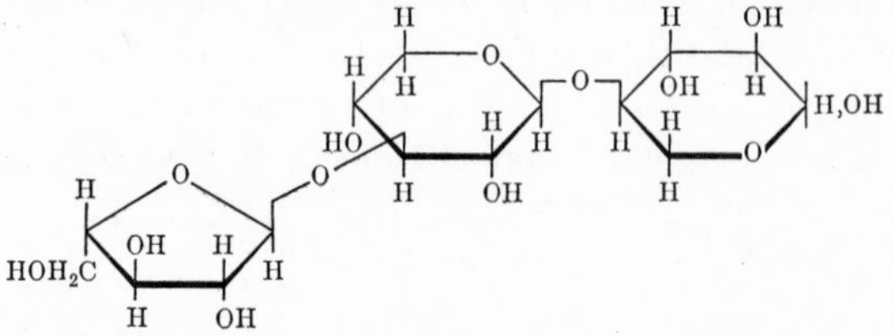

III

$-(1 \to 4)-\beta\text{-D-Xyl}p-(1 \to 4)-\beta\text{-D-Xyl}p-(1 \to 4)-(\beta\text{-D-Xyl}p)_n-(1 \to 4)-$

IV

$-(1 \to 4)-\beta\text{-D-Xyl}p-(1 \to 4)-\beta\text{-D-Xyl}p-(1 \to 4)-$
3
↑
$\beta\text{-D-Xyl}p-(1 \to 4)-(\beta\text{-D-Xyl}p)_{n-1}-1$

V

determination of formic acid released and reagent consumed during oxidation with periodate (compare with wheat-flour arabinoxylan[7]), by estimation of D-xylose residues unattacked by periodate (compare with barley-

(9) C. T. Bishop and D. R. Whitaker, *Chem. & Ind.* (London), 119 (1955).

(10) C. T. Bishop, *J. Am. Chem. Soc.*, **78**, 2840 (1956).

(10a) G. O. Aspinall, I. M. Cairncross and A. Nicolson, *Proc. Chem. Soc.*, in press (1959).

husk hemicellulose[11] and rye-flour arabinoxylan[12]), and by estimation of the proportions of nonreducing L-arabinose and D-xylose end-groups in the methylated polysaccharide (compare with barley-flour arabinoxylan[13]).

Some xylans also contain non-terminal L-arabinofuranose residues [for example, the hemicelluloses from corn (maize) cobs,[14,15] maize fiber[16,17] and maize hulls,[18,19] and barley husks[11]]. Since oligosaccharides having reducing L-arabinose residues are released under mild conditions of hydrolysis, it is probable that these oligosaccharides result from the cleavage of non-terminal furanosyl linkages. This is clearly so with barley-husk[11] and corn (maize) cob[14,15] hemicelluloses, where 2-O-β-D-xylopyranosyl-L-arabinose (VI)* has been isolated after mild acid hydrolysis, since 3,5-(and not 3,4-)di-O-methyl-L-arabinose is found on hydrolysis of the methylated polysaccharides. There is not yet sufficient evidence to show whether these non-terminal L-arabinofuranose residues are linked directly (VII) to the xylan backbone or whether they terminate longer side-chains in which one or more D-xylose residues are interposed (VIII).

VI

Many polysaccharides of the xylan group contain residues of D-glucuronic acid or 4-O-methyl-D-glucuronic acid. Since glycosiduronic acids are particularly resistant to acid hydrolysis, aldobiouronic acids may be isolated

---

* This disaccharide was originally assigned an α-glycosidic linkage,[14] but subsequent experiments describing its synthesis (see Ref. 20) and its degradation to 2-O-β-D-xylopyranosyl-glyceritol (see Ref. 21) show that the glycosidic linkage is β.

(11) G. O. Aspinall and R. J. Ferrier, J. Chem. Soc., 4188 (1957).

(12) G. O. Aspinall and R. J. Sturgeon, J. Chem. Soc., 4469 (1957).

(13) G. O. Aspinall and R. J. Ferrier, J. Chem. Soc., 638 (1958).

(14) R. L. Whistler and D. I. McGilvray, J. Am. Chem. Soc., 77, 2212 (1955); R. L. Whistler and W. M. Corbett, ibid., 77, 3822 (1955).

(15) R. L. Whistler and G. E. Lauterbach, J. Am. Chem. Soc., 80, 1987 (1958).

(16) R. L. Whistler and W. M. Corbett, J. Am. Chem. Soc., 77, 6328 (1955).

(17) R. L. Whistler and J. N. BeMiller, J. Am. Chem. Soc., 78, 1163 (1956).

(18) R. Montgomery, F. Smith and H. C. Srivastava, J. Am. Chem. Soc., 79, 698 (1957).

(19) H. C. Srivastava and F. Smith, J. Am. Chem. Soc., 79, 982 (1957).

(20) G. O. Aspinall and R. J. Ferrier, J. Chem. Soc., 1501 (1958).

(21) A. J. Charlson, P. A. J. Gorin and A. S. Perlin, Can. J. Chem., 35, 365 (1957).

$$-(1 \rightarrow 4)\text{-}\beta\text{-}\mathrm{D}\text{-}\mathrm{Xyl}p\text{-}(1 \rightarrow 4)\text{-}$$
$$3$$
$$\uparrow$$
$$\beta\text{-}\mathrm{D}\text{-}\mathrm{Xyl}p\text{-}(1 \rightarrow 2)\text{-}\mathrm{L}\text{-}\mathrm{Ara}f\text{-}1$$

VII

$$-(1 \rightarrow 4)\text{-}\beta\text{-}\mathrm{D}\text{-}\mathrm{Xyl}p\text{-}(1 \rightarrow 4)\text{-}$$
$$3$$
$$\uparrow$$
$$\beta\text{-}\mathrm{D}\text{-}\mathrm{Xyl}p\text{-}(1 \rightarrow 2)\text{-}\mathrm{L}\text{-}\mathrm{Ara}f\text{-}(1 \rightarrow 4)\text{-}(\beta\text{-}\mathrm{D}\text{-}\mathrm{Xyl}p)_n\text{-}1$$

VIII

from the graded acid hydrolysis of xylans containing hexuronic acid residues, and the mode of linkage of D-glucuronic acid to D-xylose may be established by identification of the hydrolysis products of the derived, methylated aldobiouronic acid. In this way, O-(4-O-methyl-α-D-glucosyl uronic acid)-(1 → 2)-D-xylose (IX) was isolated from aspen-wood hemicellulose.[22] D-Glucuronic acid or its 4-methyl ether are most commonly found linked to position 2 of D-xylose, although similar aldobiouronic acids containing (1 → 3)- (for example, from some samples of wheat-straw hemicellulose[23]) and (1 → 4)-linkages (for example, from corn-cob hemicellulose B[24]) have been encountered. Similarly, partially methylated aldobiouronic acids[25] may be isolated from hydrolyzates of the methylated polysaccharides. In all the polysaccharides of this type so far examined, hexuronic acid residues have been shown to be linked directly to the xylan backbone as single-unit side-chains. Thus, the isolation of O-(2,3,4-tri-O-methyl-α-D-glucosyluronic acid)-(1 → 2)-3-O-methyl-D-xylose (X) from partial hydrolyzates of methylated beechwood xylan[26] indicates the presence of the unit XI in the polysaccharide structure.

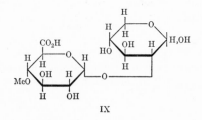

IX

(22) J. K. N. Jones and L. E. Wise, *J. Chem. Soc.*, 3389 (1952).

(23) C. T. Bishop, *Can. J. Chem.*, **31**, 134 (1953).

(24) R. L. Whistler and L. Hough, *J. Am. Chem. Soc.*, **75**, 4918 (1953).

(25) G. O. Aspinall, *Advances in Carbohydrate Chem.*, **9**, 131 (1954).

(26) G. O. Aspinall, E. L. Hirst and R. S. Mahomed, *J. Chem. Soc.*, 1734 (1954).

X

$-(1 \rightarrow 4)\text{-}\beta\text{-}D\text{-}Xylp\text{-}(1 \rightarrow 4)\text{-}$

2

↑

$4\text{-Me-}\alpha\text{-}D\text{-}GpA\text{-}1$

XI

Although the xylans from land plants are built up from chains of $(1 \rightarrow 4)$-linked β-D-xylopyranose residues, in many instances it is not yet known whether the backbone is strictly linear or whether some degree of branching occurs in these chains. In only one case, that of wheat-straw hemicellulose,[27] has a branched oligosaccharide been isolated and in no example, so far, have xylose-containing di- or tri-saccharides with $(1 \rightarrow 2)$- or $(1 \rightarrow 3)$-linkages been encountered as products of partial acid hydrolysis. When the necessary data are available, a comparison of values for number-average molecular weight (for example, by osmometry or isothermal distillation[28,29]) and average chain-length (for example, by end-group assay) may give an indication of the presence or absence of branching. If more than one nonreducing D-xylose end-group per molecule is present, there is clear evidence *for* branching. On the other hand, the presence of only one nonreducing D-xylopyranose end-group per molecule only constitutes evidence *against* branching if it is known that the D-xylose residue terminates the main chain. D-Glucuronic acid residues in xylans are commonly found attached as side-chains (as in XI), but there is no evidence yet that they may also terminate the main chain (as in XII or XIII). Graded hydrolysis of methylated xylans containing such D-glucuronic acid end-groups would yield a fully etherified aldobiouronic acid, $O\text{-}(2,3,4\text{-tri-}O\text{-methyl-}D\text{-glucosyl-}$ uronic acid)$\text{-}(1 \rightarrow 4)\text{-}2,3\text{-[or-}(1 \rightarrow 2)\text{-}3,4\text{-]-di-}O\text{-methyl-}D\text{-xylose}$, and such a methylated aldobiouronic acid has not yet been encountered in these circumstances. Several wood xylans contain only one D-xylopyranose end-group per molecule and, in the absence of evidence for structural units

$D\text{-}GpA\text{-}(1 \rightarrow 4)\text{-}D\text{-}Xylp\text{-}1\text{—}$ $D\text{-}GpA\text{-}(1 \rightarrow 2)\text{-}D\text{-}Xylp\text{-}1\text{—}$

XII   XIII

(27) C. T. Bishop, *Can. J. Chem.*, **33**, 1073 (1955).

(28) C. T. Greenwood, *Advances in Carbohydrate Chem.*, **7**, 289 (1952); **11**, 385 (1956).

(29) C. P. J. Glaudemans and T. E. Timell, *Svensk Papperstidn.*, **61**, 1 (1958).

XII or XIII, it is reasonable to assume that the xylan backbone is un-branched. In the case, however, of xylans containing L-arabinofuranose residues, it is much more difficult to obtain direct evidence for the order of linkage of sugar residues. It is doubtful if it would be possible by present methods to detect a small proportion of L-arabinofuranose residues terminating main xylan chains (as in XIV) if these residues were also attached as side-chains (I), as commonly found.

$$\text{L-Ara}f\text{-}(1 \rightarrow 4)\text{-D-Xyl}p\text{-}1\text{---}$$

XIV

Where there is known to be some degree of branching in the backbone of the xylan molecule, it is not at present possible to distinguish between structures containing single unit stubs (XV) and those containing more extended side-chains (XVI).

$$\text{-}(1 \rightarrow 4)\text{-}\beta\text{-D-Xyl}p\text{-}(1 \rightarrow 4)\text{-}(\beta\text{-D-Xyl}p)_n\text{-}1$$
$$2(\text{or } 3)$$
$$\uparrow$$
$$\beta\text{-D-Xyl}p\text{-}1$$

XV

$$\text{-}(1 \rightarrow 4)\text{-}\beta\text{-D-Xyl}p\text{-}1$$
$$2(\text{or } 3)$$
$$\uparrow$$
$$\beta\text{-D-Xyl}p\text{-}(1 \rightarrow 4)\text{-}(\beta\text{-D-Xyl}p)_n\text{-}1$$

XVI

The main structural features of the xylan group of hemicelluloses are now clear. All the polysaccharides of this type from land plants, so far examined, belong to the same general family in being built up from chains of $(1 \rightarrow 4)$-linked β-D-xylopyranose residues and may be contrasted with the xylan from the red alga *Rhodymenia palmata*[30] which contains chains of $(1 \rightarrow 3)$- and $(1 \rightarrow 4)$-linked D-xylopyranose residues. Only two xylans, devoid of other sugar residues, namely, those from esparto grass[31] and tamarind seeds,[32] have been isolated from land plants. The majority of xylans carry other sugar residues, most commonly those of L-arabinofuranose and D-glucopyranosyluronic acid which are attached as single-unit side-chains. The differences in structure within the group are mainly re-

(30) E. G. V. Percival and S. K. Chanda, *Nature*, **166**, 787 (1950); V. C. Barry, T. Dillon, B. Hawkins and P. O'Colla, *ibid.*, **166**, 788 (1950); V. C. Barry, J. E. McCormick and P. W. D. Mitchell, *J. Chem. Soc.*, 3692 (1954).

(31) S. K. Chanda, E. L. Hirst, J. K. N. Jones and E. G. V. Percival, *J. Chem. Soc.*, 1289 (1950).

(32) G. R. Savur, *J. Chem. Soc.*, 2600 (1956).

flected in the proportions and types of side-chains present and in their modes of attachment. Most of these polysaccharides are probably mixtures of closely-related molecular species in which variations in detailed structure are superimposed on the variations in molecular size commonly found in natural polymers. Indeed, hemicellulose fractions from a single source often contain the same sugar components but in different proportions, and, in an extreme case, that of esparto grass, a xylan devoid of other sugar residues[31] and a highly branched arabinoxylan[33] have been isolated.

In the following Sections, a comparison is made of the structures of xylans from different land plants.

1. Xylans from the Gramineae

Xylans from cereals and grasses are generally characterized by the presence of L-arabinofuranose residues linked to the backbone as single-unit side-chains, usually to position 3 of D-xylose, but, in many cases, D-glucuronic acid or 4-O-methyl-D-glucuronic acid residues, or both, are also present in a smaller proportion.

Early work on esparto xylan[4,34] established the basic structure of the polysaccharide, but it was not definitely known whether the 5–10% of L-arabinose residues, found in part at least in the furanose form as end groups,[34] originated from an arabinoxylan or from a contaminating arabinan. Evidence for the structural heterogeneity of this hemicellulose came from the isolation, by repeated fractionation by means of the insoluble copper complex, of an arabinose-free xylan.[31] Later, it was shown that, in the arabinose-rich fraction of esparto hemicellulose,[33] the majority of the L-arabinose residues were present in the furanose form as nonreducing end-groups, and that these could only arise from an arabinoxylan containing an essentially linear backbone of D-xylopyranose residues and carrying side-chains linked to position 3 of D-xylose and terminated by L-arabinofuranose residues. These two molecular species isolated from esparto hemicellulose are probably representative of a whole series of closely-related polysaccharides which are present in the plant. More recently, evidence was found for still greater complexity in the structure of esparto xylans. During the preparation of xylobiose and xylotriose by the partial acid hydrolysis of esparto hemicellulose,[35] a small proportion of 2-O-β-D-xylopyranosyl-L-arabinose was isolated.[20] This disaccharide probably arises from a small proportion of xylopyranosyl-arabinofuranosyl side-chains at-

(33) G. O. Aspinall, E. L. Hirst, R. W. Moody and E. G. V. Percival, J. Chem. Soc., 1631 (1953).

(34) W. N. Haworth, E. L. Hirst and E. Oliver, J. Chem. Soc., 1917 (1934); R. A. S. Bywater, W. N. Haworth, E. L. Hirst and S. Peat, ibid., 1983 (1937).

(35) G. O. Aspinall, M. E. Carter and M. Los, J. Chem. Soc., 4807 (1956).

tached to the backbone of D-xylose residues in some fractions of esparto hemicellulose.

Wheat-straw hemicelluloses have been investigated by several groups of workers and, although there is general agreement as to the main structural features, the results of these various groups differ in some respects. The most marked differences are in the proportions of D-glucuronic acid residues present. All the hemicellulose samples examined are characterized by the normal xylan backbone carrying, through position 3 of D-xylose residues, side-chains terminated by nonreducing L-arabinofuranose residues.[36-39] The isolation of the trisaccharide O-L-arabinofuranosyl-(1 → 3)-O-β-D-xylopyranosyl-(1 → 4)-D-xylopyranose (III) from the enzymic degradation[9,10] of one wheat-straw hemicellulose[36] shows that some, at least, of the L-arabinofuranose residues are present as single-unit side-chains (I). Repeated fractionation of one hemicellulose sample afforded a xylan devoid of L-arabinose residues but still containing a small proportion of D-glucuronic acid residues.[40] In one wheat-straw hemicellulose sample, the residues of D-glucuronic acid and 4-O-methyl-D-glucuronic acid are attached to D-xylose by a (1 → 3)-linkage,[23] but it is probable that, in other samples, a (1 → 2)-linkage is present.[37a,39] Another hemicellulose fraction is devoid of D-glucuronic acid residues, but contains a small proportion of D-glucose residues.[38] Since the corresponding methylated polysaccharide, when hydrolyzed, gives rise, among other compounds, to 2,6-di-O-methyl-D-glucose, it has been suggested that the D-glucose residues are an integral part of the xylan, although their precise structural significance is not yet clear.

Xylans of the same general type as those from wheat straw are found in wheat leaf,[41] oat straw,[42] and cocksfoot grass.[43] In each xylan, all the L-arabinose residues are found as terminal groups in the furanose form. In the wheat-leaf xylan, the mode of linkage of D-glucuronic acid (or its 4-methyl ether, or both) to D-xylose cannot be regarded as conclusively proved, although a (1 → 3)-linkage is claimed.[41] The evidence for (1 → 2)-linked aldobiouronic acid units in the oat-straw[42] and cocksfoot-grass[43] xylans is more certain. The partial structure XVII summarizes the main features of xylans of this type.

(36) G. A. Adams, *Can. J. Chem.*, **30**, 698 (1952).

(37) A. Roudier, *Compt. rend.*, **237**, 840 (1953); *Assoc. tech. ind. papetière Bull.*, 53 (1954).

(37a) A. Roudier, *Compt. rend.*, **248**, 1432 (1959).

(38) I. Ehrenthal, R. Montgomery and F. Smith, *J. Am. Chem. Soc.*, **76**, 5509 (1954).

(39) G. O. Aspinall and E. G. Meek, *J. Chem. Soc.*, 3830 (1956).

(40) G. O. Aspinall and R. S. Mahomed, *J. Chem. Soc.*, 1731 (1954).

(41) G. A. Adams, *Can. J. Chem.*, **32**, 186 (1954).

(42) G. O. Aspinall and K. C. B. Wilkie, *J. Chem. Soc.*, 1072 (1956).

(43) G. O. Aspinall and I. M. Cairncross, unpublished results.

-(1 → 4)-β-D-Xyl$p$-(1 → 4)-(β-D-Xyl$p$)$_n$-(1 → 4)-β-D-Xyl$p$-(1 → 4)-
　　　　3　　　　　　　　　　　　　　　　　2(or 3)
　　　　↑　　　　　　　　　　　　　　　　　↑
　　L-Ara$f$-1　　　　　　　　　　(4-Me-)α-D-GpA-1

XVII

Polysaccharides of greater complexity are found among the hemicelluloses of corn cobs,[6,14,15,24,44,45] maize fiber[16,17 46] and maize hulls[18,19,47] (the materials from these two latter sources are similar, if not identical), wheat bran,[48-50] and barley husks.[11] These xylans contain non-terminal L-arabinose residues, present mainly, if not exclusively, in the furanose form. Barley-husk hemicellulose[11] is probably the least complex polysaccharide of this type. It is similar to the xylans of cereal straws and grasses (XVII) in carrying single-unit L-arabinofuranose and D-glucuronic acid side-chains joined to D-xylose by (1 → 3)- and (1 → 2)-linkages, respectively, but it carries, in addition, side-chains terminated by 2-O-β-D-xylopyranosyl-L-arabinofuranose units and linked as in VII or VIII.

The corn-cob hemicelluloses provide examples of several structural variations. One sample[38] carries only L-arabinofuranose residues as side-chains but contains a small proportion of D-glucose residues linked through positions 1, 3, and 4. Other samples may be separated into two main fractions differing in solubility in aqueous media.[51] The hemicellulose "A fraction" approximates more closely to a pure xylan,[6] but recent studies[15] indicate that it contains some of the structural features of the more complex "B fraction." The "B fraction" is similar to barley-husk hemicellulose[11] in having terminal and non-terminal L-arabinofuranosyl residues, the latter being present in 2-O-β-D-xylopyranosyl-L-arabinofuranosyl units. Both D-glucuronic acid and its 4-methyl ether are present as constituents of the polysaccharide and are probably attached as side-chains to xylan chains, since graded hydrolysis affords the two aldobiouronic acids O-(4-O-methyl-D-glucosyluronic acid)-(1→2)-D-xylose (IX)[44] and O-(D-glucosyluronic acid)-(1 → 2)-D-xylose (XVIII).[24] In addition, a third aldobiouronic acid (XIX)[24] and an aldotriouronic acid (XX)[45] have been isolated as products of partial acid hydrolysis. Although the role of these units (XIX and XX) in the

(44) R. L. Whistler, H. E. Conrad and L. Hough, J. Am. Chem. Soc., 76, 1668 (1954).

(45) R. L. Whistler and D. I. McGilvray, J. Am. Chem. Soc., 77, 1884 (1955).

(46) R. L. Whistler and W. M. Corbett, J. Org. Chem., 21, 694 (1956).

(47) R. Montgomery, F. Smith and H. C. Srivastava, J. Am. Chem. Soc., 78, 2837, 6169 (1956); R. Montgomery and F. Smith, ibid., 79, 695 (1957).

(48) G. A. Adams, Can. J. Chem., 33, 56 (1955).

(49) G. A. Adams and C. T. Bishop, J. Am. Chem. Soc., 78, 2842 (1956).

(50) J. Schmorak, C. T. Bishop and G. A. Adams, Can. J. Chem., 35, 108 (1957).

(51) R. L. Whistler, J. Bachrach and D. R. Bowman, Arch. Biochem., 19, 25 (1948); R. L. Whistler and G. E. Lauterbach, Arch. Biochem. Biophys., 77, 62 (1958).

polysaccharide structure has not yet been established, it is possible that they result from the termination of some xylan chains by D-glucuronic acid residues.

Maize-fiber (or maize-hull) hemicellulose is a polysaccharide of extreme structural complexity and is unusual amongst polysaccharides of land plants in containing L-galactose,[16,17,52] in addition to D-galactose, as a constituent sugar. Under relatively mild conditions of acid hydrolysis, it has been possible to isolate the following oligosaccharides: 3-O-α-D-xylopyranosyl-L-arabinose (XXI),[16,18] O-L-galactopyranosyl-(1 → 4)-D-xylopyranosyl-(1 → 2)-L-arabinose (XXII),[16] 4-O-β-D-galactopyranosyl-D-xylopyranose (XXIII),[18] 5-O-β-D-galactopyranosyl-L-arabinose (XXIV),[19,53] and xylobiose.[19] It is probable that the three oligosaccharides which contain reducing L-arabinose residues (XXI, XXII, and XXIV) are formed by cleavage of

$$\alpha\text{-D-Gp}A\text{-}(1 \to 2)\text{-D-Xyl}p \quad\quad \alpha\text{-D-Gp}A\text{-}(1 \to 4)\text{-D-Xyl}p$$

XVIII   XIX

$$\alpha\text{-D-Gp}A\text{-}(1 \to 4)\text{-}\beta\text{-D-Xyl}p\text{-}(1 \to 4)\text{-D-Xyl}p$$

XX

$$\alpha\text{-D-Xyl}p\text{-}(1 \to 3)\text{-L-Ara} \quad\quad \text{L-Gal}p\text{-}(1 \to 4)\text{-D-Xyl}p\text{-}(1 \to 2)\text{-L-Ara}$$

XXI   XXII

$$\beta\text{-D-Gal}p\text{-}(1 \to 4)\text{-D-Xyl}p \quad\quad \beta\text{-D-Gal}p\text{-}(1 \to 5)\text{-L-Ara}f$$

XXIII   XXIV

L-arabinofuranosyl linkages through which they are attached as side-chains to the xylan backbone. 4-O-D-Galactopyranosyl-D-xylopyranose (XXIII) probably *also* arises from a side-chain, as methylation studies have shown that both D- and L-galactose residues are present in the polysaccharide as end groups only.[17] The xylobiose presumably represents a fragment of one of the main xylan chains. Although maize-fiber gum (or hemicellulose) contains a large variety of side-chain units, it has basal chains similar to those of other xylans, since a degraded polysaccharide composed solely of residues of D-xylose and D-glucuronic acid may be isolated after cleavage of the more acid-labile side-chains.[46] The majority of the D-glucuronic acid residues are present as single-unit side-chains attached to D-xylose in the main chains by the common (1 → 2)-linkages.[47]

Wheat-bran hemicellulose[48-50] is another polysaccharide in which L-arab-

(52) L-Galactose is a common constituent of seaweed polysaccharides [see T. Mori, *Advances in Carbohydrate Chem.*, **8**, 316 (1954)], but it has been found previously only in linseed mucilage [E. Anderson and H. J. Lowe, *J. Biol. Chem.*, **168**, 289 (1947)] amongst land plants.

(53) I. J. Goldstein, F. Smith and H. C. Srivastava, *J. Am. Chem. Soc.*, **79**, 3858 (1957).

inose residues, present in a variety of forms of combination, are linked to essentially linear chains of $(1 \to 4)$-linked β-D-xylopyranose residues. This material is unique amongst polysaccharides of the xylan group in containing a higher proportion of L-arabinose than of D-xylose residues.[48] L-Arabinose occurs in the furanose form as nonreducing end-groups and in nonterminal positions linked through positions 1 and 3, and possibly also provides branching points where it is linked through positions 1, 2, and 3, and 1, 2, and 5 (or 4). Graded hydrolysis of wheat-bran hemicellulose results in the formation of a linear degraded xylan still containing D-glucuronic acid residues[50] and is accompanied by removal of all the L-arabinose and some of the D-xylose residues. Since the hemicellulose contains a high proportion of D-xylopyranose end-groups, it is probable that some of these terminate L-arabinose-containing side-chains and are removed during the graded hydrolysis. D-Glucuronic acid and 4-O-methyl-D-glucuronic acid are constituents of the polysaccharide, and both sugars are glycosidically linked to position 2 of D-xylose.[49]

In addition to these various xylans which occur as structural polysaccharides in lignified tissues, xylans containing a high proportion of L-arabinose units are found in the so-called "gum fractions" of the flour and grain of cereals.[54] Although the biological function of these polysaccharides is not yet known, it is almost certainly different from that of the xylans from plant cell-walls, despite the presence of common structural features. The first detailed chemical study of such a material was carried out on a polysaccharide found in association with wheat β-amylase.[55] This was shown to be a highly branched molecule containing L-arabinofuranose, D-xylopyranose, and D-galactopyranose units. More recently, the cereal gums have been re-examined and shown to contain D-glucose, D-xylose, and L-arabinose as the main constituent sugars, together with smaller proportions of D-galactose and D-mannose.[56] The main components may be separated by fractional precipitation from aqueous solution with ammonium sulfate[56] or by fractionation of the derived acetylated polysaccharides.[7,13,57,58] Two main structural types have so far been encountered, linear β-glucans with $(1 \to 3)$- and $(1 \to 4)$-linkages (particularly from barley[59] and oats[60,61]) and arabinoxylans (particularly from wheat[7,55,57,58] and rye[10a,12]).

(54) I. A. Preece, "Cereal Carbohydrates," The Royal Institute of Chemistry, London, 1957.

(55) L. H. Ford and S. Peat, J. Chem. Soc., 856 (1941).

(56) I. A. Preece and K. G. Mackenzie, J. Inst. Brewing, **58**, 353, 457 (1952).

(57) R. Montgomery and F. Smith, J. Am. Chem. Soc., **77**, 2834 (1955).

(58) R. Montgomery and F. Smith, J. Am. Chem. Soc., **77**, 3325 (1955).

(59) G. O. Aspinall and R. G. J. Telfer, J. Chem. Soc., 3519 (1954).

(60) L. Acker, W. Diemair and E. Samhammer, Z. Lebensm.-Untersuch. u.-Forsch., **100**, 180 (1955); **102**, 225 (1955).

(61) S. Peat, W. J. Whelan and J. G. Roberts, J. Chem. Soc., 3916 (1957).

In some cases, α-linked glucan fractions have also been isolated,[56,62] and the preliminary investigations suggest that these consist mainly of starch-like polysaccharides.

The cereal-gum arabinoxylans contain linear chains of $(1 \rightarrow 4)$-linked β-D-xylopyranosyl residues, and all the L-arabinose residues occur as end groups in the furanose form and are probably all attached as single-unit side-chains. Some D-xylose residues carry single side-chains through one position only (usually position 3), but others are present as double branch-points (carrying *two* L-arabinofuranose units). The general structure of these arabinoxylans is shown in XXV. Two such polysaccharides have been isolated from wheat endosperm, one being soluble in water[58]; the other is water-insoluble and associated with the "squeegee fraction" of the flour,[57] but the same type of structure is found in both polymers. Mixtures of water-soluble and water-insoluble polysaccharides are also found in other cereals,[63] but the detailed structures of the water-insoluble polysaccharides have not yet been investigated.

L-Ara$f$-1   L-Ara$f$-1

↓   ↓

3(or 2)   3

-$(1 \rightarrow 4)$-β-D-Xyl$p$-$(1 \rightarrow 4)$-β-D-Xyl$p$-$(1 \rightarrow 4)$-β-D-Xyl$p$-$(1 \rightarrow 4)$-

2

↑

L-Ara$f$-1

XXV

Some of the main structural features of the xylans isolated from the *Gramineae* are outlined in Table I.

2. *Xylans from Woods*

Analyses of the hemicelluloses of woods indicate the presence of a high proportion of D-xylose residues in association with those of a methyl ether of a hexuronic acid.[64] The first evidence for the chemical structure of such wood xylans came from the isolation of xylobiose, xylotriose,[65] and the aldobiouronic acid O-(4-O-methyl-α-D-glucosyluronic)-$(1 \rightarrow 2)$-D-xylose acid (IX)[22] from partial hydrolyzates of aspen wood. The role of such oligosaccharide fragments in wood xylans became more apparent as the result of a study of a xylan from European beechwood,[26] in which it was shown

---

(62) K. A. Gilles, W. O. S. Meredith and F. Smith, *Cereal Chem.*, **29**, 314 (1952).

(63) I. A. Preece and R. Hobkirk, *J. Inst. Brewing*, **60**, 490 (1954).

(64) M. H. O'Dwyer, *Biochem. J.*, **33**, 713 (1939); **34**, 149 (1940); for further references, see reviews cited in Ref. 1.

(65) J. K. N. Jones and L. E. Wise, *J. Chem. Soc.*, 2750 (1952).

that the polysaccharide is composed of chains of $(1 \rightarrow 4)$-linked β-D-xylo-pyranose residues, with approximately every tenth D-xylose residue carry-ing (through position 2) single 4-O-methyl-D-glucuronic acid residues at-tached as side-chains. All the wood xylans subsequently examined have been of the same general type and may be represented by the partial structure XXVI. The various wood xylans differ slightly in average molec-ular size and in the proportion of hexuronic acid residues attached as side-

$$-(1 \rightarrow 4)\text{-}\beta\text{-D-Xyl}p\text{-}(1 \rightarrow 4)\text{-}\beta\text{-D-Xyl}p\text{-}(1 \rightarrow 4)\text{-}\beta\text{-D-Xyl}p\text{-}(1 \rightarrow 4)\text{-}$$

$$2$$

$$\uparrow$$

$$\text{4-Me-}\alpha\text{-D-G}p\text{A-1}$$

XXVI

chains. In general, the proportion of residues of 4-O-methyl-D-glucuronic acid is higher in the soft-wood xylans (about 15–20 %) than in those from hard woods (8–15 %). Several of these wood xylans probably contain linear xylan chains, since there is present only one D-xylopyranose end-group per molecule. The xylan from Loblolly pine,[65a] however, must contain a branched xylan chain, since there are present three D-xylopyranose end-groups per molecule, and it is probable that the xylan from North American beech-wood[66] also contains branching in the backbone. On the other hand, in oak-heartwood xylan,[67] there is present less than one D-xylopyranose end-group per molecular chain, and it is possible that some xylan chains may be terminated by hexuronic acid residues. The xylan component of aspen hemicellulose[68] also contains minor structural features which are not yet fully explained; for example, D-glucose residues linked through positions 1 and 4, and D-xylose residues linked through positions 1 and 2 only, are associated with hexuronic acids, probably as constituents of aldobiouronic acid units.

Wood xylans are characterized by the presence of residues of 4-O-methyl-D-glucuronic acid linked to position 2 of D-xylose in the main xylan chains (XXVI), and, accordingly, the aldobiouronic acid, O-(4-O-methyl-α-D-glu-cosyluronic acid)-$(1 \rightarrow 2)$-D-xylose (IX), is commonly isolated after the graded hydrolysis of such xylans. Partial acid hydrolysis of Monterey pine wood[69] furnishes this compound together with the isomeric aldobiouronic acid, O-(4-O-methyl-α-D-glucosyluronic acid)-$(1 \rightarrow 3)$-D-xylose, as a minor product, but the role of the $(1 \rightarrow 3)$-linked aldobiouronic acid unit in the

(65a) J. K. N. Jones and T. J. Painter, *J. Chem. Soc.*, 573 (1959).

(66) G. A. Adams, *Can. J. Chem.*, **35,** 556 (1957).

(67) G. O. Aspinall, M. E. Carter, R. A. Laidlaw and J. Sandstrom, unpublished results; M. E. Carter, Ph. D. Thesis, Edinburgh, Scotland (1956).

(68) J. K. N. Jones, E. Merler and L. E. Wise, *Can. J. Chem.*, **35,** 634 (1957).

(69) D. J. Brasch and L. E. Wise, *Tappi*, **39,** 581, 768 (1956).

TABLE I

Xylans from the Gramineae

Source	Mode of linkage of L-arabinofuranose end-groups[a]	Mode of linkage of D-glucuronic acid end-groups[b]	Other structural features	References
Esparto grass	none present	none present		31
Esparto grass	$(1 \to 3)$-D-Xylp	none present	β-D-Xylp-$(1 \to 2)$-L-Ara branched xylan chain	20, 33
Wheat straw	$(1 \to 3)$-D-Xylp	$(1 \to 3)$-D-Xylp (Me)		9, 10, 23 27, 36
Wheat straw	$(1 \to 3)$-D-Xylp	$(1 \to 2)$-D-Xylp		37, 37a
Wheat straw	$(1 \to 3)$-D-Xylp	none present	···4-D-Gp-1··· 3 · ·	38
Wheat straw	none present	$(1 \to 2)$-D-Xylp		40
Wheat straw	$(1 \to 3)$-D-Xylp	$(1 \to 2)$-D-Xylp (Me)	some branched xylan chains	39
Oat straw	$(1 \to 3)$-D-Xylp	$(1 \to 2)$-D-Xylp (Me)		42
Cocksfoot grass	$(1 \to 3)$-D-Xylp	$(1 \to 2)$-D-Xylp (Me)		43
Wheat leaf	$(1 \to 3)$-D-Xylp	(?) $(1 \to 3)$-D-Xylp		41
Barley husks	$(1 \to 3)$-D-Xylp	$(1 \to 2)$-D-Xylp (Me)	β-D-Xylp-$(1 \to 2)$-L-Araf branched xylan chain ···2-L-Araf-1···	11
Corn (maize) cobs	$(1 \to 3)$-D-Xylp	not known		6, 15, 51

Source	Linkages	(1 → 2)-D-Xylp (Me)	Side chains	References
Corn (maize) cobs	(1 → 3)-D-Xylp	(1 → 2)-D-Xylp (Me)	β-D-Xylp-(1 → 2)-L-Araf	6, 14, 15
Corn (maize) cobs	(1 → 3)-D-Xylp; (1 → 4)-D-Xylp	none present	···4-D-Gp-1··· 3 · · ·	24, 44, 45 38
Maize fiber	(1 → 3)-D-Xylp	not known	α-D-Xylp-(1 → 3)-L-Ara L-Galp-(1 → 4)-D-Xylp-(1 → 2)-L-Ara	16, 17
Maize hulls	not known	(1 → 2)-D-Xylp	α-D-Xylp-(1 → 3)-L-Ara β-D-Galp-(1 → 4)-D-Xylp β-D-Galp-(1 → 5)-L-Araf	18, 19 47, 53
Wheat bran	(1 → 3)-D-Xylp (1 → 3)-D-Xylp-(2 ← 1)	(1 → 2)-D-Xylp	···3-L-Araf-1···	48-50
Wheat flour	(1 → 3)-D-Xylp (1 → 3)-D-Xylp-(2 ← 1)	none present		7, 55 57, 58
Barley flour	(1 → 3)-D-Xylp (1 → 2)-D-Xylp	none present		13, 62
Rye flour	(1 → 3)-D-Xylp-(2 ← 1) (1 → 3)-D-Xylp	none present		10a, 12

a D-Xylp = D-Xylopyranose, L-Araf = L-arabinofuranose, D-Gp = D-glucopyranose, and Galp = galactopyranose residues.
b (Me) indicates that D-glucuronic acid residues are present, wholly or in part, as the 4-methyl ether.

polysaccharide from which it is derived is not yet known. In addition to end groups of 4-O-methyl-D-glucuronic acid, some wood xylans contain a small proportion of L-arabinofuranose end-groups (for example, xylans from Western-hemlock,[70] aspen,[68] and European-larch[71] woods. These L-arabinofuranose end-units are probably attached to the main xylan chains by (1 → 3)-linkages, and, although it is not yet certain whether these are attached directly or through one or more (1 → 4)-linked D-xylose residues, the former

TABLE II

Xylans from Woods

Source	Chain length[a]	DP_n , method[b]		Nature of xylan chain	Other structural features	References
European beech	75	69	*id*	linear		26
American beech	25	47[c]		branched		66
Aspen					L-Ara$f$-1 ⋯ ⋯2-D-Xyl$p$-1⋯ ⋯4-D-Gp-1⋯	68
European oak		about 110	*op*	linear		67
White birch	130	110	*op*	linear		72
White elm	145	133	*op*	linear		72a
Sugar maple	149	127	*op*	linear		72b
Western hemlock					L-Ara$f$-1⋯	70, 73
Norway spruce	99	101	*op*	linear		74
European larch	98	107	*id*	linear	L-Ara$f$-1⋯	71
Loblolly pine	26	77	*op*	branched		65a

[a] By methylation end-group assay. [b] Number-average degree of polymerization of methylated polysaccharide by *id* (isothermal distillation) or *op* (osmotic pressure) methods. [c] Viscosity-average degree of polymerization.

alternative seems more likely, as this mode of linkage is found in other xylans.

Some of the structural features of wood xylans are summarized in Table II.

Xylans from other woods have been studied in somewhat less detail, but the available evidence suggests that the xylans from Japanese elm,[75]

(70) G. G. S. Dutton and F. Smith, *J. Am. Chem. Soc.*, **78,** 3744 (1956).

(71) G. O. Aspinall and J. E. McKay, *J. Chem. Soc.*, 1059 (1958).

(72) C. P. J. Glaudemans and T. E. Timell, *J. Am. Chem. Soc.*, **80,** 941 (1958).

(72a) J. K. Gillham and T. E. Timell, *Can. J. Chem.*, **36,** 410, 1467 (1958).

(72b) T. E. Timell, *Can. J. Chem.*, **37,** 893 (1959).

(73) G. G. S. Dutton and F. Smith, *J. Am. Chem. Soc.*, **78,** 2505 (1956).

(74) G. O. Aspinall and M. E. Carter, *J. Chem. Soc.*, 3744 (1956).

(75) I. Tachi and N. Yamamori, *Nippon Nôgei-kagaku Kaishi*, **25,** 12, 130, 262 (1951–52).

European birch,[76] maple,[77] Scots pine,[78] maritime pine,[79] slash pine,[80] southern pine,[81] black spruce,[78] Sitka spruce,[82] and white spruce[83] contain the same main structural features.

The xylans from both hard and soft woods, and also from other dicotyledonous plants (see later), are characterized by side-chains of 4-O-methyl-D-glucuronic acid, but in some cases small proportions of L-arabinofuranose side-chains are also present; and the xylans from cereals and grasses are characterized by L-arabinofuranose side-chains, but, in many instances, side-chains of D-glucuronic acid or its 4-methyl ether are also present. It is clear, therefore, that there is no marked structural division between the two groups of xylans. Furthermore, in both groups the sugar residues attached as side-chains show the same preferred modes of linkage to the xylan backbone, namely L-arabinose by (1 → 3)- and D-glucuronic acid by (1 → 2)-linkages.

3. Other Xylans

Two xylans from dicotyledonous plants, namely, from straw of flax (*Linum usitatissimum*)[84] and from jute,[85,85a] possess the same essential structure (XXVI) as that of the wood xylans. Like several wood xylans, flax-straw xylan[84] contains small proportions of associated L-rhamnose residues, and hydrolysis of the methylated polysaccharide gives rise, among other compounds, to 2,4-di-O-methyl-L-rhamnose, but there is no positive evidence that these L-rhamnose residues are an integral part of the xylan. Contrary to earlier reports[86] that partial hydrolysis of jute hemicellulose yields the aldobiouronic acid, (3-O-methyl-D-glucopyranosyluronic acid)-(1→3)-D-xylose, it has now been shown[85,85a] that the acidic disaccharide is the common (4-O-methyl-D-glucosyluronic acid)-(1 → 2)-D-xylose (IX).[85,85a] Some degree of branching in the xylan chains is indicated. The hemicelluloses from milkweed floss[86a] and kapok[86b] are very similar to jute hemicellulose and also contain branched xylan chains.

(76) J. Saarnio, K. Wathen and C. Gustafsson, *Acta Chem. Scand.*, **8**, 825 (1954).

(77) L. G. Neubauer and C. B. Purves, *Can. J. Chem.*, **35**, 388 (1957).

(78) A. R. N. Gorrod and J. K. N. Jones, *J. Chem. Soc.*, 2522 (1954).

(79) A. Roudier and L. Eberhard, *Tappi*, **38**, No. 9, 156A (1955); *Compt. rend.*, 1505 (1958).

(80) R. L. Whistler and G. N. Richards, *J. Am. Chem. Soc.*, **80**, 4888 (1958).

(81) J. K. Hamilton, E. V. Partlow and N. S. Thompson, *Tappi*, **41**, 803, 811 (1958).

(82) G. G. S. Dutton and K. Hunt, *J. Am. Chem. Soc.*, **80**, 4420 (1958).

(83) G. A. Adams, *Can. J. Chem.*, **37**, 29 (1959).

(84) J. D. Geerdes and F. Smith, *J. Am. Chem. Soc.*, **77**, 3569, 3572 (1955).

(85) G. O. Aspinall and P. C. Das Gupta, *J. Chem. Soc.*, 3627 (1958).

(85a) H. C. Srivastava and G. A. Adams, *Chem. & Ind.* (London), 920 (1958).

(86) P. B. Sarkar, A. K. Mazumder and K. B. Pal, *Textile Research J.*, **22**, 529 (1952); P. C. Das Gupta and P. B. Sarkar, *ibid.*, **24**, 705 (1954).

(86a) F. W. Barth and T. E. Timell, *J. Am. Chem. Soc.*, **80**, 6320 (1958).

One of the first acidic xylans to receive a detailed investigation was that from New Zealand "flax" (*Phormium tenax*)[87] [a monocotyledonous plant entirely unrelated to flax (*Linum* sp.)], for which polysaccharide the following partial structure (XXVII) was advanced. The experimental evidence is also consistent with the direct attachment of D-glucuronic acid residues

$$-(1 \rightarrow 4)\text{-}\beta\text{-}D\text{-Xyl}p\text{-}(1 \rightarrow 4)\text{-}\beta\text{-}D\text{-Xyl}p\text{-}(1 \rightarrow 4)\text{-}\beta\text{-}D\text{-Xyl}p\text{-}(1 \rightarrow 4)\text{-}$$
$$2$$
$$\uparrow$$
$$\text{D-Gp}A\text{-}(1 \rightarrow 4)\text{-}\beta\text{-}D\text{-Xyl}p\text{-}1$$

XXVII

to the xylan backbone (XXVI), and, in view of the widespread occurrence of this latter type of structure, the former structure is unlikely. It is not known whether the hexuronic acid residues are those of D-glucuronic acid or of its 4-methyl ether.

Other xylans containing hexuronic acid residues are those from pear cell-walls[88] and peanut shells.[89] The former xylan contains only a small proportion of D-glucuronic acid residues, and, although these are linked directly to the xylan chain, the (1 → 3)-linkage cannot be considered as finally established. Peanut-shell hemicellulose[89] is typical of the xylans from dicotyledonous plants in carrying single-unit side-chains of D-glucuronic acid joined to the backbone by (1 → 2)-linkages, but in this case the hexuronic acid is not present as the methyl ether.

III. Mannans and Glucomannans

Polysaccharides based on D-mannose as the major structural unit occur in woods and in the seeds of many plants. Although polysaccharides from the latter sources are often classified as seed mucilages, this term is unsatisfactory and, in view of close similarities in structure, the two groups of polysaccharides may be considered together.

Mannans and glucomannans from plant sources all contain linear chains of (1 → 4)-linked β-D-mannose and β-D-glucose residues as their main structural features. The only true mannans (that is, polysaccharides containing 95% or more of D-mannose residues) so far examined from land plants are those from vegetable ivory (*Phytelephas macrocarpa*).[90-95] The

---

(86b) A. L. Currie and T. E. Timell, *Can. J. Chem.*, **37**, 922 (1959).

(87) R. J. McIlroy, *J. Chem. Soc.*, 121 (1949); R. J. McIlroy, G. S. Holmes and R. P. Mauger, *ibid.*, 796 (1945).

(88) S. K. Chanda, E. L. Hirst and E. G. V. Percival, *J. Chem. Soc.*, 1240 (1951).

(89) B. Radhakrishnamurthy and V. R. Srinivasan, *Proc. Indian Acad. Sci.*, **46A**, 53 (1957).

(90) F. Klages, *Ann.*, **509**, 159 (1934); **512**, 185 (1934).

(91) G. O. Aspinall, E. L. Hirst, E. G. V. Percival and I. R. Williamson, *J. Chem. Soc.*, 3184 (1953).

claims to have isolated mannans from spruce sulfite-pulp[96] and spruce holocellulose[97] have not been substantiated by determination of the composition of the polysaccharides. Indeed, in the light of the failure of subsequent attempts to obtain true mannans by the fractionation of wood glucomannans,[98-100] it is probable that the spruce polysaccharides were glucomannans. Similarly, it has yet to be shown that salep mannan[101,102] (isolated from the tubers of various species of orchids) is composed solely of D-mannose residues. A true mannan has, however, been isolated from the seaweed alga *Porphyra umbilicalis*[103] and this contains chains of $(1 \rightarrow 4)$-linked β-D-mannopyranose residues.

Several mannans and glucomannans contain, in addition, a small proportion of D-galactose residues. Since these are found mainly as nonreducing end-groups, it is clear that they are integral parts of the mannans or glucomannans, although there is no evidence yet to indicate whether the D-galactose residues are attached as single-unit side-chains to a $(1 \rightarrow 4)$-linked mannan backbone, as in galactomannans like guaran.[104]

1. *Mannans*

Two mannans may be isolated from ivory nuts. Mannan A, which is extracted with alkali, occurs in granular form,[94,95] and x-ray diffraction photographs of both the native and the extracted polysaccharide show distinct crystalline patterns.[95] Mannan B cannot, however, be extracted directly, and it is separated from cellulose by precipitation from cuprammonium solution.[91] In the plant, mannan B is built up of microfibrils analogous to those of cellulose, but the extracted polysaccharide shows no tendency to crystallize on precipitation.[95]

Although unresolved problems of fine structure still remain, no essential differences in chemical structure have yet been revealed between the two

(92) G. O. Aspinall, R. B. Rashbrook and G. Kessler, *J. Chem. Soc.*, 215 (1958).

(93) T. E. Timell, *Can. J. Chem.*, **35**, 333 (1957).

(94) H. Meier, *Electron Microscopy, Proc. Stockholm Conf. 1956*, 298 (1957).

(95) H. Meier, *Biochim. et Biophys. Acta*, **28**, 229 (1958).

(96) K. Hess and M. Lüdtke, *Ann.*, **466**, 18 (1928).

(97) E. Husemann, *J. prakt. Chem.*, **155**, 13 (1940).

(98) J. K. Hamilton, H. W. Kircher and N. S. Thompson, *J. Am. Chem. Soc.*, **78**, 2508 (1956).

(99) T. E. Timell and A. Tyminski, *Tappi*, **40**, 519 (1957).

(100) B. Lindberg and H. Meier, *Svensk Papperstidn.*, **60**, 785 (1957).

(101) H. Pringsheim and A. Genin, *Z. physiol. Chem., Hoppe-Seyler's*, **140**, 299 (1924).

(102) F. Klages and R. Maurenbrecher, *Ann.*, **535**, 175 (1938).

(103) J. K. N. Jones, *J. Chem. Soc.*, 3292 (1950).

(104) R. L. Whistler and Z. F. Ahmed, *J. Am. Chem. Soc.*, **72**, 2254 (1950); R. L. Whistler and J. L. Stein, *ibid.*, **73**, 4187 (1951); R. L. Whistler and D. F. Durso, *ibid.*, **73**, 4189 (1951); **74**, 5140 (1952); R. L. Whistler and C. G. Smith, *ibid.*, **74**, 3795 (1952).

mannans. The presence of chains of $(1 \rightarrow 4)$-linked β-D-mannopyranose residues was first established by Klages,[90] who obtained 2,3,6-tri-O-methyl-D-mannose as the main product of hydrolysis of *both* methylated polysaccharides. In more recent studies, a second trimethyl ether of D-mannose (probably the 2,3,4 isomer) was isolated as a minor product of hydrolysis of methylated mannans A *and* B, and the presence of some $(1 \rightarrow 6)$-linkages was indicated.[91] However, no oligosaccharides containing $(1 \rightarrow 6)$-linked D-mannose residues could be detected amongst the products of partial acid hydrolysis of the polysaccharides,[92] and confirmatory evidence for this mode of linkage is still awaited. In addition to end groups of D-mannose, the small proportion of D-galactose residues in the mannans are found exclusively as nonreducing end-groups.[91] Further evidence for the main type of linkage comes from the isolation of β-D-$(1 \rightarrow 4)$-linked mannobiose (XXVIII), mannotriose (XXIX), and higher homologs, as the major products of partial acid hydrolysis.[92] In addition, small proportions of two other series of oligosaccharides were isolated in these experiments. One series (XXX) contained D-glucose residues at the reducing end of the molecules, and it is not known if these oligosaccharides are of structural significance and account for the small proportion of D-glucose residues in the purified mannans or whether the D-glucose residues arise from inadvertent epimerization of mannose residues. The second series (XXXI) of oligosaccharides contained some $(1 \rightarrow 4)$-linked α-D-mannopyranose residues, and this finding indicated a previously unsuspected feature of the polysaccharides. There is no evidence that these α-linkages are formed by reversion or by acid-catalyzed anomerization at the glycosidic bond during acetolysis.[92]

$$\beta\text{-D-Man}p\text{-}(1 \rightarrow 4)\text{-D-Man}p$$

XXVIII

$$\beta\text{-D-Man}p\text{-}(1 \rightarrow 4)\text{-}\beta\text{-D-Man}p\text{-}(1 \rightarrow 4)\text{-D-Man}p$$

XXIX

$$\beta\text{-D-Man}p\text{-}(1 \rightarrow 4)\text{-}(\beta\text{-D-Man}p)_n\text{-}(1 \rightarrow 4)\text{-D-G}p$$

XXX

$$\alpha\text{-D-Man}p\text{-}(1 \rightarrow 4)\text{-}(\beta\text{-D-Man}p)_n\text{-}(1 \rightarrow 4)\text{-D-Man}p$$

XXXI

Clearly, two morphologically distinct mannans occur in ivory nuts, and, although both polysaccharides contain the same chemical features, there is evidence that they differ in molecular size. Thus, nitration of ivory-nut shavings followed by fractionation of the polysaccharide nitrates affords mannans in two quite different molecular-weight ranges.[93] Osmotic-pressure measurements on mannan A nitrate and on mannan B nitrate gave values for the number-average degrees of polymerization of 17–21 and 80, respectively.[95] A comparison of these values with those found for the chain lengths of the mannans by methylation end-group assay cannot properly be made until the nature of the structural heterogeneity is ascertained. It is not known whether two linear molecular species are present, terminated at the nonreducing end by residues of D-mannopyranose and D-galactopyranose or whether some mannan chains are linear while others carry the D-galactose units as side-chains. Furthermore, it is not known if the anomalous [?(1 → 6)-] linkages are present in all the mannan chains or only in some. Assuming all the chains to be linear, whether terminated by D-mannose or D-galactose, the methylation studies gave average chain-lengths of 10–13 for mannan A and 38–40 for mannan B.[91] On the other hand, assuming all chains to be terminated by D-mannose residues, and D-galactose residues to be attached as side-chains, the values for average chain-lengths are 12–16 and 75–80, respectively.

2. Glucomannans

Glucomannans of the same general structural type occur (a) in the seeds of various land-plants, (b) in close association with cellulose in coniferous woods, and (c) to a lesser extent in some hardwoods. In polysaccharides from both sources, the basic features are chains of (1 → 4)-linked β-D-mannopyranose and β-D-glucopyranose residues. Where the disaccharides, 4-O-β-D-mannopyranosyl-D-glucopyranose (XXXII) and 4-O-β-D-glucopyranosyl-D-mannopyranose (XXXIII), have been isolated as products of partial acid hydrolysis, it is known that true glucomannans are present rather than mixtures of closely related mannans and glucans. The possibility of some degree of structural heterogeneity (for example, glucomannans and mannans, or glucomannans with differing proportions of the constituent sugars) in these hemicellulose fractions cannot yet be excluded. Furthermore, it is not yet known whether D-mannose and D-glucose residues are linked in a regular or a random manner.

$$\beta\text{-D-Man}p\text{-}(1 \to 4)\text{-D-G}p$$

XXXII

$$\beta\text{-D-G}p\text{-}(1 \to 4)\text{-D-Man}p$$

XXXIII

Iles mannan, isolated from some *Amorphophallus* species, has been shown to be a mixture of a glucomannan and a starch-like α-glucan, from which the glucomannan may be separated by means of its insoluble copper complex.[105] The glucomannan contains chains of $(1 \to 4)$-linked β-D-manno-pyranose (70%) and β-D-glucopyranose (30%) residues. Cellobiose *and* the two disaccharides containing both D-mannose and D-glucose residues (XXXII and XXXIII) have been isolated as products of partial acid hydrolysis.[106] Surprisingly, neither mannobiose (XXVIII) nor mannotriose (XXIX) was detected on partial hydrolysis, but the available evidence requires the presence of adjacent D-mannose residues in the polysaccharides, as in partial structure XXXIV.

$-(1 \to 4)\text{-}(\beta\text{-D-Man}p)_4\text{-}(1 \to 4)\text{-}(\beta\text{-D-G}p)_2\text{-}(1 \to 4)\text{-}$

$(\beta\text{-D-Man}p)_4\text{-}(1 \to 4)\text{-}(\beta\text{-D-G}p)_2\text{-}(1 \to 4)\text{-}$

XXXIV

Similarly-constituted glucomannans have been isolated from various species of iris seeds[107] and lily bulbs,[108] the polysaccharides containing D-glucose and D-mannose residues in the proportions 1:1.1 and 1:1.9, respectively. The iris-seed glucomannans also contain a small proportion of D-galactopyranose end-groups.[107]

Glucomannans account for approximately half the hemicellulose fractions of coniferous woods. In general, they are less readily extracted with alkali than are the xylans, and some degree of separation of glucomannan from xylan may be effected by taking advantage of solubility differences. The glucomannan fractions more resistant to extraction with alkali may often be removed in the presence of added borate.[109] The different gluco-mannan fractions from the same source show only minor structural differences and no marked variations in degree of polymerization.[100,110] The fact that fractionation of glucomannans leads to fractions of the *same* composition (D-glucose and D-mannose in proportions of between 1:3 and 1:4) suggests that these polysaccharides are structurally homogeneous.[98–100,110] In some cases, however, glucomannans isolated by alkaline extraction are accompanied by a β-glucan which is probably a degraded cellulose.[71,111]

The first evidence for chemical linkage between D-mannose and D-glucose residues in wood polysaccharides came from the isolation, after partial hydrolysis of slash-pine α-cellulose,[112] of a disaccharide containing *both* sugar residues. Anthis[113] subsequently showed that two disaccharides, 4-O-β-D-

(105) P. A. Rebers and F. Smith, *J. Am. Chem. Soc.*, **76**, 6097 (1954).
(106) F. Smith and H. C. Srivastava, *J. Am. Chem. Soc.*, **78**, 1404 (1956).
(107) P. Andrews, L. Hough and J. K. N. Jones, *J. Chem. Soc.*, 1186 (1953).
(108) P. Andrews, L. Hough and J. K. N. Jones, *J. Chem. Soc.*, 181 (1956).
(109) J. K. N. Jones, L. E. Wise and J. P. Jaffe, *Tappi*, **39**, 139 (1956).
(110) I. Croon and B. Lindberg, *Acta Chem. Scand.*, **12**, 453 (1958).
(111) G. O. Aspinall, R. A. Laidlaw and R. B. Rashbrook, *J. Chem. Soc.*, 4444 (1957).
(112) J. G. Leech, *Tappi*, **35**, 249 (1952).
(113) A. Anthis *Tappi,*, **39**, 401 (1956).

glucopyranosyl-D-mannopyranose (XXXIII) and a mannosylglucose which may be 4-O-β-D-mannopyranosyl-D-glucopyranose (XXXII), may be isolated from this source. Structural investigations have been carried out on glucomannans isolated from the holocelluloses of Loblolly pine,[65a,113a] Sitka spruce,[111,113b] Norwegian spruce,[100,110] European larch,[114] and Western red cedar,[114a] and from Western-hemlock sulfite pulp.[98, 114b] In each case, from analysis either of the cleavage products of the methylated polysaccharides[65a,110,111,114,114a] or of the hydrolysis products of the reduced, periodate-oxidized polysaccharide,[98] it has been established that the glucomannans are composed of chains of (1 → 4)-linked β-D-mannopyranose and β-D-glucopyranose residues. 4-O-β-D-Mannopyranosyl-D-glucopyranose (XXXII), 4-O-β-D-glucopyranosyl-D-mannopyranose (XXXIII), mannobiose (XXVIII), and mannotriose (XXIX) have been characterized as partial-hydrolysis products of Loblolly-pine glucomannan.[113a] The absence of cellobiose from this mixture of oligosaccharides suggests that this glucomannan may contain only isolated D-glucose residues (as in partial structure XXXV), in contrast to Iles mannan[106] and to the glucomannan associated with wood cellulose from Western hemlock,[114b] which must contain blocks of at least two D-glucose residues. The glucomannans from woods of Loblolly pine,[65a] European larch,[114] and Western red cedar[114a] contain small proportions of D-galactopyranose end-groups, but it is not known how these are attached to mannan or glucomannan chains. Although only small proportions of D-mannose-containing polysaccharides occur in hardwoods, there is evidence that glucomannans of the same general type occur in aspen[68] and white-birch[114c] woods.

$$\cdots 4\text{-}\beta\text{-D-Man}p\text{-}(1 \rightarrow 4)\text{-}\beta\text{-D-G}p(1 \rightarrow 4)\text{-}(\beta\text{-D-Man}p)_3\text{-}(1 \rightarrow 4)\text{-}$$

XXXV

Wood glucomannans contain essentially linear structures, but it is not yet possible to make any general statement regarding the presence or absence of a small degree of branching in these polysaccharides. A comparison of number-average molecular weights and average chain-lengths of Sitka-spruce[111] and the two Norwegian-spruce[100,110] glucomannans suggests that the former is linear, whereas both the latter are branched. There is also the possibility of branching in a glucomannan isolated from unbleached, spruce pulp[115] by extraction with cuprammonia. This polysaccharide is

(113a) J. K. N. Jones and T. J. Painter, *J. Chem. Soc.*, 669 (1957).

(113b) G. G. S. Dutton and K. Hunt, *J. Am. Chem. Soc.*, **80**, 5697 (1958).

(114) G. O. Aspinall and J. E. McKay, unpublished results; J. E. McKay, Ph. D. Thesis, Edinburgh, Scotland (1958).

(114a) J. K. Hamilton and E. V. Partlow, *J. Am. Chem. Soc.*, **80**, 4880 (1958).

(114b) J. K. Hamilton and H. W. Kircher, *J. Am. Chem. Soc.*, **80**, 4703 (1958.)

(114c) J. K. Gillham and T. E. Timell, *Svensk Papperstidn.*, **61**, 540 (1958).

(115) E. Merler and L. E. Wise, *Tappi*, **41**, 80 (1958).

similar to other glucomannans, since partial acid hydrolysis affords mannobiose (XXVIII), mannotriose (XXIX), and 4-O-β-D-glucopyranosyl-D-
mannopyranose (XXXIII), together with other (incompletely identified)
oligosaccharides. Since not all the D-mannose and D-glucose residues are
attacked by periodate, this glucomannan must contain (1 → 3)-linkages
or branch points.

IV. GALACTANS AND ARABINOGALACTANS

Water-soluble arabinogalactans occur in many coniferous woods and are
present in largest proportion in larches. The polysaccharides of this type
so far studied are all highly branched, with (1 → 6)- and (1 → 3)-linked
D-galactopyranose residues predominating. The L-arabinose residues occur
as integral parts of arabinogalactans, and no evidence exists for the presence in woods of the pectic type of araban.[8] Although there are variations
in the relative proportions of L-arabinose and D-galactose residues in different fractions from the same source, no galactans *devoid* of arabinose
residues have been isolated from woods. Indeed, the only true galactans
known in land plants, namely, those from *Lupinus albus* pectin[116] and from
Strychnos nux vomica seeds,[117] are of an entirely different structural type in
containing essentially linear chains of (1 → 4)-linked β-D-galactopyranose
residues. However, the recent isolation of 4-O-β-D-galactopyranosyl-D-
galactopyranose from the partial, acid hydrolysis of white-birch α-cellu-
lose[114c,117a] suggests that a (1 → 4)-linked β-galactan may be present in this
wood. There is still uncertainty as to the degree of structural heterogeneity
in these polysaccharides, especially those from larch woods. Some of the
conflicting opinions as to the presence of one or more components in larch
ϵ-galactans[118] may be resolved by the demonstration that Western-larch
sapwood contains *two* water-soluble polysaccharides, whereas the heart-
wood contains only one.[119]

The most detailed structural studies to date have been carried out on
the arabinogalactans or ϵ-galactans from Western[120-124] and European[125-127]

(116) E. L. Hirst, J. K. N. Jones and W. O. Walder, *J. Chem. Soc.*, 1225 (1957).
(117) P. Andrews, L. Hough and J. K. N. Jones, *J. Chem. Soc.*, 806 (1954).
(117a) J. K. Gillham, A. S. Perlin and T. E. Timell, *Can. J. Chem.*, **36**, 1741 (1958).
(118) See Ref. 2, p. 203.
(119) G. L. Borgin, *J. Am. Chem. Soc.*, **71**, 2247 (1949).
(120) E. V. White, *J. Am. Chem. Soc.*, **63**, 2871 (1941).
(121) E. V. White, *J. Am. Chem. Soc.*, **64**, 302 (1942).
(122) E. V. White, *J. Am. Chem. Soc.*, **64**, 1507 (1942).
(123) E. V. White, *J. Am. Chem. Soc.*, **64**, 2838 (1942).
(124) H. Bouveng and B. Lindberg, *Acta Chem. Scand.*, **10**, 1515 (1956).
(125) W. G. Campbell, E. L. Hirst and J. K. N. Jones, *J. Chem. Soc.*, 774 (1948).
(126) J. K. N. Jones, *J. Chem. Soc.*, 1672 (1953).
(127) G. O. Aspinall, E. L. Hirst and E. Ramstad, *J. Chem. Soc.*, 593 (1958).

larches. An extensive investigation of Western-larch arabinogalactan was carried out by White.[120-123] The general character of the polysaccharide was indicated by the isolation of the methyl glycosides of 2,3,5-tri-O-methyl-L-arabinose,   2,3,4,6-tetra-O-methyl-D-galactose,   2,3,4-tri-O-methyl-D-galactose, and 2,4-di-O-methyl-D-galactose in the proportions of 1:2:1:3 on methanolysis of the methylated polysaccharide.[123] Evidence for the mode of attachment of the D-galactopyranose end-groups came from the isolation of the methyl glycosides of 2,3,4,6-tetra-O-methyl-β-D-galactopyranosyl-(1 $\rightarrow$ 6)-2,3,4-tri-O-methyl-D-galactopyranose and 2,3,4,6-tetra-O-methyl-β-D-galactopyranosyl-(1 $\rightarrow$ 6)-2,4-di-O-methyl-D-galactopyranose as products of the partial methanolysis of the methylated arabinogalactan. Formation of these compounds indicated the presence of the fragments XXXVI and XXXVII in the original polysaccharide.[121] As L-arabinofuranosyl linkages are more easily cleaved by acid than are D-galactopyranosyl linkages, a mild, acid hydrolysis of the arabinogalactan resulted in removal of some of the L-arabinose end-groups with relatively little modification of the galactan framework.[122] Hydrolysis of the derived, methylated, degraded arabinogalactan gave 2,3,4,6-tetra-, 2,3,4- and 2,4,6-tri-, and 2,4-di-O-methyl-D-galactose in the proportions of 2:1:1:2. The isolation of 2,4,6-tri-O-methyl-D-galactose in this experiment indicated the probable attachment of L-arabinofuranose residues to position 6 of a (1 $\rightarrow$ 3)-linked D-galactose residue. More direct evidence on this point is desirable, however, since the extent of modification of the galactan framework during the acid hydrolysis is not known.

β-D-Gal$p$-(1 $\rightarrow$ 6)-D-Gal$p$-1 $\cdots$

XXXVI

β-D-Gal$p$-(1 $\rightarrow$ 6)-D-Gal$p$-1 $\cdots$
3
.
.
.

XXXVII

On the basis of these results and of an analysis of the degraded, methylated polysaccharide remaining after partial methanolysis of the original methylated arabinogalactan,[123] White put forward the partial structure XXXVIII for the arabinogalactan.

Recent investigations by Bouveng and Lindberg[124] have shown that Western-larch arabinogalactan is more complex than previously supposed.

(127a) H. Bouveng and B. Lindberg, *Acta Chem. Scand.*, **12**, 1977 (1958).

(128) V. C. Barry and P. W. D. Mitchell, *J. Chem. Soc.*, 4020 (1954) and earlier papers.

$$
\begin{array}{ccc}
& \vdots & \\
& 6 & \\
\beta\text{-D-Gal}p\text{-1} & \cdots\text{3-D-Gal}p\text{-1} & \\
\downarrow & \downarrow & \\
6 & 6 &
\end{array}
$$

D-Galp-(1 → 3)-D-Galp-(1 → 3)-D-Galp-(1 → 3)-D-Galp-(1 → 6)-D-Galp-1···
    6   6
    ↑   ↑
   R-1   R-1

XXXVIII

(where R = D-Galp or L-Araf)

Under mild conditions of hydrolysis, 3-O-β-L-arabinopyranosyl-L-arabinose
(XXXIX) and 6-O-β-D-galactopyranosyl-D-galactose (XL) were isolated
as partial-hydrolysis products. The isolation of the arabinose-containing
disaccharide indicates that not all the L-arabinose residues are present as
end groups in the furanose form. Bouveng and Lindberg[124] have suggested
that the formation of the (1 → 6)-linked galactobiose (XL), under such
mild conditions of hydrolysis, results from cleavage of D-galactofuranosyl
linkages in the polysaccharide, but independent evidence for such furanosyl
linkages is not yet available. Similar treatment of the arabinogalactan from
European larch[126,127] gives rise to the same two disaccharides (XXXIX and
XL), but no evidence for the presence of D-galactofuranosyl residues in
the polysaccharide could be obtained.[127]

β-L-Arap-(1 → 3)-L-Ara

XXXIX

β-D-Galp-(1 → 6)-D-Galp

XL

Further investigations on the arabinogalactan from Western-larch heart-
wood by Bouveng and Lindberg[127a] have established the presence in this
material of *two* arabinogalactans (compare Ref. 119) which may be separated by fractional precipitation of their borate complexes with cetyltri-
methylammonium hydroxide. Methylation studies on the major component
have shown that this polysaccharide possesses a highly branched structure
with (1 → 3)- and (1 → 6)-linked D-galactopyranose residues, and with the
possibility of some (1 → 4)-linkages also being present. Two thirds of the
L-arabinose residues occur in the furanose form as end-groups, and the re-
mainder are present in 3-O-β-L-arabinopyranosyl-L-arabinofuranose units.

The first structural study of the arabinogalactan or ε-galactan from
European larch was carried out by Campbell, Hirst, and Jones,[125] who
showed the polysaccharide to contain residues of D-galactose and L-arabinose in the proportion of 6:1. Fractionation of the methylated polysaccharide gave, as the main component, a methylated galactan containing

only minimal quantities of L-arabinose residues, the remaining material being derived either from an arabinogalactan or from an araban and a second galactan. Hydrolysis of this main component gave equimolar proportions of 2,3,4,6-tetra-, 2,3,4-tri-, and 2,4-di-O-methyl-D-galactose, thus indicating a highly branched molecule for which several possible repeating units could be proposed (XLI, XLII, XLIII and their variants).

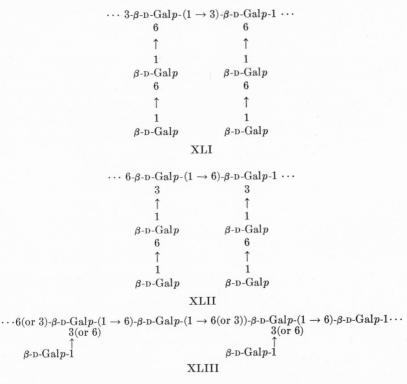

$$\cdots 3\text{-}\beta\text{-}\text{D-Gal}p\text{-}(1 \rightarrow 3)\text{-}\beta\text{-}\text{D-Gal}p\text{-}1 \cdots$$

6	6
↑	↑
1	1
β-D-Gal*p*	β-D-Gal*p*
6	6
↑	↑
1	1
β-D-Gal*p*	β-D-Gal*p*

XLI

$$\cdots 6\text{-}\beta\text{-}\text{D-Gal}p\text{-}(1 \rightarrow 6)\text{-}\beta\text{-}\text{D-Gal}p\text{-}1 \cdots$$

3	3
↑	↑
1	1
β-D-Gal*p*	β-D-Gal*p*
6	6
↑	↑
1	1
β-D-Gal*p*	β-D-Gal*p*

XLII

$$\cdots 6(\text{or } 3)\text{-}\beta\text{-}\text{D-Gal}p\text{-}(1 \rightarrow 6)\text{-}\beta\text{-}\text{D-Gal}p\text{-}(1 \rightarrow 6(\text{or } 3))\text{-}\beta\text{-}\text{D-Gal}p\text{-}(1 \rightarrow 6)\text{-}\beta\text{-}\text{D-Gal}p\text{-}1 \cdots$$

3(or 6)   3(or 6)
↑   ↑
β-D-Gal*p*-1   β-D-Gal*p*-1

XLIII

Further knowledge of the detailed structure of European-larch ε-galactan has come from later investigations.[126,127] In these studies, however, no evidence could be found for heterogeneity of the type previously encountered in the methylated derivative, and the ε-galactan itself was ultracentrifugally homogeneous.

In agreement with the earlier findings,[125] approximately equimolecular proportions of 2,3,4,6-tetra-, 2,3,4-tri-, and 2,4-di-O-methyl-D-galactopyranose were isolated as the main products of hydrolysis of methylated ε-galactan, but, in addition, small proportions of 2,3,4-tri-O-methyl-L-arabinose, 2,5-di-O-methyl-L-arabinose, and 2,4,6-tri- and 2-mono-O-methyl-D-galactose were found. Evidence in favor of partial structure XLI for the galactan framework was obtained by application to the polysaccharide of Barry's method of degradation.[128] Degradation of periodate-oxidized ε-galactan with phenylhydrazine gave a mixture of low molecular-weight phenylosazones plus a polysaccharide residue.[127] The isolation of the latter indicated the presence, in ε-galactan, of blocks of adjacent galactose units which are unattacked by periodate, and, accordingly, the various structures represented by XLIII may be rejected. Partial, acid hydrolysis of the polysaccharide residue gave 3-O-β-D-galactopyranosyl-D-galactose (XLIV) as the main disaccharide product, with only small proportions of the (1 → 6)-linked isomer (XL). It follows that a major part of the galactan structure is represented by XLI, in which each D-galactopyranose residue in a (1 → 3)-linked chain carries (through position 6) side-chains with an average of two (1 → 6)-linked D-galactopyranose residues. It is of interest that a similar type of distribution of D-galactopyranose residues containing (1 → 6)- and (1 → 3)-linkages is found in gum arabic[129] and *Acacia pycnantha* gum.[130]

$$\beta\text{-D-Gal}p\text{-}(1 \rightarrow 3)\text{-D-Gal}p$$

XLIV

$$\beta\text{-L-Ara}p\text{-}(1 \rightarrow 3)\text{-L-Ara}f\text{-}1 \cdots$$

XLV

Mild, acid hydrolysis of European-larch arabinogalactan results in the formation of 3-O-β-L-arabinopyranosyl-L-arabinose (XXXIX).[126] Although this disaccharide has been isolated as an acid-reversion product from L-arabinose,[131] it is accompanied under these conditions by two other arabinose-containing disaccharides, neither of which was detected in the larch polysaccharide hydrolyzate. Since hydrolysis of methylated ε-galactan gave approximately equimolar proportions of 2,3,4-tri-O-methyl-L-arabinose and 2,5-di-O-methyl-L-arabinose, traces of 2,3,5-tri-O-methyl-L-arabinose, and no mono-O-methyl-L-arabinose, it is clear that the L-arabinose units must arise from an arabinogalactan rather than from an arabinan, and that the majority of these must be present in 3-O-β-L-arabinopyranosyl-L-arabinofuranose side-chains (XLV) linked, in some way as yet unknown, to the framework of D-galactose units (XLI).

Other arabinogalactans from Jeffrey pine,[132] jack pine,[133] and white

(129) T. Dillon, D. F. O'Ceallachain and P. O'Colla, *Proc. Roy. Irish Acad.*, **55B,** 331 (1953); **57B,** 31 (1954); F. Smith and D. Spriestersbach, *Abstracts Papers Am. Chem. Soc.*, **128,** 15D (1955).

(130) G. O. Aspinall, E. L. Hirst and A. Nicolson, *J. Chem. Soc.*, 1697 (1959).

(131) J. K. N. Jones and W. H. Nicholson, *J. Chem. Soc.*, 27 (1958).

(132) W. H. Wadman, A. B. Anderson and W. Z. Hassid, *J. Am. Chem. Soc.*, **76,** 4097 (1954).

(133) C. T. Bishop, *Can. J. Chem.*, **35,** 1010 (1957).

spruce[134] have been studied, and the main modes of linkage of the constituent sugars have been established by characterization of the methylated sugars liberated on hydrolysis of the methylated polysaccharides. As with the larch arabinogalactans, the isolation of D-galactose as 2,3,4,6-tetra-, 2,3,4-tri-, and 2,4-di-methyl ethers on hydrolysis of the methylated polysaccharides indicates that similar, highly branched structures with (1 → 6)- and (1 → 3)-linkages are present. Jack-pine[133] and white-spruce[134] arabinogalactans both contain, as end groups, L-arabinose residues in the furanose form only. On the other hand, the Jeffrey-pine polysaccharide[132] contains a high proportion of L-arabinose residues, these being present both in terminal and non-terminal positions. Several of these polysaccharides contain small proportions (about 2%) of hexuronic acid residues, but it is not known whether the acidic groups are constituents of the arabinogalactans or whether they arise from minor contaminants.

V. OTHER POLYSACCHARIDES

In addition to the three main groups of polysaccharides based on D-xylose, D-mannose, and D-galactose, polysaccharides whose structural chemistry has been outlined in the previous Sections, brief reference will be made to polysaccharides which are based on other sugars and which occur in the cell walls of higher plants. Special mention may be made of D-glucose, for, in addition to its association with D-mannose as constituents of wood hemicelluloses, polymers of this sugar, other than starch and cellulose, have been discovered in the plant kingdom during recent years.

The water-soluble cereal gums[64] from barley and oats contain as major components β-glucans. Hydrolysis of methylated, barley β-glucan affords approximately equal proportions of 2,3,6- and 2,4,6-tri-O-methyl-D-glucose, thus indicating the presence of linear chains of β-D-glucopyranose residues with (1 → 4)- and (1 → 3)- linkages in equal proportions.[59] Although the detailed order of these two types of linkage is not known, some of the (1 → 3)-linked D-glucopyranose residues must be flanked by (1 → 4)-linked residues, as D-*arabino*-hexose phenylosazone has been isolated on degradation of the periodate-oxidized β-glucan.[135]

Oat β-glucan (or oat lichenin) is constituted similarly to the barley polysaccharide, but contains (1 → 4)- and (1 → 3)-linkages in the proportions of[60] 2:1 or[61] 3:1. Partial, acid hydrolysis of the polysaccharide yields cellobiose, laminaribiose, cellotriose, and the two trisaccharides XLVI and XLVII containing both (1 → 3)- and (1 → 4)-linkages.[61] On the basis of these results, the following partial structure (XLVIII) has been proposed.[61]

(134) G. A. Adams, *Can. J. Chem.*, **36**, 755 (1958).
(135) R. Montgomery and F. Smith, *J. Agr. Food Chem.*, **4**, 716 (1956); G. O. Aspinall, unpublished results.

$$\beta\text{-D-G}p\text{-}(1 \rightarrow 3)\text{-}\beta\text{-D-G}p\text{-}(1 \rightarrow 4)\text{-D-G}p$$

XLVI

$$\beta\text{-D-G}p\text{-}(1 \rightarrow 4)\text{-}\beta\text{-D-G}p\text{-}(1 \rightarrow 3)\text{-D-G}p$$

XLVII

$$\cdots 3\text{-}\beta\text{-D-G}p\text{-}(1 \rightarrow 4)\text{-}\beta\text{-D-G}p\text{-}(1 \rightarrow 4)\text{-}\beta\text{-D-G}p\text{-}(1 \rightarrow 3)\text{-}\beta\text{-D-G}p\text{-}(1 \rightarrow 4)\text{-}\beta\text{-D-G}p\text{-}1 \cdots$$

XLVIII

Callose[136] is a polysaccharide which accumulates on the sieve plates of the phloem of the grape vine. The low optical rotation of the polysaccharide, together with its resistance to attack by periodate, indicated that the major part of the molecular structure was composed of chains of $(1 \rightarrow 3)$-linked β-D-glucopyranosyl residues. The nature of the dominant linkage was confirmed by the isolation of 2,4,6-tri-O-methyl-D-glucose as the main product of hydrolysis of the methylated polysaccharide. A similar polysaccharide has been synthesized *in vitro* from uridine 5-(D-glucosyl dihydrogen pyrophosphate) using an enzyme preparation from mung-bean seedlings.[136a]

D-Galacturonic acid and L-rhamnose are often found as polysaccharide constituents in association with hemicelluloses. In some cases, D-galacturonic acid may arise from pectic acid, as this polysaccharide has been shown to occur in the inner bark of black spruce[137] and its presence in other woody tissues has been claimed.[138] The role of L-rhamnose as a polysaccharide component has not yet been demonstrated. L-Fucose has been isolated on hydrolysis of Scots-pine and black-spruce woods, and 3-O-methyl-L-rhamnose from black spruce.[81] 2-O-Methyl-D-xylose[139] and 2-O-methyl-L-fucose[140,140a] have been characterized as hydrolysis products of plum-leaf polysaccharides.[140a] These two sugars may, however, arise from pectic substances rather than from hemicelluloses, since they are also found on hydrolysis of pectins from sugar beet[141] and of sisal pectic acid.[142]

(136) G. O. Aspinall and G. Kessler, *Chem. & Ind.* (London), 1296 (1957); G. Kessler, *Ber. schweiz. botan. Ges.*, **68,** 5 (1958).

(136a) D. S. Feingold, E. F. Neufeld and W. Z. Hassid, *J. Biol. Chem.*, **233,** 783 (1958).

(137) W. W. Pigman, E. Anderson and R. L. Leaf, Jr., *J. Am. Chem. Soc.*, **70,** 432 (1948).

(138) Z. I. Kertesz, "The Pectic Substances," Interscience Publishers, Inc., New York, N. Y., 1951, pp. 328–329.

(139) P. Andrews and L. Hough, *Chem. & Ind.* (London), 1278 (1956).

(140) J. D. Anderson, P. Andrews and L. Hough, *Chem. & Ind.* (London), 1453 (1957).

(140a) P. Andrews and L. Hough, *J. Chem. Soc.*, 4476 (1958).

(141) P. Andrews, L. Hough, D. B. Powell and B. M. Woods, *J. Chem. Soc.*, 774 (1959).

(142) G. O. Aspinall and A. Cañas-Rodriguez, *J. Chem. Soc.*, 4020 (1958).

VI. Some Current Problems in Hemicellulose Chemistry

The primary aim of this article has been to outline recent progress in our knowledge of the structural chemistry of the hemicelluloses. However, in order that the present position may be seen in perspective, it is necessary to indicate some of the problems still receiving attention and to mention briefly a number of topics, a full consideration of which is outside the scope of the present review. The main *modes of linkage* of the sugar constituents of the hemicelluloses have now been established, although, in several instances, information regarding the *order of linkage* of the sugar units is still lacking. Probably the most urgent need, in this as in related fields, is for the development of methods for (a) the assessment of the extent of physical and chemical heterogeneity of those materials which have been examined, and (b) the fractionation, on a preparative scale, of closely-related molecular species. Here, a distinction must be made between three inter-related problems: (1) the separation of polysaccharides containing different sugar units or the same sugar units linked in different ways; (2) the separation of polysaccharides containing the same sugars linked in the same way but in different proportions; and (3) the determination of molecular weight distributions of polymer homologs. Difficulties arise, for example, in the application of established methods of polymer fractionation to the separation of hemicelluloses. It is never certain whether, in particular cases, such methods will differentiate between molecules on the grounds of molecular size or of chemical structure, or whether various types of cross-fractionation will occur.[143]

Electrophoretic methods offer considerable promise for the separation of different molecular species, and some separations have been effected using borate buffer.[144] Electrophoresis on glass-fiber paper[145] in alkali may prove a valuable diagnostic tool for assessing the degree of heterogeneity of polysaccharides, although the nature of the heterogeneity so revealed has not yet been demonstrated. An extension of this technique for preparative purposes would be of great value.

No complete picture of biological materials can be given without reference to their original condition in their natural environment. Brief consideration will, therefore, be given to the biosynthesis of the hemicelluloses and to their relationship, in the plant, to cellulose and lignin. Since much of our present knowledge of the chemistry of the hemicelluloses is based upon examination of materials isolated by alkaline extraction from plant tissues which, in many cases, have been previously treated to remove lig-

(143) See Ref. 29 and references there cited.

(144) K. W. Fuller and D. H. Northcote, *Biochem. J.*, **64**, 657 (1956).

(145) B. A. Lewis and F. Smith, *J. Am. Chem. Soc.*, **79**, 3929 (1957).

nin, the possibilities of chemical modification during isolation must be considered.

1. *Chemical Modification during Isolation*

The most complete extraction of hemicelluloses (of plant tissues) by alkali is only possible after removal of lignin. Indeed, in the case of coniferous woods (for example, Sitka spruce[146]), extraction of hemicelluloses is often impossible unless lignin has been previously removed. Of the two methods commonly employed for delignification, using chlorine[147] and acidified sodium chlorite,[148] respectively, the latter method probably has the greater degradative effect on both the residual cellulose[149] and the isolated hemicellulose.[150] It has been shown, for example, that xylans isolated by alkaline extraction of (a) white-spruce wood and (b) the corresponding chlorine holocellulose have similar average molecular weights, whereas the xylan extracted from the chlorite holocellulose has a markedly lower molecular weight.[150] Chlorous acid oxidizes reducing carbohydrates to aldonic acids,[151] but the nature of reactions causing depolymerization and involving chain scission is not known.

In a recent review,[152] the alkaline degradation of polysaccharides has been given detailed consideration. For present purposes, it is only necessary to indicate four types of reaction (resulting from the use of alkali) which may cause modification of the hemicelluloses as they occur in the plant: (1) de-esterification of partially acylated polysaccharides; (2) chemical degradation initiated at reducing groups; (3) alkaline hydrolysis of glycosidic linkages; and (4) the breaking of (formal) chemical bonds between hemicelluloses and other cell-wall components.

Woods contain a number of acyl (mainly acetyl) groups, and it is probable that these are associated with the xylan components of the hemicellulose fraction. Evidence for the original esterification of aspen-wood xylan comes from the observation that the *isolated* xylan (obtained by alkaline extraction) is readily cleaved by periodate, whereas only a small proportion of the D-xylose residues in the wood itself are oxidized under similar conditions.[65] Hemicelluloses still containing acyl groups may be extracted from wood holocelluloses by means of dimethyl sulfoxide, and further quantities

(146) R. Nelson and C. Schuerch, *Tappi*, **40**, 419 (1957).

(147) C. F. Cross and E. J. Bevan, *J. Chem. Soc.*, **55**, 199 (1889); see also, W. G. Van Beckum and G. J. Ritter, *Paper Trade J.*, **108**, 1, 27 (1939).

(148) L. E. Wise, M. Murphy and A. A. D'Addieco, *Paper Trade J.*, **122**, 35 (1946).

(149) T. E. Timell and E. C. Jahn, *Svensk Papperstidn.*, **54**, 831 (1951).

(150) C. J. P. Glaudemans and T. E. Timell, *Svensk Papperstidn.*, **60**, 869 (1957).

(151) A. Jeanes and H. S. Isbell, *J. Research Natl. Bur. Standards*, **27**, 125 (1941); W. K. Wilson and A. A. Padgett, *Tappi*, **38**, 292 (1955).

(152) R. L. Whistler and J. N. BeMiller, *Advances in Carbohydrate Chem.*, **13**, 289 (1958).

of acylated polysaccharides may be removed by subsequent extraction with water.[153] A recent study[154] has indicated that the majority of the acyl groups in woods arise from acetyl esters, and that the formic acid isolated from woods results from chemical degradation rather than from hydrolysis of formyl esters. It has now been established that the acetyl groups are substituents of D-xylose rather than of D-glucuronic acid residues, the majority probably being attached to position 3 of D-xylose.[154a]

The alkaline degradation initiated at reducing groups of polysaccharides has been reviewed recently.[152] The main type of reaction occurring in this way results in the formation of saccharinic acids,[155] with the exposure of new reducing groups. With $(1 \rightarrow 4)$-linked polymers, this "peeling" reaction will proceed in a stepwise manner until intercepted by a "stopping" reaction or until a $(1 \rightarrow 2)$- or $(1 \rightarrow 3)$-linked branch point is encountered.[152] The type of reaction likely to be initiated at the reducing groups of xylans has been exemplified in studies of the alkaline degradation of xylobiose and xylotriose.[35,156] The fact that a corn-cob xylan was not degraded by alkali has been attributed to oxidation of the reducing end-groups during the preparation of the chlorite holocellulose.[156] Chlorite delignification does not, however, necessarily oxidize all reducing end-groups, since oat-straw xylans prepared from the chlorite holocellulose[42] are degraded by alkali, with the formation of acidic products.[157] Rye-flour arabinoxylan,[12] isolated by direct aqueous extraction, is similarly degraded, but, as with hydrocellulose,[158-160] when the reducing group is modified (for example, by reduction with potassium borohydride), the polysaccharide is stabilized toward alkali.[157]

Glycosides are generally considered to be stable toward alkali, although several types of alkali-labile glycosides are known.[161] Recently, however, the alkaline hydrolysis of glycosides that are stable under normal conditions has been demonstrated to occur under drastic conditions.[162] This type

(153) E. Hägglund, B. Lindberg and J. McPherson, *Acta Chem. Scand.*, **10**, 1160 (1956).

(154) T. E. Timell, *Svensk Papperstidn.*, **60**, 762 (1957).

(154a) H. O. Bouveng, P. J. Garegg and B. Lindberg, *Chem. & Ind.* (London), 1727 (1958).

(155) J. C. Sowden, *Advances in Carbohydrate Chem.*, **12**, 36 (1957).

(156) R. L. Whistler and W. M. Corbett, *J. Am. Chem. Soc.*, **78**, 1003 (1956).

(157) G. O. Aspinall, C. T. Greenwood and R. J. Sturgeon, unpublished results; R. J. Sturgeon, Ph. D. Thesis, Edinburgh, Scotland (1958).

(158) H. Richtzenhain, B. O. Lindgren, B. Abrahamsson and K. Holmberg, *Svensk Papperstidn.*, **57**, 363 (1954).

(159) F. S. H. Head, *J. Textile Inst.*, **46**, T584 (1955).

(160) G. Machell and G. N. Richards, *Tappi*, **41**, 12 (1958).

(161) C. E. Ballou, *Advances in Carbohydrate Chem.*, **9**, 59 (1954).

(162) B. Lindberg, *Svensk Papperstidn.*, **59**, 531 (1956); E. Dryselius, B. Lindberg and O. Theander, *Acta Chem. Scand.*, **11**, 663 (1957); **12**, 340 (1958).

of alkaline hydrolysis of polysaccharides, causing the scission of glycosidic linkages, would result in the exposure of new reducing groups, at which alkaline degradation by the "peeling" reaction would be initiated. Although alkaline hydrolysis of this kind has not yet been detected under the relatively mild conditions employed during the laboratory extraction of hemicelluloses, there is evidence that cellulose may be so degraded during the alkaline refining of pulp.[163] Recent studies on the hemicelluloses from southern-pine pulps indicate that glycosiduronic acid linkages are more labile than neutral glycosidic linkages to alkaline hydrolysis, since xylans and arabinoxylans, devoid of glucuronic acid residues, may be isolated from kraft pulps.[81] Furthermore, treatment of isolated xylan fractions under kraft-pulping conditions results in the cleavage of glycosiduronic acid linkages, with the formation of neutral xylans.

Despite the lack of positive evidence for the existence of chemical bonds between lignin and hemicelluloses (see p. 467), an aryl glycosidic linkage has been postulated.[164] Some aryl glycosides are readily hydrolyzed by alkali,[161] so it would be anticipated that lignin-hemicellulose bonds would be cleaved under conditions employed for hemicellulose extractions. It has been further postulated that, during alkaline cooking of pulps, part of the hemicellulose originally linked to lignin is transferred to cellulose.[164] This type of alkaline transglycosylation reaction has recently been demonstrated with model compounds.[165]

2. Molecular Size

Relatively few molecular-weight determinations have been carried out on hemicelluloses and their derivatives, and so, detailed comment must be delayed until more data are available. The values so far recorded indicate that the majority of polysaccharides of this group have molecular sizes of about the same order of magnitude, usually within the range of 50–200 D. P. (degree of polymerization). Methods for the determination of the size and shape of polysaccharides have been reviewed recently,[28,29] and the experimental difficulties in the measurement of molecular weights of less than 20,000 (a range which is common in the hemicellulose field) have been emphasized.[28] In addition to problems of experimental method, difficulties often arise in the preparation of suitable derivatives (especially of xylans[29]) and in the interpretation of results.

The value of number-average molecular weights of methylated polysaccharides, used in conjunction with methylation end-group assays in the assessment of the degree of branching, has been stressed previously (see p. 435). Etherification is, however, normally carried out under alkaline con-

(163) O. Samuelson and A. Wennerblom, Svensk Papperstidn., 57, 827 (1954).
(164) J. W. McKinney, Paper Trade J., 122, 58 (1946).
(165) S. Häggroth and B. Lindberg, Svensk Papperstidn., 59, 870 (1956).

ditions, and the extent of degradation taking place has not yet been assessed. Degradation is probably only slight if alkali and alkylating reagent are added slowly and simultaneously in the early stages of reaction, so that glycosidation first occurs and prevents further degradation from the reducing group (compare hydrocellulose[160]). Precautions taken to exclude oxygen during etherification should minimize the type of oxidative degradation known to occur with other polysaccharides (for example, cellulose[166] and amylose[167]) in the presence of alkali and oxygen.

Although most polysaccharides may be acylated without degradation, acyl derivatives of xylans[29] are often unsatisfactory for molecular-weight determinations owing to their poor solubility characteristics. Mixed esters of xylans[143] are often superior in this respect, but there are obvious difficulties in the differential analysis of acyl groups. Hemicellulose nitrates have been used for measurements of molecular size,[168] but xylan nitrates,[29] like xylan acetates, are reported to have poor solubility characteristics.

The results of molecular-weight determinations on hemicelluloses need to be interpreted in the light of comments made earlier (see p. 461) regarding the degrees of heterogeneity possible in polysaccharides of this type.

3. Biological Synthesis

The close association, in the plant, of two groups of sugars with similar stereochemistry, namely, (a) D-galactose, D-galacturonic acid, and L-arabinose, and (b) D-glucose, D-glucuronic acid, and D-xylose, has led to the suggestion that the pentoses may be derived from the hexoses by oxidation at C6 to hexuronic acids, followed by decarboxylation. Although polysaccharides based on the three sugars in the first group are found closely associated in pectic substances,[8] direct transformation of polymer to polymer is clearly impossible, since the monosaccharide units in galactan, pectic acid, and araban differ in configuration at C1, in ring size, or in mode of linkage.[169] Greater structural similarities are found in the cell-wall polysaccharides, where cellulose, xylan, and glucomannans *all* contain basal chains of $(1 \rightarrow 4)$-linked β-D-glycopyranose units, but, again, polymer to polymer transformation seems unlikely (a) in view of the many variations in fine structure found in the xylans and (b) in the absence of evidence for the natural occurrence of poly-D-glucosiduronic acids. Indeed, D-glucuronic acid residues have, thus far, only been encountered as side chains attached to the backbones of xylans. Recent studies on the biosynthesis of xylans[170-172]

(166) D. I. McGilvray, *J. Chem. Soc.*, 2577 (1953).

(167) R. T. Bottle, G. A. Gilbert, C. T. Greenwood and K. N. Saad, *Chem. & Ind.* (London), 541 (1953).

(168) B. Immergut and B. G. Rånby, *Svensk Papperstidn.*, **60**, 573 (1957).

(169) E. L. Hirst, *J. Chem. Soc.*, 70 (1942); 522 (1949).

(170) A. C. Neish, *Can. J. Biochem. and Physiol.*, **33**, 658 (1955).

support the view that the interconversion of the component sugars takes place at the monosaccharide level,[173] and provide much evidence that the D-xylose units involved in xylan synthesis are derived from D-glucose by loss of C6.

Experiments with wheat plants fed with labeled sugars have shown that D-glucose is more efficiently converted into both cellulose and xylan than is D-xylose.[170-172] Furthermore, D-glucose-1-C^{14} is converted into xylan with little rearrangement of the carbon skeleton, since the D-xylose formed on hydrolysis of the polysaccharide contains more than 80 % of its radioactivity at C1. In contrast, hydrolysis of the xylan formed from plants fed with D-xylose-1-C^{14} yielded D-xylose with a widespread redistribution of isotopic carbon. A similar randomization of C^{14} was found in the D-glucose obtained from cellulose formed from D-xylose-1-C^{14}, and Neish[170] suggested that derivatives of D-glucose and D-xylose utilized in the synthesis of cellulose and xylan may be formed through common intermediates—possibly pentose 5-phosphates, D-glucose 6-phosphate, sedoheptulose 7-phosphate, and other compounds involved in the hexose monophosphate shunt.[173]

Further support for the hypothesis of conversion of D-glucose to D-xylose derivatives by way of derivatives of D-glucuronic acid comes from the observations that D-glucurono-1,4-lactone-1-C^{14} is equally as effective as D-glucose as a xylan precursor and that D-xylose may be isolated with 88–89 % of its isotopic carbon at[171,172] C1.

None of the intermediates involved in these sugar transformations have yet been characterized, but "uridine diphosphate glycosides" have been postulated,[171] and it is of interest that such glycosides of D-xylose, D-glucuronic acid, and L-arabinose have been identified in mung-bean seedlings.[174] Again, the intermediates involved in the biosynthesis of (1 → 4)-linked glycans are not yet known, but in view of the common occurrence of transglycosylation reactions in the synthesis of polysaccharides,[175] the formation of these various polysaccharides along parallel pathways seems probable, with such glycosides as D-xylosyl phosphate or "uridine diphosphate D-xylose" acting as glycosyl donors.

The role of L-arabinose in these biosynthetic pathways is also of interest. It seems probable that, unlike D-xylose itself, this sugar may be readily

(171) H. A. Altermatt and A. C. Neish, *Can. J. Biochem. and Physiol.*, **34**, 405 (1956).

(172) A. C. Neish, *Can. J. Biochem. and Physiol.*, **36**, 187 (1958).

(173) The present position with regard to the biological synthesis and interconversion of monosaccharides has been reviewed by L. Hough and J. K. N. Jones, *Advances in Carbohydrate Chem.*, **11**, 185 (1956).

(174) V. Ginsberg, P. K. Stumpf and W. Z. Hassid, *Federation Proc.*, **15**, 262 (1956); J. Solms, D. S. Feingold and W. Z. Hassid, *J. Am. Chem. Soc.*, **79**, 2342 (1957).

(175) S. A. Barker and E. J. Bourne, *Quart. Revs.* (London), **7**, 56 (1953); M. Stacey, *Advances in Enzymol.*, **15**, 301 (1954).

converted into the derivatives of D-xylose required for xylan synthesis, since wheat plants, when fed with L-arabinose-1-C^{14}, synthesize a xylan which, on hydrolysis, affords D-xylose with the major part of the radioactivity remaining[172] at C1. In other experiments, the formation of both D-xylose and L-arabinose (as constituents of the hemicellulose of wheat seedlings) from D-glucose-1-C^{14}, with but little rearrangement of the carbon skeleton, has been demonstrated.[176] Arabinoxylans, however, normally contain residues of D-xylose and L-arabinose in the pyranose and furanose forms, respectively, and any interconversion of the derivatives of the two pentoses used in polysaccharide synthesis must involve a change in ring size, in addition to epimerization at C4. In this case, a simple transformation of a derivative of the one pentose to a derivative of the other seems unlikely. Recent work has, however, shown that mung-bean seedlings contain a uridyl transferase and a waldenase which, together, can convert α-D-xylosyl phosphate to a mixture of "uridine diphosphate glycosides" of D-xylose and L-arabinose,[177] but probably without change in ring size.

4. Relationship with Other Cell-wall Components

In the cell walls of higher plants,[178] hemicelluloses are found in close association with cellulose and lignin, and evidence for the distribution of these three main components in the various parts of the wall has been obtained by staining techniques.[179] It is not certain, however, whether the close association of these substances can be accounted for entirely in terms of physical entanglement and secondary forces (van der Waals' and hydrogen bonding) or whether primary chemical bonds unite some of the components.

Little direct evidence is available regarding the nature of the association of hemicelluloses with cellulose in the cell wall itself. The main approach to the problem, so far, has been to examine the role of D-glucose residues in the extractable, hemicellulose fractions (see p. 459) and of sugar residues other than D-glucose in the residual cellulose. In view of the persistence of small proportions of other sugar units (especially of D-xylose and D-mannose) in cellulose, existence of covalent linkages between D-glucose and these sugars has been postulated,[180] but in no case has the presence of such chemical bonds been substantiated to date. Since only small propor-

(176) V. Ginsberg and W. Z. Hassid, *J. Biol. Chem.*, **223**, 277 (1956).

(177) V. Ginsberg, E. F. Neufeld and W. Z. Hassid, *Proc. Natl. Acad. Sci. U. S.*, **42**, 333 (1956); E. F. Neufeld, V. Ginsberg, E. W. Putman, D. Fanshier and W. L. Hassid, *Arch. Biochem. Biophys.*, **69**, 602 (1957).

(178) For a recent review of both chemical and biological investigations, see D. H. Northcote, *Biol. Revs. Cambridge Phil. Soc.*, **33**, 53 (1958).

(179) P. W. Lange, "Fundamentals of Papermaking Fibres," Tech. Sect. Brit. Paper and Board Makers Assoc., 1958, pp. 147–185.

(180) G. A. Adams and C. T. Bishop, *Tappi*, **38**, 672 (1955), and references there cited.

tions of these other sugars are involved, an unambiguous solution of the problem presents formidable experimental difficulties, and evidence which assumes the complete physical separation of polymers must always be viewed with suspicion. Two examples of the difficulties encountered in the separation of cellulose and hemicelluloses may be mentioned. Cotton cellulose, devoid of D-xylose residues, has been shown to adsorb xylans from alkaline solution under the conditions employed in wood pulping[181] in the preparation of so-called α-cellulose. Although complete separation of cellulose from hemicelluloses by fractionation of the derived nitrates has been claimed,[182] in other experiments, high molecular-weight fractions of cellulose nitrate have been found to contain D-mannose residues.[183] Such evidence alone does not, however, prove that D-mannose residues are constituents of the cellulose, since fractionation of mixtures of nitrates of ramie cellulose (of high molecular weight and D-mannose-free) with nitrates of ivory-nut mannan (of relatively low molecular weight) affords fractions of high molecular weight containing D-mannose residues.[184]

Much conflicting evidence has been presented concerning the occurrence of lignin–hemicellulose linkages.[185] The present unsatisfactory position may be illustrated by two examples of results of recent investigations. The rates of extraction of xylan from birch wood with alkali are held to be inconsistent with those of a process involving cleavage of covalent bonds between hemicelluloses and lignin.[186] On the other hand, an examination (by ionophoresis on glass-fiber paper[145]) of lignin-containing materials, isolated from milled wood under non-swelling conditions,[187] provides strong evidence for the presence of substances in which hemicelluloses and lignin are chemically linked.[188]

(181) S. Yllner and B. Enström, *Svensk Papperstidn.*, **59,** 229 (1956); **60,** 549 (1957).

(182) E. Dymling, H. W. Giertz and B. G. Rånby, *Svensk Papperstidn.*, **58,** 10 (1955).

(183) T. E. Timell, *Pulp Paper Mag. Can.*, **56,** 104 (1955).

(184) J. L. Snyder and T. E. Timell, *Svensk Papperstidn.*, **58,** 889 (1955).

(185) For a review, see J. W. T. Merewether, *Holzforschung*, **11,** 65 (1957).

(186) R. Nelson and C. Schuerch, *J. Polymer Sci.*, **22,** 435 (1956).

(187) A. Björkman, *Svensk Papperstidn.*, **60,** 329 (1957).

(188) B. O. Lindgren, *Acta Chem. Scand.*, **12,** 447 (1958).

Author Index for Volume 14

Numbers in parentheses are footnote numbers. They are inserted to indicate the reference when an author's work is cited but his name is not mentioned on the page.

A

Abraham, S., 15, 30(46), 57(46)
Abrahams, P., 147, 157(44), 159(44), 160(44)
Abrahamsson, B. 463
Abrams, A., 68, 76, 109, 114(131)
Abul-Fadl, M. A. M., 417, 421(185)
Acker, L., 441, 459(60)
Ackerman, D., 188
Acree, S. F., 304
Adachi, S., 64, 127, 133
Adams, G. A., 438, 439, 440(48, 49, 50), 441(48, 49, 50), 443, 444(36, 41), 445(48, 49, 50), 446(66), 447, 459, 467
Agranoff, B., 158, 164, 165, 192(101b)
Ågren, G., 68, 93, 101(175), 103(59)
Ahlborg, K., 43
Ahmed, Z. F., 449
Akabori, S., 70, 114(78), 115
Akiya, S., 235, 259
Alberda van Ekenstein, W., 289
Alberi, J. T., 212, 209(287), 210(287)
Alessandrini, A., 275, 281(294)
Alexander, F., 384(40), 385(40), 387, 390(40)
Ali, M. E., 23
Allen, F. W., 56
Allen, G. R., Jr., 182, 185, 187(214), 204(229), 207(214), 208(214, 229), 209(229)
Altermatt, H. A., 466
Altman, K. I., 419, 421(190)
Alyakrinskaya, E. A., 133
Ambler, J. A., 65, 69, 87, 107, 117(73)
Aminoff, D., 258(202), 259, 264
Amos, H., 288, 291(43)
Anastassiadis, P. A., 269
Andersen, W., 316, 318(144), 377(144), 378(144)
Anderson, A. B., 149, 156, 157, 166(61), 169, 170(61), 199(61, 159), 458, 459(132)

Anderson, C. A., 162
Anderson, E., 429, 440, 442(1), 460
Anderson, J. D., 460
Anderson, J. M., 238, 239(130, 131)
Anderson, L., 29, 57(110a) 137, 138(5), 143, 146, 148, 157(42, 58), 158, 160, 162, 163, 164(128), 165(31), 171, 172(53), 173(164), 179, 180(51, 53, 209), 181(209), 183(5), 184, 186, 188, 192(209), 196(53, 58, 164, 236a), 197 (58), 201(42), 203(42), 204(42, 209), 205(51, 53, 236a), 206(42, 209, 236a), 207(232, 236a, 284), 208(223, 232, 284), 210, 211(42, 51b, 236a), 212(236a)
Anderson, R. C., 141, 142(18), 168(18)
Anderson, R. H., 120
Anderson, R. J., 175, 177(183), 195(183, 267), 198
Anderson, T. F., 296
Anderson, W., 374(302), 375(302), 377 (302), 378(302), 380
Andreotte, R., 64
Andrews, P., 452, 454, 460
Anet, E. F. L. J., 70, 109, 114(235), 117, 157
Angyal, C. L., 140
Angyal, S. J., 22, 29, 57(110a), 136, 137, 138(6, 7), 140, 141, 142, 144(4), 146, 147, 148(6), 149(6), 150(6), 151, 152(56), 153(56), 154, 155, 156, 157(42, 55, 90), 163, 166, 167, 168, 169(6), 170(143), 171(7, 55, 149), 172(7, 55, 72) 173(55), 174, 178, 179(205), 180(52), 181(7, 149), 182(7), 183, 190(6), 193 (55, 256), 194(25, 86, 179, 256), 195(6, 55), 196(7, 55), 197(55), 198, 199(6, 149), 200(4, 6, 52, 86, 149), 201(4, 6, 7, 42, 43, 52, 86), 202(4, 7, 52, 86, 149), 203(7, 21, 42, 52, 149), 204(21, 42), 205(42, 52, 205), 206(42, 52), 211(6, 21, 42)

Subject Index for Volume 14

A

β-N-Acetylglucosaminidase, 270, 273, 277, 413

Adenine, 2,8-dichloro-, 328

—, 2,8-dichloro-9-(D-glucopyranosyl)-, 328

Adenosine, 3-O-acetyl-2-deoxy-5-O-tosyl-, 316

—, 2,3-O-isopropylidene-, tosylated, 315

Adenosinetriphosphoric acid, 261, 237

Aldobiouronic acids, 433, 434, 439

Aldohexose, 3,4,6-trideoxy-3-dimethyl-amino-, 326

Aldohexoses, 2-amino-2-deoxy-, derivatives of, 101, 224

Aldopentopyranose, 2,3,4-trideoxy-(Tetrahydropyran-2-ol), 119

—, 3,4-dideoxy-*glycero*-, 119

Aldosylamines, 216, 221

Aldotriouronic acid, 439

Allofuranose, 2-acetamido-2-deoxy-1,2: 5,6-di-O-isopropylidene-α-D-, 229

Allopyranoside, methyl 2,3-anhydro-α-D-, derivatives of, 218, 219

Allose, 2-amino-2-deoxy-D-, 220, 222

Altropyranoside, methyl 2-amino-4,6-O-benzylidene-2-deoxy-α-D-, 218

—, methyl 3-amino-4,6-O-benzylidene-3-deoxy-α-D-, 218

—, methyl 2,6-anhydro-α-D-, 22

Altrose, 2-amino-2-deoxy-D-, 222

—, 3,6-dideoxy-3-dimethylamino-β-D-, 232

Amadori rearrangement, 66, 72, 117, 131, 221

reversed. *See* Heyns rearrangement.

Amicetamine, 325

methyl glycoside of, 326

Amicetin, 232, 284, 322, 324, 359

Amicetin B, 326

Amino acids, N-(D-fructosyl), 118

N-(D-*arabino*-tetrahydroxy-2-oxo-hexyl), 117

reaction of, with sugars, 64, 69, 110, 122, 127

Amosamine, 232, 326

"Antiglucuronidase," 419

Apiose, D-, 17

—, 2-O-benzyl-D-, 17

Araban, 465

Arabinal, D-. *See* Ribal, D-.

Arabinofuranose, L-, in xylans, 433

Arabinoglactans, 454–458

Arabinopyranoside, methyl α-D-, 33

Arabinose, D-, 256

L-, 97, 176, 219, 430–432, 454

L-, in biosynthesis, 466

D-, C14-labeled ester of, 38

L-, estimation of, 433

L-, reaction of, with casein, 98
  with glutamic acid, 100, 115

D-, reaction of, with glycine ethyl ester, 252

—, 3-amino-3-deoxy-D-, 229

—, 3-O-β-L-arabinosyl-L-, 456, 458

—, 2,5-di-O-methyl-D-, 43

—, 2,5-di-O-methyl-L-, 457, 458

—, 3,5-di-O-methyl-L-, 433

—, 2,4-di-O-tosyl-D-, 18

—, 3-O-formyl-D-, 39

—, 3-O-β-D-galactopyranosyl-D-, 216, 275
  anilide of, 274

—, 5-O-β-D-galactopyranosyl-L-, 440

—, O-L-galactopyranosyl-(1 → 4)-D-xylo-pyranosyl-(1 → 2)-L-, 440

—, 2-O-β-D-glucopyranosyl-D-, 277

—, 2,3,4-tri-O-methyl-L-, 457, 458

—, 2,3,5-tri-O-methyl-L-, 431, 458

—, 2-O-β-D-xylopyranosyl-L-, 433, 437

—, 3-O-α-D-xylopyranosyl-L-, 440

Arabinose-1-C14, L-, 467

Arabinoside, methyl di-O-trityl-α-D-, acetylation and detritylation of, 33

—, methyl 2,3,5-tri-O-methyl-L-, 455

Arabinosylamine, D-, addition of hydrogen cyanide to, 215

Arabinoxylans, 431, 437, 441, 463
  biosynthesis of, D-glucose-1-C14 in, 467

Arginine, N-D-glucosyl-, 117

Ascorbic acid, L-, 96, 162, 382, 417, 421

497

H

Hemicelluloses, 382, 429, 439
  association with cellulose and lignin, 467
  biological synthesis of, 465
  chemistry of, some problems in, 461
  classification of, 430
  delignification of, 462, 464
  heterogeneity in, 461
  isolation of, 461
  modification by alkali, 462
  molecular-weight determination of, 464
  from natural sources, 433, 438, 440
  nitrates of, 465
  the term, 430
  transglycosylation reaction of, 464
Heparin, 277, 382, 419
Heparosine, 277, 279
Heptonic acid, D-*glycero*-D-*gulo*-, hexa-*O*-acetyl, nitrile, 55
Heptulose, D-*altro*-, 1,7-diphosphate, 43
  7-phosphate, 466
Hexodialdose, D-(and L-)*manno*-, di-*O*-isopropylidene acetal, 166
Hexokinase, 237
Hexopyranosyl bromide, tri-*O*-acetyl-2-deoxy-D-*arabino*-, 331
Hexosamines, determination of, 70, 258, 264, 425
Hexosazone, D-*arabino*-, 109, 459
  D-*xylo*-, 226
2-Hexulose, 1-*N*-(carboxyalkylamino)-1-deoxy-, 110
Hexulosylamine, D-*arabino*-, 221
  D-*lyxo*-, 221
  D-*ribo*-, 221
  L-*xylo*-, 222
Heyns rearrangement, 102, 117, 131, 252
Hyalobiouronic acid, 277, 425
Hyaluronic acid, 277, 382, 417, 425
Hyaluronidase, 277, 383, 425
Hygromycins, 185
Hypoxanthine, 292

I

Idaric acid, DL-, 29
Idopyranose, 1,6-anhydro-β-D-, 226
Idose, 2-amino-2-deoxy-L-, 222
—, 6-deoxy-6-nitro-D-, 142
Iduronic acid, L-, 426

Inosadiamines, 183, 184, 187
—, *N*,*N*'-dibenzoyl-, 185
Inosamine, pentaacetate ester, deamination of, 143
  scyllo- (Inositol, aminodeoxy-*scyllo*-), 142, 186, 187
Inosamine-1, *levo*-, 188
  myo-, deamination of, 188
  (−)-*neo*-, 187
  rac-, 186
Inosamine-2, (±)-*epi*-, 186
  levo-. See Inosamine-1, *levo*-.
  myo-, 186, 187
  neo-, 185, 187
Inosamine-3, *levo*-, 187
Inosamine-4, (±)-*myo*-, 186
Inosamine-5, *levo*-. See Inosamine-3, *levo*-.
Inosamines, 183, 186, 187, 207
"Inosatriamine," 186
Inosine, 290
—, 2-deoxy-, 292
Inositides, monophospho-, of brain, 165
Inositol, *allo*-, 144, 155, 167, 202
  C14-labeled, 136
  cis-, 146, 168
  dextro-, 145, 149, 166, 181, 199
  epi-, 145
    derivatives of, 149, 189, 201
  iso-, 166
  levo-, 145
    derivatives of, 149, 150, 166, 181, 200
    methyl ether. See (−)-Pinitol and (−)-Quebrachitol.
    3-phosphate, 174
  meso-. See Inositol, *myo*-.
  muco-, 167
  myo-, 138, 141, 144, 147, 150, 157, 159–165
    C14-labeled, 142, 163
    derivatives of, 172, 173, 177, 189, 192
    dimethyl ether. See Dambonitol.
    hexaphosphate ester. See Phytic acid.
    methyl ethers of, 169, 172. See also Bornesitol, (+)-, and Sequoyitol.
  neo-, 146, 168
  rac-, 166, 167
  scyllo-, 138, 154, 167, 189
—, 1,2-anhydro-*allo*-, 181–183
—, 2,3-anhydro-*allo*-, 182

CUMULATIVE AUTHOR INDEX FOR VOLUMES 1–13

A

ADAMS, MILDRED. *See* Caldwell, Mary L.

ANDERSON, ERNEST, and SANDS, LILA, A Discussion of Methods of Value in Research on Plant Polyuronides, I, 329–344

ASPINALL, G. O., The Methyl Ethers of Hexuronic Acids, IX, 131–148

ASPINALL, G. O., The Methyl Ethers of D-Mannose, VIII, 217–230

B

BALLOU, CLINTON E., Alkali-sensitive Glycosides, IX, 59–95

BARKER, G. R., Nucleic Acids, XI, 285–333

BARKER, S. A., and BOURNE, E. J., Acetals and Ketals of the Tetritols, Pentitols and Hexitols, VII, 137–207

BARRETT, ELLIOTT P., Trends in the Development of Granular Adsorbents for Sugar Refining, VI, 205–230

BARRY, C. P., and HONEYMAN, JOHN, Fructose and its Derivatives, VII, 53–98

BAYNE, S., and FEWSTER, J. A., The Osones, XI, 43–96

BEÉLIK, ANDREW, Kojic Acid, XI, 145–183

BELL, D. J., The Methyl Ethers of D-Galactose, VI, 11–25

BeMILLER, J. N. *See* Whistler, Roy L.

BINKLEY, W. W., Column Chromatography of Sugars and Their Derivatives, X, 55–94

BINKLEY, W. W., and WOLFROM, M. L., Composition of Cane Juice and Cane Final Molasses, VIII, 291–314

BLAIR, MARY GRACE, The 2-Hydroxyglycals, IX, 97–129

BOBBITT, J. M., Periodate Oxidation of Carbohydrates, XI, 1–41

BÖESEKEN, J., The Use of Boric Acid for the Determination of the Configuration of Carbohydrates, IV, 189–210

BONNER, WILLIAM A., Friedel–Crafts and Grignard Processes in the Carbohydrate Series, VI, 251–289

BOURNE, E. J., and PEAT, STANLEY, The Methyl Ethers of D-Glucose, V, 145–190

BOURNE, E. J. *See also*, Barker, S. A.

BRAY, H. G., D-Glucuronic Acid in Metabolism, VIII, 251–275

BRAY, H. G., and STACEY, M., Blood Group Polysaccharides, IV, 37–55

C

CAESAR, GEORGE V., Starch Nitrate, XIII, 331–345

CALDWELL, MARY L., and ADAMS, MILDRED, Action of Certain Alpha Amylases, V, 229–268

CANTOR, SIDNEY M. *See* Miller, Robert Ellsworth.

CARR, C. JELLEFF, and KRANTZ, JOHN C., JR., Metabolism of the Sugar Alcohols and Their Derivatives, I, 175–192

COMPTON, JACK, The Molecular Constitution of Cellulose, III, 185–228

CONCHIE, J., LEVVY, G. A., and MARSH, C. A., Methyl and Phenyl Glycosides of the Common Sugars, XII, 157–187

CRUM, JAMES D., The Four-carbon Saccharinic Acids, XIII, 169–188

D

DEAN, G. R., and GOTTFRIED, J. B., The Commercial Production of Crystalline Dextrose, V, 127–143

DEITZ, VICTOR R. *See* Liggett, R. W.

DEUEL, HARRY J., JR., and MOREHOUSE, MARGARET G., The Interrelation of Carbohydrate and Fat Metabolism, II, 119–160

DEULOFEU, VENANCIO, The Acylated

514

CUMULATIVE SUBJECT INDEX FOR VOLUMES 1–13

ERRATA

Volume 11

Page 277, reference 54; and page 411, column 2, last line. For "Perkins" read "Perkin."

Page 442, column 1. For "Motarotase" read "Mutarotase."

Volume 13

Page 103, line 9. For "metyl" read "methyl."

Page 142, formula XXI, line 2. Interchange "C" with the first "N."

Page 174, second formula Ib, line 2. Interchange "H" and "OH."

Page 177, second formula IIIab, line 1. For "CH₂H" read "CO₂H."

Page 216, reference 13, line 4. For "D-glucoce" read "D-glucose."

Page 234, column 3, entry 4. For "+4.2" read "−35; −25."

Page 383, column 1, line 4 up. For "pheynyl" read "phenyl."